Coincraft's Standard Catalogue
of the coins of
Scotland, Ireland, Channel Islands &
Isle of Man

Richard Lobel
Publisher

Mark Davidson
Author of Hammered Section

Allan Hailstone
Author of Milled Section

Eleni Calligas
Editor

COINCRAFT

opposite the British Museum

44 & 45 Great Russell Street London WC1B 3LU
Tel: 0171-636 1188 0171-637 8785
Fax: 0171-323 2860 0171-637 7635
Email: info@coincraft.com

London 1999

Acknowledgements

We would like to thank the following for their assistance:

Airedale Coins

Lauri Andrews

Stephen Byrne

Nigel Cox

Robert Heslip

Jersey States Treasury

Baldwins

James Brown

Barry Clayden

Chris Comber

Dix Noonan Webb

Q. David Bowers

Anthony Dowle

Bowers and Murena

Patrick Finn

Glendinings

Peter Hicks

Anton Holt

Robert Ilsley

Ian Jull

Alan Kelly

Michael Kenny

Andrew Litherland

Claire Lobel

Sylvia Mitchell

James Morton

David Murphy

Paul Nicholson

James Noble

John Rainey

Michael Sharp

Sothebys

Tony le Tissier

David Twinholm

Alan Ward

Chris Webb

The following photographs were reproduced with the kind permission of the Trustees of the National Museums and Galleries of Northern Ireland:

ic13d-010, ic1hc-010, ic1ps-005, ie41d-005, ie42d-030, ie42d-055, ih72d-015, ih72d-025, ihn1d-010, ihn1d-030, ihn1d-035, ihn1d-045, ihn1d-090, ihn1d-095, ihn1d-140, ihn1d-185, ihn1d-200, ihn1d-215, ihn1d-230, ihn1d-235, ihn1d-250, ihn1d-260, ihn1d-465, ihn1d-485, ihn1d-500.

About the Contributors

Richard Lobel

Richard was born in Cambridge Massachusetts in 1944 and moved to London in 1968. He is a member of the Professional Numismatic Guild since 1974 and of numerous numismatic societies world-wide. He holds a degree in International Business and Macro Economics from Boston University and was accepted to the Harvard Business School to study Finance but moved to England instead, mistakenly believing that he spoke the language.

His first mentor in the coin business was the late Maurice Gould, author of many numismatic research works. Over the years he has had the privilege of knowing many famous numismatists and learning from them. His serious interest in coins dates from his first paid subscription to a coin publication in June of 1955.

He founded Coincraft, which has become the second largest firm of coin dealers in the United Kingdom. Perhaps his proudest boast is that Coincraft sells more numismatic books retail than anyone else in the UK. They deal only with collectors and publish a monthly newspaper/catalogue called *The Phoenix* and an occasional magazine, *The Coin Collector*.

He has been listed in the *Guinness Book of Records* many times, for the legendary Edward VIII Collection, the unique 1954 Penny and for heading the consortium that bought the largest, heaviest and most expensive lot of banknotes ever sold at auction.

Richard stated that 'this is the second important book on numismatics that Coincraft has published, but it will not be the last. After almost 45 years in the coin business, I want to give something back to numismatics. I hope that collectors and scholars will both find something in it to amuse and delight them. Over the years, coins have been very good to me and now is my chance to repay that kindness.'

Mark Davidson

Born and raised in Surrey, Mark began collecting bun pennies by date at the age of six. Encouraged in his hobby by his parents and his uncle, he soon became a keen collector and purchased his first hammered coin from the then recently discovered Colchester hoard of Henry III and Edward I pennies. At sixteen he started working for Richard Lobel and received his 'apprenticeship in the coin trade'. He started his own business at the age of twenty, dealing in all types of coins, publishing catalogues and trading from the old Saturday Charing Cross market. When that market closed in 1987, Mark started a monthly London Coin fair with Linda Monk which still flourishes today and, on the death of John Hooper, he became a partner in Croydon Coin Auctions. Mark is very well known in the trade and attends most auctions and fairs, where he enjoys meeting collectors.

Allan Hailstone

Allan was born in Coventry in 1938, and lived in various parts of England before moving to London in 1957 to read Chemical Engineering at Imperial College. Graduating in 1960, he entered industry but rapidly found that nobody appeared to know what a Chemical Engineer was. In 1962, he noticed a wants list of coins in a shop window in Canterbury, and decided on the spot to become a coin dealer.

With an amiable eccentric nature masking a deeply flawed personality, Allan met Richard Lobel many years ago, and recognised a kindred spirit; something akin to a friendship developed.

Allan can often be found perusing old books in the British Library or hiding behind a newspaper at any one of several London coffee shops. Caring more for accuracy, language and spelling than for his fellow man, he was a natural choice for producing the milled section of this book.

Dr Eleni Calligas

Born in Athens in 1960, Eleni is, by trade, a historian of nineteenth century Greece. She finds potted autobiographies misleading but can unequivocally state that after completing her BA degree in History at the American College of Greece, she continued her studies at the London School of Economics, receiving her MA in 1987 and her doctorate in 1994. She was among the founding editors of the Greek historical journal *Histor*, has published a book-length study on child welfare in 19th century Greece and contributed articles to historical journals in both Greek and English. As well as history and the written word, she likes cats, sunshine and Alice in Wonderland humour.

Contents

Preface

Dear Collector,

I guess it must have been some ten years ago that I first actually did something about going into numismatic book publishing and how different those ten years have been. Sometimes when you go into a new venture you look at the world through rose-tinted glasses. With book publishing you look at the world through a pile of bills and invoices and say goodbye to piles of banknotes, which you will never see again. There were times at the end of the month when I felt that I was standing by a great gaping black hole, I would lift a stack of £50 notes over my head, say an incantation and throw them into the vortex, hoping to satiate its appetite for another month. Then again, there is also a moment, too infrequent unfortunately, that the black hole sends something back to you and that thing is a book. Fully printed, fully illustrated, nicely bound, a real bona fide book. At that point all the trouble, all the pain, all the effort and even all the money is worth it. You are there at the birth of a book, something which makes the gestation period of a human being seem like a brief moment in time.

I have been at the 'birth' of a couple of Coincraft's books, but this one has been the most 'fun'. Years ago, when I assumed that anyone could just knock off a book on coins in their spare time, Peter 'Maundy' Allen tried to help me out. I couldn't understand how there could be any problems. Take the information that is available, recheck it in at least two sources, make corrections where necessary and oh yes, add in a whole bunch of new information and come out with a book. Nothing to it! That first book took seven years of research and even now, we revise and add new information to it every year. Piece of cake...!

In life, to succeed you need a number of things, you need to work hard, have a fair modicum of intelligence and you need to be lucky. I feel that on the luck side, I was very lucky to know the two authors and the editor. It would have been almost impossible to do the job without those three. I admit that all I really provide is an idea for a book and the money to finance it. Perhaps with the odd 'nose in other people's business' from time to time. Patience is one word that I have had to learn and as anyone who knows me knows, I am not a patient person. I would never have had the time or the inclination to do it myself. This is one book which gives me great, great pride. I can only hope that the other books which are in various stages of progress will do the same, without me having to go to that black hole too often, without too many stacks of banknotes having to be sacrificed...

We are a team at Coincraft that loves coins, that loves getting things right, that loves creating a whole new series of books on coins, banknotes, tokens, medallions and everything numismatic. That we do it in a new fashion, that we are not afraid to break old taboos, that we do it the way collectors collect, that we do it our way, that makes life interesting! You will not get just a priced catalogue from Coincraft, you will get background information, historical information, collecting hints and a detailed catalogue which will help you further enjoy your hobby. Coincraft is trying to produce catalogues which will be useful to the collector and non-collector alike, we are trying to give you the type of catalogue that you want. We believe that if you don't enjoy what you are doing, then you shouldn't be doing it! If you are beginning as a collector we don't want to frighten you off and if you are an advanced collector we hope that you too will find something you didn't know before. We are trying to produce the kind of books that we had always wished existed. That is the reason I took the company into numismatic book publishing, that is the reason for this book and for all the books we are going to publish.

The Scottish and Irish series are a bit of a puzzle to most collectors, most dealers and not a few specialist numismatists. To understand the coin series you also have to understand the histories. In Scotland there were over 70 different denominations of coinage to deal with! In both series a lot of what was previously written had to be checked and rechecked. Many of the smaller series had not had any extensive research done on them at all. We have attempted to produce a work which will stimulate interest in these areas although, unfortunately, I do not think that it will also stimulate their collectability that much. The main reason for this is the lack of available material. You just can't get enough good Irish or Scottish coins to satiate the demand that already exists. This new book will create interest in Scottish coins, Irish coins, the coins of Jersey, Guernsey and the Isle of Man, but it can not create new supplies. Have a look through the pages of dealers' advertisements, they might just have the coin or coins you are looking for. After all, they had the courage to support this book, it is up to us to help support them. No dealer can have everything in stock all the time, today you are lucky to have enough decent material available. Support your dealers, they have supported you by advertising their existence in this catalogue.

Irish and Scottish coins have always been, in my experience, very difficult to get, especially in nice condition. I started in coins way back when I was a youngster and had my first paid subscription to a coin publication in June of 1955. I consider myself a numismatist as well as a coin dealer and am proud of the knowledge that I have gained over the past 44 years. In the Scottish series I have only ever seen three silver coins that were in Brilliant Uncirculated condition! Choice early coins just do not exist. I believe that is because the money in Scotland and in Ireland kept circulating in almost a vacuum. In 1963 I visited British Honduras in Central America, which is now Belize. Because it is surrounded on almost all sides by Guatemala, a country which used to claim it, there was not a lot of interaction on the money front. In fact, silver Victorian coins still circulated in 1963, they were being pulled out of circulation, to be sent back to London for melting, but they still circulated. It is my belief that the coins of Scotland and Ireland were really used and thus they circulated and continued to circulate within their respective areas, thus choice examples are rare. I also feel that the prices for Irish and Scottish coins are way too low and do not reflect their true rarity. At this point I must remind my readers that Coincraft does not sell coins as investments, but these coins are too cheap on today's market for their rarity. You could do a lot worse than start a nice type collection of Scottish or Irish coins. The coinage of the Channel Islands is one where the coins are accessible and the prices are again very reasonable.

It has been almost 20 years since any new catalogue of the coinage of Scotland and/or Ireland has been printed. These are fascinating areas with great numismatic histories and it is time that something was done about it. In this book we have tried to open these areas to you, to let you explore, to let you understand and to hopefully make you more aware of their rich numismatic history.

This is not a book you sit down and read from cover to cover, or at least you wouldn't unless you were proof reading it. It is a book in which you look up a specific coin and while you are doing that, you browse elsewhere in its pages. Every time you pick it up, we hope that you will learn something else, sometimes that idea of 'learning' will be large and sometimes it will be small, but you will have learned something. Not everything is going to be perfect in this first edition, which is why we have inserted special reply cards for our readers to tell us what we have done wrong. A number of you are specialist collectors in your field and as specialists you will know much more about your subject than we will. We are general practitioners, this book is not exhaustive but it is an attempt to bring to you the information that you will need and that you will want. It is an excellent first go and we are very proud of it.

As I said at the beginning, publishing a book is like giving birth, only publishing takes a lot longer. The team has been working for over four years on this book and I, as the publisher, am extremely proud of them. I hope that you, the reader, will enjoy it and use it. This book will add something to our numismatic knowledge and for that reason and for no other reason, it had to be written. I am proud of my small part in its publication and once again I thank the team that did all the work: Mark Davidson, Allan Hailstone and Eleni Calligas. It has been a long struggle but I am sure that you will feel that it has all been worth while.

Stay well, be happy and keep on collecting....

Richard Lobel
Founder of Coincraft

A guide to using the Milled Section tables

The tables for each section are generally in three parts, as detailed below.

Part 1: The Broad Definition (5 columns)

Column 1: The name of the denomination.

Column 2: The metal from which the coin is made.

Column 3: The weight of the coin in grams. If found specimens vary markedly from the official weight, a weight range of most commonly found specimens is given.

Column 4: The diameter, usually to the nearest millimetre (mm).

Column 5: The reverse alignment. This means the alignment of the reverse seen if the coin is firstly held at the rim between two fingers, top and bottom, with the obverse facing and upright, and then rotated 180 degrees between the fingers.

Further information relating to the points above may be given as a footnote to the 5-column definition table.

Part 2: The Description

Each different obverse used is listed in sequence as Obverse 1, 2, etc. and briefly described. The different portrayals of any monarch are listed as Head 1, 2, etc. and the placement of the head facing left or right is stated. The legend on the obverse then follows in block capitals, without punctuation. There are often so many variations of punctuation within a given type that it is more appropriate to refer to the relevant photograph and correlate it with punctuation varieties given in Part 3.

Any bracketed wording in italics following the legend description and date does not form part of the legend on the coin but is intended to provide information on the issue, usually in the case of commemorative issues. If this information is obvious from the legend, however, it is omitted.

The reverses are similarly listed as Reverse 1, 2, etc. following the obverse list. The edge is then described (e.g. milled) or in the case of a lettered edge, the legend is given. With all legends, bracketed information is used to describe a variable listed in Part 3, e.g. (date). The terms 'regnal date' and 'edge date' are interchangeable.

Part 3: The Main Table

The table columns usually (but not invariably) are in the following sequence for each type:

1. The Coincraft reference number of the coin.

2. The date as shown on the coin.

3. (optional) The edge date or regnal date which forms part of the legend in Part 2.

4. Features of the coin. These are the characteristics which qualify the coin as a distinct variety of the series, e.g 'proof' or 'edge plain'. If no entry appears, it is usually the date which forms the characteristic feature. An entry reading, e.g., '9 over 8' refers to an overdate, where '9' appears in the corrected date. Where the corrected date contains two or more identical digits, the entry will read, e.g., 'first 3 over 2', 'latter 7 over 6'.

5. The obverse number as in Part 2.

6. The reverse number as in Part 2.

7. The retail price in the various grades in which the coin is usually found. The prices are in Pounds Sterling and are those which one would expect to pay from a reputable dealer, including handling fees, tax, etc. For very low priced items these ancillary charges form a disproportional, and therefore substantial, fraction of the price quoted.

Many price boxes have been left blank. This is because a price is considered inappropriate; for example, the coin may not exist in the grade stated, or the only known example is in a museum. Alternatively, it may be of negligible value in the grade stipulated. In a few cases, it is impossible to estimate within reasonable limits what the item would fetch.

Footnotes to the table are cross-referenced to notes in the table itself.

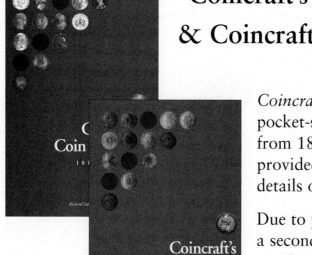

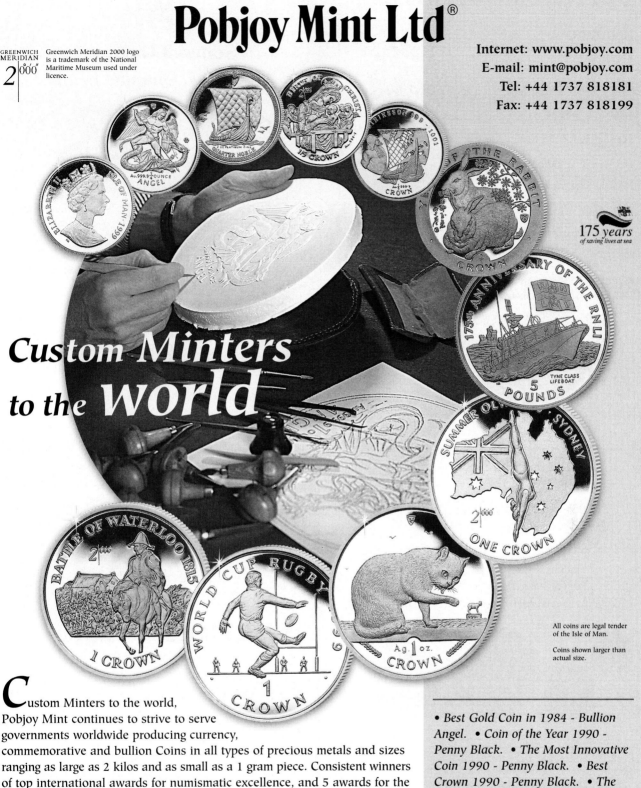
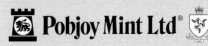

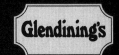

27

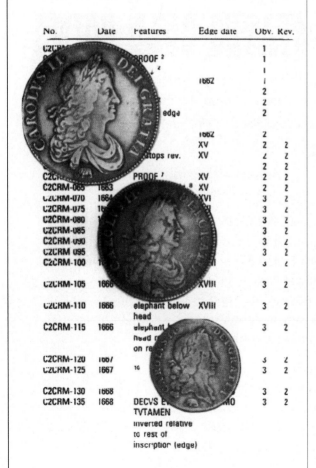

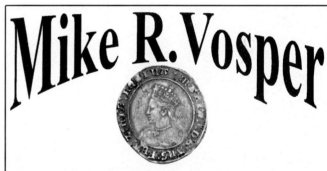

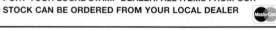

The Royal Mint: A Tradition of Excellence

An invitation to join the Royal Mint Coin Club

Coin collecting is now one of the most keenly pursued hobbies in the world. In order to satisfy the demands of the modern collector, the Royal Mint has established its own Coin Club to provide its members with the latest information on new coins from both home and abroad. Recognised as the supreme examples of the minter's art, Royal Mint collector coins, often struck in precious metals, form a tangible record of our heritage.

To find out more about how coins are created and to receive your free brochures, simply telephone **[01443] 623456** or write to the address below for further information.

**Royal Mint Coin Club
FREEPOST,
PO Box 500 Cardiff CF1 1YY**

Index of Advertisers

Scotland

The hammered coinage of Scotland

During Roman times Scotland was inhabited by the Picts, so called because they were painted (picti). The Romans built Hadrian's Wall and fortified it with garrison posts, to keep the Scots out whom they considered barbarians.

Scotland derived its name from *Scotia*, the original name for Ireland. The Scots, who were Gaelic speaking Christians, came over from Ireland and settled in the Western Islands and Argyll. Together with the English, they converted the original inhabitants, the Picts, to Christianity and in 843 Kenneth Macalpin, king of the Scots, also became the king of the Picts and the united kingdom was named Alban. The area of this kingdom varied and it was not until the reign of Duncan I (1034 – 40) that Scotland became united.

Duncan I was overthrown by Macbeth (1040 – 57) who ruled until he was killed in battle by Duncan I's son who became king Malcolm III (1057 – 93). Malcolm III was an English speaker as he had spent fifteen years in exile in the court of the English king Edward the Confessor. Malcolm invaded northern England several times but was driven back by William I of England who fortified areas of the north of England. After Malcolm's death in battle in Northumbria there followed a turbulent period, with various men ruling various parts of Scotland, until David I rose to power in 1124 and succeeded in unifying the troubled kingdom once more under his rule.

Although it is thought that no coins were struck in Scotland until the reign of David I, there is no doubt that numerous coins circulated. They would have included Roman and Celtic coins, silver pennies especially from Ireland, Viking coinage and sceats from Northumbria. English pennies, European sterlings and deniers also circulated as well as Byzantine gold coins and gold and silver dirhems from the East.

David I issued silver pennies which were fairly similar in style to English issues. They were sometimes known as sterlings and could be cut in half or quarters to produce halfpennies and farthings. They bore a crude bust of the king on the obverse and the name of the moneyer and mint on the reverse; a style of coin that continued until the reign of Alexander III.

During the English Civil War David invaded Northumbria and in 1139 signed a peace treaty with Stephen of England which gave much of northern England to Scotland. This area was ruled by David's son Prince Henry who struck coins in his name there. As with his father, only pennies were struck.

Prince Henry died in 1152 and his father David I the following year. He was succeeded in 1153 by Malcolm IV who was only eleven years old and known as The Maiden because of his appearance and the fact that he never married. He returned northern England to English rule in exchange for the earldom of Huntingdon and a stable Anglo-Scottish relationship. During this period only pennies were struck.

When Malcolm died in 1165, his younger brother William became king and was known as the Lion because he replaced the dragon on the arms of Scotland with a lion. William was captured by the English while trying to regain parts of northern England which were lost in previous reigns. He was only released by Henry II on the condition that he acknowledged Henry II as 'Lord of Scotland'. He, however, bought back his independence by paying Richard I of England 10,000 merks which Richard badly needed for the Crusades.

Again during this reign only pennies were issued but William produced a variety of coinages. The last coinage, which was struck at the end of his reign and also posthumously, is the first Scottish coin fairly easily available to collectors. It is interesting to note that these issues are sometimes found in England with metal detectors and they obviously circulated freely there.

William the Lion died in 1214 and was succeeded by his son, Alexander II, who joined the English Barons against King John of England and died while trying to regain the Hebrides from Norwegian control. He was succeed in 1249 by his son, Alexander III, who was only seven.

Numismatically this reign is very complex, with pennies the main denomination struck but also halfpennies and farthings being introduced in 1280. These were fairly similar to pennies but smaller.

Alexander III's issues can be divided into three coinages. The 'transitional coinage' was fairly similar to the previous reign and followed by the 'first coinage' which was struck between 1250 and 1280. A variety of styles of busts exist, but most issues bear a crowned head holding a sceptre on the obverse and a long cross with a star or mullet, as they are sometimes known, in each quarter on the reverse.

Underweight coins of low metal fineness were a problem throughout Europe and Scotland was no exception. It was relatively easy for a moneyer to produce an underweight coin and pass it into circulation, making a small, illegal profit on the excess silver, and to safeguard against this, the moneyer's name and mint town were placed on the reverse of coins, usually abbreviated. In the relevant chapter we list all the moneyers names as well as town abbreviations. The reverse legend starts with the moneyer's name followed by 'on', meaning 'of', and the town. Until Alexander III, all reigns that issued pennies used this system. At the time the penny was a large denomination of a high value and the need for smaller denominations was met by legally cutting coins into halves or quarters along the central cross of the reverse producing halfpennies or farthings.

Alexander's 'second coinage', struck from 1280 onwards, was of a clear style with well defined letters and design. It is interesting to note that the previous year (1279) Edward I had changed the style of the English coinage and introduced new denominations and no doubt Alexander III did not want Scotland to have inferior coinage to England. It is estimated that about fifty million pennies were struck during this recoinage and while these coins are considered common by numismatists only a fraction of those produced have survived. For the first time the moneyer's details are omitted but the number of points on the mullets or stars on the reverse linked a coin to the correct mint and perhaps moneyer. Unfortunately, much of this die information has subsequently been lost and it is uncertain where some of these coins were struck. The prolific quantity of pennies struck during this period suggests that they continued to be struck after Alexander's reign, and many circulated throughout Europe as their good design, correct weight and high metal fineness made them popular and superior to many European coins.

Alexander III married Margaret, sister of Edward I of England, and their daughter Margaret married the king of Norway. Their daughter, also named Margaret and known as the Maid of Norway, succeeded to the Scottish throne in 1286 at the age of three, when Alexander III died, riding over a cliff in the dark. When she was six Margaret was betrothed to Edward I's son, who would become Edward II of England, but she died while sailing from Norway without ever setting foot in Scotland. No coins were struck during her reign in her name but it is most probable that coins from the previous coinage of Alexander III were struck.

There was no direct successor following Margaret's death but thirteen claimants, known as the competitors, contested the throne. Edward I of England was asked to arbitrate and he set up a commission which deliberated for two years and finally decided in favour of John Baliol who was the grandson of the eldest daughter of David, Earl of Huntingdon who had died seventy years earlier.

John Baliol was crowned at Scone but had little authority against the powerful nobles in his country and in 1295 exhibited poor judgement by signing treaties with England's old enemy France which brought England and Scotland to the point of war. This resulted in many Scottish towns being lost and John abdicating and spending three years in prison in England. He was later released and died in France.

During John Baliol's reign pennies and halfpennies were produced. These were not of such a good standard as the previous issue and some issues used the number of points to the stars or mullets to link the mint while others gave the mint in the reverse legend. John Baliol during his short reign produced two coinages. They are known as the rough and smooth surface coinage, due to the fact that the first coinage has a rough surface due to intentionally produced dies with slightly irregular surfaces. The smooth surface second coinage has normally produced dies.

John Baliol abdicated in 1296 and Scotland was run as an English colony up until 1306. Edward I removed the Stone of Destiny and placed it in Westminster Abbey. It was not returned to Scotland until 1996. Edward I met sporadic resistance mainly from Sir William Wallace who was betrayed and executed in 1305.

Robert Bruce was one of the guardians appointed by Edward I of England during the interregnum. He was related to the niece of William the Lion and was one of the competitors after Margaret had died.

Robert Bruce claimed the throne in 1306 and was crowned at Scone. King Edward was not happy and Robert Bruce had to flee the country after King Edward pursued him. King Edward of England imprisoned Robert's wife and executed three of his brothers. However, Robert Bruce built resistance and finally beat the English at the battle of Bannockburn near Stirling. More unrest followed, especially in Northern England, but in 1328 England recognised Scotland's independence with the treaty of Northampton.

All coins of Robert Bruce's reign are rare, reflecting the turbulent period of his reign. The coins are similar in style to Alexander III's second coinage with pennies, halfpennies and farthings being struck.

Robert Bruce died in 1329. His son David II become king in 1331. It was not to be an easy reign because Edward Baliol, son of John Baliol also claimed the throne and was backed by Edward III of England. Edward Baliol invaded Scotland in 1332 and was crowned at Scone. King David II took exile in France, however he returned to Scotland in 1341 after Edward Baliol was forced to flee Scotland by Scottish Barons and Edward Baliol retired in England.

David II invaded England in 1346 and was captured by Edward III at the battle of Neville's Cross near Durham. He remained a prisoner of Edward III's for eleven years until he agreed to pay a ransom to Edward III over ten years. David II died in 1371.

Numismatically, David II's reign is very interesting. The coinage of David II was very much influenced by the new issues of Edward III. Firstly Scotland's first gold coin, the noble, was introduced. It is almost identical to the English issue, the only main

difference being the king's name in the obverse legend. This issue had a value of six shillings and eightpence the same as the English issue and this denomination was well known throughout most of Europe.

In 1357 the groat and halfgroat were introduced with a value of fourpence and twopence respectively. These issues show a crowned bust of the king with the king's name and title in the legend on the obverse while the reverse bears a long cross with a star or mullet in each quarter. The reverse shows two legends, the outer and the inner. The outer legend is a religious statement similar to the statements found on English coins while the inner legend shows the name of the mint.

The privy or mintmark was also introduced. On David's coins it consisted of a cross at the start of the obverse and reverse legend, the aim being that the mintmark could change for a particular issue or reign and so link a coin to a die. This idea had already been implemented on the English coinage and although the mintmarks for subsequent English reigns became more complex, the system was never properly used in Scotland, probably because fewer dies were needed.

Pennies, halfpennies and farthings were also struck during David's reign and all issues were struck at Edinburgh and Aberdeen. David II's issues were fairly prolific with a fairly large number of groats, halfgroats and pennies surviving. In 1347 an act of the Scottish Parliament allowed and encouraged English issues to circulate in Scotland. Due to the rising silver price throughout Europe, quality Scottish coins could be exported to Europe, melted down and sold at a profit because their silver content was higher than their face value. So in 1369, an act of Parliament made it illegal to carry money out of Scotland unless a tax was paid to the king.

In 1371, Robert II became king. His father Walter the Steward was related to the High Steward of Scotland in the reign of David I. The name Steward became Stewart and was to be the name of the dynasty which would last three hundred years slightly changing in spelling to Stuart. His reign was to be more peaceful than previous reigns and he very much rekindled Scotland's friendship with France.

Only silver coins were struck during his reign and were very similar in style to the previous reign. The Aberdeen mint was closed but the Perth and Dundee mints opened. Many issues show the moneyer's initial 'B', for Bonagius, by the king's head. This was an idea not used on English coins of the period. Groats, halfgroats, pennies and halfpennies were struck during this reign. The weights of Robert II's issues were reduced from the previous reign and in England in 1373 it was petitioned that groats of Robert II should only be worth threepence if traded in England.

Robert II died in 1390 and was succeeded by his son Robert, who had changed his name from John as it was thought the name John was ill-omened. Robert III had not the force to control his nobles and unrest followed. Dukedoms were created in Scotland to quell the unrest. Robert III died from shock after hearing the news that his son had been captured by the English.

During Robert III's reign for the first time gold coins in some quantity were struck for circulation. These coins were the lion and the demy lion and had a value of five shillings and two shillings and sixpence and were roughly equivalent in gold content if not value to the English half and quarter noble. The names and style of these coins is similar to French issues and were struck during the heavy and light coinage of Robert III's reign.

Due to the heavily rising gold and silver price in 1403 the weights of all denominations were reduced otherwise their metal content would have been higher than their face value. The fineness of the silver coins was also reduced causing many issues to have a very low silver content. Groats, halfgroats, pennies and halfpennies were the silver denominations struck. These coins are very crude in style and execution and were struck in Edinburgh, Aberdeen, Perth and Dumbarton. During this period more acts were passed to stop coins from being exported from Scotland and so leaving sufficient coins in circulation.

Robert III died in 1406 however his son James who was heir was only eleven and was a prisoner in England for the first eighteen years of his reign. While James I was in prison a regency was formed and James I was only released after a ransom of £40,000 was paid to the English. When James I returned to Scotland he was determined to restore law and order and he restored an uneasy peace using ruthless measures. He was murdered in 1437 by Sir Robert Graham who had a grievance with him.

During his reign the gold demy and half demy were introduced. The denomination names were of French origin and the coins had a value of nine shillings, and four shillings and sixpence respectively. The silver price during this period was still rising resulting in the groat's value being raised from fourpence to sixpence. Pennies and halfpennies were also struck during his reign, but no halfgroats or farthings. During this period there was concern in Scotland that the quality in silver content and style of the coinage was falling.

James II became king at the age of seven. Until he became old enough to rule, Scotland was ruled by Scottish lords. When James II was old enough to rule he quarrelled with the lords in particular the Douglas family. James II proposed a joint war with France against England but French support did not materialise, and he was killed in 1460 when laying siege to the English held Roxburgh castle, a bursting cannon killed him.

James II's coins were very much a continuation of James I's. However, a new gold denomination the lion and half lion with a value of ten shillings and five shillings was introduced in 1451. The silver price during this period was rising and the value of all second coinage coins was increased with the groat now being worth twelve pence. It must also be noted that coins in the second coinage were also heavier so the denomination had not doubled in value. Various acts were passed during James II's reign and during various periods it is possible that the face value of the groat varied. Most European countries which were all suffering from the rising silver price reduced the weights of the coins, however Scotland adopted the policy of increasing the value of the denomination. This must have caused confusion with the public unsure of what a particular coin from a particular issue was worth. The fact that in later reigns the fineness of some denomination was reduced could only have made the situation worse. It is probable that most merchants dealt with coins by weight and earlier issues with a higher metal content than their denomination would be melted down legally or illegally and a profit made.

James III became king in 1460 at the age of nine. He married Margaret who was daughter of Christian I, King of Denmark, Norway and Sweden. Part of the dowry James III received was the Orkney and Shetland Islands. James III became unpopular with his nobles due to his extravagant behaviour and also having particular favourites. He was murdered at the age of thirty six by a soldier pretending to be a priest after the battle of Sauchieburn.

During James III's reign new denominations and styles were introduced reflecting the new Renaissance style. Four new gold denominations were introduced. During the first gold issue the rider, half rider and quarter rider were introduced with a value of twenty three shillings, eleven shillings and sixpence and five shillings and ninepence respectively. These coins were called riders because a horseman can be found on the obverse and the rider is also a European denomination. The gold unicorn with a value of eighteen shillings was introduced during the second gold issue of 1484 – 88.

The value, weight and fineness of the silver issues varied during James III's reign. The face value of the groat varied during James

III's reign, and English coinage circulated in Scotland during this period. An English groat in Scotland was valued between fourteen and sixteen pence. During several issues of the groat and halfgroat a more lifelike portrait of the king can be found and these coins are a desirable addition to any collection. During much of James III's reign coins of very low silver content known as billon were produced. These denominations were the plack and half plack with a value of fourpence and twopence and the penny and halfpenny.

Copper and brass coins with a value of a penny and farthing were also struck during this period. The first issue was known as the regal issue and was nicknamed black money because of its lack of silver content. The second issue was probably an ecclesiastical issue struck at St Andrew's.

James IV became king at the age of fifteen. He became known as a competent but rash king and imposed peace and order in Scotland, however he lacked good judgement when dealing with England. Once again the Scots joined forces with the French against England, and James was killed at the battle of Flodden in Northumbria in 1513. His body was captured by the English, however because James IV was in dispute with the Pope over a broken peace treaty with England his body could not be buried. His body was left for some time unburied in a lead coffin in a monastery in Richmond, Surrey. During the reign of Elizabeth I of England he was buried in London.

Numismatically his coinage was continuation from previous reigns. The gold denomination the unicorn of eighteen shillings was complemented by the half unicorn with a value of nine shillings.

The denomination lion and half lion were also reintroduced and these coins now had a value of thirteen shillings and fourpence and six shillings and eightpence respectively. Groats, halfgroats and pennies were also struck and as with previous issues the value of these denominations varied. The billon coinage denominations from the previous reign were also struck and some of this issue appear to have no silver content at all.

James V became king at the age of only seventeen months. The fact that Scotland again had an infant king was exploited by the nobles who again for a period controlled the rule of Scotland. James V was declared competent to rule in 1524 although he did not rule absolutely until 1528.

He was married in 1537 to Madeleine of France however she died shortly after and he then married Mary of Guise who was the mother of Mary Queen of Scots. James V quarrelled with Henry VIII of England over Henry's ecclesiastical policies and war finally broke out. However James's nobles refused to accept his orders and James who was a sickly man died at the age of thirty.

It was to be a reign of new denominations and styles at last fully reflecting the renaissance throughout Europe.

While during the early part of his reign gold unicorns and half unicorns were still produced now with a value of twenty and ten shillings respectively, new denominations were to be issued.

These new gold denominations were the gold crown of twenty shillings, which are sometimes known as Abbey crowns because they were struck at Holyrood Abbey, the ducat of forty shillings, two thirds ducats of twenty six shillings and eightpence and one third ducat of thirteen shillings and fourpence. The ducat was also nicknamed the 'bonnet piece' because the king is wearing a bonnet. The denomination ducat is a European denomination. These gold ducats were Scotland's first dated coins with the 1539 issue being the first.

Superb groats with lifelike portraits were also struck and had a value of one shilling and sixpence. The one third groat with a value of sixpence was also introduced. During this period several acts of Parliament gave mintmasters James Achesoun and Joachim Hochstetter virtually a free hand to produce coins. These mintmasters had to pay the king for this privilege and they made their money by striking coins often with the metal content not reflecting the face value of the coin.

Billon issues were also struck during James V's reign. As well as the plack with a value of fourpence the famous bawbee and half bawbee were introduced which had a value of sixpence and three-pence respectively. The quarter bawbee of this reign is probably a pattern.

James V left no surviving legitimate children so in 1542 Mary who became known as Mary Queen of Scots became queen at the age of seven days. Her reign was to become the most famous in Scotland known for its romance and tragedies. When Mary was only seven months old she was betrothed to the five year old Prince Edward, the son of Henry VIII of England. The marriage was to take place when Mary was eleven however with the usual factions controlling Scotland during the reign of a child the Catholic followers snatched the baby and crowned her in Stirling and repudiated the betrothal. Henry VIII retaliated by invading Scotland and sacked Edinburgh. Scotland was now split in two by religious divisions. Many people supported the Protestants while others supported the Catholic faith. These divisions were to shape the history of Scotland and England during this period. After Henry VIII's death his young, sickly son Edward VI became king. He was like his father a Protestant. In 1547 the Duke of Somerset led an army to Scotland and defeated the Scots at the Battle of Pinkie near Edinburgh. From then on for the next thirteen years England was to rule Scotland and Mary went to exile in France. This was to be the last battle that England fought Scotland.

Mary married Francis the Dauphin of France in 1558 when she was fifteen. Now with French support she drove the English from Scotland and became Queen of Scotland. Francois died in 1560. While Mary had been in exile much of Scotland had become Protestant while Mary remained a Catholic. These religious differences started riots and escalated into virtual civil war, which was ended by Parliament's acceptance of the Protestant Reformation.

Mary who was known as being charming and beautiful married her first cousin, Lord Darnley, who was next in succession to the English throne after herself, so strengthening her claim to the English throne. Mary and Lord Darnley did not get on however, Mary was pregnant with his child who was going to become James VI. Mary became infatuated with the Earl of Bothwell and Bothwell strangled Lord Darnley, blew up his house, divorced his wife, abducted and married Mary.

However this was unacceptable to the Lords who were determined not to accept Bothwell as king and Mary abdicated in 1567.

Mary was imprisoned in England and in 1587 she was executed at Fotheringay Castle, Northants. She was buried in Peterborough Cathedral and then later moved to Westminster Abbey.

Mary's coinage was as complicated as her love life with large numbers of new denominations being introduced. The gold denominations included gold crowns which were similar to previous reigns, forty-four shillings, twenty-two shillings and twenty shillings, which showed Mary's monogrammed initials. The superb three pound and thirty shilling pieces were also struck between 1555 and 1558 and these two denominations show a superb life-like portrait of the queen.

The gold ducat with a value of sixty shillings was struck in 1558. The style of this coin in the obverse is similar to the shillings of Philip and Mary in England.

Two major silver denominations were issued during Mary's reign. Firstly the testoon and half testoon with a value of four shillings and two shillings respectively were issued. Many varieties of these issues exist and some issues have lovely portraits. All issues are dated and the word testoon is a European denomination.

The next major silver denomination was the crown-size ryal which was issued in 1565 – 67. It had a value of thirty shillings and was complemented by the two thirds ryal and one third ryal which had a value of twenty shillings and ten shillings. Up until 1560 it is thought that most of Mary's coinage was struck at Holyrood and then after 1560 it was struck at Edinburgh. The coinages of Mary very much reflect her life with the name and bust of Francis found on the gold ducat of sixty shillings and the name and arms of Henry Darnley found on the silver ryal series (the ryal, the two thirds ryal and the third ryal).

Billon coins were also struck in some quantity, and the twelve-penny groat or nonsunt was introduced in 1558. The popular lion or hard head as it was sometimes known was also struck during Mary's reign and had a value of three halfpence. Billon bawbees, half bawbees, placks as well as pennies were also struck during her reign. These pennies have the infant's portrait on the obverse.

James VI became king of Scotland at the age of thirteen months after the abdication of his mother Mary Queen of Scots. A council of Regency ruled during his childhood and James was well educated. For much of his early life, he was in 'protective custody' and after escaping these confinements once again tried to cultivate the alliance of Scotland and France. Elizabeth swayed his allegiances to France by paying James a 'pension' of four thousand pounds a year and also confirming he was heir to the English throne.

Elizabeth I died in 1603 and James VI became king of England in 1603. He was known as James I of England and James VI of Scotland.

James VI's religious beliefs wavered; at one stage he almost accepted Catholicism, then considered Presbyterianism. He finally settled for Protestantism, which resulted in the gunpowder plot when Catholic sympathisers tried to blow up the king in 1605. James VI very much wanted a uniting of the two nations and this was often reflected in the coinage. He died in 1625 at the age of fifty-eight from premature old age in Hertfordshire.

James VI's coinage was complicated and in 1604 new denominations were introduced which were similar in style to the English issues. This was intentional so that the two united countries could trade more easily. The denominations however were not the same value and a ratio of twelve to one between Scottish and English denominations was maintained. This in practice meant coins like the Scottish unit or sceptre piece with a value of twelve pounds was worth the same as an English gold unite of twenty shillings.

Before James VI's accession to the English throne numerous denominations were struck. The gold denominations include the spectacular twenty pound piece, the ducat of twenty shillings, lion noble of seventy-five shillings, two third noble of fifty shillings and one third noble of twenty-five shillings.

The gold thistle noble of one hundred and forty-six shillings and eightpence was also struck as well as the hat piece of eighty shillings, so called because the king is wearing a hat. Gold riders showing the king as a horseman were also struck with a value of one hundred shillings and the half rider of fifty shillings complemented the denomination. The gold sword and sceptre piece was introduced in 1601 and had a value of one hundred and twenty shillings. The half sword and sceptre piece complemented this issue and had a value of sixty shillings. They were known as sword and sceptre pieces because a sword and sceptre can be found on the reverse.

Before the accession to the English throne large quantities of silver coins were struck. The denominations included the ryal, two thirds ryal and one third ryal which were also struck during the previous reign. The two merk with a value of twenty-six shillings and eightpence was also introduced and was complemented by the merk, half merk and quarter merk. The word 'merk' came from the continental denomination 'mark'. The half merk was also sometimes known as the noble because it had the denomination of six shillings and eightpence which was the historical value of the noble.

During the third coinage more denominations were struck. They were the sixteen, eight, four and two shillings and during the fourth coinage a crown size forty shillings was issued.

The superb issue was complemented by the thirty, twenty and ten shillings coins. All of these issues were dated and showed a half length bust of the king holding a sword.

During the sixth coinage the silver balance half merk was struck. It had a value of six shillings and eightpence and was known as a 'balance' because a set of scales can be found on the reverse. It was complemented by the balance quarter merk which was struck in 1591 only.

During the seventh coinage the ten shilling, five shilling, thirty pence and twelve pence were struck. All these issues were dated and show an uncrowned bust of the king on the obverse and a crown above three thistles on the reverse.

During this period billon and copper coins were also struck. These included the eight-penny groat, four-penny and two-penny plack, hardhead and twopence and penny.

During James VI's reign silver prices were rising sharply resulting in denominations from previous reigns and early issues of James VI having a higher silver content that their face value. So in 1578 many silver coins were re-called and countermarked with a thistle to legally increase the value of the coins. During Mary's reign large quantities of billon placks and lions were produced. These two denominations were mainly issued to help the poor and unfortunately were heavily counterfeited. These unpopular counterfeits caused unrest and in 1575 they were recalled and genuine coins were countermarked with a heart and star to help restore confidence with the public. During the early part of James VI's reign coins were struck at Dalkeith, then the mint moved to Holyrood and then to Edinburgh.

After James VI's accession to the English throne both the Tower mint in London and the Edinburgh mint in Scotland remained open. Scottish coins were fairly similar to English coins and the two countries' issues would be circulated to some degree side by side, although the Scottish coins were never produced in the same number as the English.

The gold coins struck after James VI's accession were the unit or sceptre piece with a value of twelve pounds, the double crown with a value of six pounds, the Britain crown of three pounds, halfcrown of thirty shillings and thistle crown of forty-eight shillings.

All issues showed heraldry and designs of both countries and some of the coin legends were statements of unity. For example the unit of £12 reverse legend is FACIAM EOS IN GENTEM UNAM — I will make them one nation.

Silver coins were struck in various denominations. The largest coin was the crown-sized sixty shillings which showed the king on horseback on the obverse. It was complemented by the thirty shillings, which was similar in style. These denominations were very similar in style to the English crown and halfcrown. The twelve shilling and six shilling was also struck during this period. The six shilling is dated and both coins have a bust of the king on the obverse. These two coins were similar to the English shilling and sixpence. The silver two shilling and shilling completed the silver denominations. They were non-portrait issues and showed a crowned rose of England on the obverse and a crowned thistle on the reverse. These two denominations were similar to English halfgroat and penny. Details are given in the relevant chapters of how to differentiate the Scottish issues from the English ones.

No billon coins were struck after James VI acceded to the throne, however copper twopences and pennies were struck.

Charles I became king in 1625, at the age of twenty five. He was the only surviving child of James VI and his reign would result in civil war and his execution. Charles I's reign was marred by poor judgement and his constant disputes with Parliament. After a series of disputes with Parliament, Charles dissolved Parliament and imprisoned some of the leaders of the Commons. He was to govern as a dictator for eleven years. All this fuelled the civil war. As the situation got worse in 1639 the Scottish parliament established an army in Northern England. Between 1642 and 1646 England was torn apart by civil war and Charles finally surrendered to the Scottish army in 1646.

After his trial he was executed in 1649 and buried in Windsor.

Unlike many English issues, Charles I's Scottish issues did not reflect the civil war and upheaval the countries were going through. This was due to the fact that most of the conflict was in England.

Charles I's coinage can be divided into two issues. Firstly the hammered issue and secondly the machine made issue. These superb machine made issues were struck by the Frenchman Nicholas Briot and his son-in-law John Falconer. Their work was of the highest quality and was the forerunner of the milled coins of Charles II. Their work however was not popular with the mint workers who feared they might lose their jobs and be replaced by machines. The machine-made coins were also much slower to produce.

Gold coins were issued from 1625 – 42. The first coinage produced the unit, double crown and Britain crown as well as a milled angel which could be considered a commemorative issue. The first three denominations were all hammered. From 1637 to 1642 machine made coins were struck. The gold denominations struck were unit, half unit, Britain crown and Britain halfcrown.

Silver coins were struck from 1625 to 1642. The first issues from 1625 to 1634 were hammered and often rather crude in style. The denominations were sixty shillings, thirty shillings, twelve shillings, six shillings, two shillings and one shilling.

From 1636 to 1642 machine-made coins were struck for the following denominations: sixty shillings, thirty shillings, twelve shillings, six shillings, half merk, forty pence, three shillings, two shillings and twenty pence. These machine-made issues were struck by Nicholas Briot and John Falconer who on most issues put their initials B or F on the dies so they could be linked to the die master. Copper twopences were also produced in large quantities during this period and were struck up until 1650.

Charles I died in 1649. His son Charles II was proclaimed king of Scotland and was crowned at Scone in 1651. He was in exile from London for nine and a half years and in 1660 landed at Dover in southern England and reclaimed the throne. He was crowned in 1661. No coins were struck in Scotland during this period.

Scotland: David I (1124 – 1153)

David I was the first Scottish king to strike coins and the only denomination struck was the silver penny, or sterling as it was sometimes known. Pennies were cut into halves and quarters, so producing halfpennies and farthings. Although several Victorian publications list coins of earlier reigns, these listings are incorrect. The first issue used English designs as a format, with the king's name on the obverse legend. It is thought that these coins were struck by the moneyer Erebald, an Englishman living in Carlisle. After the capture of Carlisle by David I, it appears that Erebald made the dies for David I.

Penny

The coinage can be divided into four issues, all of which were struck in 0.925 sterling silver, the same as the English issues.

First Issue (1136 – 1144?)

Collecting Hints

The first and third issues are extremely rare, while the second issue is very rare. These coins can easily be confused with the more common English issues of Henry I (quadrilateral on cross fleury issue, H11D-075) or those of Stephen (Watford type, ST1D-005). Collectors should therefore be wary when purchasing or identifying a coin.

Carlisle

Obverse Legend   DAVIT REX — King David

Reverse Legend   EREBALD ON CARD — Erebald of Carlisle

Obverse   Crowned bust of king holding sceptre; similar to the English H11D-075.

Reverse   Cross moline, fleury in centre.

SD11D-005   ex. rare

Obverse Legend   STIEFNE REX — King Stephen

Reverse Legend   EREVALD ON CARD (varieties exist) — Erebald of Carlisle

Obverse   Crowned bust of king facing right and holding sceptre, as ST1D-005.

Reverse   Cross moline with a fleur in each angle.

SD11D-010   VG —   F £800   VF —

Edinburgh

Obverse Legend   NDIVID REX — King David

Reverse Legend   DERIND ON EDNDEN — Derind of Edinburgh

Obverse   As previous.

Reverse   As previous.

SD11D-015   ex. rare

Second Issue (1145 – 1149?)

Collecting Hints

The first issue is very rare and always found with badly blundered legends; the second and third issues are extremely rare.

This issue is a fairly poor copy of a Stephen issue and was struck at Edinburgh and Roxburgh.

Obverse Legend   (heavily blundered)

Reverse Legend   (heavily blundered)

Obverse   Crowned bust of king facing right and holding sceptre.

Reverse   Cross moline, a fleur in each angle.

SD11D-020   VG £400   F £1000   VF —

This issue was struck at five different mints, all of which are extremely rare. It should not be confused with the Henry I issue (cross and annulet issue, H11D-060).

The moneyers and mints for this issue are:

Berwick — (?) ON BER
Carlisle — RICARD ON CAR
Edinburgh — DERIN ON EDON or EREBALD ON ED
Perth — uncertain
Roxburgh — FOLBOLD ON ROCE

Obverse Legend   DAVID REX — King David

Reverse Legend   Moneyer's name and mint, see above for details.

Obverse   Small crowned bust of king facing left.

Reverse   Large cross, a crescent or annulet around a pellet in each quarter.

SD11D-025   ex. rare

Bishop of Carlisle Issue(?)

Obverse Legend   DAOVIDR — King David

Reverse Legend   EREBALD ON CAR — Erebald of Carlisle

Obverse   Crowned bust of king to right holding a branch.

Reverse   Cross fleury, three annulets in each angle.

SD11D-030	ex. rare

Third Issue (1149 – 1153?)

Coins were struck at the following mints:

Berwick — FOLPALT ON BERVI
Carlisle — RICARD ON CARD
Roxburgh — HUGO ON ROCASBURG (or ROCA)
St Andrews — MEINARD ON A.

Collecting Hints

This issue, while rare, is obtainable and the style and lettering is of fairly good quality. When available, coins are usually found in VG to Fine condition.

Obverse Legend   DAVID (or DAVIT) REX — King David

Reverse Legend   Moneyer's name and mint, see above for details.

Obverse   Crowned bust of king holding sceptre.

Reverse   Cross fleury, pellets in each quarter or sometimes broken annulets.

SD11D-035 VG £400	VF £1,000

Fourth or Posthumous Issue (1153 – ?)

Collecting Hints

These issues while rare are obtainable especially in the lower grades. The legends of both issues are heavily blundered or have meaningless words and the coin is very crude in style.

Obverse Legend   Blundered.

Reverse Legend   Blundered.

Obverse   Crude bust of king, with crown of pellets.

Reverse   Cross pellet in each quarter.

SD11D-040	VG £400	F £800 VF —

Obverse Legend   A variety of meaningless legends, often blundered or retrograde.

Reverse Legend   A variety of meaningless legends, often blundered or retrograde.

Obverse   As previous, but bust of better style.

Reverse   As previous, but bust of better style.

SD11D-045	VG £400	F £900 VF —

43

Scotland: Prince Henry
Earl of Northumberland & Huntingdon (1139 – 1152)

Prince Henry was David I's heir. These issues were struck in England during the English civil war of King Stephen and in many respects could be classed as English issues, however because Prince Henry was David's son, we have classed them as Scottish.

Penny

These issues circulated alongside those of David I and were struck at the mints of Carlisle, Corbridge and, possibly, Bamborough. The style of some issues was very much a copy of the coins of Stephen of England, in particular the Watford issue (see *Coincraft's Standard Catalogue of English & UK coins, 1066 to date,* ST1D-005).

Collecting Hints

All issues are very or extremely rare. Collectors should pay particular attention so as not to confuse these coins with the more common English issues.

Obverse Legend HENRIC(US) or NENCON — Henry or possibly Count Henry

Reverse Legend EREBALD ON COLEB — Erebald of Corbridge

Obverse Crowned bust holding sceptre.

Reverse Cross moline with fleurs in angles.

SPH1D-005   v. rare

Obverse Legend HENRICUS COM or N ENCI CON — Count Henry

Reverse Legend WILELM ON CAR — William of Carlisle

Obverse As previous.

Reverse Cross fleury only.

SPH1D-010   v. rare

Obverse Legend HENCI CON — Count Henry

Reverse Legend WILLELM ON CIB or CBI — William of Bamborough(?)

Obverse King holding sceptre.

Reverse Cross, cross crosslets in each quarter.

SPH1D-015   v. rare

Obverse Legend STIFENE REX — King Stephen

Reverse Legend As previous or EREBALD ON CARD — Erebald of Carlisle.

Obverse As previous.

Reverse As previous.

SPH1D-020   ex. rare

Scotland: Malcolm IV (1153 – 1165)

Only pennies were struck under Malcolm IV and all are extremely rare. The fourth, or posthumous, issue of David I was also struck during this reign but is listed under David I. As with the coins of previous reigns, the king's name is found on the obverse and the moneyer's name and mint on the reverse, although virtually all coins are in such poor condition that the mint name is illegible. The moneyer's for all issues is thought to be HUGO. Coins were struck at Roxburgh and possibly Berwick.

Penny

Collecting Hints

All issues are extremely rare.

Obverse Legend   MALCOLM REX — King Malcolm

Reverse Legend   HUGO ON ROCABURG — Hugo of Roxburgh

Obverse   Bust of king holding sceptre and facing right.

Reverse   Cross fleury, pellets or pellets and rosettes in alternate angles.

SML1D-005   ex. rare

Obverse Legend   As previous.

Reverse Legend   HUGO ON ROCABURG — Hugo of Roxburgh

Obverse   Front-facing bust king holding two sceptres.

Reverse   As previous.

SML1D-010   unique

As previous, but cross fleury over lozenge fleury on reverse.

SML1D-015   ex. rare

Obverse Legend   MALCOLM REX — King Malcolm

Reverse Legend   Uncertain due to poor striking, but probably as previous.

Obverse   Right-facing bust of the king holding a sceptre.

Reverse   Cross fleury, a pellet in each angle, two with stalks.

SML1D-020   v. rare

Obverse Legend   As previous.

Reverse Legend   As previous.

Obverse   Bust of king facing left and holding sceptre.

Reverse   Cross fleury a pellet in each angle.

SML1D-025   v. rare

Scotland: William I The Lion (1165 – 1214)

William I was the first Scottish king to produce silver pennies in some quantity, and issues towards the end of his reign are quite common. All depict a rather crude bust of the king on the obverse and a cross with a symbol in each quarter on the reverse. The reverse legend bears the name of the moneyer and the mint, often abbreviated, so that a substandard coin could be attributed to the correct mint and moneyer and be investigated.

Because the weight and fineness of these issues was the same as their English counterparts, Scottish coins circulated in some quantity in England too.

At the time, the penny was a high denomination and as the use of coinage became more common in everyday transactions, the need for smaller denominations increased. It was originally met by simply cutting coins into halves and quarters to produce half-pennies and farthings.

Penny

Collecting Hints

The 1165–74 issue is extremely rare and difficult to obtain, although examples from the latter issues are obtainable. A fair number of cut halfpennies have recently been found in England thus offering budget collectors the opportunity of obtaining an example. Coins of all issues are rarely found in better than Fine condition and often have very blundered legends.

First Issue (1165 – 1174)

Obverse Legend WILELMUS RE — King William

Reverse Legend FOLPOLD ROI — Folpold (of) Roxburgh

Obverse Crowned right facing bust holding sceptre.

Reverse Cross pattée, lis in each quarter.

SW11D-005   ex. rare

Obverse Legend As previous.

Reverse Legend (uncertain) of Berwick

Obverse As previous but king facing left or right.

Reverse Crosslet of pellets in each quarter.

SW11D-010   ex. rare

Second Issue (1174 – 1195)

This issue is often known as the crescent and pellet issue, because a crescent and pellet can be found in each quarter on the reverse.

Class I: Without mint name (1174 – 1180)

Obverse Legend WILAMERX or WILLAME REX or LE RE WILAM — King William

Reverse Legend AILBODE or WILLAME — Ailbode or William (moneyer's name)

Obverse Crowned left-facing bust of king holding a sceptre, the sceptre head is a cross pattée.

Reverse Cross pattée with crescent and pellet in each quarter, colons between letters.

SW11D-015   VG £80   F £250 VF £500

Class II: With mint name

This class can be distinguished by the design of the king's sceptre on the obverse.

Sceptre head with cross potent
The moneyers and mints of this sub-class are as follows:
ADAM ON ED .... Adam of Edinburgh
FOLPOLT (DE) PERT............ Folpolt of Perth
RAUL DE ROCEBUR or
RAUL ON ROC.................... Raul of Roxburgh
WILLAO BEREWIC .... William (of) Berwick

Obverse Legend LE REI WILLA or WILAM REX — William the King or King William

Reverse Legend Moneyer's name and mint (see details above), minor varieties of issue exist.

Obverse Bust of king facing left holding sceptre with a cross potent at the sceptre head.

Reverse As previous.

SW11D-020 VG £80 F £200 VF £400

Sceptre head with cross of four pellets
The moneyers and mints of this sub-class are as follows:

ADAM BEREWIC.................. Adam (of) Berwick
ADAM ON ED .... Adam of Edinburgh
HUE ON EDENEBU .... Hue of Edinburgh
RAUL ON ROCAS................ Raul of Roxburgh (many varieties)
WILAM BEREWI.................. William (of) Berwick (many varieties)

Obverse Legend LE REI WILAM — William the King

Reverse Legend Moneyer's name and mint (see details above).

Obverse As previous, but king's sceptre head is made up of a cross of four pellets.

Reverse As previous.

SW11D-025 VG £80 F £200 VF £400

The next issue has been attributed to the Berwick and Roxburgh mints.

Obverse Legend LE REI WILAO or WILAM — William the King

Reverse Legend RAUL DERLIG — Raul Derlig (moneyer's name)

Obverse As previous.

Reverse As previous.

SW11D-030 VG £70 F £180 VF £360

Short Cross & Stars Issue (1195 – 1230)

This issue can be distinguished by a voided cross in the centre of the reverse and a star in each quarter. The bust of the king is mainly made up of a series of pellets.

Class I (1195 – 1205)

The moneyers and mints of this issue are as follows:

HUE ON EDENBUR .... Hue of Edinburgh
RAUL ON ROCEBU .... Raul of Roxburgh
WATER ON PER .... Walter of Perth

Obverse Legend WILELMUS R(E)X — King William

Reverse Legend Moneyer's name and mint (see details above), many minor varieties exist.

Obverse Bust of pellets facing left, the king holding a sceptre.

Reverse Voided short cross, a star in each quarter.

SW11D-035 VG £80 F £200 VF £400

Obverse Legend WILEMUS REX — King William

Reverse Legend ADAM ON RORE or AIMER ADAM ON ROH — Adam of Roxburgh or Aimer Adam of Roxburgh

Obverse As previous, but head facing right.

Reverse As previous.

SW11D-040 VG £100 F £250 VF £500

Class II (1205 – 1230)

This class is sometimes known as the late issue or posthumous coinage, as it was struck at the end of William I's own reign and during that of his son, Alexander II. The style of these coins was deteriorating, with the portrait being made up of a just few lines.

Obverse Legend LE REI WILAM (many varieties) — William the King

Reverse Legend HUE WALTER — Moneyer's name. This issue was probably struck at the Edinburgh, Perth and Roxburgh mints.

Obverse Crude bust of the king.

Reverse Voided cross with a star in each quarter.

SW11D-045 VG £40 F £100 VF £200

As previous, but the moneyer's name on the reverse legend reads WALTER ADAM. This issue was struck at the Edinburgh mint.

SW11D-050 VG £100 F £300 VF —

As previous, but the reverse legend reads HUE WALTER ON RO — Hue Walter of Roxburgh. This issue was struck at Roxburgh.

SW11D-065 ex. rare

As previous, but the moneyer's name on the reverse legend reads HENRI LE RUS; the legend is sometimes retrograde. This issue was probably struck at the Roxburgh mint.

SW11D-055 VG £90 F £250 VF £500

As previous, but the reverse legend reads HENRI LE RUS PERT — Henry the Rus Perth. This issue was struck at Perth.

SW11D-060 VG £100 F £300 VF —

Scotland: Alexander II (1214 – 1249)

Most of the coins struck under Alexander II used dies from the reign of his father, William I, and there is considerable speculation as to the reasons for this. It is most unlikely that a single die could last the twenty five years of this coinage, so the shortage of dies or engravers would appear not to be a factor. Instead, it was probably due to the fact that Alexander II was only sixteen when his father died and the country was effectively ruled by the Barons. With the vast majority of the population being illiterate there was little need to alter the obverse legend, while the busts of the kings were crude and not a true likeness, thus further diminishing the need for change.

The issues with William I's portrait and name in the legend are listed under William I.

Penny

Collecting Hints

All issues are very rare, especially in better than Fine condition, and collectors will have great difficulty in obtaining an example.

Class I (1230 – 1235?)

This issue was struck in the name of William.

Obverse Legend   WILLRLMUS REX — King William (varieties exist)

Reverse Legend   PIERES ON RO — Pieres of Roxburgh or AIMER ON ROX — Aimer of Roxburgh or ADAM ON ROXHR — Adam of Roxburgh

Obverse   Crude right-facing bust of the king holding a sceptre.

Reverse   Short cross with a star in each quarter.

SA21D-005	VG £125	F £300	VF —

Class II (1235 – 1249)

This issue was struck in the name of Alexander.

Roxburgh Mint

Obverse Legend   ALEXSANDER REX — King Alexander

Reverse Legend   PIERES ON RO or RX — Pierres of Roxburgh

Obverse   Crowned bust of king facing right or left, holding a sceptre.

Reverse   Voided short cross a star in each quarter.

SA21D-010	VG £250	F £600	VF —

As previous, but uncrowned head.

SA21D-015	VG £250	F £600	VF —

As previous, but crowned head facing left.

SA21D-020	VG £250	F £600	VF —

Obverse Legend   ALEXSANDER REX — King Alexander

Reverse Legend   ADAM ANDREW ON R — Adam and Andrew of Roxburgh

Obverse   Uncrowned bust of king facing right or left, without sceptre.

Reverse   Voided short cross a star in each quarter.

SA21D-025	VG £250	F £600	VF —

Berwick Mint

Obverse Legend   ALEXANDER REX — King Alexander

Reverse Legend   WALROB ON BER — Wales and Robert of Berwick

Obverse   Uncrowned bust of bearded king facing right, wearing an ornamental (?)cap and holding a sceptre.

Reverse   As previous.

SA21D-030	ex. rare

As previous, but the king is clean shaven.

SA21D-035	ex. rare

Uncertain Mint

Obverse Legend   As previous.

Reverse Legend   WILAM IOHAN ON — Wilam Iohan (moneyer's name) of (?)

Obverse   As previous.

Reverse   As previous.

SA21D-040 ex. rare	

Scotland: Alexander III (1249 – 1286)

Alexander III's reign produced the most extensive of all Scottish medieval issues, with the penny being the most prolific coin and the halfpenny and farthing being introduced. There are great similarities between Alexander's coinage and that of the English re-coinage of Edward I. The style of Alexander III's issues was greatly improved with his second coinage (1280 – 86) and it is no coincidence that Edward I had introduced his own new coinage in 1279, again with improved style and new denominations. Both Scotland and England were prospering at the time and this was reflected in the large number of coins struck by both countries. Like their English counterparts, Scottish coins were accepted throughout Europe and are often found in hoards on the Continent.

Penny

The styles of coins can be broken up into three main issues. The transitional coinage, which was very much a continuation of Alexander II's issues was followed by the first coinage. These issues were struck at some eighteen mints and depicted a crowned king on the obverse and a long voided cross with stars in each quarter on the reverse with the moneyer's name and the mint name or abbreviation found in the legend.

The second coinage, or re-coinage as it is sometimes known, produced coins of good style and workmanship. The obverse bore a crowned bust of the king holding a sceptre and the reverse a plain long cross with a star in each quarter. Unlike previous issues, the moneyer's name and mint are not on the legends but the mints can be worked out by the number of points on the stars in the reverse legend. Various other marks were also placed on the coins so that they could easily be linked to dies. At a quick glance, all coins appear identical and this at last produced conformity which in turn contributed to the success of the coinage.

Transitional Coinage (1249 – 1250)

Collecting Hints

The first series is extremely rare and, in the case of the Roxburgh mint, unique while the next two issues are rare especially in better than Fine condition.

Obverse Legend ALEXANDER REX — King Alexander

Reverse Legend WILAM IOHAN ON — (moneyer's name)

Obverse Beardless bust of king facing left or right.

Reverse Short voided cross a star in each quarter.

SA31D-005	ex. rare

As previous, but Roxburgh mint.

SA31D-010	ex. rare

Obverse Legend As previous.

Reverse Legend ROB ON BEWIK or WALES EB ON

Obverse As previous.

Reverse Voided long cross with large hooked ends, a star in each quarter.

SA31D-015	VG £80	F £200	VF £500

Obverse Legend As previous.

Reverse Legend RO BE RTO NBE — Robert of Berwick

Obverse As previous.

Reverse A normal voided long cross with straight ends.

SA31D-020	VG £80	F £200	VF £500

First Coinage (1250 – 1280)

This issue, of which there are seven different styles, was struck at eighteen mints throughout Scotland. The moneyer's name and the mint can be found in the reverse legend. The mints were not spelt as they are today and were often abbreviated. Below we have listed the mint, the abbreviation used on the coins followed by the moneyer's name or names. Often the same obverse die was used by the same mint and it is possible moneyers toured Scotland striking coins.

On all issues, the moneyer's name is found first, followed by 'on' (meaning 'of') and the mint abbreviation, which was often shortened further if the moneyer had a long name. By contrast the moneyer's name, although sometimes misspelt, was rarely abbreviated. An example of a reverse legend is HENRI ON STRIVE — Henry of Stirling.

As mentioned earlier, varieties in the mint abbreviation exist and below we list the most common ones. If uncertain, it is important to check that the moneyer's name corresponds to the mint abbreviation.

Mint	Abbreviation	Moneyer
Aberdeen	ABE	Alexander
		Andreas
		Ion
		Rainald
Ayr	(H)ARE	Simon
Berwick	BER or IER	Arnald
		Iohan
		Robert
		Robert and Wales
		Wales
		Walter
		Willem

Dunbar	DUN	Walter
		Wilam
Edinburgh	EDEN	Alexander
		Nicol
		Wilam
Forfar	FO, FOR	Simond
		Wilam
Fres	FRE [1]	Walter
		Wilam
Glasgow	GLA	Walter
Inverness	INV	Gefrai
Kinghorn	KIN	Wilam
		Walter
Lanark	LAN	Wilam
Montrose	MUN [2]	Walter
Perth	P or PER	Ion
		Iohan Cokin
		Rainald
Renfrew	RIN	Walter
Roxburgh	R or ROX	Adam
		Andrew
		Michel
		Wilam
St Andrews	ANDER	Thomas
Stirling	STRIVE	Henri
uncertain	WILANERTER [3]	

1. Probably an abreviation of DUMFRIES.
2. Possibly a blundered die for DUN — Dunbar.
3. Full reverse reading of 'Wilanerter', no moneyer's name.

Aberdeen

Ayr

Dunbar

Fres

Glasgow

Kinghorn

Perth

Roxburgh

St Andrews

Stirling

Below we list the seven classes of issue. We then list each mint, with each class and value. It should be noted that we have adopted a different class classification system from that of previous reference works.

Class 1

Obverse Legend   ALEXANDER REX — King Alexander

Reverse Legend   Moneyer's name and mint.

Obverse   Youthful bust of king facing right and holding sceptre.

Reverse   Voided cross, a star in each quarter.

class 1

Class 2

Obverse Legend   As previous.

Reverse Legend   As previous.

Obverse   Small bust facing left and holding sceptre.

Reverse   As previous.

class 2

Class 3

Obverse Legend   As previous.

Reverse Legend   As previous.

Obverse   As previous, but king wearing a tall crown with a centred lis and decorated with large jewels.

Reverse   As previous.

class 3

Class 4

Obverse Legend   As previous.

Reverse Legend   As previous.

Obverse   As previous, but a thin bust.

Reverse   As previous.

class 4

Class 5

Obverse Legend   As previous.

Reverse Legend   As previous.

Obverse   Tall crowned bust of king facing right.

Reverse   As previous.

class 5

Class 6

Obverse Legend   As previous.

Reverse Legend   As previous.

Obverse   Crowned bust of king facing right or left. The bust very angular in style being made of straight lines.

Reverse   As previous.

class 6

Class 7

Obverse Legend   As previous.

Reverse Legend   As previous.

Obverse   Older or 'uglier' bust of king wearing a flat crown facing right or left.

Reverse   As previous.

class 7

No.	Mint	Class	VG	F	VF
SA31D-025	Aberdeen	1	50	100	225
SA31D-030		2	50	110	225
SA31D-035		6	50	110	225
SA31D-040	Ayr	1	70	160	300
SA31D-045		2	75	180	320
SA31D-050		3	75	180	320
SA31D-055		6	75	180	320
SA31D-060	Berwick	1	30	65	125
SA31D-065		2	30	60	120
SA31D-070		5	35	75	135
SA31D-075		6	35	75	135
SA31D-080		7	35	75	135
SA31D-085	Dun	2	65	150	rare
SA31D-090		3	65	150	rare
SA31D-095	Edinburgh	2	35	70	130
SA31D-100		3	35	80	150
SA31D-105		4	35	70	130

No.	Mint	Class	VG	F	VF
SA31D-110		5	35	70	130
SA31D-115		6	35	70	130
SA31D-120	Forfar	2	70	150	rare
SA31D-125	Fres	2	90	200	rare
SA31D-130		6	90	200	rare
SA31D-135		7	90	200	rare
SA31D-140	Glasgow	1	80	160	rare
SA31D-145		2	80	160	rare
SA31D-150		3	80	160	rare
SA31D-155		7	90	180	rare
SA31D-160	Inverness	2	100	200	400
SA31D-165	Kinghorn	2	100	200	rare
SA31D-170		5	100	200	rare
SA31D-175	Lanark	1	100	200	rare
SA31D-180		2	100	200	rare
SA31D-185		4	110	240	rare
SA31D-190	Montrose	2	ex.rare		
SA31D-195	Perth	1	40	80	160
SA31D-200		2	35	70	150
SA31D-205		6	40	80	160
SA31D-210		7	45	90	180
SA31D-215	Renfrew	2	ex. rare		
SA31D-220		5	ex. rare		
SA31D-225	Roxburgh	1	45	90	180
SA31D-230		2	40	80	160
SA31D-235		5	45	90	180
SA31D-240		6	45	90	180
SA31D-245		7	40	80	160
SA31D-250	St Andrews	2	75	160	rare
SA31D-255		3	75	160	rare
SA31D-260	Stirling	2	70	140	rare
SA31D-265		3	70	140	rare
SA31D-270	Wilanerter	2	ex. rare		
SA31D-275		3	ex. rare		

Second Coinage (1280 – 1286)

This issue, which was broadly timed to coincide with Edward I's recoinage, was a tremendous success in producing high quality coins of good style and proportion, as well as fineness and weight which could be trusted. It is thought that some fifty million coins were produced during this coinage. Unlike previous issues, these coins do not bear the mint or moneyer's names but the number of points to the stars on the reverse denote the mint where a coin was struck (a list is given below). This was a form of quality control so coins would be linked to dies and moneyers. And although it now results in some classification uncertainty or even inaccuracies, this is not to say that the various mint details were unreliable at the time but rather that the information has been lost subsequently.

Mint	Points
Aberdeen	23
Berwick	24
Edinburgh	20
Perth	26
Roxburgh	25
Uncertain	21, 22, 27, 28

Collecting Hints

Due to the uncertainty of the mint classification, the valuation of each mint is difficult and very few collectors collect by mint. By far the most common issue is the Berwick issue with 24 points while the scarcest issues are the uncertain mints with 21, 22, 27 and 28 points. We have decided not to give valuations for mints but list each issue by class. These issues are by far the most common coin of this period and usually available in VG to VF condition. Many have been found in hoards, often in England, and the average condition of these coins is often VF. Coins of this issue are rarely clipped or damaged and no collection is complete without a specimen.

| SA31D-300 | VG £17 | F £35 | VF £70 |

Class 1

Obverse Legend ALEXANDER DEI GRA or GSIA or GCIA — Alexander by the grace of God

Reverse Legend ESCOSSIE REX — King of Scotland

Obverse Crowned head facing left with sceptre, unbarred A in legend; mintmark cross pattée.

Reverse Long cross, four stars of six points each in quarter. The 'C' and 'E' in legend closed.

| SA31D-280 | VG £75 | F £165 | VF £350 |

As previous, but reverse legend reads REX SCOTORUM — King of Scots.

| SA31D-285 | VG £30 | F £70 | VF £140 |

Class 2

Obverse Legend ALEXANDER DEI GRA — Alexander by the grace of God

Reverse Legend ESCOSSIE REX — King of Scotland

Obverse As previous, but barred 'A' in legend.

Reverse As previous, but open 'C' and 'E' and a thin 'S' in legend.

| SA31D-290 | VG £75 | F £150 | VF £300 |

As previous, but reverse legend reads REX SCOTORUM — King of Scots.

| SA31D-295 | VG £25 | F £50 | VF £100 |

Class 3

Obverse Legend As previous.

Reverse Legend As previous.

Obverse As previous, but unbarred 'A' and mintmark plain cross at beginning of legend.

Reverse As previous, but 'S' in legend with an oval centre.

Class 4

Obverse Legend As previous.

Reverse Legend As previous.

Obverse New style bust of king, with hair swept back in three waves; mintmark cross potent.

Reverse Long cross, stars in each quarter, with a total of 24 to 26 points The 'C' in legend has fish-tailed endings.

| SA31D-305 | VG £17 | F £35 | VF £70 |

Class 5

Obverse Legend As previous.

Reverse Legend As previous.

Obverse As Class 3, but letters are curved and angular.

Reverse As previous, with the stars having a total of 20, 21, 22, 23, 24, 26, 27 or 28 points. Pellets sometimes found in field.

| SA31D-310 | VG £17 | F £35 | VF £70 |

Class 6

Obverse Legend As previous.

Reverse Legend As previous.

Obverse Sometimes a slightly larger bust. Straight sided letters with an unbarred 'A' and serifs at the end of letters.

Reverse Long cross, four stars in each quarter with a total of 21, 23, 24, 25 or 26 points.

| SA31D-315 | VG £18 | F £38 | VF £75 |

Class 7

Obverse Legend As previous.

Reverse Legend As previous.

Obverse As previous, but no serifs to letters.

Reverse As previous.

| SA31D-320 | VG £18 | F £38 | VF £75 |

Class 8

Obverse Legend   As previous.

Reverse Legend   As previous.

Obverse   Somewhat crude bust of irregular style and letters in the legend sometimes crudely formed.

Reverse   Long cross, four stars forming a total of 20, 21, 22, 23, 24, 25, 26, 27 or 28 points.

| SA31D-325 | VG £18 | F £38 | VF £75 |

Class 9

Obverse Legend   As previous.

Reverse Legend   As previous.

Obverse   Bust similar to John Baliol

Reverse   Long cross, four stars giving a total of 24 points.

| SA31D-330 | VG £25 | F £60 | VF £150 |

Halfpenny

The halfpenny was introduced under Alexander III following Edward I's introduction of this denomination in England. During earlier reigns, the need for small denominations had been met by legally cutting pennies in half or quarters to produce halfpennies and farthings and these cut pennies are ideal for collectors on a budget who simply want an inexpensive example from a particular reign.

For most reigns, halfpennies are rare and were struck in fairly small quantities. The earlier issues bear a profile bust of the king on the obverse while his name can be found at the start of the obverse legend. The reverse on the early issues has a long cross with a varying number of stars, or mullets as they are sometimes known, in the quarters. The reverse legend is either a continuation of the obverse title or the mint name.

Second Coinage (1280 – 1286)

The mints for these issues are uncertain.

Collecting Hints

While scarce, these issues are obtainable but coins in better than Fine condition are rare.

Obverse Legend   ALEXANDER DEI GRA — Alexander by the grace of God

Reverse Legend   REX SCOTORUM — King of Scots

Obverse   Crowned bust of king facing left and holding a sceptre.

Reverse   Long cross, a star in two quarters, each star with five points and a central piercing.

| SA3HD-005 | VG £50 | F £100 | VF £300 |

As previous, but the stars on the reverse have six points.

| SA3HD-010 | VG £45 | F £90 | VF £275 |

As previous, but one star on the reverse does not have a central piercing.

| SA3HD-015 | VG £60 | F £150 | VF £400 |

Farthing

The farthing, or quarter penny, was introduced under Alexander III following a similar initiative in England by Edward I. Nevertheless, very few farthings were struck during subsequent reigns and few have been found in hoards. Actually, most farthings on the market in the last ten years have been found by metal detectors in England, reflecting the fact that Scottish coins were acceptable south of the border.

The issues bear a profile bust of the king on the obverse, while the monarch's name can be found in the obverse legend. The reverse of the early issues has a long cross with a varying number of stars, or mullets as they are sometimes known, in the quarters. The legend is usually a continuation of the obverse title.

Second Coinage (1280 – 1286)

These two issues were probably struck at Berwick.

Collecting Hints

The first issue is rare and the second one is extremely rare. Coins from the first issue are usually in Fine condition, often with a porous or rough surface due to the soil they have been in, as they tend to be found singly rather than in hoards.

Obverse Legend   ALEXANDER REX — King Alexander

Reverse Legend   SCOTORUM — of Scots

Obverse   Crowned bust of king facing left and holding sceptre.

Reverse   Long cross, a star of six points in each quarter.

SA3FA-005	VG £125	F £300	VF £750

As previous, but only two stars on the reverse. It would appear that the two other stars were removed from the reverse dies.

SA3FA-010	ex. rare

Margaret (1286 – 1290)

No coins were struck in Margaret's name, although it is very probable that the second coinage of Alexander III continued to be produced during this period.

Scotland: John Baliol (1292 – 1296)

Margaret died in 1290 leaving no direct successor. With a total of thirteen individuals, known as claimants, contesting the throne, Edward I of England decided as an independent arbiter who should reign and chose John Baliol who was the grandson of the eldest daughter of David, Earl of Huntingdon.

During John Baliol's reign, only pennies and halfpennies were struck.

Penny

John Baliol pennies can be divided into two coinages: the first is slightly crude in style with noticeable rough surfaces due probably to poor dies, while the second is very similar to Alexander III's second coinage in style and quality.

First Coinage (dates uncertain)

Collecting Hints

This issue, while rare, is obtainable especially in the lower grades. Poor definition from the dies often makes coins look in a lesser grade than they actually are. Over the last few years more coins from this issue have come into the market thanks to metal detectors.

Berwick(?) Mint

Obverse Legend   IOHANNES DEI GRA — John by the grace of God

Reverse Legend   REX SCOTORUM — King of Scots

Obverse   Crowned bust of king facing left holding sceptre.

Reverse   Long cross, star with six points in each quarter.

| SJB1D-005 | VG £50 | F £150 | VF £375 |

St Andrews(?) Mint

Obverse Legend   As previous.

Reverse Legend   As previous.

Obverse   As previous.

Reverse   As previous, but two stars have six points, the other two stars have five points.

| SJB1D-010 | VG £100 | F £250 | VF — |

St Andrews Mint

Obverse Legend   As previous.

Reverse Legend   CIVITAS SANDRE — City of St Andrews

Obverse   As previous.

Reverse   As previous.

| SJB1D-015 | VG £80 | F £220 | VF — |

Obverse Legend   As previous.

Reverse Legend   As previous.

Obverse   As previous.

Reverse   As previous, but three stars have six points and one has five points.

| SJB1D-020 | VG £120 | F £300 | VF — |

Second Coinage (dates uncertain)

This issue, which is sometimes known as the smooth surface issue, is of better style and quality than the previous coinage and similar to many of the issues of Alexander III's second coinage, with the main difference being the obverse legend.

Collecting Hints

These issues are rare although the first issue is obtainable. Unlike the previous coinage, very few specimens of this coinage have been found recently with metal detectors

Berwick(?) Mint

Obverse Legend   IOHANNES DEI GRA — John by the grace of God

Reverse Legend   REX SCOTORUM — King of Scots

Obverse   Well defined bust of king facing left and holding sceptre.

Reverse   Long cross, stars of five points in each quarter.

| SJB1D-025 | VG £65 | F £150 | VF £325 |

St Andrews Mint

Obverse Legend   As previous.

Reverse Legend   CIVITAS SANDREE (varieties exist) — City of St Andrews

Obverse   As previous, but a pellet sometimes on the sceptre handle.

Reverse   Long cross, two stars of six pellets and two stars of five pellets.

| SJB1D-030 | VG £150 | F £350 | VF — |

Obverse Legend   I DI GRA SCOTORUM RX — John by the grace of God king of Scots

Reverse Legend   As previous.

Obverse   As previous.

Reverse   As previous.

SJB1D-035 ex. rare

Halfpenny

Collecting Hints

Two issues of John Baliol halfpennies are rare while three are extremely rare. Coins are rarely found in better than Fine condition and were often weakly struck with poorly defined legends.

First Coinage (dates uncertain)

This coinage has a rough surface in the coin's field.

Berwick(?) Mint

Obverse Legend   IOHANNES DEI GI — John by the grace of God

Reverse Legend   REX SCOTORUM — King of Scots

Obverse   Crowned bust of king facing left and holding sceptre.

Reverse   Long cross, a star of six points in each quarter.

SJBHD-005   VG £100   F £250   VF rare

Uncertain Mint

As previous, but two stars have five points.

SJBHD-010   ex. rare

St Andrews Mint

Obverse Legend   As previous.

Reverse Legend   CIVITAS SANDRE — City of St Andrews

Obverse   As previous.

Reverse   As SJBHD-005.

SJBHD-015   ex. rare

Second Coinage (dates uncertain)

This coinage has a smooth surface in the coin's field.

Uncertain Mint

Obverse Legend   IOHANNES DEI GRA — John by the grace of God

Reverse Legend   REX SCOTORUM — King of Scots

Obverse   Crowned bust of king in a neater, more lifelike style, looking left and holding a sceptre.

Reverse   Two stars of six points in two quarters. The stars are found either in the first and third or in the second and fourth quarters.

SJBHD-020   VG £150   F £350   VF rare

St Andrews Mint

Obverse Legend   As previous.

Reverse Legend   CIVIATAS SANDRE(E)— City of St Andrews

Obverse   As previous.

Reverse   As previous.

SJBHD-025   ex. rare

Scotland: Robert Bruce (1306 – 1329)

During this famous reign pennies, halfpennies and farthings were struck.

Penny

Only one issue was struck during this reign; it is similar to John Baliol's second coinage in style but bears the name of Robert. It is uncertain which mint struck this coin.

Collecting Hints

This issue is rare especially in Fine or better condition and is always popular with collectors because of Robert Bruce's historical importance.

Obverse Legend ROBERTUS DEI GRA — Robert by the grace of God

Reverse Legend SCOTORUM REX — King of Scots

Obverse Bust of king facing left and holding sceptre. The 'A' in GRA is sometimes unbarred.

Reverse Long cross, star of five points in each quarter.

SRB1D-005	VG £150	F £400	VF £950

Halfpenny

Collecting Hints

This issue is very rare, especially in better than Fine condition. On some coins the legends show weaknesses in strike.

It is uncertain which mint produced this issue.

Obverse Legend ROBERTUS DEI GRA — Robert by the grace of God

Reverse Legend SCOTORUM REX — King of Scots

Obverse Crowned bust of king facing left and holding a sceptre.

Reverse Long cross, two stars of five points in two opposite quarters.

SRBHD-005	VG £200	F £600	VF v. rare

Farthing

It is uncertain which mint produced this issue.

Collecting Hints

This issue is very rare.

Obverse Legend ROBERTUS DEI GRA — Robert by the grace of God

Reverse Legend SCOTTORUM REX — King of Scots

Obverse Crowned bust of king facing left and holding sceptre.

Reverse Long cross, a star of five points in each quarter.

SRBFA-005	v. rare

Edward Baliol (1332 – 1338)

During this period no coins were struck in the name of Edward Baliol and it is unlikely that any were struck in the name of previous kings either.

Scotland: David II (1329 – 1371)

This was a time of growing prosperity, a fact that was reflected in the coinage. As trade with Europe increased, David II was keen that the Scottish coinage should be on a par with that of Europe and especially England, in terms both of style and denomination structure. He often copied the English denominations and style and even used English legends, which is hardly surprising since English coins were highly thought of in Europe at the time, as much for their style as for their correct metal content and weight. Thus, in 1357, David II introduced three new denominations in Scotland, the noble, the groat and the halfgroat. The noble, which was struck in gold and had a value of six shillings and eightpence, was discontinued after the first issue but the silver groat and half-groat with a value of four pence and two pence became established denominations, although their value fluctuated quite dramatically in subsequent years and must have caused considerable confusion among the public. One of the main problems during this period was the constantly rising price of silver which was originally addressed by a reduction of the weight of the coins and, in later reigns, by an increase in the value of the denomination.

Noble

The style, weight and value of this extremely rare gold denomination virtually replicated contemporary English nobles of Edward III which were then the envy of Europe. It is however very likely that most Scottish specimens were melted down, either at a later date when the value of the coin's metal content exceeded its face value or perhaps by the English who recieved a huge ransom, perhaps in Scottish nobles, when king David was released in 1357.

Collecting Hints

This issue is extremely rare.

Obverse Legend DAVID DEI GRA REX SCOTORUM — David by the grace of God King of Scots

Reverse Legend IHC AUTEM TRANCIENS P MEDIUM ILLORUM IBAT — But Jesus passing through their midst went His way

Obverse King in ship holding sword and shield.

Reverse Ornate cross with a crown and lion in each quarter.

SD2NB-005	ex. rare

Groat

This denomination was introduced in 1357 and derived its name from the French *gros* and the Italian *grosso*, which both mean large or great. The Scottish groat was similar in size to the *gros tournois*, which had been introduced in France around 1260; by 1357, the groat had also been introduced in England and become an important part of Edward III's denomination structure. However, the rising price of silver posed continual problems and in an effort to retain the value of the groat at a constant level, it became necessary to reduce its weight in the third coinage, just ten years after it had been introduced.

The king's name is to be found at the beginning of the obverse legend but many coins are difficult to identify and collectors might have to look through various reigns to accurately place an issue. It is important that collectors look for various marks such as pellets or small crosses known as saltires. All issues are slightly different and this was done so that coins could be easily linked to dies and thus ensure a form of quality control should the coin be of substandard weight or fineness.

The reverse of all issues shows a long cross with a design in each quarter. Of the two legends found on the reverse, the outer one is a religious statement while the inner one bears the mint name, indicating where the coin was struck and is particularly important when identifying an issue. During David II's reign, groats were struck at the Edinburgh and Aberdeen mints.

Second Coinage (1357 – 1367)

Groats were not introduced until the second coinage of 1357 – 67.

Collecting Hints

This issue, which had numerous varieties, was produced in large quantities of which a fair number survive. Collectors should have relatively little trouble obtaining a specimen, many of which have been found in large hoards. These coins saw considerable circulation and coins in VF or better condition are rare. Most issues show signs of weakness, especially in parts of the legend, but this is due to poor striking rather than wear. Some coins also appear to be slightly clipped which, again, is often due to striking rather than deliberate clipping. Of the two mints that were active during this reign, Edinburgh and Aberdeen, all issues from the latter are rare.

Edinburgh Mint

Obverse Legend DAVID DEI GRA REX SCOTORUM — David by the grace of God King of Scots

Outer Reverse Legend DNS PTECTOR MS F LIB ATORMS — God is my defender and my redeemer

Inner Reverse Legend VILLA EDINBURGH — Town of Edinburgh

Obverse Small crowned young bust facing left and holding sceptre.

Reverse Long cross with a star in each quarter.

SD24D-005	VG £30	F £60	VF £150

As previous, but trefoils in the arcs of the tressure on the obverse. The tressure is the curves between the portrait and the inner circle pellets which separate the legend.

SD24D-010	VG £30	F £60	VF £150

As previous, but rosettes in the arcs of the tressure.

SD24D-015	VG £40	F £100	VF £275

As previous, but pellets in the arcs of the tressure.

SD24D-020	VG £80	F £200	VF rare

Obverse Legend   As previous.
Reverse Legends   As previous.
Obverse   Larger young bust of king.
Reverse   As previous.

SD24D-025	VG £40	F £90	VF £240

As previous, but a cross in one quarter of the reverse.

SD24D-030	VG £30	F £60	VF £150

As previous, but a 'D' in one quarter of the reverse, representing the initial mark of mint master Donatus Mulekin.

SD24D-035	VG £40	F £100	VF £250

Obverse Legend   As previous.
Reverse Legends   As previous.
Obverse   Older style head with larger nose and pierced pellet eyes.
Reverse   As previous, but no 'D'.

SD24D-040	VG £30	F £60	VF £160

As previous, but a 'D' in one quarter of the reverse.

SD24D-045	VG £45	F £100	VF £240

Obverse Legend   As previous.
Reverse Legends   As previous.
Obverse   Uglier bust similar to that of Robert II and tilting forward slightly. The king has pellet eyes.
Reverse   As previous.

SD24D-050	VG £30	F £60	VF £160

As previous, but pellet behind crown and in one quarter on the reverse.

SD24D-055	VG £40	F £100	VF £240

As SD24D-050, but a pellet on the sceptre handle on the obverse.

SD24D-060	VG £40	F £100	VF £240

Aberdeen Mint

Obverse Legend   As previous.

Outer Reverse Legend   As previous.

Inner Reverse Legend   VILLA ABERDON — Town of Aberdeen

Obverse   As SD24D-005.

Reverse   As SD24D-005.

SD24D-065	VG £120	F £350	VF —

As SD24D-025 except for inner reverse legend which reads VILLA ABERDON.

SD24D-070	VG £140	F £450	VF —

Third Coinage (1367 – 1371)

This issue, often referred to as the light coinage because the weight of the groat was reduced by about 15%, can be easily distinguished by a star found on the obverse. All coins were struck at Edinburgh.

Collecting Hints

This issue is slightly scarcer than the previous one, but obtainable. Collecting Hints are similar to the previous issue, with coins usually available in Fine condition and those in VF being difficult to obtain.

Obverse Legend   As previous.

Outer Reverse Legend   As previous.

Inner Reverse Legend   VILLA EDINBURGH — Town of Edinburgh

Obverse   Older bust of king with a star behind the head.

Reverse   Long cross with a star in each quarter.

SD24D-075	VG £70	F £180	VF £420

Obverse Legend   As previous.

Reverse Legends   As previous.

Obverse   Older bust similar to that of Robert II and a star on the sceptre handle.

Reverse   As previous.

SD24D-080	VG £40	F £100	VF £240

As previous, but trefoils in tressures on the obverse.

SD24D-085	VG £45	F £110	VF £250

Halfgroat

Introduced in 1357 as part of David's new denomination series, the halfgroat had a value of twopence and bore a profile bust of the king holding a sceptre on the obverse and a long cross with a star in each angle on the reverse. The outer reverse legend bore a religious statement, while the inner legend had the mint name, starting with VILLA (town) and followed by the town name. During this period both Edinburgh and Aberdeen mints produced halfgroats. This style is very similar to that of Robert II so it is important that collectors pay particular attention to the beginning of the obverse legend where the king's name is found.

Halfgroats were struck during the second and third coinages. As with the groat, the halfgroat of the third coinage was reduced in weight as a response to the rising price of silver. These issues, known also as the light coinage, all bear a star located somewhere in the obverse.

Collecting Hints

In general, halfgroats are rarer than groats, which is perhaps worth considering when deciding what to collect. While scarce, these issues are obtainable especially in VG or Fine condition. Many coins are slightly clipped and show signs of weakness in the legends due to poor striking. The groat from this reign is more common and perhaps a better choice for the collector just wanting one example from the reign.

Second Coinage (1357 – 1367)

Edinburgh Mint

Obverse Legend   DAVID DEI REX SCOTORUM — David (by the grace of) God King of Scots

Outer Reverse Legend   DNS PROTECTOR MEUS — God is my defender

Inner Reverse Legend   VILLA EDINBURGH — Town of Edinburgh

Obverse   Crowned young left-facing bust of king holding sceptre.

Reverse   Long cross with a star in each quarter.

| SD22D-005 | VG £35 | F £80 | VF £200 |

| SD22D-025 | VG £35 | F £85 | VF £200 |

As previous, but a 'D' in one quarter on the reverse.

| SD22D-030 | VG £35 | F £90 | VF £200 |

Obverse Legend DAVID DEI GRA REX SCOTORUM — David by the grace of God King of Scots

Reverse Legends As previous.

Obverse Larger, young bust.

Reverse As previous.

As SD22D-025, but a pellet behind the crown on the obverse and in one quarter of the reverse.

| SD22D-035 | VG £40 | F £100 | VF £220 |

| SD22D-010 | VG £35 | F £80 | VF £200 |

Aberdeen Mint

Obverse Legend As previous.

Outer Reverse Legend As previous.

Inner Reverse Legend VILLA ABERDON — Town of Aberdeen

Obverse As SD22D-005.

Reverse As SD22D-005.

As previous, but a small cross added to one quarter on the reverse.

| SD22D-015 | VG £40 | F £90 | VF £220 |

| SD22D-040 | VG £100 | F £250 | VF rare |

As SD22D-010, but a 'D' in one quarter on the reverse, which is the initial of the mintmaster Donatus Mulekin.

Obverse Legend As previous.

Outer Reverse Legend As previous.

Inner Reverse Legend VILLA ABERDON — Town of Aberdeen

Obverse As SD22D-010.

Reverse As SD22D-010.

| SD22D-020 | VG £40 | F £90 | VF £220 |

| SD22D-045 | VG £170 | F £450 | VF rare |

Third Coinage (1367 – 1371)

Edinburgh Mint

This issue is often known as the light coinage, because the weight of coins was reduced by about 15% due to the rising price of silver.

Obverse Legend As previous.

Outer Reverse Legend As previous.

Inner Reverse Legend VILLA EDINBURGH — Town of Edinburgh

Obverse Older left-facing bust of the king holding a sceptre, with a star behind the king's head.

Obverse Legend As previous.

Reverse Legends As previous.

Obverse Older bust of king.

Reverse As SD22D-010.

Reverse Long cross with a star in each quarter.

| SD22D-050 | VG £70 | F £160 | VF £350 |

As previous, but a star on the king's sceptre only.

| SD22D-055 | VG £35 | F £90 | VF £200 |

As previous, but the king's bust is of a similar style to that on Robert II's coinage.

| SD22D-060 | VG £35 | F £90 | VF £200 |

Penny

There were three coinages during the long reign of David II and pennies were struck from 1333 until the end of the reign.

First Coinage (1333 – 1356)

Second Issue

Collecting Hints

This issue is the most common of David's coinages. Coins are slightly crude in style often with rough surfaces and are usually found in Fine to VF condition. Coins are rarely clipped but are sometimes found damaged. It is thought these coins were struck in Edinburgh.

Obverse Legend   DAVID DEI GRACIA — David by the grace of God

Reverse Legend   REX SCOTORUM — King of Scots

Obverse   Crowned bust of king facing left and holding sceptre. Legend uses large or small letters.

Reverse   Long cross, star of six points in each quarter, large letters in legend.

| SD21D-005 | VG £20 | F £50 | VF £100 |

Obverse Legend   As previous (minor varieties).

Reverse Legend   REX SCOTTORUM — King of Scots

Obverse   As previous, but small letters in legend.

Reverse   As previous, but small letters in legend.

| SD21D-010 | VG £18 | F £45 | VF £90 |

Second Coinage (1357 – 1367)

This coinage, which was struck at the Edinburgh and Aberdeen mints, can be easily differentiated from the previous issue by the mint's name in the reverse legend.

Collecting Hints

This coinage of which there are many varieties especially in the marks and punctuation found in the legend is available in Fine condition but is much scarcer in the higher grades reflecting the fact that many of these coins saw considerable circulation.

Edinburgh Mint

Obverse Legend   DAVID REX SCOTORUM — David king of Scots

Reverse Legend   VILLA EDINBURGH — Town of Edinburgh

Obverse   Small young crowned bust facing left and holding sceptre.

Reverse   Long cross, stars of five points in each quarter.

| SD21D-015 | VG £30 | F £65 | VF £130 |

Obverse Legend   As previous.

Reverse Legend   As previous.

Obverse   Large young crowned bust facing left and holding sceptre.

Reverse   As previous.

| SD21D-020 | VG £35 | F £75 | VF £150 |

As previous, but a small cross in one quarter of the reverse.

| SD21D-025 | VG £45 | F £100 | VF £200 |

As previous, but a letter 'D' in one quarter of the reverse.

SD21D-030	VG £35	F £75	VF £150

Obverse Legend As previous.
Reverse Legend As previous.
Obverse Old bust of king with larger nose and pierced pellet eyes.
Reverse As SD21D-015.

SD21D-035	VG £40	F £90	VF £180

Obverse Legend As previous.
Reverse Legend As previous.
Obverse Large ugly bust of king with pellet eyes. This bust is similar to that of Robert II.
Reverse As previous.

SD21D-040	VG £40	F £90	VF £180

As previous, but pellet behind king's crown and in one quarter.

SD21D-045	VG £40	F £90	VF £180

Aberdeen Mint

Obverse Legend As previous.
Reverse Legend VILLA ABERDON — Town of Aberdeen
Obverse Small young crowned bust of king facing left and holding sceptre.
Reverse Long cross stars with five points in each quarter.

SD21D-050	VG £180	F £400	VF v. rare

As previous, but large young crowned bust.

SD21D-055	VG —	F £500	VF rare

Third Coinage (1367 – 1371)

This coinage, which was only struck in Edinburgh, was reduced in weight by about 15% from the previous issues due to the rising silver price. A star is to be found on the obverse to distinguish coins from previous issues.

Collecting Hints

The first issue with a star behind the king's head is rare while the second issue is scarce but obtainable.

Obverse Legend As previous (minor varieties).
Reverse Legend VILLA EDINBURGH — Town of Edinburgh
Obverse Crowned bust of king, facing left and holding sceptre. This bust is very similar to that of Robert II. A star behind the king's head.
Reverse Long cross a star of five points in each quarter.

SD21D-060	VG —	F £300	VF rare

As previous, but a star on the king's sceptre and not behind the king's bust.

SD21D-065	VG £40	F £80	VF £160

Halfpenny

The halfpenny was struck during the first and second coinages.

Collecting Hints

All issues are rare and difficult to obtain in better than Fine condition while several are extremely rare.

First Coinage (1330 – ?1333)
Berwick(?) Mint
First Issue (1330 – 1333)

Obverse Legend MONET(A) REGIS D. — Money of King D (continued on reverse)
Reverse Legend AVID SCOTOR — (D)avid of Scots
Obverse Crowned bust facing left and holding sceptre.
Reverse Long cross, a star of five points in two quarters.

SD2HD-005	VG £200	F £450	VF rare

Obverse Legend DAVID DEI GRA REX — David by the grace of God
Reverse Legend As previous.
Obverse As previous.
Reverse As previous.

SD2HD-010	ex. rare

Obverse Legend As previous.
Reverse Legend REX SCOTORUM — King of Scots
Obverse As previous.
Reverse As previous.

SD2HD-015 ex. rare

Obverse Legend DAVID DEI GRACIA — David by the grace of God

Reverse Legend As previous.

Obverse As previous.

Reverse As previous.

SD2HD-020 ex. rare

Second Issue (1333 – uncertain)

These issues were probably struck at Edinburgh.

Obverse Legend DAVID DEI GRACIA — David by the grace of God

Reverse Legend REX SCOTORUM — King of Scots

Obverse Crowned bust of king facing left and holding a sceptre.

Reverse Long cross, a star of six points in three quarters.

SD2HD-025 VG £125 F £300 VF rare

As previous, but an 'I' (the initial of mintmaster James Mulekin) behind the bust on the obverse and 'I' and mullets in alternate angles on the reverse.

SD2HD-030 ex. rare

Second Coinage (1357 – 1367)
Edinburgh Mint

Obverse Legend DAVID REX SCOTOR — David King of Scots

Reverse Legend VILLA EDINBURGH — Town of Edinburgh

Obverse Young small bust of crowned king facing left and holding sceptre.

Reverse Long cross, a star in two quarters.

SD2HD-035 ex. rare

Farthing

Under David II, farthings were produced only during first coinage and it is thought that all three issues were struck at Berwick mint.

Collecting Hints

All issues are of the highest rarity.

Obverse Legend MONETA REGIS .D. — Money of King D (continued on reverse)

Reverse Legend AVID SCOTOR — (D)avid of Scots

Obverse Crowned bust of king facing left and holding sceptre.

Reverse Long cross, a star of five points in each quarter.

SD2FA-005 ex. rare

Obverse Legend DAVID DEI GRACIA — David by the grace of God

Reverse Legend AVID SCOTTOR — (D)avid of Scots

Obverse As previous.

Reverse As previous.

SD2FA-010 ex. rare

Obverse Legend As previous.

Reverse Legend REX SCOTORUM — King of Scots

Obverse As previous.

Reverse As previous.

SD2FA-015 ex. rare

Scotland: Robert II (1371 – 1390)

Robert II's reign was very much a continuation in style from the previous reign of David II, with groats, halfgroats, pennies and halfpennies being struck.

Groat

This issue is very much a continuation from the previous reign, the main difference being in the obverse legend which reads ROBERTUS instead of DAVID. Three mints were active during this period, Edinburgh, Dundee and Perth, and their names are found in the reverse inner circle. They read as follows:

VILLA DE PERTH — Town of Perth
VILLA DUNDE — Town of Dundee
VILLA EDINBURGH — Town of Edinburgh

Although Robert III also produced groats, his issues bear a front-facing portrait unlike those of Robert II which have a profile portrait.

Collecting Hints

While scarce, this issue is obtainable especially the first variety. Coins are usually available in Fine condition, which are often slightly clipped and have weaknesses in legend. Coins in VF or better condition are rare but sometimes obtainable. The Dundee mint is rare.

Edinburgh Mint

Obverse Legend ROBERTUS DEI GRA REX SCOTORU(M) — Robert by the grace of God King of Scots

Outer Reverse Legend DNS PTECTOR MS F LIB ATORMS — God is my defender and my redeemer

Inner Reverse Legend VILLA EDINBURGH — Town of Edinburgh

Obverse Crowned bust facing left, a star sometimes on the base of the sceptre and trefoils in the tressures.

Reverse Long cross with a star in each quarter.

| SR24D-005 | VG £30 | F £65 | VF £150 |

As previous, but a 'B' behind the king's head which was the initial mark for the moneyer Bonagius.

| SR24D-010 | VG £60 | F £140 | VF £320 |

As SR224D-005, but a saltire behind the king's head.

| SR24D-015 | VG £60 | F £140 | VF £320 |

As SR224D-005, but saltires within tressure.

| SR24D-020 | VG £60 | F £140 | VF £320 |

Dundee Mint

Obverse Legend As previous.

Outer Reverse Legend As previous.

Inner Reverse Legend VILLA DUNDE — Town of Dundee

Obverse Crowned bust facing left, a 'B' behind the bust.

Reverse Long cross, a star in each quarter.

| SR24D-025 | VG £120 | F £300 | VF rare |

Perth Mint

Obverse Legend   As previous.

Outer Reverse Legend   As previous.

Inner Reverse Legend   VILLA DE PERTH — Town of Perth

Obverse   Crowned bust facing left, trefoils within tressures.

Reverse   Long cross, a star in each quarter.

SR24D-030	VG £40	F £80	VF £180

As previous, but a 'B' behind the king's head which was the initial mark of the moneyer Bonagius.

SR24D-035	VG £50	F £125	VF £300

Halfgroat

Halfgroats for this reign were very much a continuation from the previous one and continued to feature a profile bust. Three mints were active, Edinburgh, Dundee and Perth and the mint name can be found in the inner circle of the reverse. Robert III also produced halfgroats, but his issues all show a front-facing bust unlike Robert II which bear a profile bust.

Collecting Hints

Most issues are scarce but obtainable, especially in VG to Fine condition. Many coins are slightly clipped or chipped and have weak spots in the legend due to poor striking. Issues from the Dundee mint are rare.

Edinburgh Mint

Obverse Legend   ROBERTUS DEI GRA REX SCOTORUM — Robert by the grace of God King of Scots

Outer Reverse Legend   DNS PROTECTOR MEUS — God is my defender

Inner Reverse Legend   VILLA EDINBURGH — Town of Edinburgh

Obverse   Crowned left-facing bust of king holding sceptre with a star on the handle.

Reverse   Long cross with a star in each quarter.

SR22D-005	VG £40	F £100	VF £240

As previous, but a 'B' behind the king's head which was the initial mark of the moneyer Bonagius.

SR22D-010	VG £80	F £180	VF rare

As SR22D-005, but a saltire behind the king's head.

SR22D-015	VG £60	F £140	VF £320

Dundee Mint

Obverse Legend   ROBERTUS REX SCOTORUM — Robert King of Scots

Outer Reverse Legend   As previous.

Inner Reverse Legend   VILLA DUNDE — Town of Dundee

Obverse   Crowned left-facing bust holding a sceptre with plain handle, a saltire behind the king's head.

Reverse   Long cross with a star in each quarter.

SR22D-020	ex. rare

As previous, but with a 'B' instead of a saltire behind the king's head and a saltire on the king's sceptre.

SR22D-025	VG £100	F £250	VF rare

Perth Mint

Obverse Legend   As SR22D-005.

Outer Reverse Legend   As SR22D-005.

Inner Reverse Legend   VILLA DE PERTH — Town of Perth

Obverse   As SR22D-005.

Reverse   As SR22D-005.

SR22D-030	VG £35	F £80	VF £160

As previous, but a 'B' behind the king's bust and a cross on the sceptre handle.

SR22D-035 ex. rare

Penny

This issue is very much a continuation from the previous reign, however the bust of the king has rather more chiselled features. Three mints are active during this reign, Edinburgh, Dundee and Perth and the mint's name can be found on the reverse. The letter 'B' which is found on some issues is thought to be the initial mark of the moneyer Bonagius.

Collecting Hints

Several of these issues while scarce are obtainable especially in Fine or less condition. Coins in VF are rare but are obtainable. Several of these issues are extremely rare and we have listed these.

Edinburgh Mint

Obverse Legend ROBERTUS REX SCOTTOR — Robert King of Scots

Reverse Legend VILLA EDINBURGH — Town of Edinburgh

Obverse Crowned bust of king facing left, holding a sceptre with a star on the handle.

Reverse Long cross, a star in each quarter.

SR21D-005	VG £30	F £70	VF £150

As previous, but a trefoil behind the king's head.

SR21D-010   ex. rare

As previous, but a 'B' behind head.

SR21D-015 ex. rare

As RT1D-005, but no star on the sceptre handle.

SR21D-020	VG £30	F £70	VF £150

Dundee Mint

Obverse Legend As previous.

Reverse Legend VILLA DUNDE — Town of Dundee

Obverse Crowned bust of king facing left and holding sceptre, a 'B' behind the king's bust.

Reverse As previous.

SR21D-025   ex. rare

Perth Mint

Obverse Legend As previous.

Reverse Legend VILLA DE PERTH — Town of Perth

Obverse As previous.

Reverse As previous.

SR21D-030   ex. rare

Obverse As previous, but omitting the 'B' behind the bust. A variety of sceptre styles, the most common of which has a star at the base.

Reverse As previous.

SR21D-035	VG £50	F £120	VF £250

Halfpenny

The halfpenny was struck at Edinburgh and Dundee.

Collecting Hints

The Edinburgh issue while rare is obtainable especially in lower grades. The Dundee issue is extremely rare.

Edinburgh Mint

Obverse Legend ROBERTUS REX S — Robert King of Scotland

Reverse Legend VILLA EDINBUR (or EIDINBUG) — Town of Edinburgh (size of letters varies)

Obverse Crowned bust of king facing left and holding a sceptre.

Reverse Long cross, a star in each quarter.

SR2HD-005	VG £60	F £160	VF £450

Dundee Mint

Obverse Legend As previous.

Reverse Legend VILLA DUNDE — Town of Dundee

Obverse As previous.

Reverse As previous.

SR2HD-010 ex. rare

Scotland: Robert III (1390 – 1406)

At the close of the fourteenth century, Scotland was rather behind the rest of Europe which was by then producing gold coins in some quantity due to a more plentiful supply of gold. In response Robert introduced the gold lion and demi lion, or half lion as it is also known, and they became the first gold Scottish coins to become established in circulation. The production of silver coins continued with groats, halfgroats, pennies and halfpennies, all of which departed from the obverse design of previous monarchs and depict a front-facing bust of the king, as that found on the English coins.

However, the price of both gold and silver rose steadily throughout Europe during this period and by 1403 it necessitated a drastic reduction in the weight of Scottish coins by about a third. The resultant issues are known as the light coinage, with the earlier ones termed the heavy coinage. It is interesting to note that during this period, the weight of English silver coins was reduced by less than Scottish issues, reflecting the relative strength of England's economy.

Lion

The gold lion, with a value of five shillings, was introduced during the reign of Robert III. All issues were struck at Edinburgh and bear a large crowned shield on the obverse and St Andrew crucified on the reverse. This issue was sometimes known as a St Andrews. Varieties in the reverse legend reading exist.

Collecting Hints

These issues, while rare, are obtainable. Coins are usually found undamaged in Fine to VF condition and probably originate from hoards. The light issue tends to be cruder in style.

Heavy Coinage (1390? – 1403)

This issue weighs 61.5 grains (3.98 grams).

Obverse Legend ROBERTUS DEI GRA REX SCOTORUM — Robert by the grace of God King of Scots

Reverse Legend XPCRE GRATXPC VINCI TXPACIMP (varieties exist) — Christ reigns, Christ conquers, Christ commands

Obverse Crown over shield, a lion rampant in the shield.

Reverse St Andrew crucified on the cross which reaches to the edge of the coin, a lis either side of the cross.

SR3LI-005	VG —	F £550	VF £1,350

Obverse Legend ROBERTUS DEI GRACIA REX SCOTTORUM — Robert by the grace of God King of Scots

Reverse Legend XPC REGNAT XPAC VINCIT XPC IMPERAT — Christ reigns, Christ conquers, Christ commands

Obverse Smaller crown over smaller shield, a lion rampant in the shield.

Reverse St Andrew crucified on the cross, the ends of the cross reach to the inner circle, a lis either side of cross.

SR3LI-010	VG —	F £600	VF £1,500

Light Coinage (1403 – 1406)

This issue weighs 38 grains (2.46 grams).

Obverse Legend ROBERTUS DEI GRACIA REX SCO — Robert by the grace of God King of Scotland

Reverse Legend XP CREGNATX PC IM PERAT (varieties exist) — Christ reigns, Christ conquers, Christ commands

Obverse Crown of poor style over shield, a lion rampant in the shield.

Reverse St Andrew crucified on a more narrow cross, a lis either side of the cross.

SR3LI-015	VG —	F £600	VF £1,500

Obverse Legend As previous, but many varieties.

Reverse Legend DNS P TEATOR MS LIBER (varieties exist) — God is my defender and my redeemer

Obverse As previous.

Reverse As previous, sometimes with cross not visible, probably due to poor dies.

SR3LI-020	VG —	F £600	VF £1,500

Demi Lion

The demi lion or half lion was introduced during the reign of Robert III with a value of two shillings and sixpence although its face value increased during later reigns due to the rising price of gold.

The denomination, which complemented the gold lion of five shillings, was part of a coinage designed to use the increasing supply of gold and commercial activity not only in Scotland but also in Europe.

Collecting Hints

Several of the issues are extremely rare or even unique but two, while rare, are obtainable usually in Fine or VF condition.

Heavy Coinage (1390? – 1403)

This issue weighed 30.5 grains (1.98 grams).

Obverse Legend   ROBERTUS DEI GRACIA REX — Robert by the grace of God King

Reverse Legend   XPC REG RAT XPC VIN — Christ reigns, Christ conquers, Christ commands

Obverse   Royal shield within tressure of eight arcs.

Reverse   A St Andrews cross to the edge of the coin, a lis in two of the quarters, a large trefoil in the other two.

SR3DLI-005	ex. rare

Obverse Legend   ROBERTUS REX SCOTORUM (many varieties) — Robert King of Scots

Reverse Legend   As previous.

Obverse   Royal shield with no tressure.

Reverse   As previous.

SR3DLI-010	VG £200	F £450	VF £1,100

Obverse Legend   ROBERTUS DEI G. REX SCOTO — Robert by the grace of God King of Scots

Reverse Legend   XPC VINCIT XPC REGNAT — Christ reigns, Christ conquers, Christ commands

Obverse   As previous.

Reverse   As previous, but the trefoil is closed in style.

SR3DLI-015	ex. rare

Light Coinage (1403 – 1406)

This issue weighs 20 grains (1.30 grams).

Obverse Legend   ROBERTUS D. G. REX SCO (many varieties) — Robert by the grace of God King of Scots

Reverse Legend   XPC REGNAT TX QG VIN — Christ reigns, Christ conquers, Christ commands

Obverse   As previous, but smaller and lighter.

Reverse   As previous.

SR3DLI-020	VG —	F £500	VF £1,200

As previous, but king's name and title on both obverse and reverse.

SR3DLI-025	unique

Obverse Legend   ROBERTUS DEI G REX A SCO — Robert by the grace of God King of Scotland

Reverse Legend   DNS P TEATORM — Lord protect and guard

Obverse   As previous.

Reverse   As previous.

SR3DLI-030	ex. rare

Groat

The design of the obverse changed at this time to depict a front-facing bust of the king like the English issues, although the style of the Scottish groats is somewhat cruder.

During the heavy coinage groats were struck at Edinburgh, Aberdeen and Perth, while the three mints that were active during the light coinage were Edinburgh, Dumbarton and Aberdeen. The mint's name can be found in the inner reverse legend and are as follows:

VILLA ABERDEN — Town of Aberdeen
VILLA DE PERTH — Town of Perth
VILLA DUNBERTAN — Town of Dumbarton
VILLA EDINBURGH — Town of Edinburgh

Heavy Coinage (1390? – 1403)

Collecting Hints

While scarce, this issue is obtainable. The coins rarely look attractive due to rather poorly engraved dies. Although rarely clipped or damaged, they are often weakly struck, making them appear to be of a lower grade than is actually the case. Coins are usually available in Fine condition while VF specimens are rare.

Edinburgh Mint
First Issue

Obverse Legend   ROBERTUS DEI GRA REX SCOTTORUM — Robert by the grace of God King of Scots

Outer Reverse Legend   DNS PTECTOR MS F LIB ATORMS (minor varieties exist) — God is my defender and my redeemer

Inner Reverse Legend   VILLA EDINBURGH — Town of Edinburgh

Obverse   Tall crowned bust of king, tressure of seven arcs with three pellets at each cusp.

Reverse   Long cross with three pellets in each quarter.

| SR34D-005 | VG £30 | F £60 | VF £140 |

As previous, but a fleur de lis in the legend.

| SR34D-010 | VG £30 | F £70 | VF £150 |

As SR34D-005, but nine arcs to the tressure.

| SR34D-015 | ex. rare |

As SR34D-005, but the bust breaks through the tressure and there are no pellets at the cusps.

| SR34D-020 | VG £65 | F £180 | VF — |

Second Issue

Obverse Legend   As previous.

Reverse Legends   As previous.

Obverse   Slightly smaller, neater bust of the king, sometimes with three pellets at the cusps.

Reverse   Long cross with three pellets in each quarter.

| SR34D-025 | VG £30 | F £70 | VF £150 |

As previous, but annulets in spandrels.

| SR34D-030 | VG £35 | F £85 | VF £170 |

Aberdeen Mint

Obverse Legend   As previous.

Outer Reverse Legend   As previous.

Inner Reverse Legend   VILLA DE ABERDEN or ABIRDENE — Town of Aberdeen

Obverse   As SR34D-025.

Reverse   As SR34D-030.

| SR34D-035 | VG £50 | F £125 | VF £280 |

As SR34D-030, except for the inner reverse legend which reads VILLA DE ABERDEN — Town of Aberdeen.

| SR34D-040 | VG £50 | F £125 | VF £280 |

Perth Mint

Obverse Legend   As previous.

Outer Reverse Legend   As previous.

Inner Reverse Legend   VILLA DE PERTH — Town of Perth

Obverse   As SR34D-025.

Reverse   As previous.

| SR34D-045 | VG £40 | F £80 | VF £180 |

As SR34D-030 except for the inner reverse legend which reads VILLA DE PERTH — Town of Perth.

| SR34D-050 | VG £40 | F £80 | VF £180 |

Light Coinage (1403 – 1406)

SR34D-070	VG £130	F £325	VF rare

> # Collecting Hints
>
> This issue is smaller and over a third lighter than the previous coinage. Most coins appear to be poorly struck, perhaps due to the thinness of the flan. They are usually unclipped, although many issues have flat spots in the legends due to poor striking. All issues are rare, especially those of Dumbarton and Aberdeen and coins are rarely available in better than Fine condition.

As previous, but five arcs to tressure.

SR34D-075	ex. Rare

Edinburgh Mint

Obverse Legend ROBERTUS DEI GRA REX SCOTTOR — Robert by the grace of God King of Scots

Outer Reverse Legend As previous.

Inner Reverse Legend VILLA EDINBURGH — Town of Edinburgh

Obverse Smaller crowned bust of front-facing king, a single pellet on cusps of tressure.

SR34D-055	VG £50	F £125	VF £300

Halfgroat

As with other silver denominations, the halfgroat bore a front-facing bust of the king similar to the English issues. The reverse was also similar to the English issues, with the stars or mullets in the angles of the cross being replaced by three pellets. However, these issues are much cruder than the English ones. Halfgroats were struck at the mints of Edinburgh and Perth but only during the heavy coinage of 1390? – 1403.

> # Collecting Hints
>
> These issues are scarce but obtainable, especially in the lower grades. They were poorly struck, often leaving areas of weakness over parts of the coin. All coins in VF condition are rare.

As previous, but three or four pellets on cusps, four pellets on head.

SR34D-060	VG £50	F £125	VF £300

Aberdeen Mint

Obverse Legend As previous.

Outer Reverse Legend As previous.

Inner Reverse Legend VILLA ABERDEN or ABIRDENE — Town of Aberdeen

Obverse Small bust of crowned king facing front; of similar style to that of James I.

Reverse Long cross with three pellets in each quarter.

Heavy Coinage (1390? – 1403)

Edinburgh Mint

First Issue

Obverse Legend ROBERTUS DEI G REX SCOTOR (varieties exist) — Robert by the grace of God King of Scots

Reverse Legend DNS PTETORMS LIBATO — God is my defender and my redeemer (abbreviated)

Inner Reverse Legend VILLA EDINBURGH — Town of Edinburgh

Obverse Tall bust of crowned king, pellets on cusps of tressure.

Reverse Long cross with three pellets in each quarter.

SR34D-065	VG £130	F £325	VF rare

SR32D-005	VG £40	F £90	VF £250

Dumbarton Mint

Obverse Legend ROBERTUS DEI GRACIA REX SC. — Robert by the grace of God King of Scotland

Outer Reverse Legend DNS P TECTOR MS LIBERAT — God is my defender and my redeemer

Inner Reverse Legend VILLA DUNBERTAN — Town of Dumbarton

Obverse Crowned bust of king.

Reverse As previous.

As previous, but no pellets in cusps. The king's bust is taller and breaks the tressure.

SR32D-010	VG £80	F £180	VF rare

Second Issue

New, much neater, bust of king sometimes with trefoils on cusps of tressure.

SR32D-015	VG £40	F £85	VF £200

Perth Mint

Obverse Legend   As previous (varieties exist).

Reverse Legend   As previous.

Inner Reverse Legend   VILLA DE PERTH — Town of Perth

Obverse   As previous.

Reverse   As previous.

SR32D-020	VG £45	F £100	VF £220

Penny

The obverse of the penny again depicted a front-facing crowned bust of the king, with the reverse showing a long cross with three pellets in each quarter. These issues are very similar to the English ones, which were very popular throughout Europe at the time and more commonly found today. Collectors should therefore pay particular attention to the legends so as not to confuse the two. Three mints, whose names can be found on the reverse legend, were active during the light coinage. These coins were struck in debased silver of 0.617 fineness.

Collecting Hints

All of these issues are very rare and are usually found in no better than VG condition. These coins were poorly struck and often when struck were in no better than Fine condition. Due to this fact, we do not list coins in VF condition as they possibly do not exist.

Edinburgh Mint

Obverse Legend   ROBERTUS REX SCOTOR — Robert King of Scots

Reverse Legend   VILLA EDINBURGH — Town of Edinburgh

Obverse   Crowned bust of king with crude styling.

Reverse   Long cross, three pellets in each quarter.

SR31D-005	VG £150	F £300

As previous, but obverse legend is divided by fleur de lis above a crescent. The legend reads ROBERTUS DEI G. R. — Robert by the grace of God

SR31D-010	ex. rare possibly unique

As SR31D-005 but neater, less crude bust and the king wears a larger crown.

SR31D-015	VG £120	F £280

Obverse Legend   As previous.

Reverse Legend   REX SCOTORUM — King of Scots

Obverse   As previous.

Reverse   As previous.

SR31D-020	VG £120	F £280

Obverse Legend   ROBERTUS DEI REX SCO — Robert by the grace of God King of Scotland

Reverse Legend   ROB DEI GRA REX — Robert by the grace of God King

SR31D-025	ex. rare

Perth Mint

Obverse Legend   ROBERTUS REX SCOTORUM — Robert King of Scots

Reverse Legend   VILLA DE PERTH — Town of Perth

Obverse   As SR31D-015.

Reverse   As SR31D-015.

SR31D-030	VG £250	F £330

Aberdeen Mint

Obverse Legend   ROBERTUS DEI GRA REX — Robert by the grace of God King

Reverse Legend   VILLA DE ABRDEN — Town of Aberdeen

Obverse   As previous.

Reverse   As previous.

SR31D-035	VG £275	F £650

Halfpenny

These issues were struck in silver of low fineness (0.617) and, although very similar, should not be confused with the more common English issues. Collectors should pay particular attention to the legends.

Collecting Hints

All three issues are very rare and crude in style and strike.

Edinburgh Mint

Obverse Legend   ROBERTUS REX SCOT — Robert King of Scotland

Reverse Legend   VILLA EDINBUR (?) — Town of Edinburgh

Obverse   Rough, crowned front-facing bust of the king.

Reverse   Long cross, three pellets in each quarter.

| SR3HD-005 | VG £180 | F £450 | VF rare |

As previous, but the king's bust is neater.

| SR3HD-010 | VG £180 | F £450 | VF rare |

Perth Mint

Obverse Legend   As previous.

Reverse Legend   VILLA DE PERT(H) — Town of Perth

Obverse   As previous.

Reverse   As previous.

| SR3HD-015 | VG £250 | F £600 | VF rare |

Scotland: James I (1406 – 1437)

Due to the rising metal price, the old denominations were rendered obsolete and new ones introduced in their place to minimize confusion. Thus, two gold denominations were introduced under James I, the demy and the half demy, although silver groats, pennies and halfpennies continued to be struck. However, the value of silver continued to rise steadily throughout Europe and no country could immune itself from the problems this created. Various monarchs tackled the issue in different ways, with a reduction of the weight of coins being the most common initial response. This had been resorted to in Scotland by Robert III but proved an unpopular measure so, as the silver prices continued to rise and there was often a shortage of bullion, it was decided in the reign of James I to vary the value of the silver denominations depending on their silver content. This practice continued in later reigns and often each issue had different values as well as weights, no doubt causing great difficulty amongst an uneducated, illiterate population. Moreover, as the price of silver rose, coins in circulation would have a higher silver content than their value, prompting unscrupulous individuals to melt them down and sell the bullion at a profit, thus exacerbating the work of the mints.

Demy

The denomination comes from the French for half because the Scots tried to base the value of the demy on an English half noble; the issue is sometimes spelt 'demi'. Introduced under James I with a value of nine shillings; the demy was struck in gold and weighed 54 grains (3.5 grams). All issues were struck at Edinburgh and depict a lion rampant in a lozenge on the obverse and a saltire cross within a tressure on the reverse. The demy was also struck under James II and, as the two reigns are very similar, collectors should refer to both when identifying an issue.

Collecting Hints

These issues, while scarce, are obtainable especially in Fine to VF condition and are usually found undamaged. As many of these coins were found in hoards, they had seen little circulation.

Obverse Legend IACOBUS DEI GRACIA REX SCOT (varieties exist) — James by the grace of God King of Scotland

Reverse Legend SALUUM FAC POPULUM TUUM DNB — O Lord save Thy people

Obverse Lion rampant in lozenge; mintmark crown at the start of the legend.

Reverse Large saltire cross, a lis either side within a fleured tressure of six arcs, small quatrefoils in arcs of tressure.

| SJ1DM-005 | VG £200 | F £500 | VF £1,000 |

As previous, but large quatrefoil with open centres on reverse.

| SJ1DM-010 | VG £220 | F £600 | VF £1,200 |

As previous, but a chain pattern in inner and outer circles.

| SJ1DM-015 | v. rare |

As SJ1DM-010, but small pellets in centre of quatrefoils.

| SJ1DM-020 | VG £220 | F £600 | VF £1,200 |

Half Demy

The gold half demy was introduced during the reign of James I to complement the demy, with a value of four shillings and sixpence.

Collecting Hints

This issue is very rare and usually found in Fine condition.

Obverse Legend IACOBUS DE I GRACIA R — James I by the grace of God King

Reverse Legend SALUUM FAC POPULUM TUUM — O Lord save Thy people

Obverse Lion rampant in lozenge.

Reverse Saltire cross in the centre, a lis either side in fleured tressure of six arcs.

75

| SJ1HDM-005 | VG — | F £600 | VF £1,300 |

| SJ14D-005 | VG £50 | F £140 | VF £325 |

As previous, but seven arcs in reverse tressure.

As previous, but sceptre to the right.

| SJ1HDM-010 | v. rare |

| SJ14D-010 | VG £70 | F £180 | VF — |

Groat

As previous, but the inner circles are like chains.

| SJ14D-015 | VG £125 | F £300 | VF — |

In an attempt to compensate for the rising price of silver it was decided to re-value the groat at sixpence and raise its weight slightly. The groats of James I are fairly similar to those of James II but all issues bear a sceptre, usually to the left of the king's bust. The reverse is slightly different; although the long cross is retained, there are only three pellets in two quarters and, in a departure from previous designs, two lis in the other two.

Four mints were active under James I: Edinburgh, Perth, Linlithgow and Stirling and, as with previous issues, the mint's name can be found in the inner circle of the reverse. They are as follows:

VILLA DE LINLITHGO — Town of Linlithgow
VILLA DE PERTH — Town of Perth
VILLA EDINBURGH — Town of Edinburgh
VILLA STREVELIN — Town of Stirling

Second Issue

Obverse Legend   As previous.

Reverse Legends   As previous.

Obverse   Cruder bust of king wearing a larger crown with a larger central fleur.

Reverse   As previous, often with an extra small pellet in two quarters and an annulet in one quarter.

| SJ14D-020 | VG £50 | F £140 | VF £325 |

Perth Mint

First Issue

Obverse Legend   As previous.

Outer Reverse Legend   As previous.

Inner Reverse Legend   VILLA DE PERTH — Town of Perth

Obverse   As SJ14D-005.

Reverse   As SJ14D-005.

| SJ14D-025 | VG £80 | F £200 | VF — |

Second Issue

Obverse Legend   As previous.

Reverse Legends   As previous.

Obverse   As SJ14D-020.

Reverse   As SJ14D-005, but sometimes with a lis in the central cross.

Collecting Hints

All issues are rare, especially the ones from the provincial mints. Coins were often poorly struck and are rarely found in better than Fine condition.

Edinburgh Mint

First Issue

Obverse Legend   IACOBUS DEI GRACIA REX SCOTO(R) (many varieties) — James by the grace of God King of Scots

Outer Reverse Legend   DNS PTECTOR MS LIBATORM — God is my defender and my redeemer

Inner Reverse Legend   VILLA EDINBURGH — Town of Edinburgh

Obverse   Small crowned front-facing bust of king holding sceptre to the left.

Reverse   Long cross with three pellets in two quarters and a lis in the remaining two quarters.

| SJ14D-030 | VG £125 | F £300 | VF — |

Linlithgow Mint
First Issue

Obverse Legend   As previous.

Outer Reverse Legend   As previous.

Inner Reverse Legend   VILLA DE LINLITHGO — Town of Linlithgow

Obverse   As SJ14D-005.

Reverse   As SJ14D-005.

| SJ14D-035 | VG £130 | F £325 | VF — |

Second Issue

Obverse Legend   As previous.

Reverse Legends   As previous.

Obverse   As SJ14D-020.

Reverse   As SJ14D-030.

| SJ14D-040 | VG £140 | F £340 | VF — |

Stirling Mint
Second Issue

Obverse Legend   As previous.

Outer Reverse Legend   As previous.

Inner Reverse Legend   VILLA STREVELIN — Town of Stirling

Obverse   As SJ14D-020.

Reverse   As SJ14D-005.

| SJ14D-045 | VG £140 | F £350 | VF — |

Penny

With growing prosperity, gold issues in circulation and rising silver prices, the penny was becoming a denomination of fairly little value. The revaluation of the groat also led to the devaluation of the penny, which was produced with a low silver content which reflected the rising silver price. Three mints were active, Edin-

burgh, Aberdeen and Inverness and their name can be found on the reverse of the coins.

Collecting Hints

These rather ugly issues which are often chipped, probably due to the metal content are usually found in VG or Fine condition. Coins are sometimes corroded again due to the mixed metal content and should only be cleaned by experts. Coins in VF condition are very rare while all issues from the Inverness mint are extremely rare.

Edinburgh Mint

Obverse Legend   IACOBI DEI GRACIA R. (varieties exist) — James by the grace of God King

Reverse Legend   VILLA EDINBURGH — Town of Edinburgh

Obverse   Front-facing crowned bust of king, which is very similar to Robert III.

Reverse   Long cross, three pellets in each quarter.

| SJ11D-005 | VG £40 | F £100 | VF £250 |

As previous, but a lis either side of the king's neck.

| SJ11D-010 | VG £70 | F £200 | VF — |

Obverse Legend   IACOBUS DEI GRACIA R — James by the grace of God King

Reverse Legend   As previous.

Obverse   Large head with no neck.

Reverse   As previous.

| SJ11D-015 | VG £70 | F £200 | VF — |

Obverse Legend   As previous.

Reverse Legend   As previous.

Obverse   New-style crowned bust of king with neck, as first issue groats, but no sceptre.

Reverse   As previous; mintmark cross in legend.

| SJ11D-020 | VG £40 | F £100 | F £250 |

As previous, but saltires (or small crosses) by the king's neck or crown.

| SJ11D-025 | VG £40 | F £100 | VF £250 |

As previous, but also annulets by crown; reverse as SJ11D-005.

| SJ11D-030 | ex. rare |

As previous, but very small bust which is a die from the halfpenny. This is possibly a trial or pattern.

SJ11D-035   v. rare

Aberdeen Mint

Obverse Legend   IACOBI DEI GRA REX (?) — James by the grace of God King

Reverse Legend   VILLA DE ABERDEN — Town of Aberdeen

Obverse   Crowned front-facing bust of the king.

Reverse   Long cross three pellets in each quarter.

SJ11D-040   VG £200   F £500 VF —

Obverse Legend   IACOBI DEI G REX SCOT — James by the grace of God King of Scotland

Reverse Legend   VILLA DE ABRDEN — Town of Aberdeen

Obverse   Crowned bust of king, a lis to the right of neck. Sometimes with annulets by bust.

Reverse   Long cross, three pellets in each quarter.

SJ11D-045   VG £200   F £500   VF —

Inverness Mint

Obverse Legend   IACOBUS DEI GRA REX SC — James by the grace of God King of Scotland

Reverse Legend   VILLA INVERNIS — Town of Inverness

Obverse   Crowned bust of king as SJ11D-005

SJ11D-050   ex. rare

Obverse Legend   As SJ11D-045.

Reverse Legend   As previous.

Obverse   New style of bust, a lis by the king's neck.

Reverse   As previous.

SJ11D-055   ex. rare

Halfpenny

Both of these issues were struck at the Edinburgh mint and were struck in billon.

Collecting Hints

While rare, the first issue is obtainable especially in the lower grades but the second issue is extremely rare. Also, coins from the first issue in better than Fine condition are extremely rare as they were poorly struck and saw considerable circulation. Both issues were struck in base silver.

Obverse Legend   IACOBUS DEI GRA REX SCOTOR — James by the grace of God King of Scots

Reverse Legend   VILLA EDINBURGH — Town of Edinburgh

Obverse   Small, neat bust of crowned king.

Reverse   Long cross, three pellets in each quarter.

SJ1HD-005   VG £80   F £200   VF v. rare

Obverse Legend   As previous.

Reverse Legend   As previous.

Obverse   As previous, but the bust is of poorer design and the king's crown has a taller central fleur.

Reverse   As previous.

SJ1HD-010   ex. rare

Scotland: James II (1437 – 1460)

James II's reign is divided into two coinages by the revaluation of 1451. In terms of gold coins, the demy was struck during the first coinage (1437 – 51) with a value of nine shillings and was replaced in the second coinage (1451 – 60) by the lion and demi lion which had a value of ten and five shillings respectively. Of the silver coins struck, the groat was produced throughout the reign but was increased in both weight and value during the second coinage while the halfgroat was only struck for the later period and the penny, also produced throughout the reign, was decreased in weight during the second coinage.

Demy

The gold demy continued to be struck during the first coinage of James II with a value of nine shillings. All issues were produced at Edinburgh and depict a lion rampant in a lozenge on the obverse and a saltire cross within a tressure on the reverse. In terms of style, the issue is very similar to the previous reign while its weight and value were unchanged.

First Coinage (1437 – 1451)

Obverse Legend   IACOBUS DEI GRACIA REX SCOTO — James by the grace of God King of Scots

Reverse Legend   SALUM FAC POPULUM TUUM DIIE (varieties exist) — O Lord save Thy people

Obverse   Lion rampant in lozenge.

Reverse   Large saltire cross, a lis either side within a fleured tressure of six arcs, quatrefoils with large central pellets in arcs of tressure, annulet stops in legend.

| SJ2DM-005 | VG £220 | F £550 | VF £1,200 |

As previous, but an annulet in centre of the reverse cross.

| SJ2DM-010 | VG £250 | F £600 | VF £1,300 |

As SJ2DM-005 but saltire stops in legends.

| SJ2DM-015 | VG £250 | F £600 | VF £1,300 |

Lion

Struck during the second coinage, James II's lion was very much a continuation in style from the issues of Robert III. However, due to the rising price of gold, the face value of the coin was increased to ten shillings and its weight reduced. This issue is sometimes known as a Scottish crown.

Second Coinage (1451 – 1460)

This issue weighs 54 grains (3.5 grams).

Obverse Legend   IACOBUS DEI GRA REX SCOTTOR(UM) — James by the grace of God King of Scots

Reverse Legend   SALUUM FAC POPULUM TUUM — O Lord save Thy people

Obverse   Crown over shield, a lion rampant in the shield, a crown either side of the shield; mintmark cross fourchée in legend.

Reverse   St Andrew on cross between two lis.

| SJ2LN-005 | VG — | F £900 | VF £2,200 |

Obverse Legend   IACOBUS D' GRACIA REX SCOTOR — James by the grace of God King of Scots

Reverse Legend   XPC REGNAT XPC VINCITX — Christ reigns, Christ conquers, Christ commands

Obverse   As previous, but mintmark crown in legend.

Reverse   As previous.

| SJ2LN-010 | VG — | F £1,000 | VF £2,300 |

Obverse Legend   As previous.

Reverse Legend   As previous.

Obverse   As previous, but a lis on either side of the shield; mintmark crown.

Reverse   As previous, but the lis is joined to the crown on either side of the cross; mintmark crown at the start of the legend.

| SJ2LN-015 | VG — | F £800 | VF £1,750 |

Demi Lion

The gold demi lion was produced during James II's second coinage but now had a value of five shillings, due to the increasing price of gold. It weighed 27 grains (1.75 grams) which was less than the issues of Robert III.

Collecting Hints

These issues are rare in any condition. For a collector who just wants a gold coin from James II's reign, the demi or lion are more attractive coins and more common.

Obverse Legend   IACOBUS D' GRA REX SCOTOR — James by the grace of God King of Scots

Reverse Legend   XPC REGNA TXPC VIN CITX — Christ reigns, Christ conquers, Christ commands

Obverse   Uncrowned shield.

Reverse   St Andrew on cross, a crown either side of the saint.

| SJ2DL-005 | VG — | F £1,000 | VF £2,000 |

As previous, but small crown over shield.

| SJ2DL-010 | VG — | F £1,100 | VF £2,200 |

Groat

James II's reign can be divided into two coinages, the first of which (1437 – 51) produced groats at three mints with a value of sixpence. These issues are very similar to those of James I with the king holding a sceptre. Minor varieties of both reigns exist and collectors should pay attention to the position of the sceptre as well as the size and style of the crown.

The second coinage (1451 – 60) saw a dramatic increase in the weight of the groat with a corresponding increase of its face value to twelve pence. In real terms, the value of the groat in silver content had been reduced due to the steadily rising silver price. The main difference of this issue is that the coin is obviously larger and the king is not holding a sceptre.

First Coinage (1437 – 1451)

Collecting Hints

The Edinburgh issue while scarce is obtainable especially in VG or Fine condition. Coins in VF condition are rare mainly due to poor striking. Coins of the two provincial mints Linlithgow and Stirling are extremely rare.

Edinburgh Mint

Obverse Legend   IACOBUS DEI GRACIA REX SCOTOR (varieties exist) — James by the grace of God King of Scots

Outer Reverse Legend   DN SP TE CTOR MS LIBIRATO — God is my defender and my redeemer

Inner Reverse Legend   VILLA EDINBURGH — Town of Edinburgh

Obverse   Crowned bust of king holding sceptre to right, the king's crown is thinner and the king's hair is bushy.

Reverse   Long cross, three pellets in two quarters, a lis in the other two quarters.

| SJ24D-005 | VG £45 | F £100 | VF £300 |

As previous, but sceptre to left.

| SJ24D-010 | VG £90 | F £225 | VF £425 |

As SJ24D-005, but the obverse legend is repeated on the outer reverse legend.

| SJ24D-015 | ex. rare |

As SJ24D-005, but the king has very wavy hair and wears an ornate crown with a large central lis.

| SJ24D-020 | VG £60 | F £150 | VF £350 |

Linlithgow Mint

Obverse Legend   As previous.

Outer Reverse Legend   As previous.

Inner Reverse Legend   VILLA DE LINLITHGO — Town of Linlithgow

Obverse   As SJ24D-005.

Reverse   As SJ24D-005.

| SJ24D-025 | ex. rare |

Stirling Mint

Obverse Legend   As previous.

Outer Reverse Legend   As previous.

Inner Reverse Legend   VILLA STEVELII or STREVELE — Town of Stirling

Obverse   As SJ24D-005.

Reverse   As SJ24D-005.

| SJ24D-030 | ex. rare |

Second Coinage (1451 – 1460)

Collecting Hints

While several varieties are rare, and the provincial issues are extremely rare, a coin from this issue is obtainable. These issues tend to be better produced possibly due to the fact that they are larger than the previous issue. Coins are usually available in Fine condition, sometimes clipped and scarce VF coins exist. The portraits of these coins are very similar to those of English kings, in particular Edward IV, so the collector should check the issue carefully in particularly the obverse legends.

Edinburgh Mint

Obverse Legend   IACOBUS DEI GRA REX SCOTTORUM — James by the grace of God King of Scots

Outer Reverse Legend   ATORME LIBERATOR ME DNS PTE (many varieties) — God is my defender and my redeemer

Inner Reverse Legend   VILLA EDINBURGH — Town of Edinburgh

Obverse   Crowned bust of king, no sceptre.

Reverse   Long cross, three pellets in two quarters, a crown in two quarters.

| SJ24D-035 | VG £150 | F £450 | VF rare |

Obverse Legend   As previous.

Outer Reverse Legend   DNS PROTECTORM S LIBER ATORMS — God is my defender and my redeemer

Inner Reverse Legend   As previous.

Obverse   Larger crowned bust of king, an annulet either side of neck, pellet pointed spikes in crown.

Reverse   As previous, but an annulet usually amongst the three pellets.

| SJ24D-040 | VG £65 | F £200 | VF £400 |

As previous, with more modern looking lettering, no annulets at neck.

| SJ24D-045 | VG £65 | F £200 | VF £400 |

As previous, but a saltire or small cross either side of neck.

| SJ24D-050 | VG £80 | F £300 | VF rare |

As SJ24D-045, but the crown has trefoil pointed spikes.

| SJ24D-055 | VG £50 | F £110 | VF £250 |

As previous, but a trefoil either side of the king's neck and sometimes by the pellets on the reverse.

SJ24D-060   VG £45   F £100   VF £225

As SJ24D-055, but crosses or saltires at neck.

SJ24D-065   VG £50   F £110   VF £240

Obverse Legend   As previous.

Reverse Legends   As previous.

Obverse   New plain unjewelled crown, beaded inner circles with the lettering similar to issues of the next reign.

Reverse   As previous.

SJ24D-070   ex. rare

Perth Mint

Obverse Legend   As previous.

Outer Reverse Legend   As previous.

Inner Reverse Legend   VILLA DE PERTH — Town of Perth

Obverse   As SJ24D-065.

Reverse   As SJ24D-065.

SJ24D-075   ex. rare

Aberdeen Mint

Obverse Legend   As previous.

Outer Reverse Legend   As previous.

Inner Reverse Reverse   VILLA ABIRDEN — Town of Aberdeen

Obverse   As previous, but sometimes no saltires.

Reverse   As previous.

SJ24D-080   v. rare

Roxburgh Mint

Obverse Legend   As previous.

Outer Reverse Legend   As previous.

Inner Reverse Legend   VILLA ROXBURGH — Town of Roxburgh

Obverse   As previous, always with saltires at neck.

Reverse   As previous.

SJ24D-085   ex. rare

Stirling Mint

Obverse Legend   As previous.

Outer Reverse Legend   As previous.

Inner Reverse Legend   VILLA STERLING — Town of Stirling

Obverse   As previous, with saltires or lis at neck.

Reverse   As previous.

SJ24D-090   VG —   F £500   VF v. Rare

Halfgroat

Halfgroats were struck during the second coinage of 1451 – 60, at the mints of Edinburgh, Aberdeen and Perth. Due to the rising silver prices during this period, the value of the halfgroat was increased to sixpence, in line with the groat which was struck with a value of twelve pence.

All of these issues depict a crowned, front-facing bust of the king with no sceptre and are fairly similar to more common English issues. Low grade coins may also be confused with groats, as well as halfgroats from later reigns, so collectors should pay particular attention to the obverse legend, the style of crown and portrait as well as the marking in the quarters of the reverse.

Second Coinage (1451 – 1460)

Collecting Hints

The issue from the Edinburgh mint is rare while those from Aberdeen and Perth are extremely rare.

Edinburgh Mint

Obverse Legend IACOB DEI GRACIA REX SCOTOR — James by the grace of God King of Scots

Reverse Legend DNS PTECTOROB MS LIBERATOB — God is my defender and redeemer

Inner Reverse Legend VILLA EDINBURG(E) — Town of Edinburgh

Obverse Crowned, front-facing bust of king; sometimes mintmark cross at the beginning of the legend.

Reverse Long cross with three pellets in two of the quarters and a crown in the other two, sometimes annulets between the pellets; mintmark crown.

SJ22D-005	VG —	F £650	VF v. rare

Aberdeen Mint

Obverse Legend As previous.

Reverse Legend As previous.

Inner Reverse Legend VILLA ABERDON — Town of Aberdeen

Obverse As previous.

Reverse As previous.

SJ22D-010	ex. rare

Perth Mint

Obverse Legend As previous.

Reverse Legend As previous.

Inner Reverse Legend VILLA DE PERTH — Town of Perth

Obverse As previous.

Reverse As previous.

SJ22D-015	ex. rare

Penny

The continuing rise in silver price, growing prosperity and inflation culminated in the reign of James II with groats now being valued at twelve pence. They were however at this time roughly the same weight and therefore value as the English groat the value of which remained at fourpence. This produced serious consequences for the penny which was now billon (part silver and part base metal) as the denomination had little spending power.

The issues can be divided into two coinages. The main differences is that the weight of the second coinage was heavily reduced by about 35%.

First Coinage (1437 – 1451)

> # Collecting Hints
>
> Both mints are extremely rare.

Obverse Legend IACOBUS DEI TRACIIIA RE — James by the grace of God King (misspelt)

Reverse Legend VILLA EDINBURG — Town of Edinburgh

Obverse Tall thin bust with bushy hair.

Reverse Long cross, three pellets in the angles.

SJ21D-005	ex. rare

Stirling Mint

Obverse Legend As previous.

Reverse Legend VILLA STERLIN (?) — Town of Stirling

Obverse As previous.

Reverse As previous.

SJ21D-010	ex. rare

Second Coinage (1451 – 1460)

> # Collecting Hints
>
> While four mints in total were active, Edinburgh, Aberdeen, Perth and Roxburgh, all issues are extremely rare or unique, except for several issues of Edinburgh. However even these issues are rare and are usually found in less than Fine condition and are often damaged. Varieties of legend including mis-spellings exist.

Edinburgh Mint

Obverse Legend IACOBUS DI GRACIA REX (?) — James by the grace of God King

Reverse Legend VILLA EDINBURG — Town of Edinburgh

Obverse Crowned thin bust of king.

Reverse Long cross three pellets in two quarters only.

SJ21D-015	ex. rare

Obverse Legend

Reverse Legend

Obverse As previous.

Reverse Long cross, a crown in one quarter, three pellets around an annulet in each other quarter.

SJ21D-020	ex. rare

Obverse Legend   IACOUS DI GRA REX SITORU (varieties) — James by the grace of God King of Scots

Reverse Legend   As previous.

Obverse   Crowned bust of king; mintmark crown at beginning of legend.

Reverse   Long cross, three pellets in each quarter.

SJ21D-025   VG £125   F £300   VF —

Obverse Legend   IACO REC GRA REX SCOTORU(M) — James by the grace of God King of Scots

Reverse Legend   As previous.

Obverse   As previous, but a saltire either side of the king's neck.

Reverse   As previous, but a saltire usually between the pellets.

SJ21D-030   VG £140   F £350   VF —

Obverse Legend   IACO REI G REX SCOTRUM — James by the grace of God King of Scots

Reverse Legend   As previous.

Obverse   Crowned bust of king a lis either side of neck.

Reverse   As previous.

SJ21D-035   VG £180   F £400   VF —

Aberdeen Mint

Obverse Legend   IACO REI GRA REX SCOTRUM — James by the grace of God King of Scots

Reverse Legend   VILLA ABIRDEN — Town of Aberdeen

Obverse   Crowned bust of king, a saltire either side of neck.

Reverse   Long cross three pellets in each quarter with a saltire in the centre.

SJ21D-040   unique

Perth Mint

Obverse Legend   As previous.

Reverse Legend   VILLA PERTH (?) — Town of Perth

Obverse   As SJ21D-025.

Reverse   As SJ21D-025.

SJ21D-045   ex. rare

Roxburgh Mint

Obverse Legend   As SJ21D-040.

Reverse Legend   VILLA ROXBU — Town of Roxburgh

Obverse   Crowned bust of king, lis either side of neck.

Reverse   Long cross, three pellets in each quarter.

SJ21D-050   unique

Scotland: James III (1460 – 1488)

Due to the rising gold price, new gold denominations were introduced during James III's reign, the rider, half rider and quarter rider as well as the unicorn. Low denomination coins were also needed so the billon plack and half plack were introduced with a value of fourpence and twopence respectively, as was the copper farthing. Due to the rising silver price there were a fair number of silver issues and both the weight and the value of the groat and the halfgroat flucutated.

As previous, but below the king there is a small 'A', the initial of the mintmaster Alexander Livingston.

SJ3RD-010	v. rare

Rider

The gold rider, so called after the equestrian figure of the king on the obverse, was first introduced under James III and had a value of twenty-three shillings. The denomination was short-lived, being struck between 1475 and 1483 and subsequently replaced by the gold unicorn which had a value of eighteen shillings. However, the rider re-emerged under James VI, with a value of 100 shillings.

Obverse Legend   As previous reverse.

Reverse Legend   As previous obverse.

Obverse   As SJ3RD-005, but the king is riding to the left.

Reverse   As SJ3RD-005.

SJ3RD-015	v. rare

First Issue (1475 – 1483)

Obverse Legend   IACOBUS DEI GRA REX SCOTOR — James by the grace of God King of Scots

Reverse Legend   SALUM FAC POPULUM TUUM DNE — O Lord save Thy people

Obverse   Helmeted king in armour, on horseback with drawn sword riding to the right.

Reverse   A shield with a lion rampant over a cross, a crown above the shield.

SJ3RD-005	VG —	F £1,750	VF £3,500

Unicorn

The gold unicorn was introduced during the reign of James III with a value of eighteen shillings and some numismatists consider this first issue to have been a pattern or trading coin for the European market, as its weight and fineness were identical to the French gold crown. While there is some doubt as to how many James III issues circulated, it is clear that during later reigns the unicorn became an important and popular denomination. This non-portrait issue derived its name from its obverse design of a unicorn.

Some numismatic works list a half-unicorn for this reign, however it is now considered that this coin was issued by James IV.

Second Gold Issue (1484 – 1488)

Obverse Legend   EXURGAT DE ET DISIPERT NIMICIES — Let God arise and His enemies be scattered

Reverse Legend   As obverse.

Obverse   Unicorn and royal shield; mintmark cross crosslet at start of legend.

Reverse   Large star with wavy rays over a cross fleury; mintmark lis at start of legend.

| SJ3UC-005 | VG — | F £1,000 | VF £3,000 |

Half Rider

The gold half rider was first issued during the reign of James III. With a value of eleven shillings and sixpence, it formed part of a new denomination structure which, however, proved unpopular and was replaced in later reigns by the unicorn series. Nevertheless, the half rider itself was re-introduced for a short period under James VI, with a value of fifty shillings.

First Gold Issue (1475 – 1483)

Collecting Hints

The first issue is extremely rare while the second issue is very rare.

Obverse Legend IACOBUS DEI GRA REX SCOTORUM — James by the grace of God King of Scots

Reverse Legend SALWM FAC POPULUM TWM DOMINE — O Lord save Thy people

Obverse Royal arms.

Reverse King on horseback riding to the left.

| SJ3HRD-005 | ex. rare |

As previous, but a lis below the king's sword.

| SJ3HRD-010 | v. rare |

Quarter Rider

Introduced under James III with a value of five shillings and ninepence, the quarter rider depicts the king on horseback, hence the name rider, and was part of a new denomination structure which, however, proved unsuccessful and was replaced by the unicorn.

Collecting Hints

This issue is very rare in any grade.

First Gold Issue (1475 – 1483)

Obverse Legend IACOBUS DEI GRA REX SCOTORU — James by the grace of God King of Scots

Reverse Legend SALWM FAC POPULUM TWM DOMIN — O Lord save Thy people

Obverse Crown above royal arms over a cross.

Reverse King holding sword riding to the left, a lis below the sword.

| SJ3QRD-005 | v. rare |

Groat

Under James III a variety of groats of different styles, weights, values and fineness were struck, mainly in Edinburgh. The varying weight and values of these issues must have caused considerable confusion to the public. The old fashioned medieval styles were being phased out during this period and replaced with Renaissance inspired portraits which were far more lifelike.

Light Issue of 1467

These issues had a value of twelve pence and were made of 0.925 silver.

Collecting Hints

These issues are very much a continuation from the previous reign. However minor varieties of each issue separate the reigns, in particular the designs in the centre of the reverse. These issues are rare and were fairly poorly struck. Coins in VF or better are extremely rare, however these issues are rarely found clipped or damaged.

Edinburgh Mint

Obverse Legend IACOBUS D GRA REX SCOTO(RUM) — James by the grace of God King of Scots

Outer Reverse Legend DNS PROTECTOR MS LIBERATO (many varieties exist) — God is my defender and my redeemer

Inner Reverse Legend VILLA EDINBURG — Town of Edinburgh

Obverse Front-facing crowned bust, the crown is 'low' or 'flat' in style, a saltire or cross either side of neck.

Reverse Long cross, two stars in two quarters, three pellets and a saltire in two quarters.

| SJ34D-005 | VG £75 | F £175 | VF £500 |

As previous, but larger, heavier bust, no saltires at neck or usually on reverse.

| SJ34D-010 | VG £70 | F £160 | VF £450 |

As previous, but 'T' and 'L' either side of neck, probably the initials of the mintmasters Thomas Tod and Alexander Livingston.

| SJ34D-015 | VG £100 | F £240 | VF £600 |

Berwick Mint

Obverse Legend As previous.

Outer Reverse Legend As previous.

Inner Reverse Legend VILLA BERWICHI — Town of Berwick

Obverse As previous.

Reverse As previous.

| SJ34D-020 | VG £120 | F £300 | VF rare |

Base Issue (1471 – 1483)

This issue had a value of sixpence and was made of silver of 0.770 fineness. It was struck at Edinburgh only.

Collecting Hints

This attractive issue shows the new style realistic portrait. This coin is rare especially in better than Fine condition and is sometimes found clipped or damaged.

Obverse Legend IACOBUS DEI GRA REX SCOTORUM (varieties exist) — James by the grace of God of Scots

Reverse Legend VILLA EDINBURGH — Town of Edinburgh

Obverse Crowned three quarter facing bust to right.

Reverse Cross with floriated ends, a thistle in two quarters, a mullet in remaining two quarters, the position of these four marks can vary.

| SJ34D-025 | VG £80 | F £200 | VF £550 |

As previous, but a 'T' to left of king, this is the initial of the mintmaster Thomas Tod.

| SJ34D-030 | VG £180 | F £450 | VF rare |

Light Issue of 1475

These groats had a value of twelve pence and a silver content of 0.925. They are fairly similar to the light issue of 1467, as well as some of the issues of James II, although they are smaller in size and bear minor marks and varieties which differentiate them. One major variety is the style of the king's crown, which often varies. Coins were struck at Edinburgh and Berwick.

Collecting Hints

The first two types while scarce are obtainable especially in the lower grades, while the third type as well as issues from the Berwick mint are rare. All coins are rare in VF or better condition.

Edinburgh Mint

Obverse Legend IACOBUS DEI GRA REX SCOTOR(U)M — James by the grace of God King of Scots

Outer Reverse Legend DNS PTEACTOR MS Z LIBERTU — God is my defender and my redeemer

Inner Reverse Legend VILLA EDINBURGH — Town of Edinburgh

Obverse Small crowned bust of king; the crown is fairly flat with five tall fleurs as decoration.

Reverse Long cross, three pellets in two quarters, a mullet or star in two quarters of six points.

| SJ34D-035 | VG £50 | F £100 | VF £300 |

As previous, but the king's face is slightly larger and his crown has three fleurs.

| SJ34D-040 | VG £50 | F £100 | VF £300 |

As SJ34D-035 but saltires or small stars either side of bust.

| SJ34D-045 | VG £100 | F £225 | F £500 |

Berwick Mint

Obverse Legend As previous.

Outer Reverse Legend As previous.

Inner Reverse Legend VILLA BERWICHI — Town of Berwick

Obverse As SJ34D-035.

Reverse As SJ34D-035.

| SJ34D-050 | VG £110 | F £225 | VF — |

Obverse Legend   As previous.

Outer Reverse Legend   As previous.

Inner Reverse Legend   VILLA BERWICHI — Town of Berwick

Obverse   As SJ34D-040.

Reverse   As SJ34D-040.

| SJ34D-055 | VG £120 | F £250 | VF — |

Light Issue of 1482

This issue, which was only struck at Edinburgh, had a value of twelve pence and was made of 0.925 silver. It is very similar to that of the light issue of 1475, the main differences being the spelling of Edinburgh and the number of points on the stars or mullets on the reverse. The style of portrait is also much neater. The king on both types of the 1482 issues wears a crown with five equal-sized lis.

Collecting Hints

The first type is rare, especially in better than fine condition. Coins are rarely found clipped but are often heavily worn. The second variety is extremely rare.

Obverse Legend   IACOBUS DEI GRA REX SCOTORM — James by the grace of God King of Scots

Outer Reverse Legend   DNS PTEATORMS Z LIBERATURMS — God is my defender and my redeemer

Inner Reverse Legend   VILLA EDENBEOURGE — Town of Edinburgh

Obverse   Neat bust of king wearing a flat crown of five lis of equal height

Reverse   Long cross, three pellets in two quarters, two stars of five points in the other two quarters.

| SJ34D-060 | VG £70 | F £160 | VF £400 |

Obverse   As previous.

Reverse   As SJ34D-035. This issue is a mule and used the die from the previous issue.

| SJ34D-065 | ex. Rare |

Heavy Issue (1484 – 1488)

This issue is often known as the rough or irregular issue. It had a value of fourteen pence and was made of 0.925 silver. It can easily be identified by the annulet on the king's breast and the spelling of Edinburgh.

Collecting Hints

This coin is rare in any grade.

Obverse Legend   IACOBUS DEI GRACIA REX SCOT — James by the grace of God King of Scotland

Outer Reverse Legend   DNS PROTORUM AVMAT MEVOR — God is my defender and my redeemer

Inner Reverse Legend   VILLA EDINBR(U)G — Town of Edinburgh

Obverse   Crowned bust with five fleur de lis in the crown, an annulet on the king's breast, all within a tressure of twelve arcs.

Reverse   Three pellets in two quarters, a crown in the other two quarters.

| SJ34D-070 | VG — | F £500 | VF — |

Main Issue (1484 – 1488)

This issue was struck in Edinburgh and Aberdeen in 0.925 silver and had a value of fourteen pence. It is very popular with collectors, depicting a new style, lifelike portrait of the king on the obverse while the reverse is similar to previous issues.

Collecting Hints

This issue is scarce but obtainable especially in the lower grades. Coins in VF or better condition are rare and many have chipped edges or are cracked, possibly due to poor striking.

Edinburgh Mint

Obverse Legend   IACOBUS DEI GRACIA REX SCOTORU (many varieties exist) — James by the grace of God King of Scots

Outer Reverse Legend   DNS PROTECTOR ERATO (varieties exist) — God is my defender and my redeemer

Inner Reverse Legend   VILLA EDINBRUGH — Town of Edinburgh

Obverse   Crowned bust, three quarter face to left with arched crown.

Reverse   Long cross, three pellets and an annulet in two quarters, a crown in two quarters.

| SJ34D-075 | VG £65 | F £150 | VF £450 |

As previous, but a crown and saltire in front of bust and a lis behind.

| SJ34D-080 | ex. rare |

As SJ34D-075, but an annulet in the inner circle of the obverse.

SJ34D-085	VG £65	F £150	VF £450

As SJ34D-075, but an annulet in front of the bust.

SJ34D-090	VG £65	F £150	VF £450

As SJ34D-075, but an annulet behind the king's head.

SJ34D-095	VG £65	F £150	VF £450

Aberdeen Mint

Obverse Legend   As previous.

Outer Reverse Legend   As previous.

Inner Reverse Legend   VILLA DE ABRDA — Town of Aberdeen

Obverse   As SJ34D-075.

Reverse   As SJ34D-075.

SJ34D-100	VG £180	F £400	VF rare

Obverse Legend   As previous.

Outer Reverse Legend   As previous.

Inner Reverse Legend   VILLA DE ABRDA or ABBDEN — Town of Aberdeen

Obverse   As SJ34D-085.

Reverse   As SJ34D-055.

SJ34D-105	VG £180	F £400	VF rare

Halfgroat

Halfgroats, which were struck during most of James III reign, all tend to be rare and we have given Collecting Hints for each issue.

Light Issue (1467) value sixpence

Collecting Hints

Both of the Edinburgh issues are unique, while the Berwick issue is extremely rare.

Edinburgh Mint

Obverse Legend   IACOBUS 3 D. GRA REX SCOTOR — James III by the grace of God King of Scots

Outer Reverse Legend   DNS PTEATOB MS LEBERAT — God is my defender and redeemer

Inner Reverse Legend   VILLA EDINBURGH — Town of Edinburgh

Obverse   Crowned front-facing bust of king, a cross either side of neck; mintmark cross patée with end fourchée, at start of legend.

Reverse   Long cross, three pellets in two quarters, a mullet or star of six points in two quarters.

SJ32D-005	unique

As previous, but no numeral '3' after the king's name.

SJ32D-010	unique

Berwick Mint

Obverse Legend   As SJ32D-005.

Outer Reverse Legend   As previous.

Inner Reverse Legend   VILLA BERVICHI or BERWICI — Town of Berwick

Obverse   As previous.

Reverse   As previous.

SJ32D-015	ex. rare

Base Issue (1471 – 1483)

This issue, which was only struck at Edinburgh, had a value of threepence and the silver content was reduced from 0.925 to 0.770. It depicts a realistic lifelike crowned bust of the king on the obverse reflecting the new Renaissance style which was spreading throughout Europe. The reverse bears a floriate cross with thistleheads and mullets in alternate angles.

Collecting Hints

This issue is extremely rare in any grade. The groat from this issue is much more common and is probably a better choice for the collector who wants an example from the issue.

Obverse Legend   IACOBUS DEI GRA REX SCOTORUM or SC — James by the grace of God King of Scots

Reverse Legend   VILLA EDINBURGH — Town of Edinburgh

Obverse   Crowned bust of king with lifelike portrait.

Reverse   Floriate cross, with mullets and thistleheads in alternate angles.

| SJ32D-020 | VG — | F £600 | VF v. rare |

Light Issue of 1475 (Berwick Mint)

This rare issue was only struck at Berwick with a silver content of 0.925 and a value of sixpence. Unlike the previous issue, it has the earlier 'medieval' style and a fairly distinctive crown. It tends to be smaller in size than issues from previous reigns.

Collecting Hints

This issue is very rare and, when obtainable, is found in the lower grades.

Obverse Legend   IACOBUS DEI GRA REX SCOT — James by the grace of God King of Scotland

Outer Reverse Legend   DNS PERTECTOR MS Z LIIBERATO — God is my defender and my redeemer

Inner Reverse Legend   VILLA BERVICCHII or BERWICII — Town of Berwick

Obverse   Crowned front-facing bust of the king, the crown has three tall fleurs.

Reverse   Long cross, three pellets in two of the quarters and two stars in the other two.

| SJ32D-025 | VG £400 | F £850 | VF v. rare |

Light issue of 1482 (Edinburgh Mint)

This issue was similar but slightly less crude than the previous issue. Made of 0.925 silver and with a value of sixpence, it was struck at the Edinburgh mint. The obverse crown bears four fleurs. The initials 'A', 'L' and 'T' of the mintmasters Alexander Livingston and Thomas Tod can also be found on the coin.

Collecting Hints

This issue is very rare, especially in better than VF condition.

Obverse Legend   IACOBUS DEI GRA REX SCOTOTUM — James by the grace of God King of Scots

Outer Reverse Legend   DNS PT EATORM S Z LIBERATURMS — God is my defender and my redeemer

Inner Reverse Legend   VILLA EDENBEOURGE — Town of Edinburgh

Obverse   Front-facing crowned bust of king with a crown of four fleurs. There is an 'L' above the crown and an 'A' and 'T' either side of the king's neck.

Reverse   Long cross with a mullet in two of the quarters, three pellets in the other two, and an 'L' in the centre of the cross.

| SJ32D-030 | VG £200 | F £450 | VF v. rare |

As previous, but without the mintmasters' initials.

| SJ32D-035 | probably unique |

No halfgroats were struck for the heavy issue of 1484 – 88.

Main Issue (1484 – 1488)

This issue was struck at Edinburgh, of 0.925 silver and with a value of seven pence. It is rare and bears a lifelike crowned portrait of the king with a long cross on the reverse.

Collecting Hints

This issue is rare especially in VF or better condition.

Obverse Legend   IACOBUS DIE GRACIA REX — James by the grace of God King

Outer Reverse Legend   DNS PRATETOR ME RATO — God is my defender and my redeemer

Inner Reverse Legend   VILLA EDINBUI (many varieties exist) — Town of Edinburgh

Obverse   Crowned bust facing half left with bushy hair; mintmark cross fleury at the start of the legend.

Reverse   Long cross with a crown in two angles, three pellets and an annulet in two quarters; mintmark plain cross.

| SJ32D-040 | VG £100 | F £250 | VF rare |

As previous, but no mintmark on reverse.

| SJ32D-045 | v. rare |

Plack

The plack was struck at Edinburgh, probably throughout the whole of James III's reign, and does not bear a portrait of the monarch. It had a value of fourpence, the historical value of the groat, and a metal content of 50% silver and 50% copper which led it to be known as the billon coinage. Placks were also issued during subsequent reigns, so collectors should refer to later dates when identifying a coin as the various issues tend to be fairly similar; collectors should also pay particular attention to the styles and design of the reverse.

Collecting Hints

This issue is rare in all grades. Crude contemporary forgeries of this issue are known to exist.

Obverse Legend   IACOBUS D. GRA REX SCOTTORU(M) — James by the grace of God King of Scots

Reverse Legend   VILLA DE EDINBURGH — Town of Edinburgh

Obverse   The Scottish arms in a shield with a crown above, within a tressure.

Reverse   Floreate cross fourchée, a central panel with a small cross within, a crown in each angle.

SJ3PL-005   rare

As previous, but a star in the centre of the reverse.

SJ3PL-010   ex. rare

As previous, but an 'I' in the centre of the reverse.

SJ3PL-015   ex. rare

Half Plack (dates uncertain)

This billon issue was known as a half plack rather than a half-groat but had a value of twopence, which is the historical value of the halfgroat. It was struck in 0.500 silver in Edinburgh.

Collecting Hints

This issue is fairly similar to the ones of James IV and collectors should refer to both when identifying a coin. The first type of James III halfplack is rare, it is usually found worn and is very rare in VF or better condition. The later issues are extremely rare.

Obverse Legend   IACOBUS D. GRA REX SCOTTOR — James by the grace of God King of Scots

Reverse Legend   VILLA DE EDINBURGH — Town of Edinburgh

Obverse   Crowned shield of tressure of three arcs, a lion rampant in shield, a cross pattée either side of shield.

Reverse   Floreate cross fourchée, a saltire in the central panel, a crown in each angle.

SJ3HPL-005 VG £60   F £125   VF £300

As previous, but no marks by the shield.

SJ3HPL-010 ex. rare

As SJ32D-050, but an 'I' instead of a saltire on the reverse.

SJ3HPL-015 ex. rare

Penny

As with the groats and halfgroats, James III pennies can be divided into several issues. Firstly, there was the light silver issue of 1475 which was made of good quality silver and had a value of threepence, as did the light issue of 1482. The billon issue, which was struck between 1481 and 1488, produced pennies of very low fineness but with a value of a penny. The ecclesiastical issues were struck at St Andrews, probably by Bishop James Kennedy. They were copper coins and could perhaps be considered tokens.

This wide diversity in the coinage must have caused great difficulty in trading especially amongst a mostly illiterate and uneducated population. However the centralisation of coin production at Edinburgh at this time undoubtedly contributed to greater conformity during later reigns.

Silver Issue of 1475 (Edinburgh Mint)

Collecting Hints

This issue is rare especially in the higher grades and is made of good quality silver.

Obverse Legend   IACOBUS DE GRA REX SO — James by the grace of God King of Scotland

Reverse Legend   VILLA EDEINBOUR — Town of Edinburgh

Obverse   Crowned, neat, front-facing bust of the king.

Reverse   Long cross, two stars of six points in two quarters. Three pellets in two quarters.

SJ31D-005   VG £80   F £200   VF —

Light Issue of 1482 (Edinburgh Mint)

This issue was slightly lighter in weight than the previous one.

Collecting Hints

This issue is rare in any grade.

Obverse Legend   As previous.

Reverse Legend   As previous.

Obverse   As previous.

Reverse   As previous, but the stars have five points

SJ31D-010   VG £150   F £350   VF —

Billon Coinage (1484 – 1488)
(Edinburgh Mint)

Collecting Hints

While rare, this issue is obtainable especially in lower grades. Coins are often found chipped with much of the legend either missing or flat. Coins with full flans are worth more that the prices listed below.

Obverse Legend   IACOBUS DEI GRA REX (varieties exist) — James by the grace of God King

Reverse Legend   VILLA EDINBUR(G) — Town of Edinburgh

Obverse   Crowned front-facing bust of king, mintmark cross fourchée at start of legend.

Reverse   Long cross, three pellets in each quarter.

SJ31D-015   VG £40   F £80   VF rare

Obverse Legend   IACOBUS DEI GRA REX S — James by the grace of God King of Scotland

Reverse Legend   As previous.

Obverse   As previous.

Reverse   Short cross, slipped trefoils or quatrefoils in angles.

SJ31D-020   VG £60   F £120   VF rare

Obverse Legend   As SJ31D-015

Reverse Legend   As previous.

Obverse   Crowned bust of king with five fleurs to crown; mintmark plain cross at start of legend.

Reverse   Long cross, three pellets in each quarter.

SJ31D-025   VG £50   F £100   VF £220

As previous, with three fleurs in crown.

SJ31D-030   VG £55   F £120   VF £260

Obverse Legend   IACOBUS DEI REX SCO — James [by the grace of] God King of Scotland

Reverse Legend   As previous.

Obverse   Crowned bust of king, facing slightly left with long bushy hair. An annulet either side of the crown and sometimes above.

Reverse   Long cross, three pellets in each quarter; mintmark cinquefoil.

SJ31D-035   VG £125   F £300   VF   rare

Bishop James Kennedy Pennies

These coins are sometimes considered as tokens. Made of copper with no silver content at all, they did not bear a portrait of the king. Sometimes known as 'crux pellit' coins, they were unpopular with the public, with many people refusing to accept them as payment. This issue was also known as Crosraguel pennies because a large hoard was found there but not, as some sources state, because the coins were produced there.

Collecting Hints

These coins are common especially in the lower grades, however they are rarely found in better than Fine condition reflecting the considerable circulation these coins saw.

Obverse Legend   IACOBUS DEI GRA REX — James by the grace of God King

Reverse Legend   CRUX PELLIT OIE CRIM — The cross drives away all sin

Obverse   An orb tilted downwards.

Reverse   Cross in quatrefoil.

SJ31D-040   VG £30   F £80   VF   rare

Obverse Legend   As previous reverse legend.

Reverse Legend   As previous.

Obverse   As previous.

Reverse   As previous.

SJ31D-045   VG £50   F £140   VF rare

Obverse Legend   As SJ31D-040.

Reverse Legend   As previous.

Obverse   Orb tilted upwards.

Reverse   As previous.

SJ31D-050   VG £30   F £80   VF rare

As previous, but a jewel in each third of the orb.

SJ31D-055   ex. rare

As SJ31D-040, but a rosette in the centre of the orb.

SJ31D-060	ex. rare

Halfpenny

This issue, which should not to be confused with the penny, was struck at Edinburgh in billon of such low fineness that it looks like copper.

Collecting Hints

This coin is unique.

Obverse Legend   IACOBUS D.G. REX SCO — James by the grace of God King of Scotland

Reverse Legend   VILLA EDIN — Town of Edinburgh

Obverse   Front-facing, crowned bust of king, three fleurs to crown.

Reverse   Long cross, three pellets in each quarter.

SJ3HD-005	unique

Farthing

Two main farthing issues were struck during this period, in copper or, sometimes, brass, as the farthing was by now a very low denomination of little value. The first issue is known as the royal or regal issue and nicknamed 'black money' because it had no silver content; the second was probably an ecclesiastical issue struck in St Andrews.

Collecting Hints

All issues are rare and most coins obviously saw considerable circulation, those in better than Fine condition are very rare.

Royal Issue

1466

Obverse Legend   I REX SCOTORUM — James King of Scots

Reverse Legend   VILLA EDINBUR(G) — Town of Edinburgh

Obverse   Large crown.

Reverse   St Andrews cross with a small saltire on either side.

SJ3FA-005	VG £100	F £250	VF rare

1470

Obverse Legend   IACOBUS DIE GRA — James by the grace of God

Reverse Legend   VILLA EDINBUR — Town of Edinburgh

Obverse   Crown with I.R. (Iacobus Rex) below.

Reverse   Crown over St Andrews cross, small saltires in each angle.

SJ3FA-010	VG £80	F £200	VF £450

Ecclesiastical Issue

Obverse Legend   IACOBUS D.G.R. — James by the grace of God

Reverse Legend   MONE PAVP — Money for the poor

Obverse   Crown over I.R.

Reverse   Cross in inner circle, a crown in two of the quarters and a star in the other two.

SJ3FA-015	VG £130	F £300	VF rare

Obverse Legend   None

Reverse Legend   MONE PAUP — Money for the poor

Obverse   Three lis in three broken circles, a star in the centre and three crowns in angles of circles on the edge of the coin.

Reverse   As previous.

SJ3FA-020	VG £110	F £250	VF rare

As previous, but reverse legend reads MO PAUPER — Money for the poor.

SJ3FA-025	VG £110	F £250	VF rare

Scotland: James IV (1488 – 1513)

During this period, the unicorn continued to be struck and was complemented by the half unicorn. A gold lion and half lion were also re-introduced with a value of thirteen shillings and fourpence, and six shillings and eightpence respectively. These denominations were equivalent to the popular values of two angels and one angel. Silver groats, halfgroats and pennies as well as billon placks, half placks and billon pennies were also produced. As with previous reigns, the face value of the silver coinage varied under James IV, with a groat being worth either fourteen or twelve pence, the halfgroat either seven pence or six pence, while the silver penny which was only struck during the light coinage had a value of threepence. The billon pennies had a value of one penny.

Unicorn

Produced only at Edinburgh, the unicorn was struck in 19 or 21 carat gold and had a value of eighteen shillings. James IV unicorns differ from those of the previous reign in that they all bear the king's name on the obverse, they are however fairly similar to the issues of James V, so collectors should refer to both these reigns when identifying a coin.

Collecting Hints

All issues are rare but occasionally obtainable, whereupon they are usually found undamaged in Fine to VF condition.

Obverse Legend IACOBUS DEI GRACIA REX SCOTORU (varieties exist) — James by the grace of God King of Scots

Reverse Legend EXURGAT DES ET DISIPERTUR INIM (varieties exist) — Let God arise and His enemies be scattered

Obverse Unicorn and royal shield, a crown of three lis around the unicorn's neck. The words of the legends are punctuated by six pointed star stops.

Reverse Large star with wavy rays over a cross fleury, Lombardic 'N' in legend and the words punctuated as on the obverse.

| SJ4UC-005 | VG — | F £800 | VF £2,000 |

As previous, but 'V's or broken star stops in legends; mintmark cross pommée.

| SJ4UC-010 | VG — | F £800 | VF £2,000 |

Obverse Legend As previous.

Reverse Legend EXURGAT DEUS DISSIPERT INMICI EI — Let God arise and His enemies be scattered

Obverse As previous, but a crown of five lis around the unicorn's neck, lis or pellet stops in legend; mintmark cross pattée at start of legend, sometimes no chain by the unicorn.

Reverse As previous, lis or pellet stops in legend.

| SJ4UC-015 | VG — | F £800 | VF £2,000 |

Obverse As previous.

Reverse As previous, but Roman style lettering in legend.

| SJ4UC-020 | VG — | F £1,000 | VF £2,200 |

Obverse Legend IACOBUS 4 DEI GRA REX SCOTORUM — James IV by the grace of God King of Scots

Reverse Legend EXURGAT DEUS DISIPENT INIMICI EIU — Let God arise and His enemies be scattered

Obverse As previous, but a '4' after the king's name, star stops in legend; mintmark crown at start of legend and no chain below the unicorn.

Reverse As previous, but star stops in legend.

| SJ4UC-025 | v. rare |

These are the five most common types, but mules from them are not uncommon and minor varieties of legends exist.

Lion

This issue is very much a continuation from the lions of James II. However, due to the constantly rising price of gold, the value of the lion was increased again, to thirteen shillings and fourpence, and its gold content was reduced from 23 carat to approximately 18–20 carat. Its weight was 52.25 grains (3.48 grams). This issue is sometimes also known as a 'St Andrew' or a crown.

Collecting Hints

The first issue is unique while the second issue is very rare. As with previous issues, when available, coins are usually found in Fine to VF condition.

Obverse Legend   IACOBUS D. GRACIA REX SCO — James by the grace of God King of Scotland

Reverse Legend   SALUUM FAC POPULUM TUU DNE — O Lord save Thy people

Obverse   Crown over shield, a lion in the shield, a lis either side of the shield; mintmark crown.

Reverse   St Andrew holding cross.

SJ4LI-005	unique

Obverse Legend   IACOBUS DEI GRA REX SCOTTORUM IIII — James IV by the grace of God King of Scots

Reverse Legend   SALMUM FAC PPLUU TUUM DNE — O Lord save Thy people

Obverse   Crown over royal shield, a lis either side; mintmark crown.

Reverse   St Andrew crucified, the cross extends to the edge of the coin.

SJ4LI-010	VG —	F £1,500	VF £3,000

Half Unicorn

First struck under James IV, the gold half unicorn complemented the unicorn which had been introduced during the previous reign. Its value was nine shillings, rising to ten shillings under James V. All issues were struck in Edinburgh and depict a unicorn and royal shield on the obverse and a large star on the reverse.

Collecting Hints

The first three issues are rare but obtainable, while the last two are extremely rare. Coins from the first three issues are usually found in Fine to VF condition and undamaged.

Obverse Legend   IACOBUS DEI GRACIA REX SCT (varieties exist) — James by the grace of God King of Scots

Reverse Legend   EXURGAT D S ET DISIPERTUR IN — Let God arise and His enemies be scattered

Obverse   Unicorn and shield, star stops in legend.

Reverse   Large star with wavy rays with four floriated ends, Lombardic 'N's in legend; mintmark lis.

SJ4HUC-005	VG —	F £1,000	VF £2,200

As previous, but Roman 'N's in reverse legend, and sometimes no stops in legends.

SJ4HUC-010	VG —	F £1,000	VF £2,200

Obverse Legend   IACOBUS DEI GRACIA REX SCO — James by the grace of God King of Scotland

Reverse Legend   EXURGAT DS ET DISIPERT INIM — Let God arise and His enemies be scattered

Obverse   As previous, but 'V's or broken star stops in legend.

Reverse   As previous, stops in legend.

SJ4HUC-015	VG —	F £1,000	VF £2,200

Obverse Legend   IACOBUS DEI GRACIA REX SCO QR — James by the grace of God King of Scotland the fourth

Reverse Legend   As previous(?)

Obverse   As previous, but mintmark cross potent.

Reverse   'I' (for IACOBUS) in centre of star, with fourteen wavy rays.

SJ4HUC-020	ex. rare

As previous, but mintmark crown. A small star in the centre of the reverse star instead of an 'I'.

SJ4HUC-025	ex. rare

Demi Lion

Due to the rising gold price, James IV demi lions were struck with a value of six shillings and eightpence while their metal fineness was reduced to between 18 and 20 carats. Sometimes known as a 'half St Andrew', this issue is similar stylistically to those of previous reigns.

Obverse Legend   IACOBUS DEI GRACIA REX SCO — James by the grace of God King of Scotland

Reverse Legend   SALVVIII FAC PPLV TV DN — O Lord save Thy people

Obverse   Crown over royal shield, a crowned lis on either side of the shield; mintmark crown.

Reverse   St Andrew on cross which extends to the edge of the coin, a crowned lis on either side of the cross.

| SJ4DLI-005 | VG — | F £1,800 | VF — |

As previous, but the legend ends with 'IIII' denoting James IV.

| SJ4DLI-010 | VG — | F £2,000 | VF — |

Groat

As most modern collectors tend to prefer the groat with a lifelike portrait, it is rather unfortunate that James IV reverted to producing groats in the older medieval style, perhaps because the diversity of groats of varying weight, design and fineness of previous reigns would have caused confusion and error amongst a generally uneducated and illiterate public.

Many of James IV's groats are similar to those of previous reigns, although varieties in style of bust as well as reverse marks help differentiate them. Most of James' early issues use the mintmark cross fleury which can be found at the beginning of the obverse and reverse legends; earlier issues of previous reigns did not use this mintmark except for the light issue of 1482.

James IV groats were produced in Edinburgh and can be divided into two coinages by virtue of their weight, value and silver content. The heavy coinage (1489 – 96) was struck in 0.925 silver and had a value of fourteen pence, while the light coinage (1496 – 1513) was of reduced weight and value, twelve pence, due to rising silver prices.

Collecting Hints

Both the heavy and the light coinages are rare in any grade and although coins are rarely clipped they are sometimes damaged. Light coinage specimens are usually found in VF or better condition, but the heavy coinage issue is rarely found in better than Fine condition.

Heavy Coinage (1489 – 1496)

This issue had a value of fourteen pence and was made of 0.925 silver.

Obverse Legend   IACOBUS DEI GRA REX SCOTOR (varieties exist) — James by the grace of God King of Scots

Inner Reverse Legend   VILLA EDIBUR or EDINBURG — Town of Edinburgh

Outer Reverse Legend   DNS PROTEATOR MEUSE (varieties exist) — God is my defender (and my redeemer)

Obverse   Crowned bust wearing crown of five lis; mintmark cross fleury.

Reverse   Long cross with three pellets and an annulet in two of the quarters, a crown in the other two and a lis in the centre of the cross.

| SJ44D-005 | VG £150 | F £350 | VF — |

As previous, but taller bust with no lis on the central cross of the reverse.

| SJ44D-010 | VG £110 | F £250 | VF £600 |

As SJ44D-010 but with 'IIII' (4) after the king's name in the obverse legend.

| SJ44D-015 | VG £150 | F £350 | VF — |

Obverse Legend   As SJ44D-005.

Reverse Legend   As SJ44D-005.

Obverse   Front-facing bust with very thin face and cheeks, the crown as previous but somewhat flatter, an annulet on the king's breast.

Reverse   Long cross with a crown in one of the angles, a lis in another and three pellets and an annulet in the other quarters.

| SJ44D-020 | VG £150 | F £350 | VF — |

Obverse Legend   As previous.

Reverse Legend   As previous.

Obverse   New style bust and crown, the king has heavy eyelids and wears a crown of three fleurs.

Reverse   As SJ44D-005.

| SJ44D-025 | VG £140 | F £330 | VF rare |

As previous, but tall spikes between the lis of the crown.

| SJ44D-030 | VG £140 | F £330 | VF rare |

Light Coinage (1496 – 1513)

With a face value of twelve pence, this issue was made of 0.925 silver and bore a mintmark crown at the start of the obverse legend. These coins are very neat in style compared to previous issues.

Obverse Legend   IACOBUS DEI GRA REX SCOTTORUM — James by the grace of God King of Scots

Outer Reverse Legend   SALUU FAC POPULU TUU D — O Lord save Thy people

Inner Reverse Legend VILLA EDINBURGH — Town of Edinburgh

Obverse Neat crowned bust of king facing mintmark crown.

Reverse Long cross with three pellets in two of the quarters and two mullets or stars in the other two.

SJ44D-035	VG £175	F £375	VF £800

As previous, but the numeral '4' at the end of the obverse legend.

SJ44D-040	VG —	F £500	VF £1,000

As previous, but a star on either side of the king's neck.

SJ44D-045	ex. rare

As SJ44D-035, but 'QRA' or 'QT' (QUARTU — four in Latin) at the end of the obverse legend.

SJ44D-050	VG £160	F £350	VF £700

As previous, but a star on either side of the king's neck.

SJ44D-055	VG £180	F £400	VF £800

As previous., but the numeral 'IIII' at the end of the obverse legend instead of 'QRA' or 'QT'.

SJ44D-060	VG £180	F £400	VF £800

Maundy Issue (1512)

This issue was struck as Maundy money and had a value of twelve pence. It bears a bearded bust of the king which is unique to this issue.

Obverse Legend As SJ44D-035 with a '4' after the king's name.

Outer Reverse Legend EXURGAT DEUS DISSIPENTUR INIMICI EIUS — Let God arise and His enemies be scattered

Inner Reverse Legend As previous.

Obverse Bearded bust of king.

Reverse As previous.

SJ44D-065	ex. rare

Halfgroat

James IV struck silver halfgroats during both the heavy and the light coinages, all at Edinburgh. Both issues reverted to the medieval style and depict an un-lifelike crowned front-facing portrait of the king. These coins, which are all rare, are fairly similar to some halfgroats of James II and III as well as English ones. Collectors should pay particular attention to the obverse legend, style of bust and crown as well as the marks found in the reverse quarters.

Heavy Coinage (1489 – 1496)

These issues had a value of seven pence and were made of 0.925 silver.

Collecting Hints

This issue is very rare and rarely found in better than Fine condition.

Obverse Legend IACOBUS DI GRA REX SCOTORUM Q (or 4) — James IV by the grace of God King of Scots

Outer Reverse Legend BNS PBPTEETB MEUM — God is my defender and my redeemer

Inner Reverse Legend VILLA EDINBUG — Town of Edinburgh

Obverse Tall crowned front-facing bust of king, the crown has four fleurs.

Reverse Long cross, a lis sometimes in the centre, a crown in two of the quarters, three pellets and an annulet in the other two.

SJ42D-005	VG £160	F £375	VF v. rare

97

As previous, but no 'Q' or '4' at the end of the obverse legend.

SJ42D-010	VG £220	F £500	VF v. rare

Light Coinage (1496 – 1513)

This issue had a value of sixpence and was made of 0.925 silver.

Collecting Hints

This issue is not quite as rare as the previous one, but rarely found in better than Fine condition.

Obverse Legend   IACOBUS DEI GRA REX SCOTTORU — James by the grace of God King of Scots

Outer Reverse Legend   SALVV FAC POPULV TVVDNE — O Lord save Thy people

Inner Reverse Legend   VILLA EDINBURGH — Town of Edinburgh

Obverse   Neat, front-facing crowned bust of king.

Reverse   Long cross with three pellets in two of the quarters and a mullet in the other two.

SJ42D-015	VG £140	F £300	VF rare

As previous, but with a star on either side of the king's neck.

SJ42D-020	ex. rare

Obverse Legend   IACOBUS DEI GRA REX SCOTTORU IIII — James IV by the grace of God King of Scots

Outer Reverse Legend   SALVV FAC POPULVV TVDNE — O Lord save Thy people

Inner Reverse Legend   As previous.

Obverse   As SJ42D-015.

Reverse   As previous.

SJ42D-025	VG £180	F £400	VF rare

Plack

Also known as the billon issue, the plack had a value of four pence.

Collecting Hints

This issue is fairly common, especially in lower grades, and coins in VF condition are obtainable albeit scarce. Many issues are also slightly clipped or bent.

Obverse Legend   IACOBUS DEI GRA REX SCOTORUM QRA — James IV by the grace of God King of Scots

Reverse Legend   VILLA DE EDINBURGH — Town of Edinburgh

Obverse   Shield with lion rampant with a crown on either side all within tressure.

Reverse   Floriated cross fourchée with a large compartment in the centre that encloses a saltire and a crown in each angle.

SJ4PL-005	VG £40	F £100	VF £250

As previous, but no 'QRA' at the end of the legend.

SJ4PL-010	VG £15	F £35	VF £80

As previous, but plain Roman lettering on ether the obverse or the reverse.

SJ4PL-015	VG £15	F £35	VF £80

As previous, but Roman lettering on both sides, a '4' after the king's name and star stops sometimes in legend. It is possible that this issue was struck during the reign of James V too.

SJ4PL-020	VG £15	F £35	VF £80

Half Plack

This issue had a value of twopence and seems to have been made using a very low silver content, probably about 25%. Some issues appear to have been made of pure copper and might be contemporary forgeries.

Collecting Hints

The first type is extremely rare, while the other ones are scarce but obtainable, especially in the lower grades. Coins in VF condition are rare.

Obverse Legend   IACOBUS DEI GRA REX SCOTTOR QR. — James IV by the grace of God King of Scots

Reverse Legend   VILLA (de) EDINBURGH — Town of Edinburgh

Obverse   Royal shield, a crown at the side and above, all within a tressure.

Reverse   Floriated cross fourchée with a saltire in the central panel and a crown in each quarter.

SJ4HPL-005	ex. rare

As previous, but no 'QR' in the obverse legend.

SJ4HPL-010	VG £50	F £125	VF £300

As previous, but no crowns by the shield on the obverse.

SJ4HPL-015	VG £50	F £125	VF £300

As previous, but a lis by the shield on the obverse.

SJ4HPL-020	VG £50	F £125	VF £300

Penny

James IV produced two issues of pennies for his reign, the silver issue of 0.925 silver which was struck during the light coinage (1496 – 1513) and had a value of threepence and the billon issue which only had a value of one penny and were struck in billon or copper. Many varieties of the billon issue exist although all coins were struck in Edinburgh.

Light Coinage (1496 – 1513)

Collecting Hints

This coin is extremely rare.

Obverse Legend IACOBUS DEI GRA REX SCOTTO — James by the grace of God King of Scots

Reverse Legend SALVV FAC PPLVVTVVME — O Lord save Thy people

Obverse Crowned bust of king; mintmark crown.

Reverse Long cross, a star of five points in two quarters, three pellets in two quarters.

SJ41D-005 ex. rare

Billon Issue

The dates for this issue are uncertain, but coins were probably struck during most if not all of the reign.

Collecting Hints

These issues which are often made of pure copper are scarce but obtainable, especially the last three issues. Coins are often found chipped and worn and are rare in VF or better condition.

Obverse Legend IACOBUS DEI GRA REX SCOTO (many varieties) — James by the grace of God King of Scots

Reverse Legend VILLA (DE) EDINBURG — Town (of) Edinburgh

Obverse Tall bust with an annulet either side of neck, crown with five fleurs.

Reverse Cross, three pellets (sometimes fourth small one or annulet?) in each quarter.

SJ41D-010	VG £60	F £140	VF rare

As previous, but no annulet by neck.

SJ41D-015	VG £40	F £100	VF £200

Obverse Legend As previous.

Reverse Legend SALU FAC POP TUUME (?) — O Lord save Thy people

Obverse Small crowned bust of king.

Reverse Long cross, a crown in two quarters, a lis in two other quarters.

SJ41D-020	v. rare

Obverse Legend As SJ41D-010.

Reverse Legend As SJ41D-010.

Obverse Small neater bust of crowned king.

Reverse As previous.

SJ41D-025	VG £30	F £80	VF £180

As previous, but a larger, uglier bust.

SJ41D-030	VG £30	F £80	VF £180

As previous, but a smaller, neater bust usually struck on a smaller but thicker copper flan.

SJ41D-035	VG £25	F £65	VF £130

Scotland: James V (1513 – 1542)

Due to the rising gold price there was a need throughout James V's reign to introduce new denominations to keep pace with the gold price.

Ducat

The gold ducat was struck during the third coinage of James V with a value of forty shillings. Also know as 'bonnet piece' because it depicts the king wearing a bonnet, it is the first Scottish gold coin with a lifelike portrait. However, what is perhaps most interesting it the fact that the ducat bears a date thus making it not only the first Scottish coin to be dated, but the first British one. Minted from native Scottish gold mined in Crawford Muir and Corehead, the coins were presented to the king in a tureen at a royal banquet in 1539 and described as 'the fruit of the earth'.

Collecting Hints

Gold ducats dated 1539 are extremely rare, while those dated 1540 are very rare. The issue of 1539 is sometimes considered to be a pattern.

Third Coinage (1539 – 1542)

Obverse Legend   IACOBUS 5 DEI G R SCOTORU 1539 — James V by the grace of God King of Scots 1539

Reverse Legend   HONOR REGIS IVDCUM DILIGIT — The king's power loveth judgement

Obverse   Bearded lifelike bust of king wearing a bonnet and facing right.

Reverse   Crowned shield over cross fleury.

SJ5DU-005   ex. rare

Obverse Legend   IACOBUS 5 DEI GRA R SCOTOR 1540 — James V by the grace of God King of Scots 1540

Reverse Legend   HONOR REGIS IVDICIVM DILIGIT — The king's power loveth judgement

Obverse   As previous, but an annulet behind the king's head.

Reverse   Open crowned shield over cross fleury.

SJ5DU-010   v. rare

Two Thirds Ducat

With a value of twenty-six shillings and eightpence, this issue was only struck in 1540 as part of James V's new third coinage which for the first time bore a lifelike portrait of the king. The third coinage is often referred to as the bonnet coinage because the king is depicted wearing a bonnet.

Collecting Hints

This issue is very rare in any grade.

Third Coinage (1539 – 1542)

Obverse Legend   IACOBUS D.G.R. SCOTORUM 1540 — James by the grace of God King of Scots 1540

Reverse Legend   HONOR REGIS IUDICIUM DILIGIT — The king's power loveth judgement

Obverse   King wearing bonnet facing right, an annulet behind his head.

Reverse   Crown over royal shield, 'I 5' (IACOBUS V) divided by shield.

SJ5TTDU-005   v. rare

Unicorn

The gold unicorn was issued for the first coinage with an increased value of twenty shillings, which was later increased further to twenty two shillings so as to keep it in line with the denomination's metal value. These were the last issues of the unicorn which was replaced by the gold crown produced in later issues.

Collecting Hints

The first issue in extremely rare, while the following two are very rare. When available, coins are usually found in Fine to VF condition. The style of these issues tends not to be as good as that of the previous ones and coins often appear to be struck on small flans or, possibly, clipped.

First Coinage (1518? – 1526)

Obverse Legend   IACOBUS DEI GRA REX SCOTORUM — James by the grace of God King of Scots

Reverse Legend   EXURGAT DEUS DISSIPENT IIMICI EIUS (varieties exist) — Let God arise and His enemies be scattered

Obverse   Unicorn and shield, an 'X' or 'XC' below the unicorn; mintmark crown at start of legend.

Reverse Star over cross fleury, a cinquefoil countermark in the field. This cinquefoil is the family device of the Earl of Arran and it is probable that he supplied the gold for this rare issue.

SJ5UC-005 ex. rare

Obverse As previous.

Reverse A pellet or mullet in the centre of the star; a cinquefoil counterstamp.

SJ5UC-010 VG — F £1,500 VF v. rare

As previous, but no countermark.

SJ5UC-015 VG — F £1,600 VF v. rare

Crown of Twenty Shillings

The gold crown of twenty shillings was first struck during the second coinage of James V (1526 – 39) and is known as the Abbey crown because it was produced at the Abbey mint of Holyrood. All issues bear a crown over a royal shield on the obverse and a cross fleury on the reverse.

Second Coinage (1526 – 1539)

Collecting Hints

These issues are rare, although the third and fourth ones are the most common and can be obtained by the determined collector. Coins are usually found in Fine to VF condition and are rarely damaged.

Obverse Legend IACOBUS 5 DEI GRA REX SCOTOR — James by the grace of God King of Scots

Reverse Legend PER LIGNV CRUCIS SALVI SUMUS — By the wood of the Cross we are saved

Obverse Arched crown over shield of Scotland, an 'X' either side of shield denoting 20 shillings.

Reverse Cross fleury with a thistle in each angle.

SJ5C20-005 VG — F £2,200 VF £4,500

Obverse Legend As previous.

Reverse Legend CRUCIS ARMA SEQUAMUR — Let us follow the arms of the Cross

Obverse Small open crown over a royal shield, an 'X' either side of the shield, double annulet stops in the legend.

Reverse Cross fleury with a thistle in each angle.

SJ5C20-010 VG — F £1,400 VF £3,000

As previous, but obverse shield with rounded base and there are trefoil stops in legend.

SJ5C20-015 VG — F £800 VF £1,750

As previous, but pellet stops in the legend.

SJ5C20-020 VG — F £800 VF £1,750

As previous, but a very small crown above the shield.

SJ5C20-025 unique

Third Ducat

Struck in 1540, the gold third ducat had a value of thirteen shillings and fourpence and was part of James V's new third coinage, which depicted the king wearing a bonnet and so became known as the bonnet coinage; it was also the first coinage that a lifelike portrait of the king was used on a gold coin.

Collecting Hints

This issue is very rare in any grade.

Third Coinage (1539 – 1542)

Obverse Legend IACOBUS D.G.R. SCOTOR 1540 — James by the grace of God King of Scots 1540

Reverse Legend HON REGIS IUDICU DILICIT — The king's power loveth judgement

Obverse King wearing bonnet facing right, a pellet behind his head.

Reverse Crown over royal shield, 'I 5'(IACOBUS V) dividing shield.

SJ5TDU-005   v. rare

Half Unicorn

With a value of ten shillings, James V's first coinage was the last time that the gold half unicorn was produced. The denomination was not replaced by a gold coin because of rising gold prices, however silver coins with a value of ten shillings were struck in later reigns.

First Coinage (1518? – 1526)

Collecting Hints

This issue is very rare in any grade.

Obverse Legend   IACOBUS DEI GRACIA REX SCOTORUM — James by the grace of God King of Scots

Reverse Legend   FXURGAT DFUS FT DISIPENT INIMICI FINS (varieties exist) — Let God arise and His enemies be scattered

Obverse   A unicorn and royal shield, all 'S's in legend are reversed; mintmark crown.

Reverse   A star with wavy rays and a small star at its centre, all 'E's in the legend usually omit the lower bar; mintmark crown.

SJ5HUC-005   v. rare

Groat

While the old style of groat was popular with much of the population, Scotland was changing, being heavily influenced by the Renaissance in Europe. Coins did not escape this influence and the groat issue of James V produced coins of a superb design with lifelike portraits.

Second Coinage (1526 – 1539)

This groat had a value of eighteen pence and was struck in 0.833 silver, which was a popular European fineness. Due to the rising silver price the weight of silver had been greatly reduced from the previous issue.

Collecting Hints

These attractive coins will always be popular with collectors but they saw considerable circulation at the time. They are scarce but available in less than Fine condition, and coins in VF or better are rare and desirable. Like many previous issues the legends are often clipped, possibly due to poor production.

Obverse Legend   IACOBUS 5 DEI GRA REX SCOTOR (varieties exist) — James by the grace of God King of Scots

Reverse Legend   VILLA EDINBURGH (varieties exist) — Town of Edinburgh

Obverse   Crowned bust facing right, the king's crown is double arched.

Reverse   Shield with lion rampant over a large cross fourchée.

SJ54D-005   VG £120   F £300   VF £800

Obverse Legend   As previous.

Reverse Legend   OPPIDU EDINBURGI — Town of Edinburgh

Obverse   As previous, but the crown has a single arch, a trefoil sometimes behind the bust.

Reverse   As previous.

SJ54D-010   VG £80   F £200   VF £550

As previous, but the king's coat is open, the reverse shield is fairly oval in shape.

SJ54D-015   VG £60   F £125   VF £350

As previous, but the king has a more pointed nose, no trefoils behind the bust.

SJ54D-020   VG £60   F £125   VF £350

Third Groat

The silver third groat with a value of sixpence was struck during James V's second coinage. The groat had a value of one shilling and sixpence at the time, therefore the value for this denomination was ideal. Nevertheless, in later issues and reigns it was replaced by the popular bawbee, which also had a value of sixpence (see p.103).

Collecting Hints

This issue is rare but obtainable, especially in the lower grades. It has a silver content of 83%, however some specimens suggest that the alloys were poorly mixed or that mint records are inaccurate as some issues appear to be of baser metal.

Second Coinage (1526 – 1539)

Obverse Legend   IACOBUS 5 DEI GRA R. SCOTO(RO) — James V by the grace of God King of Scots

Reverse Legend   OPPIDU EDINBURGI — Town of Edinburgh

Obverse   Crowned bust facing right.

Reverse   Royal shield over cross fourchée; sometimes mintmark lis at the start of the legend.

SJ5TGR-005	VG £70	F £200	VF rare

Bawbee

The famous and popular bawbee was first introduced under James V and had a value of sixpence and a silver metal content of 25%. All issues bore a thistle on the obverse and a crown on the reverse.

The bawbee was also struck under Mary, and the main difference between the two reigns is the reading of the obverse legend.

The half bawbee, with a value of threepence, complemented this denomination structure. Many dies were used for these issues which resulted in numerous minor varieties in spelling and punctuation. Unlike other base metal issue coins and for reasons that remain unclear, the bawbee tended not to be forged.

Collecting Hints

These issues are fairly common, especially in the lower grades. Many coins were weakly struck producing flat areas on the design, particularly the crown on the reverse cross.

Third Coinage (1538 – 1542)

Edinburgh Mint

Obverse Legend   IACOBUS D.G. REX SCOTORUM — James by the grace of God King of Scots

Reverse Legend   OPPIDUM EDINBURGH — Town of Edinburgh

Obverse   Crowned thistle dividing 'I 5' (IACOBUS V).

Reverse   Crown over saltire cross, a lis either side; mintmark lis.

SJ5BB-005	VG £15	F £35	VF £90

As previous, but an annulet over the 'I' or in inner circle.

SJ5BB-010	VG £25	F £70	VF £180

As previous, but an annulet over the 'I' and the '5', or sometimes just an annulet over the '5'.

SJ5BB-015	VG £25	F £70	VF £180

Plack

Billon Coinage (1513 – 1533)

These issues had a value of four pence and were made of low content billon or in some cases just copper. The copper issues are probably contemporary forgeries.

Collecting Hints

The first issue is fairly common especially in the lower grades. However coins in VF condition are available to the patient collector. The second issue is unique.

Obverse Legend   IACOBUS DEI GRA REX SCOTORUM — James IV by the grace of God King of Scots

Reverse Legend   VILLA DE EDINBURG — Town of Edinburgh

Obverse   Shield with lion rampant, a crown on either side, all within a tressure.

Reverse   Floreated cross fourchée with an open compartment in the centre enclosing a mullet, a crown in two quarters, a plain cross in two quarters.

SJ5PL-005	VG £20	F £50	VF £120

Obverse Legend   As previous.

Reverse Legend   As previous.

Obverse   As previous, but ornamental lettering, annulets in spandrels around shield.

Reverse   As previous, but crowns in all four quarters.

SJ5PL-010	unique

Half Bawbee

The half bawbee with a value of threepence was first introduced under James V in 1538 and was also struck under Mary. Made of billon with a silver content of about 25%, it complemented the much more popular and common bawbee. All issues were struck at Edinburgh.

Third Coinage (1538 – 1542)

Collecting Hints

These coins are very scarce and rarely found in better than Fine condition.

Obverse Legend   IACOBUS D.G.R. SCOTORUM — James by the grace of God King of Scots

Reverse Legend   OPPIDUM EDINBURG — Town of Edinburgh

Obverse   Crown over a thistle, with 'I.5' (Iacobus V) on either side.

Reverse   A crown over a saltire cross.

SJ5HBB-005	VG £100	F £200	VF £500

As previous, but an annulet over the 'I'.

| SJ5HBB-010 | VG £100 | F £200 | VF £500 |

As SJ5HBB-005, but an annulet over the '5'.

| SJ5HBB-015 | VG £100 | F £200 | VF £500 |

Quarter Bawbee

The quarter bawbee of James V is a pattern and therefore not listed here.

Scotland: Mary (1542 – 1567)

Gold Portrait Ryal or Three Pound Piece

This superb issue, which was only struck for three years during Mary's reign, had a value of sixty shillings. The obverse shows a lifelike portrait of the queen facing left although experts have commented that the engraver did not manage to capture her true beauty. The reverse bears a crown over the royal arms. This coinage should not to be confused with the silver ryal issues.

First Period (1542 – 1558)

Collecting Hints

Coins dated 1555 are very rare while those dated 1557 and 1558 are extremely rare. Forgeries of this issue exist.

Obverse Legend MARIA DEI G. SCOTOR REGINA — Mary by the grace of God Queen of Scots

Reverse Legend IUSTUS FIDE VIVIT 1555 — The just man lives by faith

Obverse Bust of the queen facing left.

Reverse Crown over royal shield.

SMAPR-005   v. rare

As previous, but dated 1557.

SMAPR-010   ex. rare

As previous, but dated 1558.

SMAPR-015   ex. rare

Ducat

This large gold issue had a value of sixty shillings and was only struck in 1558, during Mary's short marriage to Francis, son of Henry II of France. The obverse bears the facing busts of Mary and Francis while the reverse shows a cross of eight interlinked dolphins. The obverse design of this coin was obviously inspired by the English Philip and Mary shilling although the engraver's work is not as fine.

Second Period (1558 – 1560)

Collecting Hints

This issue is extremely rare.

Obverse Legend FRAN ET MA D.G R R SCOTOR DELPHIN VIEN — Francis and Mary by the grace of God King and Queen of Scots Dauphin and Dauphiness of Vienne

Reverse Legend HORUM TUTA FIDES 1558 — The faith of these is whole 1558

Obverse Facing busts of Francis and Mary with a crown above.

Reverse Cross made of eight interlinked dolphins, a crown at each end, Lorraine crosses in angles.

SMAD60-005   ex. rare

Forty Four Shillings

First Period (1542 – 1558)

These four gold issues were only struck in 1553 and 1557. The value of the coins reflected the constantly changing price of gold and the fluctuations in the supply of metal. The obverse depicts a crown over a royal shield. Some of the issues also bear the initials 'I G', divided by the shield. They stand for IACOBUS GUBERNATOR who was Regent and Governor of the kingdom at that time but, because his initials were considered unpopular, they were replaced by his family emblem, a cinquefoil. The reverse of the coin shows a crown over a monogram.

Collecting Hints

All issues are rare or extremely rare while the 1557 issue is unique.

Obverse Legend MARIA DEI GRA SCOTORUM — Mary by the grace of God (Queen) of Scots

Reverse Legend DILIGITE IUSTICIAM 1553 — Observe justice 1553

Obverse Crown over royal shield 'I G' divided by shield.

Reverse 'M.R.' (MARIA REGINA) in monogram dividing 'I G'.

SMA44S-005   ex. rare

As previous, but cinquefoil in place of 'I G' on both sides.

SMA44S-010   ex. rare

Obverse   As SMA44S-005.
Reverse   As SMA44S-010.

SMA44S-015   v. rare

Obverse Legend   As previous.

Reverse Legend   As previous, but dated 1557.

Obverse   Crown over royal shield dividing 'M.R.'.

Reverse   Crowned monogram of Maria with a crowned cross potent either side.

SMA44S-020   unique

Gold Half Ryal

This superb gold issue, with a value of thirty shillings, was only struck for three years during the reign of Mary. It complemented the portrait ryal and bore similar obverse and reverse designs. This coinage should not be confused with the silver ryals.

First Period (1542 – 1558)

Collecting Hints

Coins dated 1555 are very rare, the 1557 issue is unique and the 1558 extremely rare.

Obverse Legend   MARIA DEI G. SCOTOR REGINA — Mary by the grace of God Queen of Scots

Reverse Legend   IUSTUS FIDE VICIT 1555 — The just man lives by faith 1555

Obverse   Bust of queen facing left.

Reverse   Crown over shield, 1555

SMAHPR-005   v. rare

As previous, but dated 1557.

SMAHPR-010   unique

As previous, but a plainer reverse crown, dated 1558.

SMAHPR-015   ex. rare

Silver Ryal or Dollar

The ryal was first struck in 1565. Produced in silver with a value of thirty shillings, it is also sometimes known as a dollar or Cookeston dollar, because the palm tree on the reverse was mistaken for a famous yew tree in Cookeston where Mary and Henry were supposed to have sat during their courtship. Actually, the palm tree and tortoise depicted on the reverse are thought to be heraldic designs from Henry Darnley's family. The obverse bears the more traditional crown over royal shield. Countermarked coins are listed under James VI.

Collecting Hints

Although the first issue is unique, the second is obtainable especially in Fine condition; coins in VF condition are rare. Unlike many Scottish coins, these are bold and usually well struck and are an asset to any collection.

Fourth Period (1565 – 1567)

First Issue

Obverse Legend   HENRICUS & MARIA D. GRA R & R SCOTOTRUM — Henry and Mary by the grace of God Kind and Queen of Scots

Reverse Legend   QUOS DEUS COIVNXIT HOMO NON SEPARET 1565 — Those whom God hath joined together let no man put asunder 1565

Obverse   Facing portraits of Henry and Mary with date below.

Reverse   Crown over shield, a thistle on each side of shield.

SMARY-005   ex. rare

Second Issue

Obverse Legend MARIA & HENRIC DEI GRA R & R SCOTORU — Mary and Henry by the grace of God King and Queen of Scots

Reverse Legend EXURGAT DEUS & DISSIPENT INIMICI EI (varieties in size and style of lettering exist) — Let God arise and His enemies be scattered

Obverse Crown over royal shield, a thistle either side.

Reverse A tortoise climbing a palm tree, a crown above the tree and the date 1565 divided by the trunk.

SMARY-010	VG £125	F £250	VF £800

As previous, but dated 1566.

SMARY-015	VG £125	F £250	VF £800

As previous, but dated 1567.

SMARY-020	VG £150	F £325	VF £1,000

Fifth Period (1567)

This issue is very similar to the previous one, but the obverse legend bears only Mary's name, reflecting her recent widowhood. All coins are dated 1567 and 'Collecting Hints' of the fourth period, second issue apply.

Obverse Legend MARIA DEI GRA SCOTORUM REGINA — Mary by the grace of God Queen of Scots

Reverse Legend As previous.

Obverse As previous.

Reverse As previous, dated 1567.

SMARY-025	VG £125	F £300	VF £900

Twenty Two Shillings

This gold issue was struck during the reign of Mary in 1553. It complemented the forty-four shillings issue and was fairly similar, although the obverse crown divides the legend. The initials 'I.G.' divide the obverse shield and stand for IACOBUS GUBERNA-TOR who at this time was Regent and Governor of the kingdom. The reverse shows a crown over a monogram.

First Period (1542 – 1558)

Collecting Hints

This issue is rare but obtainable especially in Fine condition. VF examples are extremely rare.

Obverse Legend MARIA D.G.R. SCOTORUM — Mary by the grace of God Queen of Scots

Reverse Legend DILIGITE IUSTICIAM 1553 — Observe justice 1553

Obverse Large crown over royal shield breaking legend, 'I.G.' either side of shield.

Reverse A crown over 'M.R.' monogram, a cinquefoil either side.

SMA22S-005	VG —	F £1,200	VF v. rare

Crown or Abbey Crown

This gold issue was struck during the first period of Mary's reign, before her marriage (1542 – 58). It had a value of twenty shillings in 1542 but this was raised to twenty-two shillings and tenpence the following year. Struck at Hollyrood Abbey, it resembles the previous issue of James V in style except that there is no mark of value on the obverse. In other catalogues, it has been referred to as an ecu and is also sometimes known as the Abbey crown because it was struck at Hollyrood Abbey.

First Period (1542 – 1558)

Collecting Hints

This issue is rare and when available is usually found in Fine or VF condition.

Obverse Legend   MARIA DEI GRA REGINA SCOTORUM — Mary by the grace of God Queen of Scots

Reverse Legend   CRUCIS ARMA SEQUAMUR — Let us follow the arms of the Cross

Obverse   Crown over royal shield, a cinquefoil on either side of shield.

Reverse   A cross fleury with a thistle in each angle.

| SMAC20-005 | VG — | F £1,800 | VF £3,500 |

The gold crown of 1561 is considered a pattern and has therefore not been listed here.

Twenty Shillings

This gold coin was only struck in 1543 and had a value of twenty shillings. It was struck because the gold content of the previous issue was by then higher than its face value due to the rising price of gold.

First Period (1542 – 1558)

Collecting Hints

This coin is extremely rare.

Obverse Legend   MARIA D.G.R. SCOTORUM 1543 — Mary by the grace of God Queen of Scots 1543

Reverse Legend   ECCE ANCILLA DOMINI — Behold the hand-maid of the Lord

Obverse   Crowned royal arms.

Reverse   Crown over monogram 'MR', a cinquefoil below.

| SMA20S-005 | ex. rare |

Silver Two Thirds Ryal or Two Thirds Dollar

The silver two thirds ryal was introduced in 1565 and often known as the two thirds dollar. It had a value of twenty shillings and complemented the crown-size ryal (or Cookeston dollar), forming part of a new denomination structure and shared a similar, unusual reverse design. Countermarked issues are listed under James VI.

Collecting Hints

Two of the dates (1565 and 1566) while scarce, are obtainable, especially in Fine condition. All coins in VF condition are rare.

Fourth Period (1565 – 1567)

Obverse Legend   MARIA & HENRIC DEI GRA R & R SCOTORU — Mary and Henry by the grace of God King and Queen of Scots

Reverse Legend   EXURGAT DEUS ET DISSIPENTR INIMICI EIVS — Let God arise and His enemies be scattered (varieties exist in spelling as well as size of letters)

Obverse   Crown above royal shield dividing two thistles.

Reverse   A tortoise climbing the palm tree; undated.

| SMATTRY-005 | ex. rare |

As previous, but the palm tree divides the date, 1565.

| SMATTRY-010 | VG £85 | F £225 | VF £750 |

As previous, but dated 1566.

SMATTRY-015	VG £85	F £225	VF £750

As previous, but dated 1567.

SMATTRY-020	ex. rare

Fifth Period (1567)

This issue was struck during Mary's second widowhood and bears only her own name in the obverse legend.

Obverse Legend MARIA DEI GRA SCOTORU(M) REGINA — Mary by the grace of God Queen of Scots

Reverse Legend EXURGAT DEUS & DISSIPENTR INIMICI EI — Let God arise and His enemies be scattered

Obverse As previous.

Reverse As previous, dated 1567.

SMATTRY-025	VG £100	F £250	VF £850

Silver Third Ryal or Third Dollar

The third ryal, or third dollar as it was sometimes known, was introduced in 1565 and produced during the fourth and fifth periods. Struck in silver, it had a value of ten shillings and complemented the larger denominations of ryal and two thirds ryal, bearing a similar reverse design. Countermarked coins are listed under James VI.

Collecting Hints

Collectors should pay particular attention to the obverse legend when identifying an issue. Although VF specimens are rare, these coins are obtainable, especially in Fine condition.

Fourth Period (1565 – 1567)

Obverse Legend MARIA ET HENRIC DEI GRA R ET R SCOTORUM — Mary and Henry by the grace of God King and Queen of Scots

Reverse Legend EXURGAT DEUS DISSIPENT INIMICI EIUS — Let God arise and His enemies be scattered (varieties in legend and size of lettering exist)

Obverse Crown over royal shield with a thistle on either side of the shield.

Reverse Crown over a palm tree, a tortoise climbing the tree which divides the date 1565.

SMATRY-005	VG £80	F £200	VF £700

As previous, but dated 1566.

SMATRY-010	VG £125	F £325	VF £1,000

Fifth Period (1567)

Obverse Legend MARIA DEI GRA SCOTORUM REGINA — Mary by the grace of God Queen of Scots

Reverse Legend As previous.

Obverse As previous.

Reverse As previous, dated 1566.

SMATRY-015	ex. rare

As previous, but dated 1567.

SMATRY-020	VG £100	F £250	VF £900

Testoon

The silver testoon was only struck during the reign of Mary. When it was introduced in 1553, it had a value of four shillings but this was increased to five shillings two years later due to the rising price of silver, which also resulted in fluctuations in the metal fineness of issues. All coins were dated and many varieties exist as these issues were, undoubtedly, both popular and prolific.

First Period (1542 – 1558)

Portrait Testoon (1553)

Struck in 1553, this issue had a metal fineness of 0.916 and a value of four shillings.

Collecting Hints

This issue is extremely rare and not usually found in better than Fine condition.

Obverse Legend   MARIA DEI GRA R SCOTORUM — Mary by the grace of God Queen of Scots

Reverse Legend   DA PACEM DOMINE 1553 — Give peace O Lord 1553

Obverse   Crowned bust of queen facing right.

Reverse   Crown over royal shield, a cinquefoil on either side.

SMATS-005	ex. rare

Crowned 'M' issue (1555)

This issue was only struck in 1555, with a value of five shillings and a silver content of 0.725. The obverse bears a crowned 'M' while the reverse shows a shield over a cross potent. Counter-marked coins of this issue and testoons of latter issues are listed under James VI.

Collecting Hints

While scarce, this issue is obtainable especially in Fine condition. Coins often have an uneven coloured surface due to the fairly low silver content but contemporary forgeries with a copper core also exist.

Obverse Legend   MARIA DEI G SCOTOR REGINA 1555 — Mary by the grace of God Queen of Scots 1555

Reverse Legend   DILICIE DNI COR HUMILE (varieties exist) — A humble heart is the delight of the Lord

Obverse   A crown above a large 'M', a crowned thistle on either side.

Reverse   Shield over cross potent.

SMATS-010	VG £75	F £150	VF £450

As previous, but an annulet over the left thistle.

SMATS-015	VG £75	F £150	VF £450

Crown over Royal Shield Issue (1556 – 1558)

This issue retained a value of five shillings, but was slightly smaller in size as the silver content was 0.916. All coins are dated and many varieties exist. Several mules have been recorded with different dates in the obverse and reverse. These are very rare.

Collecting Hints

Most of these coins are fairly common, especially in the lower grades, but those in VF or better condition are rare.

Obverse Legend   MARIA DEI G SCOTOR REGINA 1556 — Mary by the grace of God Queen of Scots 1556

Reverse Legend   IN VERTUTE TUA LIBERA ME 1556 (varieties exist) — In Thy strength deliver me 1556

Obverse   Small high arched crown over shield dividing 'M.R.' (MARIA REGINA), an annulet below the 'M' and the 'R'.

Reverse   Large cross potent, a small cross in each quarter.

SMATS-020	VG £65	F £150	VF £400

As previous, but dated 1557.

SMATS-025	VG £65	F £160	VF £425

As SMATS-020, but no annulets on obverse.

SMATS-030	VG £90	F £180	VF £500

As previous, but dated 1557 or 15557 (die error).

SMATS-035	VG £110	F £250	VF rare

Obverse Legend   As previous.

Reverse Legend   As previous, dated 1557.

Obverse   Larger, wider, low arched crown above royal shield dividing 'M.R.'.

Reverse   As previous.

SMATS-040	VG £90	F £180	VF £450

As previous, but dated 1558.

SMATS-045	VG £80	F £150	VF £375

As SMATS-040, but an annulet below the 'M' and 'R'.

SMATS-050	VG £90	F £180	VF £450

As previous, but dated 1558.

SMATS-055	VG £90	F £180	VF £450

As previous, but an 'A' below the 'R' on the obverse. This is the initial of the mintmaster Acheson.

SMATS-060	VG £150	F £400	VF —

Second Period (1558 – 1560)

This issue was struck during Mary's brief marriage to Francis, son of Henry II of France, and includes Francis' name in the legend while his heraldic arms can be found on the coins. The 1560 issues also reflect that Francis had become king of France. The value of all issues was five shillings and their metal content 0.916.

Collecting Hints

These issues are scarcer that the previous ones, but still obtainable in Fine condition although rare in VF or better. Coins often appear slightly clipped, which could be due to the striking.

Obverse Legend   FRAN ET MA D.G.R.R. SCOTOR D.D. VIEN — Francis and Mary by the grace of God King and Queen of Scots Dauphin and Dauphiness of Vienne

Reverse Legend   FECIT VTRAQUE UNUM 1558 — He has make both one

Obverse   Shield over a cross potent, the arms on the shield are of Scotland, Mary and Francis.

Reverse   Crown over monogram 'F.M.', a Lorraine cross either side.

SMATS-065	VG £75	F £180	VF £450

As previous, but dated 1559.

SMATS-070	VG £80	F £200	VF £475

Obverse Legend   FRAN ET MA DG RR FRANCO SCOTOR — Francis and Mary by the grace of God King and Queen of France and Scots

Reverse Legend   VICIT LEO DE TRIBV IVDA 1560 — The lion of the tribe of Judah hath prevailed

Obverse   Crown over royal shield, the shield is divided into Scottish and French arms, a cross to the left of the shield, a saltire to the right, 1560.

Reverse   Crown over 'F.M.' monogram with a crown over a lis on one side of the monogram and a crown over a thistle on the other.

SMATS-075	VG £90	F £200	VF £500

As previous, but no small crowns over lis and thistle on the reverse.

SMATS-080	VG £100	F £250	VF —

As previous, but a wider, flatter crown over royal arms on the obverse, dated 1560.

| SMATS-085 | VG £90 | F £200 | VF £500 |

As previous, but dated 1561.

| SMATS-090 | VG £125 | F £350 | VF — |

As previous, but dated 1565 in error.

| SMATS-095 | ex. rare |

As SMATS-075, but obverse legend reads FRAN ET MA D.G.R.R. SCOTOR D.D. VIEN. This is either a Transitional piece or an error.

| SMATS-100 unique |

Third Period (1560 – 1565)

This issue, which bears a superb bust of the queen on the obverse, was struck in silver of 0.916 fineness and had a value of five shillings. The reverse shows a crown above the shield. All coins were dated 1561 or 1562.

Collecting Hints

Both dates are very rare, especially in better than Fine condition.

Obverse Legend MARIA DEI GRA SCOTORUM REGINA 1561 — Mary by the grace of God Queen of Scots 1561

Reverse Legend SALUUM FAC POPULUM TUUM DOMINE — Lord save Thy people

Obverse Bust of queen facing left, the queen is wearing a bonnet and high-necked dress, the legend starts at 7 o'clock and the coin is dated under the bust.

Reverse Crown over shield, the arms of France and Scotland in shield, crowned 'M' either side of shield.

| SMATS-105 | VG — | F £1,250 | VF — |

As previous, but dated 1562.

| SMATS-110 | VG — | F £1,500 | VF — |

Half Testoon

The half testoon was only struck during Mary's reign and, with a value of two shillings and sixpence, complemented the testoon. Issues were struck in silver of varying fineness which we have listed in each case. The 1553 issue with an uncrowned bust of the queen on the obverse is considered a pattern, and is therefore not listed here.

First Period (1542 – 1558)

Collecting Hints

While many of these issues are extremely rare, several are obtainable albeit scarce. When available, examples are usually found undamaged in Fine condition, often with weaknesses in the legends due to poor strike and with an unclear date due to the small size of the coin.

1555 Issue (0.725 silver fineness)

Obverse Legend MARIA DEI G SCOTOR REGINA 1555 — Mary by the grace of God Queen of Scots 1555

Reverse Legend DILICIE DNICOR HUMILE — A humble heart is the delight of the Lord

Obverse A crown over a large 'M', a crowned thistle on either side.

Reverse Royal shield over cross potent.

| SMAHTS-005 | VG £75 | F £200 | VF £550 |

1556 – 1558 Issues (0.916 silver fineness)

Obverse Legend   MARIA D.G. SCOTOR REGINA 1556 — Mary by the grace of God Queen of Scots 1556

Reverse Legend   IN VIRTUTE TUA LIBERA ME 1556 — In Thy strength deliver me 1556

Obverse   High arched crown above the royal arms, 'M' and 'R' on either side of the shield with an annulet below each letter.

Reverse   Large cross potent, a small cross in each quarter; mintmark crown.

SMAHTS-010   ex. rare

As previous, but an annulet above the 'R' on the obverse.

SMAHTS-015   ex. rare

As SMAHTS-010, but dated 1557.

SMAHTS-020   ex. rare

As SMAHTS-010, but no annulets below the 'M' or 'R', dated 1556.

SMAHTS-025   VG £70   F £180   VF £500

As previous, but dated 1557.

SMAHTS-030   VG £80   F £200   VF £550

As previous, but dated 1558.

SMAHTS-035   ex. rare

As previous, but dated 1558 on reverse only.

SMAHTS-040   VG £100   F £250   VF —

As SMAHTS-035, but an 'A' by the shield below the 'M', the 'A' was the initial of the mintmaster Acheson; date on the reverse only.

SMAHTS-045   ex. rare

Second Period (1558 – 1560)

This issue was struck in silver of 0.916 fineness.

> # Collecting Hints
>
> While scarce, these issues are obtainable and should not be confused with the earlier issues which have a different design. Examples are usually found undamaged in Fine condition, although some issues tend to have weak legends due to poor striking.

Obverse Legend   FRAN ET MA D.G. R.R. SCOTOR D.D. VIEN — Francis and Mary by the grace of God King and Queen of Scots Dauphin and Dauphiness of Vienne

Reverse Legend   FECIT VTRAQUE UNUM 1558 — He has made both one 1558

Obverse   Shield over a cross potent.

Reverse   Crown over monogram 'F.M.', a Lorraine cross either side, dated 1558.

SMAHTS-050   VG £100   F £250   VF £600

As previous, but dated 1559.

SMAHTS-055   VG £120   F £300   VF £650

Obverse Legend   FRAN ET MA D.G. R.R. FRANCO SCOTOR (Q or B) — Francis and Mary by the grace of God King and Queen of France and Scots

Reverse Legend   VICIT LEO DE TRIBU IVDA 1560 — The lion of the tribe of Judah hath prevailed

Obverse   Crown over royal shield, a cross to the left and a saltire to the right of the shield.

Reverse   Crown over monogram 'F.M.', a crowned lis and a crowned thistle on either side of the monogram.

SMAHTS-060	VG £85	F £200	VF £450

As previous, but the obverse crown is wider and flatter and has five lis instead of three.

SMAHTS-065	VG £85	F £200	VF £450

Third Period (1560 – 1565)

This issue shows a superb lifelike bust of the queen and was struck in silver of 0.916 fineness. It was counterstamped in James VI's reign, see p.139.

Collecting Hints

This superb issue of beautiful artistic design is very rare in any grade.

Obverse Legend   MARIA DEI GRA SCOTORUM REGINA 1561 — Mary by the grace of God Queen of Scots 1561

Reverse Legend   SALUUM FAC POPULUM TUUM DOMINE — O Lord save Thy people

Obverse   Bust of queen facing left and wearing a bonnet, date below the bust. The legend starts at 7 o'clock.

Reverse   Crown over a royal shield, a crowned 'M' on either side of the shield.

SMAHTS-070	v. rare

As previous, but dated 1562.

SMAHTS-075	ex. rare

Bawbee

Under Mary, the bawbee was struck during the first billon coinage of 1542 – 58. Two main issues were produced: the regular one of Mary struck in Edinburgh, and the issue of Mary of Guise which was produced in Stirling in 1544, when Mary of Guise took over the regency.

During this period, the bawbee continued to have a value of sixpence and a silver metal content of 25% with the remaining content being base metal. Many minor varieties in spelling and punctuation exist for all issues.

Collecting Hints

Mary's own issues are fairly common and usually found in the lower grades, often being weakly struck. The issues struck at Stirling are considerably scarcer and more difficult to obtain.

First Period (1542 – 1558)

This issue was struck at Edinburgh.

Obverse Legend   MARIA D.G. REGINA SCOTORUM — Mary by the grace of God Queen of Scots

Reverse Legend   OPPIDUM EDINBURGI — Town of Edinburgh

Obverse   Crowned thistle dividing 'M.R.' (MARIA REGINA); mintmark plain cross. The crown has three slender crosses.

Reverse   Plain saltire cross through a crown with a cinquefoil on either side.

SMABB-005	VG £15	F £35	VF £90

As previous, but cinquefoils are closed or voided.

SMABB-010	VG £25	F £50	VF £140

As SMABB-005, but a voided saltire cross on the reverse.

SMABB-015	VG £25	F £50	VF £140

As SMABB-005, but five fleur de lis on the obverse crown.

SMABB-020	VG £25	F £50	VF £140

As SMABB-005, but three cross fleury on the obverse crown.

SMABB-025	VG £25	F £50	VF £140

Many varieties of all the above issues exist and muling of varieties is not uncommon. Research shows at least one hundred slightly different dies were used to strike this issue.

Stirling Mint Issue

This issue was struck in Sterling for Mary of Guise, between June and November 1544.

Obverse Legend   MARIA D.G. REGINA SCOTORU — Mary by the grace of God Queen of Scots

Reverse Legend   OPPIDUM STIRLINGI — Town of Stirling

Obverse   Crowned thistle dividing 'M.R.' (MARIA REGINA), the crown has three slender cross fleury.

Reverse   A large cross potent with a small plain cross in each quarter; mintmark crown.

SMABB-030	VG £40	F £80	VF £225

Groat

This was a billon issue, dated 1558 or 1559, and known as a groat or nonsunt. It had a value of twelve pence.

Second Period (1558 – 1560)

This issue had a silver content of 50%.

Collecting Hints

This issue while scarce is obtainable especially in the lower grades. Coins in VF condition are scarce and it appears unlike many billon issues, this issue was not forged.

Obverse Legend   FRAN ET MA D G RR SCOTOR D.D. VIEN — Francis and Mary by the grace of God King and Queen of Scots Dauphin and Dauphiness of Vienne

Reverse Legend   IAM NON SUNT DUO SED UNA CARO 1558 or 1559 — They are no more twain but one flesh

Obverse   Crown above 'F' and 'M' monogram, a crown above a dolphin with the dolphin looking right to left of monogram, a crowned thistle to right of monogram.

Reverse   Legend in square 'box', date below box.

SMA4D-005	VG £20	F £40	VF £100

As previous, but the dolphin is looking left, dated 1559 only.

SMA4D-010	VG £50	F £120	VF £260

Plack

The billon plack was struck in 1557 with a value of fourpence.

First Period (1542 – 1558)

This issue has a silver content of about 8% and a value of fourpence.

Collecting Hints

These issues are fairly common, especially in the lower grades. Coins in VF condition are scarce but obtainable. Many coins were countermarked with a star within a heart during the reign of James VI. This was due to the large number of contemporary forgeries of this denomination which were circulating during James VI's reign. The counterstamp reassured the public that the coin had been checked by an official at the mint and was genuine. We list these counterstamped coins under James VI.

These contemporary forgeries should cause little problem to collectors today as the style of these forgeries in particular the legends is very poor. In fact they might add an interesting addition to any collection.

Obverse Legend   MARIA DEI G SCOTOR REGINA 1557 — Mary by the grace of God Queen of Scots 1557

Reverse Legend   SERVIO ET VSV TEROR 1557 — I serve and am worn by use 1557

Obverse   Crown above shield, lion rampant within shield, 'M' and 'R' either side of shield.

Reverse   Ornate cross with large central panel, a cross in centre, a crown in each quarter.

SMAPL-005	VG £12	F £25	VF £65

Half Bawbee

Made of billon with a silver content of about 25%, the half bawbee complemented the much more popular and common bawbee. All issues were struck at Edinburgh. Mary's issue was very much a continuation from the previous reign, the main difference being in the obverse legend. This issue had a value of threepence.

First Period (1542 – 1558)

Collecting Hints

This issue is scarce but obtainable, although coins in better than Fine condition are rare.

Obverse Legend   MARIA D.G.R. SCOTORUM — Mary by the grace of God Queen of Scots

Reverse Legend   OPPIDUM EDINBURGI — Town of Edinburgh

Obverse   Crown over a thistle dividing 'M.R.'.

Reverse   Plain cross over crown, a cinquefoil below.

SMAHBB-005	VG £30	F £75	VF £225

Obverse   As previous.

Reverse   As previous, but a voided saltire cross over the crown.

SMAHBB-010	VG £35	F £85	VF £240

Copper Lion

The copper lion, or hardhead as it was sometimes known, was issued during the reign of Mary between 1555 and 1560. Issues had such a small silver content, of less than 10%, that they are classed as copper rather than billon issues. At three halfpence, the value of the denomination was the same as the French *denier*, reflecting the close relationship between Scotland and France.

All issues bear a crowned 'M' or 'FM' on the obverse and a crowned lion on the reverse. Varieties exist and we have listed them all. In James VI's reign, due to the large number of forgeries circulating, some genuine coins were officially countermarked with a star within a heart countermark to assure the public that these coins were genuine. We have listed them under James VI.

Collecting Hints

Most issues are fairly common especially in the lower grades. These coins tended to be poorly struck with often part of the legend or design missing. The issue dated 1551 is a forgery. Also, coins dated '58' instead of '1558' are all considered contemporary forgeries but, as they have a value of about £20.00, they make an interesting addition to any collection. Coins with incorrect legends are also considered forgeries.

First Period (1542 – 1558)

Obverse Legend   MARIA D.G. SCOTOR REGINA — Mary by the grace of God Queen of Scots

Reverse Legend   VICIT VERITAS 1555 — Truth has conquered 1555

Obverse   Crown over 'M'.

Reverse   Crowned lion rampant.

SMACL-005	VG £15	F £30	VF £80

As previous, but annulets either side of obverse 'M', dated 1556.

SMACL-010	ex. rare

As SMACL-005, but dated 1556.

SMACL-015	ex. rare

As SMACL-005, but a pellet within the 'M' on the obverse, dated 1558.

SMACL-020	VG £15	F £30	VF £80

Second Period (1558 – 1560)

Obverse Legend   FRA ET MA D.G.R.R. SCOT D.D. VIEN — Francis and Mary by the grace of God King and Queen of Scotland Dauphin and Dauphiness of Vienne

Reverse Legend   VICIT VERITAS 1559 — Truth has conquered 1559

Obverse   Crowned 'F.M.' monogram, a dolphin each side looking right.

Reverse   Crowned lion rampant.

SMACL-025	VG £15	F £30	VF £80

As previous, but dolphins facing left, dated 1558.

SMACL-030	VG £12	F £25	VF £65

As previous, but dated 1559. The obverse legend sometimes begins 'ET'.

SMACL-035	VG £15	F £30	VF £80

As previous, but dated 1560. The obverse legend is as SMACL-025

SMACL-040	VG £20	F £45	VF £120

Penny

Pennies were struck in fairly small quantities during Mary's reign, between 1547 and 1556. These coins were called billon even though they contained less than 10% silver and have the appearance of copper. The first issues show a crowned bust of the queen which was rarely found on coins of Mary. All issues are rare and a collector looking for a denomination of this historic reign could look for a bawbee or plack if on a budget, as these denominations are fairly plentiful.

First Period (1542 – 1558)

1547 Issue

Collecting Hints

All issues are rare, especially in better than fine condition.

Obverse Legend   MARIA D.G.R SCOTORUM — Mary by the grace of God Queen of Scots

Reverse Legend   OPIDUM EDNBUR — Town of Edinburgh

Obverse   Crowned bust of young queen, the crown is arched.

Reverse   Long cross, a crown in two angles, a cinquefoil in two angles.

SMA1D-005	VG £60	F £150	VF —

As previous, but the queen wears an unarched open crown and Edinburgh is spelt EDINBURG.

SMA1D-010	VG £60	F £150	VF —

Obverse Legend   As previous.

Reverse Legend   OPIDU EDINBURGI — Town of Edinburgh

Obverse   As previous, but older bust.

Reverse   As previous.

SMA1D-015	VG £80	F £180	VF —

1554 Issue

Obverse Legend   As previous.

Reverse Legend   OPPIDUM EDINBURG — Town of Edinburgh

Obverse   Crowned bust of queen, no inner circles between legend and bust; mintmark lis at start of legend.

Reverse   Long cross, no inner circles, a crown in two quarters, a lis in two quarters.

SMA1D-020	VG £125	F £300	VF —

1556 Issue

Obverse Legend   MARIA D G SCOTOR REGINA — Mary by the grace of God Queen of Scots

Reverse Legend   VICIT VERITAS 1556 — Truth prevails 1556

Obverse   Large cross potent, a small cross in each quarter.

Reverse   Legend and date in three lines, a crown above.

SMA1D-025	VG £60	F £160	VF £400

Scotland: James VI (1567 – 1625)

James VI's coinage was prolific in the number of coins struck as well as the large number of denominations, which was mainly due to a fluctuating gold and silver price and James's accession to the English throne in 1603. After the Accession, James's Scottish coinage became similar in style to the Englsh coinage, and details on how to distinguish one from the other are given below whenever relevant. The Scottish denomination structure after James' accession to the English throne was designed using a formula to be compatable with the English issues. While issues had about the same metal content, the Scottish denomination was 12 times the English one. For example, the Scottish silver sixty shillings was the same size and value as the English five shillings.

Twenty Pound Piece

This gold piece, the most spectacular Scottish coin ever struck, was produced for only two years. It was struck in 22ct gold and bears a profile bust of the king on the obverse and a crowned shield on the reverse.

Second Gold Coinage (1572 – 1580)

> ## Collecting Hints
>
> This superb coin has always been sought after by collectors. It is the most valuable Scottish coin and, while extremely rare, specimens do come on the market from time to time. Coins are usually available undamaged in Fine to VF condition; examples in low grades probably do not exist.

Obverse Legend IACOBUS 6 DEI GRA REX SCOTOR — James by the grace of God King of Scots

Obverse Legend Below Bust IN VTRUNQUE PARATUS 1575 — Prepared for either (peace or war, symbolised by the king holding a sword and olive branch)

Reverse Legend PARCERE SUBIECTIS & DEBELLARE SUPERBOS — To spare the humbled and subdue the proud

Obverse Crowned half length bust of king holding a sword and olive branch.

Reverse Crown over royal shield.

SJ620P-005	VG —	F rare	VF rare

As previous, but dated 1576.

SJ620P-010	VG —	F rare	VF rare

Unit or Sceptre piece

The gold unit was struck during the reigns of James VI and Charles I, with the first such piece being struck during the ninth gold coinage (1604 – 9) following James VI's accession to the English throne. The coins had a value of twelve pounds in Scotland or twenty shillings in England. The Scottish unit is very similar in design to the English unite which had a value of twenty or twenty-two shillings depending on when it was struck. The main differences between the two are the style of bust, the reverse shield and the mintmark. All Scottish units use the mintmark thistle, which can be found at the start of the legends, while only some English issues bear this mintmark. It is interesting to note that the obverse legend of the Scottish pieces now refers to Great Britain rather than Scotland. Another minor difference between the English and Scottish issues is that all English issues use 'ET' for 'and', while the Scottish issues use the abbreviation '&'. The Scottish issues are much rarer than the English ones, so collectors should check carefully the correct identification of a coin.

Ninth-Tenth Gold Coinage (1604 – 1625)

> ## Collecting Hints
>
> These two issues are rare and usually found in Fine to VF condition. Collectors might consider purchasing the more common English unite instead, as it is similar in style.

Obverse Legend IACOBUS D.G. MAG BRIT FRAN & HIB REX — James by the grace of God King of Great Britain France and Ireland

Reverse Legend FACIAM EOS IN GENTEM UNAN — I will make them one nation

Obverse Crowned bust of king holding orb and sceptre; mintmark thistle at start of legend.

Reverse Crown over royal shield dividing 'I.R.' (IACOBUS REX), English arms in the first and fourth quarters.

| SJ6UT-005 | VG — | F £900 | VF £2,200 |

| SJ6TN-005 | v. rare |

As previous, but Scottish arms in the first and fourth quarters of the reverse shield.

| SJ6UT-010 | VG — | F £750 | VF £1,650 |

Thistle Noble

This coin, struck during James VI's fifth gold coinage (1588), was also known as a Scottish rose noble and had a value of 146 shillings and eightpence or eleven merks.

It was struck in 23.333 ct gold and intended to constitute a new denomination structure but, although dies were made for a half thistle noble, it would appear that no coins were struck and the denomination was superseded by the hat piece and the rider of the sixth and seventh coinages.

Fifth Gold Coinage (1588)

Collecting Hints

This coin is very rare and, when available, is usually found in Fine condition. It is interesting to note that its style and design looks very dated compared to other James VI issues.

Obverse Legend IACOBUS 6 DEI GRATIA REX SCOTORUM — James VI by the grace of God King of Scots

Reverse Legend FLORENT SCEPT PIIS REGNA HIS IOUA DAT NUMERATQ (varieties exist) — Sceptres flourish with the pious, Jehovah gives them kingdoms and numbers them

Obverse Crowned shield on ship with a thistle below.

Reverse Thistle plant with crossed sceptres and lions rampant in panel surrounded by eight thistles.

Sword & Sceptre Piece

The gold sword and sceptre piece with a value of 120 shillings was issued during James VI's eighth gold coinage (1601–4). It was struck in 22ct gold and called a sword and sceptre piece after the main feature of the reverse design.

Collecting Hints

While scarce, these coins are obtainable especially in Fine to VF condition. They tend to be well struck but are sometimes found holed, probably to be made into jewellery pieces.

Eighth Gold Coinage (1601 – 1604)

Obverse Legend IACOBUS 6 D.G.R. SCOTORUM — James VI by the grace of God King of Scots

Reverse Legend SALUS POPULI SUPREMA LEX — The safety of the people is the supreme law

Obverse Crown over royal shield

Reverse Crossed sword and sceptre with a thistle either side, a crown above and the date 1601 below.

| SJ6SS-005 | VG — | F £500 | VF £1,100 |

As previous, but dated 1602.

| SJ6SS-010 | VG — | F £500 | VF £1,100 |

As previous, but dated 1603.

SJ6SS-015   v. rare

SJ6HUT-005   ex. rare

As previous, but dated 1604.

SJ6SS-020   v. rare

As previous, but Scottish arms in first and fourth quarters on the reverse.

SJ6HUT-010   VG —   F £1,200   VF £2,500

Half Unit or Six Pound Piece

The gold six pound piece, half unit or double crown as it was sometimes known, was first issued during the ninth and tenth gold coinages of James VI. It was struck in 22 ct gold and had a value in England of ten shillings.

It is fairly similar in style to the English half sovereign and double crown of James I. However, during this reign, all Scottish issues use mintmark thistle so it is important that collectors check that the mintmark and both obverse and reverse legends are correct. Should the mintmark or legend be different, the coin is an English issue and can be found in *Coincraft's Standard Catalogue of English & UK Coins*.

The gold half unit was also struck under Charles I, but the style is very different from the English issues.

Ninth-Tenth Gold Coinage (1604 – 1625)

Collecting Hints

The first issue is extremely rare, while the second one is very rare. A collector might consider purchasing an English issue instead, since they are much more common and extremely similar.

Obverse Legend   IACOBUS D.G. MAG BRIT FRAN ET HIB REX — James by the grace of God King of Great Britain France and Ireland

Reverse Legend   HENRICUS ROSAS REGNA IACOBUS — Henry (united) the roses James the kingdoms

Obverse   Crowned bust of king facing right; mintmark thistle at start of legend.

Reverse   Crown over royal shield dividing 'I.R.' (JACOBUS REX), English arms in first and fourth quarter; mintmark thistle at start of legend.

Rider

The gold rider was struck by James VI towards the end of the 16th century and all issues are dated. The coins had a value of one hundred shillings and like several other issues from the reign of James VI depict the king on horseback on the obverse, hence the name rider. They were struck in 22 carat gold.

Seventh Gold Coinage (1593 – 1601)

Collecting Hints

While these coins saw circulation they are rarely found in less than Fine condition. They are however sometimes pierced and probably made popular jewellery pieces. Coins in VF or better condition are rare and desirable.

Obverse Legend   IACOBUS 6 DG R SCOTORUM — James by the grace of God King of Scots

Reverse Legend   SPERO MELIORA — I hope for better things

Obverse   King in armour holding sword on horseback going right, the date 1593, 1594, 1595, 1598 or 1599 below the groundline.

Reverse   Crown over royal shield.

SJ6RD-005   VG —   F £600   VF £1,750

Obverse Legend   As previous.

Reverse Legend   SPERO MELIORA — I hope for better things

Obverse   As previous, but dated 1598 or 1601.

Reverse   As previous.

SJ6RD-010	ex. rare

Ducat of Eighty Shillings

This rare coin was struck during James VI's third gold coinage (1580) in 21 ct gold. It bears an uncrowned bust of the king on the obverse.

Third Gold Coinage (1580)

Collecting Hints

This coin is very rare in any grade but when available is usually found in Fine to VF condition.

Obverse Legend   IACOBUS 6 DEI GRA REX SCOTORUM — James VI by the grace of God King of Scots

Reverse Legend   EXURGAT DE ET DISSIP INIMICI EIUS — Let God arise and His enemies be scattered

Obverse   Uncrowned bust of king facing left and wearing a ruff.

Reverse   Crown over royal shield dividing date 1580.

SJ6D80-005	v. rare

Hat Piece

The hat piece of eighty shillings, so called because the king is wearing a large hat, was issued during James VI's sixth coinage (1591–93). All coins were struck in 22 ct gold and on the reverse there is an unusual inscription in Hebrew translated as 'Jehovah'.

Sixth Gold Coinage (1591 – 1593)

Collecting Hints

This issue is very rare and, when available, is usually found in Fine to VF condition.

Obverse Legend   IACOBUS 6 D.G.R. SCOTORUM — James VI by the grace of God King of Scots

Reverse Legend   TE SOLUM VEREOR 1591 — Thee alone do I fear 1591

Obverse   Bust of king facing right and wearing a hat, a thistle behind his head.

Reverse   Crowned lion seated holding a sceptre, a cloud above with 'Jehovah' in Hebrew, 1591.

SJ6HAT-005	VG —	F rare	VF rare

As previous, but dated 1592.

SJ6HAT-010	VG —	F rare	VF rare

As previous, but dated 1593.

SJ6HAT-015	VG —	F rare	VF rare

Lion Noble

This non-portrait issue was struck in 21.5 ct gold and called a lion noble after the lion depicted on the obverse. All issues were struck during the fourth gold coinage of James VI and had a value of seventy-five shillings. A two third and a third noble complemented the denomination structure.

Fourth Gold Coinage (1584 – 1588)

Collecting Hints

This issue is very rare in any grade. Coins when available are usually in Fine or VF condition.

Obverse Legend POST 5 & 100 PROA INVICTA MANENT HEC — After one hundred and five ancestors these remain unconquered

Reverse Legend DEUS INDICUM TUUM REGI DA 1584 — Give the King Thy Judgements O Lord 1584

Obverse Crowned lion holding a sword and sceptre.

Reverse Four crowned 'IR's in a form of a cross, an 'S' in centre.

SJ6LN-005	v. rare

As previous, but dated 1585.

SJ6LN-010	v. rare

As previous, but dated 1586.

SJ6LN-015	v. rare

As previous, but dated 1588.

SJ6LN-020	v. rare

Half Sword & Sceptre Piece

The gold half sword and sceptre piece with a value of sixty shillings was issued during the eighth gold coinage. It was struck in 22 ct gold and called a sword and sceptre piece after its reverse design. The issue complemented the full sword and sceptre piece also issued during this coinage with a value of 120 shillings.

Collecting Hints

While scarce, these coins are obtainable especially in Fine to VF condition. Coins tend to be well struck with all of the legend clear.

Eighth Gold Coinage (1601 – 1604)

Obverse Legend IACOBUS 6 D.G.R. SCOTORUM ⚜ James VI by the grace of God King of Scots

Reverse Legend SALUS POPULI SUPREMA LEX — The safety of the people is the supreme law

Obverse Crown over royal shield.

Reverse Crossed sword and sceptre, a thistle either side, a crown above the sword and sceptre and the date 1601 below.

SJ6HSS-005	VG —	F £400	VF £900

As previous, but dated 1602.

SJ6HSS-010	VG —	F £450	VF £1,000

As previous, but dated 1603.

SJ6HSS-015	VG —	F £800	VF £1,500

As previous, but dated 1604.

SJ6HSS-020	VG —	F £450	VF £1,000

Three Pound Piece or Britain Crown

Struck in 22 ct gold, this issue was first struck in the reign of James VI during the ninth-tenth gold coinage and is very similar to the English gold crown of James I. The main difference is that the Scottish issue only used the mintmark thistle, collectors should therefore check the mintmark and the obverse and reverse legends carefully when identifying an issue.

Ninth-Tenth Gold Coinage (1604 – 1625)

Obverse Legend IA D.G. MAG BRIT FRAN ET HIB REX — James by the grace of God King of Great Britain France and Ireland

Reverse Legend HENRICUS ROSAS REGNA IACOBUS — Henry (united) the roses James the kingdoms

Obverse Crowned bust of king facing right; mintmark thistle at start of legend.

Reverse Crown over royal shield dividing 'IR' (IACOBUS REX), English arms in first and fourth quarter; mintmark thistle at start of legend.

SJ63P-005 ex. rare

As previous, but Scottish arms in first and fourth quarters on the reverse.

SJ63P-010	VG —	F £650	VF £1,500

Sixty Shillings

The silver sixty shillings was introduced under James VI after his accession to the English throne and was also struck during the reign of Charles I. Both issues show the king on horseback on the obverse and the shield of Great Britain on the reverse.

The issue of James VI are very similar to the English crowns of James I. The main differences are the following: the Scottish issue uses mintmark thistle only while the English issue uses a variety of mintmarks including mintmark thistle. The mintmark can be found at the start of the obverse and reverse legend. The English issue uses the mintmark thistle twice during the first and third coinage (J1CR-040 and J1CR-050) The English first coinage uses a different reverse legend while the third coinage legends are very similar to the Scottish issue. The easiest way to differentiate the two issues is that in the obverse legend the English issue uses 'ET' for 'and' while the Scottish issue uses a '&'. The styles of both issues are also different in many other minor ways.

After accession to English throne (1603 – 1625)

Obverse Legend IACOBUS D. G. MAG BRIT FRAN & HIB REX — James VI by the grace of God King of Great Britain France and Ireland

Reverse Legend QUAE DEUS CONIVXIT NEMO SEPARET — What God hath joined together let no man put asunder

Obverse King on horseback holding a sword; mintmark thistle at start of legend.

Reverse Royal shield, arms of England in first and fourth quarters; mintmark thistle at start of legend.

SJ660S-005	VG £125	F £350	VF £1,200

As previous but Scottish arms in first and fourth quarters.

SJ660S-010	VG £125	F £350	VF £1,200

Two Thirds Lion Noble

This non-portrait issue was struck in 21.5 ct gold and had a value of fifty shillings. Produced during the fourth gold coinage, it formed part of the lion noble denomination structure which included a noble and a third noble; they derived their name from the lion found on the obverse.

Fourth Gold Coinage (1584 – 1588)

Collecting Hints

This issue is very rare in any grade. When available, coins are usually found in Fine or VF condition.

Obverse Legend   POST 5 & 100 PROA INVICTA MANET HEC — After one hundred and five ancestors these remain unconquered

Reverse Legend   DEUS IUDICIUM TUUM REGI DA 1584 — Give the king Thy judgements O Lord 1584

Obverse   Crowned lion holding a sword and sceptre.

Reverse   Four crowned 'IR' in the form of a cross, an 'S' in centre, an annulet usually in first quarter.

| SJ6TTLN-005 | v. rare |

As previous, but dated 1585.

| SJ6TTLN-010 | v. rare |

As previous, but dated 1587.

| SJ6TTLN-015 | v. rare |

Half Rider

The gold half rider had a value of fifty shillings.

Seventh Gold Coinage (1593 – 1601)

Collecting Hints

While scarce, James VI half riders are obtainable and usually found in Fine condition. Specimens in VF condition are rare but nonetheless obtainable. All coins are dated, and those dated 1595, 1598 and 1601 are extremely rare.

Obverse Legend   IACOBUS 6 D. G. R. SCOTORUM — James by the grace of God King of Scots

Reverse Legend   SPERO MELIORA — I hope for better things

Obverse   King on horseback holding sword, galloping to right, dated 1593, 1594, 1595, 1598, 1599 or 1601 below groundline.

Reverse   Crown above royal arms.

| SJ6HRD-005 | VG £200 | F £500 | VF £1,000 |

Thistle Crown

Struck in 22 ct gold and with a value of forty eight shillings, the thistle crown was fairly similar in style to the English issue of James I (J1CR-025). Most English issues bear the initials 'I.R.' either on the obverse or the reverse or on both sides and, even though one English issue omits the 'I.R.' totally, the mintmarks which are found at the start of both obverse and reverse legends are different for each issue. The Scottish issue does not bear the initials 'IR' and only uses the mintmark thistle, while the English ones use a variety of other mintmarks.

Ninth-Tenth Gold Coinage (1604 – 1625)

Collecting Hints

This issue is rare, especially in VF or better condition.

Obverse Legend   IA D.G. MAG BR F & H. REX — James by the grace of God King of Great Britain France and Ireland

Reverse Legend   TUEATUR UNITA DEUS — May God guard these united (kingdoms)

Obverse   Crown over rose; mintmark thistle.

Reverse   Crown over thistle; mintmark thistle.

| SJ648S-005 | VG - F £500 | VF £1500 |

Forty Shillings

The crown size silver forty shillings was only struck in 1582, in silver of 0.916 fineness.

Fourth Silver Coinage (1581 – 1586)

Collecting Hints

This superb coin shows a half length bust of the king and is most attractive; unfortunately it is also very rare.

Obverse Legend   IACOBUS 6 DEI GRATIA REX SCOTORUM — James VI by the grace of God King of Scots

Reverse Legend   HONOR REGIS IUDICIUM DILIGIT 1582 — The King's power loveth judgement

Obverse Half-length left facing, crowned bust of the king holding a sword; mintmark cross at start of legend.

Reverse Crown over royal shield dividing 'I.R.' (IACOBUS REX) with 'XL' (forty) on one side of shield and 'S' (shillings) on the other.

SJ640S-005	v. rare

Ryal or Dollar

The impressive, crown-size silver ryal was introduced under Mary and is sometimes known as sword dollar, from the sword on the reverse which however is different in style from Mary's ryal. It continued to be struck during James VI's first silver coinage and was very much a continuation from the previous reign with the value remaining at thirty shillings, although the weight of the issue was slightly reduced. Like other denominations, many ryals were countermarked with a crowned thistle in 1578 to raise their value.

First Silver Coinage (1567 – 1571)

Collecting Hints

All dates, while scarce, are obtainable. Coins are usually found in Fine or VF condition, although EF examples also exist.

Obverse Legend IACOBUS 6 DEI GRATIA REX SCOTORUM — James VI by the grace of God King of Scots

Reverse Legend PRO ME SI MEREOR IN ME — For me but against me if I deserve

Obverse Crown over royal shield which divides crowned 'I.R.'.

Reverse Crowned vertical sword, hand pointing to XXX (thirty shillings), date 1567 divided by sword.

SJ6RY-005	VG £85	F £225	VF £700

As previous, but dated 1568.

SJ6RY-010	VG £100	F £275	VF £800

As previous, but dated 1569.

SJ6RY-015	VG £85	F £225	VF £700

As previous, but dated 1570.

SJ6RY-020	VG £85	F £225	VF £700

As previous, but dated 1571.

SJ6RY-025	VG £85	F £250	VF £750

Countermarked Ryal (1578)

Even though the last ryal was struck in 1571, large quantities of coins from both reigns were still in circulation in 1578. By then however, due to the steep rise in the price of silver during this period, the metal content of the ryal was higher than its face value. It was therefore decided to countermark a number of denominations, including the ryal, to officially raise their face value and in 1578 the face value of countermarked ryals increased from thirty shillings to thirty-six shillings and ninepence. The countermark used for all issues was the crowned thistle. Below we list all issues with their values if countermarked but it should be noted that the prices for countermarked coins are for the most common dates. Scarcer dates, which are listed in the relevant section under the monarch, are of course worth more.

Collecting Hints

While scarce, all countermarked ryals are obtainable but, because all issues that were countermarked had seen some circulation, coins in better than Fine condition are rare.

Countermarked Mary Ryal

Mary ryal of the fourth period, second issue (SMARY-010 to -020, see p.106) countermarked with a crowned thistle.

| SJ6RY-030 | VG £125 | F £250 | VF £900 |

Mary ryal of the fifth period (SMARY-025) countermarked with a crowned thistle.

| SJ6RY-035 | VG £125 | F £300 | VF £900 |

Countermarked James VI Ryal

James VI ryal (SJ6RY-005 to -025) countermarked with a crowned thistle.

| SJ6RY-040 | VG £85 | F £225 | VF £700 |

Thirty Shillings

The silver thirty shillings was issued during the reigns of James VI and Charles I. The first issue bears a half length bust of the king, while latter ones depict the king on horseback.

Fourth Silver Coinage (1581 – 1586)

This issue was struck in silver of 0.916 fineness.

Collecting Hints

This issue is fairly rare as a whole; some specific dates are extremely rare and coins in better than Fine condition are very rare.

Obverse Legend IACOBUS G DEI GRATIA REX SCOTORUM — James VI by the grace of God King of Scots

Reverse Legend HONOR REGIS IUDICIUM DILIGIT 1581 — The king's power loveth judgement

Obverse Crowned half length bust of king holding a sword.

Reverse Crown over royal arms dividing letters 'I.R.' (IACOBUS REX), the value 'XXX' (thirty) and 'S' (shillings) divided by the shield.

| SJ630S-005 | ex. rare |

As previous, but dated 1582.

| SJ630S-010 | VG £100 | F £225 | VF rare |

As previous, but dated 1583.

| SJ630S-015 | VG £125 | F £300 | VF rare |

As previous, but dated 1584.

SJ630S-020	VG £125	F £300	VF rare

As previous, but dated 1585.

SJ630S-025	ex. rare

As previous, but dated 1586.

SJ630S-030	ex. rare

After Accession to English Throne (1603 – 1625)

This issue depicts the king on horseback and is very similar to, but more common than, the English halfcrowns of James I (J1HC-025 to -045). There are several points in which the two issues differ. Although the English coins use a variety of mintmarks including thistle, the Scottish ones only bear the mintmark thistle at the start of both the obverse and the reverse legends. Similarly, the English issues exhibit some differences in the obverse legends. On the reverse, the Scottish shield is much plainer than that on the English issues, with the Irish harp often being quite different. The English third coinage bears a bird-headed harp while the edge of the Scottish issue harp is just turned in.

Collecting Hints

This issue is fairly common especially in the lower grades, although specimens in VF or better condition are difficult to obtain. Coins are often found deliberately damaged, possibly due to the king's unpopularity with some of his subjects.

Obverse Legend IACOBUS D.G. MAG BRIT FRAN & HIB REX — James by the grace of God King of Great Britain France and Ireland

Reverse Legend QUAE DEUS CONIVNXIT NEMO SEPARET — What God hath joined together let no man put asunder

Obverse King on horse back holding sword; mintmark thistle.

Reverse Shield with English arms in the first and fourth quarters; mintmark thistle.

SJ630S-035	VG £60	F £160	VF £400

As previous, but Scottish arms in first and fourth quarters.

SJ630S-040	VG £45	F £135	VF £300

Half Crown of Thirty Shillings

The gold halfcrown of thirty shillings was introduced during James VI's ninth-tenth gold coinage (1604 – 25). It is similar to the much more common English halfcrown but, whereas the Scottish issue only uses the mintmark thistle, the English halfcrown with the identical legend uses different mintmarks. The style of the shield on the reverse is also sometimes different in the Scottish issue.

Ninth-Tenth Gold Coinage (1604 – 1625)

Collecting Hints

This coin is rare and is not usually found in better than Fine condition.

Obverse Legend I D. G ROSA SINE SPINA — James by the grace of God a rose without a thorn

Reverse Legend TUEATUR UNITA DEUS — May God guard these united (kingdoms)

Obverse Crowned bust of king facing right; mintmark thistle at start of legend.

Reverse Crown over royal shield; mintmark thistle, English arms in first and fourth quarters.

SJ6HC30-005	VG —	F £650	VF £1,800

As previous, but with the Scottish arms in the first and fourth quarters on the reverse.

SJ6HC30-010	VG —	F £500	VF £1,350

Two Merks or Thistle Dollar

This silver issue was struck during the second silver coinage of James VI. Struck in silver of 0.916 fineness, it had a value of twenty six shillings and eightpence and was known as a thistle dollar because a thistle can be found on the reverse.

Second Silver Coinage (1572 – 1580)

Collecting Hints

This issue is very rare as a whole and coins dated 1580 are extremely rare.

Obverse Legend   IACOBUS 6 DEI G. REX SCOTORUM — James by the grace of God King of Scots

Reverse Legend   NEMO ME IMPUNE LACESSET 1578 — No one shall hurt me with impunity 1578

Obverse   Crown over royal shield.

Reverse   Thistle dividing 'I.R.' (IACOBUS REX); mintmark crown at start of legend.

SJ62MK-005	v. rare

As previous, but dated 1579.

SJ62MK-010	v. rare

As previous, but dated 1580.

SJ62MK-015	ex. rare

Third Lion Noble

This non-portrait issue was struck in 21.5 carat gold and known as a third lion noble after the lion found on the obverse. Struck in 1584 during the fourth gold coinage, it had a value of twenty five shillings and completed the lion noble series with a value of seventy-five shillings and two thirds lion noble of fifty shillings.

Fourth Gold Coinage (1584 – 1588)

Collecting Hints

This issue is very rare in any grade but, when available, coins are usually found in Fine or VF condition.

Obverse Legend   POST 5 & 100 PROA INVICTA MANENT HEC — After one hundred and five ancestors these remain unconquered

Reverse Legend   DEUS IUDICIUM TUUM REGI DA 1584 — Give the King Thy judgements O Lord 1584

Obverse   Crowned lion holding sword and sceptre.

Reverse   Four crowned 'I.R. in the form of a cross with an 'S' in the centre.

SJ6TLN-005	v. rare

Two Thirds Ryal

The two thirds ryal, which had been introduced under Mary with a value of twenty shillings, continued to be struck during James VI's first silver coinage and retained its value. Sometimes known as a two thirds sword dollar due to the vertical sword found on the reverse, it complemented the crown-sized ryal. In 1578 many two third ryals of both reigns were countermarked with a crowned thistle to raise their value from twenty shillings to twenty-four shillings and sixpence, due to the rising silver price which had resulted in the denomination having a higher silver content than its face value.

First Silver Coinage (1567 – 1571)

> # Collecting Hints
>
> While scarce, all issues are obtainable in Fine condition but coins in a better condition are rare.

Obverse Legend IACOBUS 6 DEI GRATIA REX SCOTORUM — James VI by the grace of God King of Scots

Reverse Legend PRO ME SI MEREOR IN ME 1567 — For me but against me if I deserve

Obverse Crown over royal shield, crowned 'I.R.' (IACOBUS REX) divided by shield.

Reverse Crown over vertical sword, a hand pointing to XX (twenty shillings), 1567 divided by sword.

SJ6TTRY-005	VG £100	F £250	VF £850

As previous, but dated 1568.

SJ6TTRY-010	VG £125	F £350	VF —

As previous, but dated 1569.

SJ6TTRY-015	VG £100	F £250	VF £850

As previous, but dated 1570.

SJ6TTRY-020	VG £100	F £250	VF £850

As previous, but dated 1561. The date should read 1571 and this is an engraver's error.

SJ6TTRY-025	rare

As previous, but dated 1571.

SJ6TTRY-030	VG £100	F £250	VF £850

As previous, but no crowns over the 'I.R.' on reverse.

SJ6TTRY-035	VG £125	F £300	VF £950

Countermarked Two Thirds Ryal (1578)

The crown over thistle countermark increased the value of the two thirds ryal to twenty four shillings and sixpence.

> # Collecting Hints
>
> These issues are scarce in Fine condition and rare in VF condition.

Mary two thirds ryals of the fourth period (SMATTRY-010 to -020) with a crown over thistle countermark on either the obverse or reverse.

SJ6TTRY-040	VG £100	F £250	VF £850

Mary two thirds ryal of the fifth period (SMATTRY-025) with a crown over thistle countermark on either the obverse or reverse.

SJ6TTRY-045	VG £100	F £250	VF £850

James VI two thirds ryal of the first coinage (SJ6TTRY-005 to -035) with a crown over thistle countermark on either the obverse or reverse. Please note that the price given for SJ6TTRY-050 is for the common dates only.

SJ6TTRY-050	VG £100	F £250	VF £850

Twenty Shillings

The silver twenty shillings was issued during the fourth silver coinage of James VI as part of a new denomination structure which included the thirty and the ten shillings but was nonetheless superseded by the sixth coinage of 1591. All issues bear a half-length bust of the king on the obverse; the denomination 'XX S' (twenty shillings) can be found dividing the shield on the reverse.

Fourth Silver Coinage (1581 – 1586)

Collecting Hints

While scarce, the first two years of issue are obtainable especially in VG to Fine condition; the last three years are extremely rare.

Obverse Legend IACOBUS 6 DEI GRATIA REX SCOTORUM — James VI by the grace of God King of Scots

Reverse Legend HONOR REGIS IUDICIUM DILIGIT 1582 — The king's power loveth judgement 1582

Obverse Half-length bust of king holding sword.

Reverse Crown over royal shield dividing 'I.R.', the denomination 'XX' and 'S' either side of shield.

| SJ620S-005 | VG £100 | F £225 | VF £850 |

As previous, but dated 1583.

| SJ620S-010 | VG £110 | F £250 | VF £950 |

As previous, but dated 1584.

| SJ620S-015 | ex. rare |

As previous, but dated 1585.

| SJ620S-020 | ex. rare |

As previous, but dated 1586.

| SJ620S-025 | ex. rare |

Sixteen Shilling Piece

Struck in 1581, this silver coin was made of metal of 0.916 fineness.

Third Silver Coinage (1581)

Collecting Hints

A very rare issue in any grade, it is fairly similar in style to the two merks of the previous coinage except for the date.

Obverse Legend IACOBUS 6 DEI GRATIA REX SCOTORUM — James VI by the grace of God King of Scots

Reverse Legend NEMO ME IMPUNE LACESSET 1581 — No one shall hurt me with impunity

Obverse Crown above royal shield.

Reverse Crown over thistle dividing 'I.R.' (IACOBUS REX).

| SJ616S-005 | v. rare |

Merk

This silver issue had a value of thirteen shillings and fourpence.

Second Silver Coinage (1572 – 1580)

This issue was sometimes known as a half thistle dollar.

Collecting Hints

This issue is very rare and should not be confused with the sixteen shillings of the third coinage, which is dated 1581.

Obverse Legend IACOBUS 6 DEI G. REX SCOTORUM — James VI by the grace of God King of Scots

Reverse Legend NEMO ME IMPUNE LACESSET 1579 — No one shall hurt me with impunity

Obverse Crown above royal shield.

Reverse Thistle dividing 'I.R.' (IACOBUS REX); mintmark crown at the start of the legend.

| SJ6MK-005 | v. rare |

Scotland: James VI (1567 – 1625)

As previous, but dated 1580.

SJ6MK-010	v. rare

Eighth Silver Coinage (1601 – 1604)

This issue is often known as a thistle merk because a thistle can be found on the reverse. It had the same value as the previous issue.

Collecting Hints

This issue is fairly common, especially in the lower grades but a number of these coins are poorly struck resulting in areas being flat or weak and it is unfortunate that the date on these issues is often unclear.

Obverse Legend IACOBUS 6 D.G.R. SCOTORUM — James VI by the grace of God King of Scots

Reverse Legend REGEM IOVA PROTEGIT 1601 — Jehovah protects the King

Obverse Crown above royal shield.

Reverse Crown above a thistle.

SJ6MK-015	VG £30	F £70	VF £250

As previous, but dated 1602.

SJ6MK-020	VG £30	F £70	VF £250

As previous, but dated 1603.

SJ6MK-025	VG £30	F £70	VF £250

As previous, but dated 1604.

SJ6MK-030	VG £35	F £80	VF £275

Twelve Shillings

The silver twelve shillings was struck under both James VI and Charles I. Although they resemble contemporary English shillings quite closely, Scottish twelve shillings are much cruder in style. Also, the Scottish issues only use the mintmark thistle, while the English ones use a variety of mintmarks, including the thistle and, finally, there are varieties in the legends.

After accession to English throne (1603 – 1625)

Collecting Hints

These coins are fairly scarce, particularly in better than Fine condition, as they were badly made with poorly prepared dies and often slightly irregular flans.

Obverse Legend IACOBUS D.G. MAG BRIT FRAN & HIB REX — James by the grace of God King of Great Britain France and Ireland

Reverse Legend QUAE DEUS CONIVNXIT NEMO SEPARET — What God hath joined together let no man put asunder

Obverse Crowned bust of king facing right, the value 'XII' (twelve) behind the bust; mintmark thistle at the start of the legend.

Reverse Shield of royal arms with English arms in the first and fourth quarters; mintmark thistle at the start of the legend.

SJ612S-005	VG £75	F £175	VF £450

As previous, but Scottish arms in the first and fourth quarters of the reverse shield.

SJ612S-010	VG £60	F £150	VF £400

As previous, but no mintmark in the obverse legend.

SJ612S-015	v. rare

Third Ryal

The third ryal, or third sword dollar as it was sometimes known because a sword can be found on the reverse, was struck during James' first silver coinage and had a value of ten shillings. In 1578 however, due to the rising price of silver, many third ryals of both this and the previous reign were countermarked with a thistle and crown to increase their value to twelve shillings and threepence. This issue complemented the ryal and two thirds ryal series.

First Silver Coinage (1567 – 1571)

Collecting Hints

While rare, these issues are obtainable especially in Fine condition; VF examples however are very rare.

Obverse Legend IACOBUS 6 DEI GRATIA REX SCOTORUM — James VI by the grace of God King of Scots

Reverse Legend PRO ME SI MEREOR IN ME — For me but against me if I deserve

Obverse Crown over royal shield, crowned 'I' and 'R' (IACOBUS REX) divided by shield.

Reverse Crown above vertical sword, a hand pointing to 'X' (ten), the date 1567 divided by the sword.

| SJ6TRY-005 | VG £100 | F £225 | VF £800 |

As previous, but dated 1568.

| SJ6TRY-010 | VG £150 | F £300 | VF £1,000 |

As previous, but dated 1569.

| SJ6TRY-015 | VG £100 | F £225 | VF £800 |

As previous, but dated 1570.

| SJ6TRY-020 | VG £150 | F £400 | VF v. rare |

As previous, but dated 1571.

| SJ6TRY-025 | VG £100 | F £225 | VF £800 |

Countermarked Third Ryal (1578)

The crown over thistle countermark increased the value of third ryals to twelve shillings and threepence.

Collecting Hints

These issues are rare but sometimes obtainable, although rarely found in better than Fine condition.

Mary third ryal (SMATRY-005 to -010) with a countermark on either the obverse or the reverse.

| SJ6TRY-030 | VG £100 | F £225 | VF £800 |

Mary third ryal (SMATRY-020) with a countermark on either the obverse or the reverse.

| SJ6TRY-035 | VG £110 | F £250 | VF £900 |

James VI third ryal (SJ6TRY-005 to -025) with a countermark on either the obverse or the reverse. Please note that the prices listed for SJ6TRY-040 are for the most common dates.

| SJ6TRY-040 | VG £110 | F £250 | VF £900 |

Ten Shilling Piece

The silver ten shilling piece was struck during James VI's fourth and seventh coinages and, in both cases, constituted part of new denomination structures. All issues are dated and bear the king's bust on the obverse.

Fourth Silver Coinage (1581 – 1586)

Collecting Hints

This issue is scarce, particularly in better than Fine condition. The value 'X S' (ten shillings) is found on the reverse and easily identifies the denomination.

Obverse Legend IACOBUS 6 DEI GRATIA REX SCOTORUM — James VI by the grace of God King of Scots

Reverse Legend HONOR REGIS IUDICIUM DILIGIT 1582 — The king's power loveth judgement 1582

Obverse Half-length bust of king holding sword.

Reverse Crown over royal shield dividing 'I.R.', the denomination 'X S' divided by of the shield.

| SJ610S-005 | VG £80 | F £175 | VF £500 |

As previous, but dated 1583.

| SJ610S-010 | VG £100 | F £250 | VF £650 |

As previous, but dated 1584.

| SJ610S-015 | VG £100 | F £250 | VF £650 |

Seventh Silver Coinage (1593 – 1601)

Collecting Hints

This issue is fairly common especially in the lower grades but examples in VF or better condition are rare. These coins are attractive and show a lifelike portrait of the king.

Obverse Legend IACOBUS 6. D.G.R. SCOTORUM — James VI by the grace of God King of Scots

Reverse Legend NEMO ME IMPUNE LACESSET 1593 — No one shall hurt me with impunity

Obverse Uncrowned bust of king; mintmark quatrefoil at start of legend.

Reverse Small crown above triple-headed thistle; mintmark quatrefoil at the start of the legend.

| SJ610S-020 | VG £40 | F £90 | VF £350 |

As previous, but dated 1594.

| SJ610S-025 | VG £40 | F £90 | VF £350 |

As previous, but dated 1595.

| SJ610S-030 | VG £40 | F £90 | VF £350 |

As previous, but dated 1598.

| SJ610S-035 | VG £45 | F £110 | VF £380 |

As previous, but dated 1599.

| SJ610S-040 | VG £40 | F £90 | VF £350 |

As previous, but dated 1600.

| SJ610S-045 | VG £45 | F £110 | VF £380 |

As previous, but dated 1601.

| SJ610S-050 | VG £60 | F £150 | VF rare |

Eight Shilling Piece

This silver coin was only struck in 1581.

Third Silver Coinage (1581)

This issue was struck in 0.916 silver.

Collecting Hints

This issue is very rare in any grade.

Obverse Legend   IACOBUS 6 DEI GRATIA REX SCOTORUM — James VI by the grace of God King of Scots

Reverse Legend   NEMO ME IMPUNE LACESSET 1581 — No one shall hurt me with impunity

Obverse   Crown over royal shield.

Reverse   Crown over thistle dividing 'I.R.' (IACOBUS REX).

SJ68S-005	v. rare

Half Merk

The silver half merk, with a value of six shillings and eightpence, was first introduced during the second coinage of James VI and sometimes referred to as a noble because it had the same value, six shillings and eightpence, as the gold noble produced in medieval Scotland and England.

Second Silver Coinage (1572 – 1580)

Collecting Hints

This issue, struck in silver of 0.666 fineness, is fairly common especially in lower grades. Coins are sometimes poorly struck resulting in poor definition and design.

Obverse Legend   IACOBUS 6 DEI GRATIA REX SCOTORUM — James VI by the grace of God King of Scots

Reverse Legend   SALUUM FAC POPULUM TUUM DNE 1572 — Lord save Thy people 1572

Obverse   Crown over royal shield dividing the digits '6' and '8' (six shillings and eight pence).

Reverse   Ornate cross with two thistles and two crowns in alternate angles.

SJ6HMK-005	VG £35	F £80	VF £225

As previous, but dated 1573.

SJ6HMK-010	VG £40	F £100	VF £250

As previous, but dated 1574.

SJ6HMK-015	VG £35	F £80	VF £225

As previous, but dated 1575.

SJ6HMK-020	VG £40	F £100	VF £250

As previous, but dated 1576.

SJ6HMK-025	VG £65	F £200	VF £450

As previous, but dated 1577.

SJ6HMK-030	VG £35	F £80	VF £225

As previous, but dated 1580.

SJ6HMK-035	VG £65	F £200	VF £450

Sixth Silver Coinage (1591 – 1593)

This issue was struck in silver of 0.875 fineness and is smaller in size than the previous one. It is often known as the balance half merk because a pair of scales can be found on the reverse.

Collecting Hints

This issue is quite rare and rarely found in better than Fine condition.

Obverse Legend   IACOBUS 6 D.G.R. SCOTORUM 1591 — James VI by the grace of God King of Scots 1591

Reverse Legend   HIS DIFFERT REGE TYRANNUS — In these a tyrant differs from a king

Obverse   Crown above royal shield, a thistle either side of the shield.

Reverse   A balance with a sword behind.

| SJ6HMK-040 | VG £90 | F £225 | VF £850 |

As previous, but dated 1592.

| SJ6HMK-045 | VG £100 | F £250 | VF £900 |

As previous, but dated 1593.

| SJ6HMK-050 | VG £130 | F £325 | VF £1,100 |

Eighth Silver Coinage (1601 – 1604)

This issue is often known as the half thistle merk, after the thistle found on the reverse. It was struck in 0.916 silver.

Collecting Hints

This issue is fairly common especially in the lower grades. It is often found badly worn in poor to VG condition and obviously saw considerable circulation. Coins in VF or better condition are rare.

Obverse Legend IACOBUS 6 D.G.R. SCOTORUM — James VI by the grace of God King of Scots

Reverse Legend REGEM IOVA PROTEGIT 1601 — Jehovah protects the king 1601

Obverse Crown over royal shield.

Reverse Crown over a thistle.

| SJ6HMK-005 | VG £30 | F £60 | VF £225 |

As previous, but dated 1602.

| SJ6HMK-060 | VG £30 | F £60 | VF £225 |

As previous, but dated 1603.

| SJ6HMK-065 | VG £30 | F £60 | VF £225 |

As previous, but dated 1604.

| SJ6HMK-070 | VG £35 | F £80 | VF £275 |

Six Shillings

The silver six shillings was issued during the reigns of James VI and Charles I. James's issues, which are dated, were produced after the king's accession to the English throne and are similar to the English sixpence but considerably cruder in both style and production. Furthermore, the Scottish issues only use mintmark thistle, while the English sixpence uses a variety of mintmarks including the thistle.

After accession to English throne (1603 – 1625)

Collecting Hints

These coins are rare and, due to the way they were often struck, rarely found in better than Fine condition.

Obverse Legend IACOBUS D G. MAG BRIT FRAN & HIB REX — James by the grace of God King of Great Britain France and Ireland

Reverse Legend QUAE DEUS CONIVNXIT NEMO SEPARET — What God hath joined together let no man put asunder

Obverse Crowned bust of king, value 'VI' behind bust; mintmark thistle at start of legend.

Reverse Royal shield with arms of England in first and fourth quarters; mintmark thistle at start of legend, date 1605 above shield.

| SJ66S-005 | VG £90 | F £200 | VF rare |

As previous, but dated 1606.

| SJ66S-010 | VG £90 | F £200 | VF rare |

As previous, but dated 1609/7. Altered die.

| SJ66S-015 | rare |

Obverse As previous.

Reverse As previous, but Scottish arms in first and fourth quarter. Date 1610 above shield.

SJ66S-020	VG £90	F £200	VF rare

As previous, but dated 1611.

SJ66S-025	VG £90	F £200	VF rare

As previous, but dated 1612.

SJ66S-030	VG £90	F £200	VF rare

As previous, but dated 1613.

SJ66S-035	VG £90	F £200	VF rare

As previous, but dated 1614.

SJ66S-040	VG £90	F £200	VF rare

As previous, but dated 1615.

SJ66S-045	VG £90	F £200	VF rare

As previous, but dated 1616.

SJ66S-050	VG £90	F £200	VF rare

As previous, but dated 1617.

SJ66S-055	VG £90	F £200	VF rare

As previous, but dated 1618.

SJ66S-060	VG £90	F £200	VF rare

As previous, but dated 1619.

SJ66S-065	VG £90	F £200	VF rare

As previous, but dated 1622.

SJ66S-070	VG £90	F £200	VF rare

Testoon (Countermarked)

No testoons were struck during the reign of James VI but coins from the previous reign were still circulating in quite large numbers. However, because of the constantly rising price of silver, the silver content of these coins was fast becoming higher than their face value. It was therefore decided in 1578 to countermark many earlier denominations, including the testoon, to officially raise their face value. A crowned thistle was the countermark used on all denominations and the testoon was raised in value from five shillings to seven shillings and fourpence. While it is difficult to class these issues in a denomination structure, it has been decided in the interests of continuity to list them here.

Collecting Hints

As one would expect, due to the fact that these coins had been in circulation for several decades, they are rarely found in better than Fine condition. A strong, clear, well-positioned countermark adds to the value of a coin. The countermarked earlier issues (SMATS-010 to -090) are scarce but obtainable, while the third issue (SMATS-105 or -110) is very rare. Prices are for the most common dates.

SMATS-010 to -090 with crowned thistle countermark on either the obverse or the reverse.

SJ6TS-005	VG £80	F £200	VF £500

SMATS-105 or -110 with crowned thistle countermark on either the obverse or the reverse.

SJ6TS-010	v. rare

Five Shilling Piece

The silver five shilling piece was issued during James VI's seventh coinage. All issues are dated and bear an uncrowned bust of the king on the obverse.

Seventh Silver Coinage (1593 – 1601)

Collecting Hints

All coins from this issue are scarce but the last two dates are extremely rare. Coins in better than Fine condition are difficult to obtain.

Obverse Legend IACOBUS 6 D.G.R. SCOTORUM — James by the grace of God King of Scots

Reverse Legend NEMO ME IMPUNE LACESSET 1593 — No one shall hurt me with impunity 1593

Obverse Uncrowned bust of king; mintmark quatrefoil at the start of the legend.

Reverse Crown above triple-headed thistle; mintmark quatrefoil at the start of the legend.

SJ65S-005	VG £60	F £150	VF rare

As previous, but dated 1594.

SJ65S-010	VG £50	F £125	VF £300

As previous, but dated 1595.

SJ65S-015	VG £50	F £125	VF £300

As previous, but dated 1598/6. Altered die for a year that was unissued.

SJ65S-020	VG £80	F £200	VF rare

As previous, but dated 1599.

SJ65S-025	VG £60	F £150	VF rare

As previous, but dated 1600.

SJ65S-030	ex. rare

As previous, but dated 1601.

SJ65S-035	ex. rare

Four Shilling Piece

This silver coin was only struck in 1581.

Third Silver Coinage (1581)

Collecting Hints

This issue is very rare in any grade.

Obverse Legend IACOBUS 6 DEI GRATIA REX SCOTOR — James VI by the grace of God King of Scots

Reverse Legend NEMO ME IMPUNE LACESSET 1581 — No one shall hurt me with impunity

Obverse Crown over royal shield.

Reverse Crown over a thistle dividing 'I.R.' (IACOBUS REX), the 'N's in the legend are reversed.

SJ64S-005	v. rare

Quarter Merk

The silver quarter merk, or half noble as it was sometimes known, was only struck during the reign of James VI. It had a value of three shillings and fourpence which was the medieval denomination of the half noble, hence the name.

Quarter merks were struck during the second, third and eighth coinages, and we will give 'Collecting Hints' for each.

Second Silver Coinage (1572 – 1580)

This issue was struck in silver of 0.666 fineness.

Collecting Hints

While scarce, this issue is available especially in the lower grades. Coins in better than Fine condition are rare and this issue was poorly struck resulting in some of the design often being unclear.

Obverse Legend IACOBUS 6 DEI GRATIA REX SCOTORUM — James VI by the grace of God King of Scots

Reverse Legend SALUUM FAC POPULUM TUUM DNE 1572 — O Lord save Thy people 1572

Obverse Crown over royal shield, dividing the value '3' and '4'.

Reverse Ornate cross with a crown or thistle in each angle.

| SJ6QMK-005 | VG £35 | F £80 | VF £280 |

As previous, but dated 1573 or 15733 (die error).

| SJ6QMK-010 | VG £35 | F £80 | VF £280 |

As previous, but dated 1574.

| SJ6QMK-015 | VG £35 | F £80 | VF £280 |

As previous, but dated 1576.

| SJ6QMK-020 | VG £35 | F £80 | VF £280 |

As previous, but dated 1577.

| SJ6QMK-025 | VG £35 | F £80 | VF £280 |

As previous, but dated 1580.

| SJ6QMK-030 | VG £60 | F £150 | VF £450 |

Sixth Silver Coinage (1591 – 1593)

This issue is often known as a balance quarter merk because a balance can be found in the reverse. It was struck in silver of 0.875 fineness, and complemented the larger denomiantion of balance half merk. Its value was the same as that of the previous issue.

Collecting Hints

This issue is rare in any grade.

Obverse Legend IACOBUS 6 D.G.R. SCOTORUM 1591 — James VI by the grace of God King of Scots 1591

Reverse Legend HIS DIFFERT REGE TYRANNUS — In these a tyrant differs from a king

Obverse Crown above royal shield.

Reverse A balance with sword behind.

| SJ6QMK-035 | VG £150 | F £400 | VF v. rare |

Eighth Silver Coinage (1601 – 1604)

This issue is often known as the quarter thistle merk as a thistle can be found on the reverse. It had the same value as the previous issue. The value of the issue, which was struck in 0.916 silver, remained the same.

Collecting Hints

As many coins from this issue undoubtedly saw considerable circulation, specimens are fairly common in less than Fine condition. Examples in VF condition are also obtainable but scarce.

Obverse Legend IACOBUS 6 D.G.R. SCOTORUM — James VI by the grace of God King of Scots

Reverse Legend REGEM IOVA PROTEGIT 1601 — Jehovah protects the King 1601

Obverse Crown over royal shield.

Reverse Crown over thistle.

| SJ6QMK-040 | VG £25 | F £60 | VF £150 |

As previous, but dated 1602.

| SJ6QMK-045 | VG £25 | F £60 | VF £150 |

As previous, but dated 1603.

SJ6QMK-050	VG £35	F £85	VF £210

As previous, but dated 1604.

SJ6QMK-055	VG £25	F £60	VF £150

Thirty Pence

The silver thirty pence was issued during the seventh coinage of James VI as part of a new denomination structure which, however, was superseded in the eighth coinage. All issues are dated and bear an uncrowned bust of the king on the obverse. Care should be taken when differentiating this denomination from the five or ten shilling pieces which are identical except for their size and, in some instances, the date.

Seventh Silver Coinage (1593 – 1601)

Collecting Hints

This issue is fairly common in the lower grades but coins in VF or better condition are rare. The date on some specimens is often unclear due to the way the die was made.

Obverse Legend IACOBUS 6 D.G.R. SCOTORUM — James VI by the grace of God King of Scots

Reverse Legend NEMO ME IMPUNE LACESSET 1594 — No one shall hurt me with impunity

Obverse Uncrowned bust of king; mintmark quatrefoil at the beginning of the legend.

Reverse Small crown above three headed thistle; mintmark quatrefoil at the beginning of the legend.

SJ630D-005	VG £35	F £80	VF £300

As previous, but dated 1595.

SJ630D-010	VG £35	F £80	VF £300

As previous, but dated 1596.

SJ630D-015	VG £35	F £80	VF £300

As previous, but dated 1598/6, altered die.

SJ630D-020	VG £40	F £90	VF £320

As previous, but dated 1599.

SJ630D-025	VG £40	F £80	VF £300

As previous, but dated 1601.

SJ630D-030	VG £50	F £125	VF £400

Half Testoon (Countermarked)

No half testoons were struck during the reign of James VI as coins from the previous reign were still circulating in quite large numbers. However, because the price of silver was rising, the silver content of these coins was fast becoming higher than their face value. It was therefore decided in 1578 to countermark many earlier denominations, including the half testoon, to officially raise their value which in the case of the half testoon was increased from two shillings and six pence to three shillings and eightpence. A crowned thistle was the countermark used on all denominations.

Collecting Hints

All issues are extremely rare and while a countermark on the third issue (SMAHTS-070) has been recorded, it is uncertain which other issues exist countermarked.

Mary third period half testoon with a crowned thistle countermark on either the obverse or the reverse.

SJ6HTS-005	ex. rare

Two Shilling Piece

This silver issue was struck during the reigns of James VI and Charles I.

Third Silver Coinage (1581)

The silver two shillings was produced during the third coinage in 1581 and then again during the eighth coinage; both issues were struck in 0.916 silver.

Collecting Hints

This issue is extremely rare.

Obverse Legend IACOBUS 6 DEI GRATIA REX SCOTOR — James VI by the grace of God King of Scots

Reverse Legend NEMO ME IMPUNE LACESSET 1581 — No one shall hurt me with impunity 1581

Obverse Crown over royal shield.

Reverse Crown over a thistle dividing 'I.R.' (IACOBUS REX).

SJ62S-005 ex. rare

Eighth Silver Coinage (1601 – 1622)

This issue, which was struck in 0.916 silver, is very similar to the more common English halfgroat of James I (J12D-010 to -020), but the crowns on the Scottish issue are much flatter. Also the Scottish issue only uses the mintmark thistle while the English issues use a variety of mintmarks, including the thistle.

Collecting Hints

These coins are fairly common and usually found in Fine condition.

Obverse Legend I D.G. ROSA SINE SPINA — James by the grace of God a rose without a thorn

Reverse Legend TUEATUR UNITA DEUS — May God guard these united (kingdom)

Obverse Crowned rose; mintmark thistle.

Reverse Crowned thistle; mintmark thistle.

SJ62S-010 VG £25 F £60 VF £150

Eighth Thistle Merk

This silver issue was only struck during the eighth coinage of James VI and had a value of one shilling and eightpence. All issues are non-portrait, with crowned arms on the obverse and a crowned thistle on the reverse. If a coin is larger than the illustration, it could be a quarter, half or full thistle merk. The main difference between these denominations is their size.

Eighth Silver Coinage (1601 – 1604)

Collecting Hints

This issue is fairly common, especially in the lower grades. The dates on some coins are often unclear and coins are often found damaged.

Obverse Legend IACOBUS 6 D.G.R. SCOTORUM — James VI by the grace of God King of Scots

Reverse Legend REGEM IOVA PROTEGIT 1601 — Jehovah protects the king 1601

Obverse Crown above royal shield.

Reverse Crown above a thistle.

SJ6ETM-005 VG £25 F £50 VF £150

As previous, but dated 1602.

SJ6ETM-010 VG £25 F £50 VF £150

As previous, but dated 1603.

SJ6ETM-015 VG £45 F £100 VF rare

Twelve Pence

This silver issue was struck during the seventh coinage of James VI. While similar to the larger denominations of this issue (ten shillings, five shillings and thirty pence) it can be identified by a single pellet or line behind the king's head. All issues are dated, although the date is often unclear, and bear an uncrowned bust of the king on the obverse.

Seventh Silver Coinage (1593 – 1601)

Collecting Hints

This coin is scarce and rarely found in better than Fine condition. It is not uncommon for the date to be unclear.

Obverse Legend IACOBUS 6 D.G.R. SCOTORUM — James VI by the grace of God King of Scots

Reverse Legend NEMO ME IMPUNE LACESSET 1594 — No one shall hurt me with impunity

Obverse Uncrowned bust of king, a pellet or line behind the bust; mintmark quatrefoil at the start of the legend.

Reverse Crown above triple-headed thistle; mintmark quatrefoil at the start of the legend.

SJ612D-005 VG £40 F £95 VF rare

As previous, but dated 1595.

SJ612D-010 VG £45 F £95 VF rare

As previous, but dated 1596.

SJ612D-015 v. rare

Shilling

The silver shilling was struck during the reigns of James VI and Charles I. Both issues are non-portrait and bear a rose with a thistle on either side. They are fairly similar to the English pennies of James I and Charles I, but the Scottish issues only use the mintmark thistle while the English ones use a variety of mintmarks but not the thistle.

After accession to English throne (1603 – 1625)

Collecting Hints

This issue is scarce but obtainable, although rarely found in better than Fine condition.

Obverse Legend I D.G. ROSA SINE SPINA — James by the grace of God a rose without a thorn

Reverse Legend TUAETUR UNITA DEUS — May God guard these united (kingdoms)

Obverse A rose, mintmark thistle at the start of the legend.

Reverse A thistle; mintmark thistle at the start of the legend.

SJ6SH-005	VG £25	F £55	VF £135

Groat

Two groats were struck during James VI's reign, both under the billon coinage. The first was the eightpenny groat which was fairly similar to the plack and bawbee from previous reigns. The second issue was the fourpenny plack which is very rare. Due to large quantities of forgeries in circulation, placks of Mary were countermarked with a star within a heart. Detail of the original issue (SMAPL-005) are in the previous chapter but we have priced it as a countermarked coin here (SJ64D-025). Mint officials countermarked coins to confirm their authenticity.

Billon Issue (1583 – 1590)

The 'eightpenny' groat had a value of eightpence and had a 25% silver content.

Collecting Hints

This issue is fairly common, especially in the lower grades. Coins in VF are scarce but obtainable. It appears forgeries were not a problem for this issue.

Obverse Legend IACOBUS 6 D. G. R. SCOTOR — James VI by the grace of God King of Scots

Reverse Legend OPPIDUM EDINBURGH — Town of Edinburgh

Obverse Crown above the royal shield, no inner circle.

Reverse A crown above a thistle, no inner circle.

SJ64D-005	VG £12	F £25	VF £70

Obverse Legend As previous, but IACOB instead of IACOBUS.

Reverse Legend OPPID EDINB — Town of Edinburgh

Obverse As previous, sometimes with a hairline inner circle.

Reverse As previous, sometimes with a hairline inner circle.

SJ64D-010	VG £15	F £30	VF £80

As previous, but with beaded inner circle on both sides of the coin.

SJ64D-015	VG £15	F £30	VF £80

Fourpenny Plack (1594)

This issue had a silver content of about 4% and a value of fourpence.

Collecting Hints

This issue is rare in any grade.

Obverse Legend IACOB 6 D. G. R. SCO — James VI by the grace of God King of Scotland

Reverse Legend OPPID EDINB — Town of Edinburgh

Obverse A thistle on a saltire over two sceptres.

Reverse A lozenge with a thistle head at each point.

SJ64D-020	VG £80	F £200	VF v. rare

Countermarked Issue (1575) on Mary placks

The details of the original Mary plack (SMAPL-005) are discussed under Mary, p.115.

Collecting Hints

This countermarked coin is fairly common. Due to the fact that these coins were in circulation some time before they were countermarked, they are rarely found in better than Fine condition.

Obverse Plack of Mary with countermark of star within a heart.

Reverse Plack of Mary.

SJ64D-025	VG £20	F £40	VF RARE

Plack of Twopence

A variety of coins with a value of twopence were struck during the long reign of James VI. All issues were struck in Edinburgh but while the plack was made of billon and had a 25% silver content, the halfgroats were made of copper. By this time the coins' face value represented very little buying power and they could be compared to tokens as their metal content was less than their value.

Twopenny Plack (1583 – 1590)

Collecting Hints

This issue is scarce, especially in better than Fine condition, and is often found weakly struck.

Obverse Legend   IACOB 6 D.G.R. SCO — James VI by the grace of God King of Scotland

Reverse Legend   OPPID EDINB — Town of Edinburgh

Obverse   Crown over royal shield, no inner circle or hairline inner circle.

Reverse   A crown over a thistle, no inner circle or hairline inner circle.

| SJ6PL-005 | VG £50 | F £125 | VF £300 |

As previous, but beaded inner circles.

| SJ6PL-010 | VG £50 | F £125 | VF £300 |

Hardhead of Twopence

Hardhead (1588)

This issue had a silver content of about 4.5% and a value of twopence.

Collecting Hints

The first issue is rare in any grade but the second issue is quite common, especially in the lower grades.

Obverse Legend   IACOB 6 D G R SCOTO — James by the grace of God King of Scots

Reverse Legend   VINCIT VERITAS — Truth prevails

Obverse   The letters IR (IACOBUS REX) below a crown.

Reverse   Crowned shield.

| SJ62D-005 | VG £50 | F £125 | VF £300 |

Obverse Legend   IACOB 6 D G R SCO — James VI by the grace of God King of Scotland

Reverse Legend   VINCIT (or VENCIT) VERITAS — Truth prevails

Obverse   As previous.

Reverse   Lion rampant with two pellets behind.

| SJ62D-010 | VG £12 | F £30 | VF £80 |

Turner or Twopence

This issue was made of copper and had a value of twopence. The word turner probably comes from the French denomination tournois.

1597 Issue

Collecting Hints

While scarce, this issue is obtainable and usually found in Fine to VF condition.

Obverse Legend   IACOBUS 6 D.G R SCOTORUM — James VI by the grace of God King of Scots

Reverse Legend   OPPIDUM EDINBURGI — Town of Edinburgh

Obverse   Uncrowned right facing bust of king.

Reverse   Three thistle heads.

| SJ62D-015 | VG £25 | F £50 | VF £150 |

1614 & 1623 Issue

This issue was made of copper and had a value of twopence.

Collecting Hints

This issue is very common, especially in the lower grades. These coins saw considerable circulation not only in Scotland but also in England, where they probably circulated with tokens during the latter half of the seventeenth century.

1614 Issue

Obverse Legend   IACOBUS DEI GRA MAG BRIT — James by the grace of God of Great Britain

Reverse Legend   FRANCIE ET HIBERNIE REX — France and Ireland King

Obverse   A three-headed thistle.

Reverse   A lion rampant, two pellets by the lion's tail indicating the value.

SJ62D-020   VG £10   F £20   VF £55

1623 Issue

Obverse Legend   IACOBUS D.G. MAG BRIT — James by the grace of God of Great Britain

Reverse Legend   FRAN & HIB REX — France and Ireland King

Obverse   As previous.

Reverse   As previous.

SJ62D-025   VG £10   F £20   VF £55

Countermarked Issue (1575) on Mary Lion

Collecting Hints

Due to the fact that these coins had been in circulation for some time before they were countermarked, they are rarely found in better than fine condition. Countermarks are found on the obverse or reverse.

Obverse   As SMACL-005 and -020 to -040, with star within heart countermark.

Reverse   As SMACL-005 and -020 to -040.

SJ62D-030   VG £20   F £40   VF —

Penny

During the reign of James VI, pennies were struck in copper. The issues can be divided into two and both are rare. The first one was struck before James's accession to the English throne, while the second issue was struck after his accession and it is probable that many of these coins circulated in England as 'tokens' of the value of about a farthing. We give separate Collecting Hints for each issue, as they vary.

Before accession to English throne (1567 – 1603)
Non-portrait Penny Plack

Collecting Hints

This issue which must not be confused with the much more common hardhead or twopence, is rare in any grade and rarely found in better than Fine condition. It should measure approximately 12 mm in diameter while the twopence measures approx. 18 mm.

Obverse Legend   IACOB 6 D.G.R. SCO — James VI by the grace of God King of Scotland

Reverse Legend   VINCIT VERITAS — Truth prevails

Obverse   Crown above I.R.

Reverse   Lion rampant.

SJ61D-005   VG £60   F £150   VF —

Portrait Penny of 1597

Collecting Hints

This coin is rare and is rarely found in better than Fine condition.

Obverse Legend   IACOBUS 6 D.G.R. SCOTORUM — James VI by the grace of God King of Scots

Reverse Legend   OPPIDUM EDINBURGI — Town of Edinburgh

Obverse   Uncrowned bust of king with a pellet denoting denomination (one penny) behind bust.

Reverse   Three thistle heads.

SJ61D-010   VG £60   F £150   VF —

After accession to English throne (1603 – 1625)

Collecting Hints

This issues are scarce unlike the common twopence which was produced in some quantity. These two issues are similar, however the penny has a single pellet by the lion while the twopence has two pellets. Coins are rarely found in better than Fine condition.

1614 Issue

Obverse Legend   IACOBUS DEI GRA MAG BRIT — James by the grace of God of Great Britain

Reverse Legend   FRANCIE ET HIBERNIE REX — France and Ireland King

Obverse   Three thistles.

Reverse   Lion rampant, single pellet by tail.

SJ61D-015   VG £25   F £60   VF £120

1623 Issue

Obverse Legend   IACOBUS D.G. MAG BRIT — James by the grace of God of Great Britain

Reverse Legend   FRAN & HIB REX — France and Ireland King

Obverse   As previous.

Reverse   As previous.

SJ61D-020	**VG £30**	**F £70**	**VF £140**

Scotland: Charles I (1625 – 1649)

Charles I tried to bring more conformity with his denomination structures than his father, James VI had managed to. Denominations were struck in gold, silver and copper, with the unit or sceptre piece being the highest denomination.

Unit or Sceptre piece

The gold unit had a value of twelve pounds. Charles I struck three main varieties of units which, unlike previous issues, all varied considerably from their English counterparts. The first Charles I issue was struck during the first coinage and is very similar to James VI's last, the only difference being that the obverse legend bears Charles' name and his initials can be found on the reverse; also the king's beard is slightly shorter. In 1635 Nicholas Briot, a Frenchman who had worked for the French and English mints, received an appointment as Master of the Scottish mint. He was later joined by his son-in-law John Falconer and both men produced the unit during the third coinage (1637–42). The issues of Briot and Falconer were not hammered but machine-made, using a mill and screw press. As in England, this form of production was unpopular with mint workers, who feared that it would deprive them of a job. The result of these machine-made coins was magnificent and Briot's work is renowned for being of the highest quality.

First Coinage (1625 – 1634)

Collecting Hints

This issue is rare but, when available, is usually found undamaged in Fine to VF condition.

Obverse Legend CAROLUS D.G. MAG BRIT FRAN & HIB REX — Charles by the grace of God King of Great Britain France and Ireland

Reverse Legend FACIAM EOS IN GENTEM UNAM — I will make them one nation

Obverse Crowned bust of king holding orb and sceptre; mintmark thistle at start of legend.

Reverse Crown above royal shield dividing 'C.R.' (Carolus Rex); mintmark thistle at start of legend.

| SC1UT-005 | VG — | F £1,150 | VF £2,400 |

Third Coinage (1637 – 1642)
Briot's Issue

Collecting Hints

The first issue is rare; when available, it is usually found undamaged in Fine to VF condition. It is superb in style and production and has to be one of the finest Scottish coins. The second issue is extremely rare.

Obverse Legend CAROLUS D.G. MAG BRITAN FRAN ET HIB REX — Charles by the grace of God King of Great Britain France and Ireland

Reverse Legend HIS PRAESUM VT PROSIM — I am set over them that I may be profitable to them

Obverse Crowned bust of king holding orb and sceptre, a thistle and 'B' (for Briot) at end of legend.

Reverse Crown over royal shield dividing crowned 'C.R' (Carolus Rex).

| SC1UT-010 | VG — | F £900 | VF £2,400 |

As previous, but obverse legend begins with 'B' and ends with a thistle head.

| SC1UT-015 | ex. rare |

Falconer's Issue

Collecting Hints

This issue is extremely rare.

Obverse Legend   As previous.

Reverse Legend   As previous.

Obverse   As SC1UT-010 but a thistle and 'F' after the obverse legend.

Reverse   As SC1UT-015, but a thistle and 'F' after the reverse legend.

SC1UT-020	ex. rare

Half Unit or Six Pound Piece or Double Crown

The gold half unit was struck during the first and third coinages of Charles I. The first coinage issue is very similar to the issues of James VI, the main difference being that the obverse legend is in Charles' name. During the third coinage, Briot and Falconer produced machine-made half units of superb style and strike. All issues had a value of six pounds.

First Coinage (1625 – 1634)

Collecting Hints

This issue is extremely rare.

Obverse Legend   CAROLUS D.G. MAG BRIT FRAN & HIB REX — Charles by the grace of God King of Great Britain France and Ireland

Reverse Legend   HENRICUS ROSAS REGNA IACOBUS — Henry (united) the roses, James the kingdoms

Obverse   Crowned bust of king similar to that of James VI; mintmark thistle at the start of the legend.

Reverse   Crown over royal shield dividing 'C.R.', mintmark thistle at the start of the legend.

SC1HUT-005	ex. rare

Third Coinage (1637 – 1642)

Collecting Hints

Briot's issue is very rare and, when available, usually found in Fine or VF condition. Falconer's issue is extremely rare.

Briot's Issue

Obverse Legend   CAR D.G. MAG BRIT FRAN ET HIB REX — Charles by the grace of God King of Great Britain France and Ireland

Reverse Legend   UNITA TUEMUR — These united we guard

Obverse   Crowned bust facing left, the legend starts at the bottom of the coin, a small 'B' (for Briot) below bust.

Reverse   Crown over royal arms dividing crowned 'CR'.

SC1HUT-010	VG —	F £1,200	VF £2,800

Falconer's Issue

As previous, but an 'F' (for Falconer) instead of a 'B' in legend.

SC1HUT-015	ex. rare

Three Pound Piece or Britain Crown

The gold Britain crown or three pound piece was struck during the first and third coinages. The first coinage issue is very similar to those of James VI except that the obverse legend is in Charles' name. Briot and Falconer's third coinage Britain crowns were machine-made and of superb style and strike.

First Coinage (1625 – 1634)

Collecting Hints

This issue is extremely rare.

Obverse Legend   CAROLUS D.G. MAG BRIT FRAN & HIB REX (?) — Charles by the grace of God King of Great Britain France and Ireland

Reverse Legend   HENRICUS ROSAS REGNA IACOBUS — Henry (united) the roses James the kingdoms

Obverse   Crowned bust of king facing right; mintmark thistle at start of legend.

Reverse   Crown over royal shield dividing 'CR' (Carolus Rex); mintmark thistle at start of legend.

SC13PB-005	ex. rare

Third Coinage (1637 – 1642)

Briot's Issue

Collecting Hints

Both issues are very rare; when available, they are usually found in Fine condition.

Obverse Legend   CAR D.G. MAG BRIT FR ET HIB REX — Charles by the grace of God King of Great Britain France and Ireland

Reverse Legend   UNITA TUEMUR — These united we guard

Obverse   Crowned bust of king facing left, the legend starts at the bottom of the coin, a 'B' for Briot is found at the end of the legend.

Reverse   Crown over royal shield dividing crowned 'C.R.'

SC13PB-010	ex. rare

As previous, but a 'B' at the start of the obverse legend.

SC13PB-015	v. rare

Sixty Shillings

The sixty shillings was struck during the first and third coinage of Charles I. While these coins are fairly similar to the English crowns, all Scottish issues use the mintmark thistle while none of the English ones do. The mintmark can be found at the start of the obverse and reverse legend.

Third coinage issues were struck by Briot and the workmanship and production of these machine-made coins is superb. The third coinage sixty shillings was complemented by the thirty, twelve and six shillings, which were all produced either by Briot himself or, in the case of some later issues, by his son-in-law John Falconer.

First Coinage (1625 – 1634)

Collecting Hints

This issue is rarer than the previous reign's sixty shillings. Coins are rarely found in better than Fine condition and are often badly damaged and worn.

Obverse Legend CAROLUS D.G. MAG BRIT FRAN & HIB REX — Charles by the grace of God King of Great Britain France and Ireland

Reverse Legend QUAE DEUS CONIVNXIT NEMO SEPARET — What God hath joined together let no man put asunder

Obverse King on horseback holding sword (identical to James VI issue); mintmark thistle at start of legend.

Reverse Royal shield; mintmark thistle at start of legend.

SC160S-005	VG £200	F £450	VF rare

Third Coinage (1637 – 1642)

Briot's Issue

Collecting Hints

This coin is usually found undamaged in Fine condition. Coins in VF or better condition are rare.

Obverse Legend CAROLUS D.G. MAGN BRITANN FRANC ET HIBERN REX — Charles by the grace of God King of Great Britain France and Ireland

Reverse Legend QUAE DEUS CONIVNXIT NEMO SEPARET — What God hath joined together let no man put asunder

Obverse King on horseback holding upright sword; mintmark thistle and small 'B' (for Briot) at start of legend.

Reverse Crown over royal shield; mintmark thistle and a 'B' on its side at the end of the legend.

SC160S-010	VG £225	F £450	VF £1,500

Half Crown of Thirty Shillings

Gold halfcrown were produced during the third coinage (1637 – 42) and were machine-made. The dies for this coinage were the work of Nicholas Briot and his initial 'B' can be found on each issue. Unlike his predecessor, Charles only produced silver halfcrowns in England, so this issue cannot be confused with any English issues.

Third Coinage (1637 – 1642)

Briot's Issue

Collecting Hints

While scarce, this coin is the most common Scottish gold coin and usually found in Fine or VF condition.

Obverse Legend CAR D.G. MAG BRIT FRAN ET HIB REX — Charles by the grace of God King of Great Britain France and Ireland

Reverse Legend UNITA TUEMUR — These united we guard

Obverse Crowned bust of king facing left, a small 'B' below the bust, the legend starts at the bottom of the coin.

Reverse Crown over royal shield dividing 'C.R.'.

| SC1HC-005 | VG £150 | F £300 | VF £750 |

As previous, but a 'B' and lozenge over the crown on the reverse.

| SC1HC-010 | VG £165 | F £350 | VF £850 |

Thirty Shillings

Silver thirty shillings were struck during the first and third coinages of Charles I. The first issue was hammered and similar in style to the issues of the previous reign, the main difference being the obverse legend. There are several varieties of the third coinage issues, all of which were machine-made by either Nicholas Briot or John Falconer.

First Coinage (1625 – 1634)

This issue is scarcer than the previous James VI issues and rarely found in better than Fine condition. It is important to note that if the mintmark and style of a coin are different, it might be an English Charles I halfcrown. No English halfcrowns of Charles I used the thistle mintmark.

Collecting Hints

This issue, while scarce, is obtainable but difficult to find in better than Fine condition.

Obverse Legend CAROLUS D.G. MAG BRIT FRAN & HIB REX — Charles by the grace of God King of Great Britain France and Ireland

Reverse Legend QUAE DEUS CONIVNXIT NEMO SEPARET — What God hath joined together let no man put asunder

Obverse King on horseback holding a sword; mintmark thistle.

Reverse Royal shield; mintmark thistle.

| SC130S-005 | VG £65 | F £175 | VF £400 |

Third Coinage (1637 – 1642)

Collecting Hints

These machine-made coins are superb in style and design. They are available in most grades with coins in Fine or VF being the most prolific. Many coins appear to be slightly bent or oval in shape, which is due to the way that they were produced. The dies were made by either Nicholas Briot or John Falconer and we have listed each one's work separately.

Briot's Issue

Obverse Legend CAROLUS D.G. MAGN BRITAN FRAN ET HIB REX B — Charles by the grace of God King of Britain France and Ireland B(riot)

Reverse Legend QUAE DEUS CONIVNXIT NEMO SEPARET — What God hath joined together let no man put asunder

Obverse King on horseback holding sword; mintmark flower and 'B'. This is an English die for a London issue (SC1HC-105).

Reverse Crown over royal shield; mintmark 'B' and thistle.

| SC130S-010 | VG £65 | F £150 | VF £400 |

Intermediate Issue

As previous, but no 'B' in legend; mintmark thistle on both sides.

| SC130S-015 | VG £55 | F £135 | VF £350 |

Falconer's Issue

As previous, but an 'F' by the horse's hoof, smooth ground below the horse; mintmark leaved thistle on both sides of the coin.

SC130S-020	VG £45	F £120	VF £300

As previous, but rough ground below the horse, 'F' by the horse's hoof.

SC130S-025	VG £45	F £120	VF £300

As previous, but an 'F' over the crown on the reverse.

SC130S-030	VG £55	F £135	VF £350

Falconer's Anonymous Issue

As previous, but no 'F' on either the obverse or the reverse.

SC130S-035	VG £55	F £120	VF £350

Twelve Shillings

The Charles I twelve shillings was struck during the first and third coinages. Coins from the first coinage are very similar to those of the previous reign, being poorly struck with badly prepared dies; the main difference between the two reigns is the obverse legend. Charles' portrait also looks very similar to that of James VI and is in fact often considered to be James's bust. Coins from the third coinage, on the other hand, were machine-made and superb in design and production. They were the work of Briot and Falconer and various minor marks on the coins denote which mintmaster was responsible for which issue.

First Coinage (1625 – 1634)

Collecting Hints

This crudely struck issue is scarce and rarely found in better than Fine condition.

Obverse Legend CAROLUS D.G. MAG BRIT FRAN & HIB REX — Charles by the grace of God King of Great Britain France and Ireland

Reverse Legend QUAE DEUS CONIVNXIT NEMO SEPARET — What God hath joined let no man put asunder

Obverse Crowned bust of king with the value 'XII' (twelve) behind; mintmark thistle at the start of the legend.

Reverse Royal shield; mintmark thistle at the start of the legend.

SC112S-005	VG £50	F £170	VF £500

Third Coinage (1637 – 1642)

Collecting Hints

These issues are of superb style and production and examples can be found in all grades from VG to EF. Coins are sometimes found creased and also with flecking or haymarking in the field due to the striking.

Briot's Issue

Obverse Legend CAR D.G. MAG BRIT FRAN ET HIB REX — Charles by the grace of God King of Great Britain France and Ireland

Reverse Legend QUAE DEUS CONIVNXIT NEMO SEPARET — What God hath joined together let no man put asunder

Obverse Crowned bust of king starting at the bottom of the coin, the denomination (XII) behind the bust, the legend starts nearly at the bottom of the coin, a 'B' at the end of the legend.

Reverse Crown over royal shield, dividing crowned 'C.R.', a small 'B' at the end of the legend.

SC112S-010	VG £35	F £85	VF £225

Intermediate Issue

Obverse Legend CAR D.G. MAG BRITAN FR ET HIB REX — Charles by the grace of God King Great Britain France and Ireland

Reverse Legend QUAE DEUS CONIVNXIT NEMO SEPARET — What God hath joined together let no man put asunder

Obverse Crowned bust of king reaching to the bottom of the coin, the denomination (XII) behind the bust, the obverse legend starts nearly at the bottom of the coin.

Reverse Crown over royal shield dividing crowned 'C.R.', a thistle over the crown.

SC112S-015	VG £35	F £90	VF £250

Falconer's Issue

Obverse   As previous.

Reverse   As previous, but a small 'F' instead of a thistle over the crown.

SC112S-020	VG £35	F £90	VF £250

Obverse Legend   CAROLUS D.G. MAGN BRITAN FRANC ET HIB REX (minor varieties exist) — Charles by the grace of God King of Great Britain France and Ireland

Reverse Legend   QUAE DEUS CONIVNXIT NEMO SEPARET — What God hath joined let no man put asunder

Obverse   Crowned bust of king with full legend around the coin starting at the top, denomination 'XII' behind bust; mintmark thistle at start of legend and an 'F' at end of legend.

Reverse   Crown over royal shield dividing crowned 'C.R.'

SC112S-025	VG £45	F £110	VF £275

As previous, but on the reverse there is a thistle at the start of the legend and an 'F' over the crown.

SC112S-030	VG £45	F £110	VF £275

As previous, but the king's bust is slightly smaller and wholly within the inner circle.

SC112S-035	VG £45	F £110	VF £275

Obverse Legend   CAROLUS D.G. MAG BRIT FRAN & HIB REX — Charles by the grace of God King of Great Britain France and Ireland

Reverse Legend   QUAE DEUS CONIVNXIT NEMO SEPARET — What God hath joined together let no man put asunder

Obverse   Crowned bust within the inner circle, the denomination behind bust; mintmark thistle at the start of the legend.

Reverse   Crown over royal shield dividing crowned 'C.R.'; mintmark thistle at the start of the legend.

SC112S-040	VG £50	F £120	VF £300

Angel

The gold angel, with a value of ten shillings, was only produced in 1633. Struck to commemorate Charles's coronation in Scotland, it was a milled coin, produced in 23 carat gold by Nicholas Briot. It should not to be confused with the English angel of Charles I (C1AG-005 to -015), which was hammered.

First Coinage (1625 – 1634)

Collecting Hints

This coin is of the highest rarity.

Obverse Legend   uncertain

Reverse Legend   AMOR POPULI PRAESIDIUM REGIS — The love of the people is the king's protection

Obverse   St Michael spearing a dragon, value 'X' (10) to the right of the figure.

Reverse   Ship with English arms, a 'B' (for Briot) before the ship's bow.

SC1AN-005	ex. rare

Half Merk

The half merk, still with a value of six shillings and eightpence, was struck during Nicholas Briot's two coinages. All issues were produced in silver of 0.916 fineness.

Second Coinage (1636)

This hammered issue was struck for just one year. The machine-made issue which is dated 1636 is a pattern and therefore not listed in this Catalogue.

Collecting Hints

Despite the fact that this issue was only struck for one year, it is fairly common in the lower grades. The king's portrait is often weak due to a poor die or worn striking and specimens in VF or better condition are rare.

Obverse Legend CAROLUS D.G. SCOT ANG FR & HIB R — Charles by the grace of God King of Scotland France and Ireland

Reverse Legend CHRISTO AUSPICE REGNO — I reign under the auspices of Christ

Obverse Crowned bust of king facing left, the value 'VI8' (six shillings and eightpence) behind the king's head, the legend starts at the bottom of the coin.

Reverse Crown over royal arms.

| SC1HMK-005 | VG £30 | F £75 | VF £300 |

Third Coinage (1637 – 1642)

This issue, which was struck by Nicholas Briot, was machine-made.

Briot's Issue

Collecting Hints

This issue is slightly scarcer than the previous one and, because the coins were machine-made, they are of superior style and quality.

Obverse Legend CAR D.G. SCOT ANG FR ET HIB R. — Charles by the grace of God King of Scotland England France and Ireland

Reverse Legend CHRISTO AUSPICE REGNO — I reign under the auspices of Christ

Obverse Crowned bust of king facing left, the value 'VI8' (six shillings and eightpence) behind the king's head, the legend starts at the bottom of the coin, a 'B' (for Briot) under the bust.

Reverse Crown over royal shield, dividing crowned 'C.R.' (Carolus Rex).

| SC1HMK-010 | VG £40 | F £90 | VF £350 |

As previous, but a 'B' (for Briot) at the end of the reverse legend.

| SC1HMK-015 | VG £40 | F £90 | VF £300 |

Six Shillings

The silver six shillings was introduced by James VI and continued to be struck under Charles I, during the first and third coinages. Charles I's Scottish issues are very different from the equivalent English sixpence. First coinage issues were all dated while the ones from the third coinage were undated and machine-made by Briot and Falconer, whose initials can usually be found on the coins. The first coinage bust is similar to that of James VI.

First Coinage (1625 – 1634)

Collecting Hints

These rare coins are rarely found in better than Fine condition as they were often poorly struck using badly made dies.

Obverse Legend CAROLUS D.G. MAG BRIT FRAN & HIB REX — Charles by the grace of God King of Great Britain France and Ireland

Reverse Legend QUAE DEUS CONIVNXIT NEMO SEPARET — What God hath joined together let no man put asunder

Obverse Crowned bust of king, value 'VI' behind bust; mintmark thistle at start of legend.

Reverse Royal shield with date 1625 above; mintmark thistle at start of legend.

| SC16S-005 | VG £80 | F £200 | VF rare |

As previous, but dated 1626.

| SC16S-010 | VG £80 | F £200 | VF rare |

As previous, but dated 1627.

| SC16S-015 | rare |

As previous, but dated 1628.

| SC16S-020 | VG £100 | F £250 | VF rare |

As previous, but dated 1630.

SC16S-025	VG £100	F £250	VF rare

As previous, but dated 1631.

SC16S-030	rare

As previous, but dated 1632.

SC16S-035	VG £80	F £200	VF rare

As previous, but dated 1633.

SC16S-040	VG £80	F £200	VF rare

As previous, but dated 1634.

SC16S-045	rare

Third Coinage (1637 – 1642)

Collecting Hints

These machine-made coins are superior in design and style to previous issues. They are usually found in Fine condition although coins in VF condition are obtainable. Should collectors just want an example from this denomination series, the twelve shillings or thirty shillings are far more attractive than the six shillings.

Briot's Issue

Obverse Legend   CAR D.G. MAG BRIT FRAN ET HIB REX — Charles by the grace of God King of Great Britain France and Ireland

Reverse Legend   QUAE DEUS CONIVNXIT NEMO SEPARET — What God hath joined let no man put asunder

Obverse   Crowned bust to the edge of the coin, a 'B' at the end of the legend which starts near the bottom of the coin.

Reverse   Crown over royal shield dividing a crowned 'C.R.'.

SC16S-050	VG £40	F £90	VF £250

As previous, but a 'B' and lis at the end of the obverse legend.

SC16S-055	VG £40	F £90	VF £250

As previous, but a 'B' over the crown on the reverse.

SC16S-060	VG £40	F £90	VF £250

As SC16S-050, but a 'B' at the end of the reverse legend.

SC16S-065	VG £40	F £90	VF £250

Falconer's Issue

Obverse Legend   CAR D.G. MAG BRITAN FR ET HIB REX — Charles by the grace of God King of Great Britain France and Ireland

Reverse Legend   QUAE DEUS CONIVNXIT NEMO SEPARET — What God hath joined let no man put asunder

Obverse   Crowned bust of king to the bottom of the coin, value 'VI' behind king's bust, legend starts near the bottom of the coin.

Reverse   Crown over royal shield dividing crowned 'C.R.', 'F' over crown.

SC16S-070	VG £40	F £90	VF £250

Obverse   As SC16S-050.

Reverse   As previous.

This issue is a mule using dies from two different issues.

SC16S-075	VG £45	F £100	VF £270

Obverse Legend   CAROLUS D.G. MAG BRIT FR ET HIB REX — Charles by the grace of God King of Great Britain France and Ireland

Reverse Legend   QUAE DEUS CONIVNXIT NEMO SEPARET — What God hath joined let no man put asunder

Obverse   Crowned bust of king, legend starts at the top of the coin; mintmark thistle at the beginning of the legend.

Reverse   Crown over royal shield dividing crowned 'C.R.', 'F' above crown.

SC16S-080	VG £40	F £90	VF £250

Obverse Legend As previous.

Reverse Legend As previous.

Obverse New bust of slightly smaller style set entirely within the inner circle.

Reverse As previous, but crowned arms within inner circle and no 'F' above crown.

SC16S-085	VG £40	F £90	VF £250

Forty Pence

The silver forty pence was issued under Charles I and all the dies were made by Briot or Falconer. The value can be found in the form of 'XL' (40) behind the king's bust.

Second Coinage (1636)

Briot's Hammered Issue

Collecting Hints

This issue is fairly common, especially in the lower grades. Coins in better than Fine condition are rare and often found damaged.

Obverse Legend CAR D.G. SCOT ANG FR & HIB R. — Charles by the grace of God King of Scotland England France and Ireland

Reverse Legend SALUS REIP SVPR LEX — The safety of the state is the supreme law

Obverse Crowned bust of king with value 'XL' behind, the bust and the legend start at the bottom of the coin.

Reverse Crown over thistle.

SC140D-005	VG £25	F £55	VF £200

Third Coinage (1637 – 1642)

These issues were machine-made.

Collecting Hints

This issue is fairly common and, because it was machine-made, it is available in Fine or VF condition. Coins in EF exist but are rare.

Briot's Issue

Obverse Legend CAR D.G. SCOT ANG FR ET HIB R — Charles by the grace of God King of Scotland England France and Ireland

Reverse Legend SALUS REIPVIBLICE SUPREMA LEX (varieties exist) — The safety of the state is the supreme law

Obverse Crowned bust of king to the edge of the coin, value 'XL' behind the bust, the legend starts near the bottom of the coin, letter 'B' (for Briot) usually at the end of the legend.

Reverse Crown over thistle, 'B' usually at the end of the legend or over the crown.

SC140D-010	VG £20	F £45	VF £125

As previous, but a 'B' below the bust (obv.) and the thistle (rev.) but not at the end of the reverse legend.

SC140D-015	VG £20	F £45	VF £125

Falconer's Issue

As previous, but an 'F' (for Falconer) at the end of the reverse legend.

SC140D-020	VG £20	F £45	VF £125

As previous, but an 'F' over the crown on the reverse.

SC140D-025	VG £20	F £45	VF £125

Mule Issue

This issue is a mule, using two different dies from two issues.

Obverse As SC140D-010.

Reverse As SC140D-025.

SC140D-030	VG £35	F £75	VF £200

Three Shillings

The silver three shillings was only struck during the reign of Charles I. Although it does not bear a mark of value, it has a thistle behind the king's bust to differentiate it from other denominations.

Fourth Coinage (1642)

Collecting Hints

This coin is fairly scarce and rarely found in better than Fine condition.

Obverse Legend   CAR D.G. SCOT ANG FRAN & HIB R — Charles by the grace of God King of Scotland England France and Ireland

Reverse Legend   SALUS REIP SUPR LEX — The safety of the state is the supreme law

Obverse   Crowned bust with thistle behind the head.

Reverse   Crown over royal shield.

| SC13S-005 | VG £30 | F £70 | VF £200 |

Two Shilling Piece

The silver two shilling piece was struck during the first and fourth coinages. Coins from the first coinage closely resemble the issue of James VI, except for differences in the obverse legend. They are also similar to an English halfgroat issue of Charles I (C12D-005 to -010) with the main difference being the mintmark, which is thistle on the Scottish coins while the English ones use a variety of other mintmarks. Fourth coinage pieces have a unique design and are therefore easily distinguished from other issues.

First Coinage (1625 – 1634)

Collecting Hints

This issue is obtainable but scarce, and rarely found in better than Fine condition.

Obverse Legend   C.D.G. ROSA SINE SPINA — Charles by the grace of God a rose without a thorn

Reverse Legend   TUEATUR UNITA DEUS — May God guard these united (kingdoms)

Obverse   Crowned rose; mintmark thistle.

Reverse   Crowned thistle; mintmark thistle.

| SC12S-005 | VG £35 | F £90 | VF £300 |

Fourth Coinage (1642)

Collecting Hints

The first issue is fairly common while the second two issues are quite scarce. Coins are difficult to obtain in VF or better condition.

Obverse Legend   CAR D.G. SCOT ANG FRAN & HIB R. — Charles by the grace of God King of England France and Ireland

Reverse Legend   IUST THRONUM FIRMAT — Justice strengthens the throne.

Obverse   Crowned bust of king facing left, large 'II' (two shillings) behind the king's head.

Reverse   Crown over Scottish shield.

| SC12S-010 | VG £18 | F £40 | VF £100 |

As previous, but the value 'II' is smaller.

| SC12S-015 | VG £35 | F £80 | VF £200 |

Obverse Legend   CAR D.G. MAG BRIT FRAN ET HIB R. — Charles by the grace of God King of Great Britain France and Ireland

Reverse Legend   As previous.

Obverse   Crowned bust facing left, there is no mark of value behind the king but a 'B' (for the mintmaster Nicholas Briot) is found below the bust; the legend starts at the bottom of the coin.

Reverse   As previous.

| SC12S-020 | VG £45 | F £120 | VF £300 |

As previous, but struck on a very thick flan. This issue is probably a presentation piece or pattern.

| SC12S-025 | ex. rare |

Twenty Pence

The silver twenty pence was issued during the second and third coinages and was the work of either Briot or Falconer. A mark of value (XX) can be found behind the king's bust on all issues.

Second Coinage (1636)
Briot's Hammered Issue

Collecting Hints

This hammered issue, which should not to be confused with the more common machine-made one of the third coinage, is scarce but obtainable especially in the lower grades. Coins in VF or better condition are rare.

Obverse Legend   CAR D.G. SCOT ANG FR & HIB R. — Charles by the grace of God King of Scotland England France and Ireland

Reverse Legend   IUST THRONUM FIRMAT — Justice strengthens the throne

Obverse   Crowned bust of king with value 'XX' behind, the bust and the legend start at the bottom of the coin.

Reverse   Crown over a thistle.

| SC120D-005 | VG £30 | F £75 | VF rare |

Third Coinage (1637 – 1642)

This issue is machine-made.

Collecting Hints

This issue is common, especially in the lower grades and even coins in VF condition, while scarce, are obtainable.

Briot's Issue

Obverse Legend CAR D.G. SCOT ANG FR ET HIB R. — Charles by the grace of God King of Scotland England France and Ireland

Reverse Legend IUSTITIA THRONUM FIRMAT — Justice strengthens the throne

Obverse Crowned bust of king starting at the bottom of the coin, value 'XX' behind bust, a 'B' for Briot below bust. The legend starts near the bottom of the coin.

Reverse Crown over a thistle, a 'B' at the end of the reverse legend.

| SC120D-010 | VG £15 | F £30 | VF £75 |

As previous, but a 'B' over crown on reverse.

| SC120D-015 | VG £15 | F £30 | VF £75 |

As previous, 'B' over crown on obverse.

| SC120D-020 | VG £15 | F £30 | VF £75 |

As previous, but 'B' before bust; reverse as last.

| SC120D-025 | VG £15 | F £30 | VF £75 |

As previous, but 'B' within crown on reverse.

| SC120D-030 | VG £15 | F £30 | VF £75 |

As SC120D-010, but 'B' at end of reverse legend.

| SC120D-035 | VG £15 | F £30 | VF £75 |

It is probable that mules of Briot's issues exist.

Falconer's Issue

As previous, but a 'B' at the end of the obverse legend and an 'F' at the end of the reverse legend.

| SC120D-040 | VG £25 | F £60 | VF £125 |

As previous, but no 'B' at the end of the obverse legend.

| SC120D-045 | VG £20 | F £40 | VF £85 |

As previous, but no initials at the end of the legends, an 'F' above the crown on the reverse. Varieties in the obverse legend exist.

| SC120D-050 | VG £15 | F £30 | VF £75 |

As previous, but the coin is within, or just within, the inner circle. The legend starts at the top of the coin.

| SC120D-055 | VG £15 | F £30 | VF £75 |

As previous, but no 'F' above the crown.

| SC120D-060 | VG £17 | F £35 | VF £85 |

Shilling

The non-portrait silver shilling introduced by James VI continued to be struck during Charles I's first coinage. Again, it bore a rose with a thistle on one side and was fairly similar to the English pennies of James I and Charles I, although the Scottish issues only use the mintmark thistle while the English ones use a variety of mintmarks but not a thistle, during the English issues of Charles I.

First Coinage (1625 – 1634)

This issue is an altered die from the previous reign.

Collecting Hints

This issue is extremely rare.

Obverse Legend C over I D.G. ROSA SINE SPINA — Charles by the grace of God a rose without a thorn

Reverse Legend TUEATUR UNITA DEUS — May God guard these united kingdoms

Obverse A rose; mintmark thistle at the start of the legend.

Reverse A thistle; mintmark thistle at the start of the legend.

| SC1SH-005 | ex. rare |

Halfgroat

Three main issues of halfgroat were struck during the reign of Charles I. Made of copper with a value of twopence, they were often known as 'turners', which was probably derived from the French copper denomination 'tournois'.

1629 Issue

Collecting Hints

This issue is very common, especially in VG to Fine condition and is very similar to the James VI issue, except for the fact that the obverse legend reads CAROLUS — Charles. Collectors will have little difficulty in obtaining an example.

Obverse Legend   CAROLUS D. G. MAG BRIT — Charles by the grace of God of Great Britain

Reverse Legend   FRAN & HIB REX — France and Ireland King

Obverse   Three thistles.

Reverse   A lion rampant, two pellets behind the lion's tail.

| SC12D-005 | VG £6 | F £15 | VF £35 |

The Earl of Stirling's Issues (1632 – 1639)

These issues, which were struck under licence by the Earl of Stirling, can be considered token coinage, firstly because their metal content did not reflect their face value and secondly because they were struck outside the mint. They are of similar historical importance as the English copper farthings of James I and Charles I and also saw considerable circulation in England, where they would have had a value of a farthing. Like the English coins, the Scottish ones used a complex mintmarking system to link dies to coins as a form of quality control. The style of the crown on the obverse was also altered on the various issues and many minor varieties exist.

Collectors should be aware that contemporary forgeries of these issues exist. They are easily identified by the lettering, which is very crude, and the striking of the coin, which is often very poor. All issues with mintmarks lion and lis are forgeries.

Collecting Hints

All issues are very common and found in VG to VF condition. Some are weakly struck, while others can have flans of irregular shape due to poor manufacture.

Many varieties of the legends exist and the central bar in the 'N's is often inverted.

Obverse Legend   CAR D.G. SCOT ANG FR ET HIB R — Charles by the grace of God King of Scotland, England, France and Ireland

Reverse Legend   NEMO ME IMPUNE LACESSET — No one shall hurt me with impunity

Obverse   English crown above a large 'II', denoting twopence, dividing 'C.R.'; mintmark lozenge or flower.

Reverse   A thistle; mintmark lozenge, rosette or flower.

| SC12D-010 | VG £5 | F £10 | VF £28 |

Obverse Legend   As previous.

Reverse Legend   As previous.

Obverse   Scottish crown with jewelled bands and arches above a large 'II' (denoting twopence), dividing 'C.R.'; mintmark lozenge, stop or trefoil.

Reverse   A thistle; mintmark star, rosette, flower, saltire or lozenge.

| SC12D-015 | VG £5 | F £10 | VF £28 |

Obverse Legend   As previous.

Reverse Legend   As previous.

Obverse   As previous, but the crown is plain; mintmark flower or lozenge.

Reverse   As previous; mintmarks star, lozenge, rosette or flower.

| SC12D-020 | VG £5 | F £10 | VF £28 |

Obverse Legend   As previous.

Reverse Legend   As previous.

Obverse   Crown of five fleur de lis over a large 'II', dividing 'C.R.'; mintmark saltire or lozenge.

Reverse   As previous; mintmark saltire, flower or rosette.

| SC12D-025 | VG £7 | F £15 | VF £35 |

1642 – 1650

These copper twopences were also known as turners and bodles and were the only coins in Scotland struck during the civil war. They were struck in Edinburgh in 1642, 1644, 1648 and 1650.

Collecting Hints

These issues are very common, especially in the lower grades, and there is no doubt that many of them saw considerable circulation not only in Scotland but also in England, where they would have circulated as farthings.

Obverse Legend   CAR D G SCOT ANG FRA ET HIB R — Charles by the grace of God King of Scotland England France and Ireland

Reverse Legend   NEMO ME IMPUNE LACESSET or LACESSIT — No one shall hurt me with impunity

Obverse   Crown over 'C.R.'.

Reverse   A thistle.

SC12D-030	VG £5	F £12	VF £30

As previous, but smaller, neater lettering.

SC12D-035 ex. rare

Penny

While there is evidence that pennies were issued twice (in 1629 and in the Earl of Stirling's issues), only issues from the 1629 coinage exist. Complementing the much more common twopence issue and made of copper, they are very similar to the twopence as well as the last issue of James VI's twopence except for the obverse legend. This issue can easily be distinguished from the larger twopence issue as it has a single pellet denoting one penny by the lion on the reverse while the twopence has two pellets. This issue was sometimes known as a half turner.

Collecting Hints

This issue is rare, especially in better that Fine condition.

Obverse Legend   CAROLUS DG MAG BRIT — Charles by the grace of God of Great Britain

Reverse Legend   FRAN & HIB REX — France and Ireland King

Obverse   Three thistles.

Reverse   Lion rampant, single pellet behind.

SC11D-005	VG £25	F £65	VF —

The 1992 Scottish 25 Ecu
The Coin that Never Was...

These are privately issued patterns for a coinage that was never to be. Everyone thought that the new currency was going to be called the Ecu, so in 1992 the International Currency Bureau issued this crown sized piece. On the obverse is a Unicorn with the Lion of Scotland and on the reverse is Europa with Liberty standing.

We can offer these full crown sized pieces in Brilliant Uncirculated condition at prices which will please and delight you.

NSC9225	1992 Scotland 25 Ecu Cupro Nickel	£7.95
NSC9227	1992 Scotland 25 Ecu Sterling Silver	£24.50
NSC9222	1992 Scotland 25 Ecu Sterling Silver Piedfort	£38.50
NSC9290	1992 Scotland 25 Ecu All 3 (Save £10.00)	£61.50
NSC9228	1992 Scotland 25 Ecu 9ct Gold	£250.00

The Ecu Mint Set

This beautiful seven piece Mint Set contains the 1992 United Kingdom Ecus. Each collection comes in a full colour package, which gives you information about the pieces while keeping them safe.

Each Mint Set contains the 1/10th Ecu, 1/4 Ecu, 1/2 Ecu, 1, 2, 5 and 10 Ecus. The Crown sized 5 Ecu takes pride of place in the centre of the collection. With full colour packaging these make excellent gifts for collectors both in this country and overseas.

You get the whole seven piece collection in the full colour packaging for only £18.95 or order three for only £52.50. You will want one for yourself and your friends.

LEU9205	Ecu Mint Set in Full Colour Package	£18.95
LEU9290	3 Ecu Mint Sets in Full Colour Packages	£52.50

For both the Scottish 25 Ecu and the Ecu Mint Set, order by post or telephone quoting SIC990604 and the individual order codes above. Please add £1.95 per order for handling. Allow 14 days for delivery.

We accept Mastercard, Visa, Diners and American Express (quote card number and expiry date).

Send your order to Coincraft Customer Services at –

COINCRAFT

44 & 45 Great Russell Street, London WC1B 3LU
Tel: 0171-636 1188 Fax: 0171-637 7635
Email: info@ coincraft.com

The milled coinage of Scotland

By way of background to the period of milled coinage of Scotland, it is not generally appreciated that the changeover to a calendar year beginning in January occurred in Scotland not in 1752/53 as in England, but in 1599/1600. As the Act of the Privy Council issued at Holyrood House on 17th December 1599 eloquently decreed: 'In all tyme cuming, the first day of the year sal begin yierlie upon the first day of Januar'. This discrepancy between the English and Scottish calendar systems, lasting for about 150 years, has in the past caused some confusion amongst numismatists when considering the dating of Scottish coinage.

The first conventional milled coinage for Scotland was under the rule of Charles II after his restoration in 1660, although the Earl of Stirling turners of 1632–39 and later pieces were machine made. On 12th June 1661, a remit was made to the Privy Council for a proposed range of silver coinage comprising four-merk, two-merk, merk, half-merk and forty-penny pieces. In addition to these, Thomas Simon in London was commanded on 14th November 1662 to execute puncheons for these coins and for an anticipated twenty-merk, ten-merk, five-merk and two and a half-merk in gold and to deliver them to Charles Maitland, general of the Edinburgh mint. It does not appear that the puncheons for the gold pieces were ever completed, but over 150 puncheons were prepared for the other pieces, for which Simon was paid £100. Maitland observed on 20th January 1663 that he had not received puncheons for 'the severall speties of gold', but he passed the puncheons for the silver coins on to Joachim Harder for the manufacture of the dies. On 20th October 1663, an Act of Privy Council ordered the striking of the two, one and half merk, with the four merk being similarly ordered on 24th March 1664. These denominations were struck from 1664, but the 40 pence coin appears to have sunk without trace.

In addition to the silver coinage, a separate Act provided for the striking of 3000 stones weight of copper turners by way of continuation of the issue of Charles I. After refurbishment of the mint machinery, the Master of the Mint, Sir John Falconer (aka Faulkner) of Balmaker reported that, although the mint was now ready to strike the new coinage, no design had been ordained, and Falconer asked to be allowed to strike pieces similar to the Charles I issue but including a symbol II to indicate the present monarch (some authorities, however, are not convinced that the II is not a mark of value). The undated turners were struck from the end of July 1663, with the order to be completed by 1666. However, the production overran, and by July 1668 23 million had been struck. The dies were then destroyed.

On 24th April 1662 the Lords of the Privy Council had issued a proclamation forbidding the importation of any foreign copper coins, but because of the delays in the production of the new coinage, they permitted on a temporary basis the use of the French 'doitts' at a rate of one penny Scots each.

The early silver coins have a thistle below the head, later replaced by a letter F. Although this denotes Falconer, the Master of the Mint, it is not the Falconer above, but his son, also John, who had succeeded him in the post. The elder Falconer died in 1671.

In 1674, the Roettier brothers John, Joseph and Philip were commanded to prepare puncheons for a new series of silver coinage. Again, a gold piece was contemplated but did not materialize. An Act of Privy Council of 25th February 1675 authorized the new issue and described the coins in detail. In April 1675 the brothers received £150 for their work, and the striking began at Edinburgh in November of the same year, after new machinery had been bought from the London mint. It is interesting to note that the receipt for the £150 from the Roettiers refers to the coinage by English names, 20-shillings to sixpence. A feature of this coinage is that the Roettier portrait faces left, whereas the Simon portrait had faced right. This reversal of attitude in the middle of a reign is unusual, to say the least, and was possibly carried out in order to distinguish the Scottish coins from similarly sized English pieces.

Although the silver coins are nowadays referred to as the dollar together with its divisions half, quarter, eighth and sixteenth, it appears likely that this nomenclature arose considerably later. The Proclamation of 28th April 1708 calling in this issue referred to the coins as 4, 2, 1 and half merks, and 3 shilling and 6 pence pieces. However, Thomas Kirke, writing in 1677, records that 'their money is commonly dollars, or mark-pieces (sic), coined at Edenbrough', and in the coin auction catalogue of Martin Folkes of January 1756, the 40 pence is described as 'the sixteenth part of a Scotch dollar'. Towards the end of the seventeenth century there was some controversy about the fluctuation in value of the coinage; presumably it is possible that renaming them unofficially may have had something to do with this. The Mint register records that this new silver coinage was completed by 1681, but coins of this series dated 1682 are known.

By 1676, copper coins had become very scarce, and a great deal of French copper coinage was in circulation. On 27th February 1677 an Act of the Privy Council commanded that 3000 stones weight of copper should be coined into sixpenny and twopenny pieces, known also respectively as bawbees and turners (bodles). Unlike with the earlier issue, the coinage was completed within three years, but later assessments put the weight of coinage struck under this contract at over 21,000 stones.

On 4th March 1681 an 'increase of money' was proclaimed, with one ounce of coined silver to be equivalent to £3.4.0 Scots; the four merks was revalued from £2.13.4 to £2.16.0 (56 shillings) Scots, with the smaller pieces pro rata.

In 1682, King Charles set up a commission to look into the affairs of the Mint. The commissioners reported in August of that year that the amount of copper coinage greatly exceeded the quantity authorized, and that much of the coinage was of low weight and fineness. Many of the required assays for the silver coinage had not been carried out, and the commission estimated that about £700,000 Scots (i.e. about £58,000 sterling) had been embezzled. The Mint was immediately closed, and various officials, including Sir John Falconer, Alexander Maitland, and Archibald Falconer, were prosecuted for corruption, and, in 1683, found guilty.

When James VII ascended the throne in 1685, the Mint was still closed, but on 20th May of that year a proclamation forbade the importation of foreign copper coins, declaring that none should pass except those bearing the Royal stamp. On 14th June 1686 the ratio of Scottish:English money was adjusted from 12:1 to just over 13:1. On the same date, the use of the edge lettering on silver coinage was authorized, as had been the case in England for several years. No copper coins were struck for James VII.

After the accession of William and Mary a full range of silver coins should have been coined almost immediately, but confusion arose with the closure of the Mint and when some of the puncheons and dies were mislaid. A minute of the Privy Council dated 26th September 1690 records that the Mint was to reopen on 15th October 1690, and the Royal Warrant for the new coinage had been issued some months earlier. On 3rd November 1691 a similar minute records that the punches for the sixty shilling and five shilling pieces had 'been in their Lordships' hands now these two months', but apparently they were nowhere to be found. On 22nd April 1692 some sealed boxes were found during the search, and on breaking them open the missing punches were discovered. It follows from the above that the 40 shillings of 1689 and the 60 and 5 shillings of 1691 were struck after the date appearing on them.

An Act of Parliament of 19th July 1690 authorized the striking of 3000 stones weight of copper into sixpenny and twopenny pieces in a respective weight ratio of 1:2, over a period of six years. The death of Mary intervened, and on 2nd January 1695 the Privy Council ordered that dies with the late Queen's portrait must be no longer used. On the following day the Master of the Mint petitioned the Privy Council to be allowed to proceed with making blanks while new dies were cut by John Clark, since the end of the six-year time limit was approaching. This was granted, and, although a further 3000 stones weight of copper were authorized in October 1699, no coins were struck.

On the death of Mary, William took the title of William I (i.e William without a numeral) on the coins of Scotland rather than William II, as he considered himself the first William of the greater territory encompassing Scotland and regions south thereof. A warrant of 11th July 1695 authorized the use of dies for the 40 and 10 shilling pieces prepared by James Clark. The next day, a Proclamation raised the rates of silver coinage by 10%, and Sir William Denholme, Master of the Mint, proposed to place the new value on the coins. The Lords of the Privy Council did not envisage that the new rates would be permanent, and rejected the proposal. On 2nd June 1696 the Scottish silver coinage was 'cried down' to its former value.

In October 1696 an Act provided that no copper should be coined without an express warrant from the King, and that if any amounts were struck in excess of the quantities allowed by former Acts, the coins should be regarded as counterfeit and the coiners punished for forgery. The old merk and half merk pieces of James VI were ordered by the Privy Council to be brought into the Mint as bullion at a rate of £3.4.0 Scots per ounce, and a further Act was passed against counterfeiters. On 28th December 1696 the Privy Council made a curious order about two soldiers of the Earl of Tullibardine's regiment, who were suspected (but not convicted) of forgery. They were ordered to be handed over to the officers from Flanders, transported there, never to return to Scotland, and the officers were to give to the captains in the regiment two recruits in their place.

From 1695 to 1699, most of the silver coins were struck every year; a sixty shillings of 1699 has been reported, but is unknown today. A small gold issue of pistole and half pistole were also issued in 1701 (for further historical details on this, see the pistole listings).

William III died in March 1702, to be succeeded by Anne. In January 1705 the Privy Council authorized James Clark to prepare dies for ten and five shilling pieces for the new monarch. These were struck from March 1705.

In Article XVI of the Treaty of Union of Scotland and England agreed on 22nd July 1706, to take place on 1st May 1707, it was stipulated that coinage should be of the same standard and value throughout the United Kingdom as it was in England, but that a mint should continue to operate in Scotland under the same rules as in England. A quantity of £411,117.10.9 of silver coin was brought into the mint at Edinburgh for recoining into English-style pieces bearing the mintmark E, but it appears that a considerable amount was reissued as Scottish coinage, particularly 40 shilling pieces. Records show that the actual weight

coined at Edinburgh was 103,346 lbs. In 1708, Scottish coinage was again called in to be recoined. It is possible that coins bearing the star next to the E mintmark are struck from silver from this second recall of Scottish coinage. The halfcrown and shilling of 1709, both with E (for Edinburgh) beneath the head of Anne were the last coins struck at the Scottish Mint intended to circulate. These pieces presumably use the English 'old style' calendar year starting on 25th March.

The Mint closed around 1709 and the lack of protest at the takeover from London may have been occasioned by the fact that the posts and salaries of some authorized staff, including those of the Governor, remained in place, indeed until as late as 1817. The Mint buildings were sold that year and demolished in 1877.

Scottish coins, more particularly the larger silver denominations, are much rarer than comparable English pieces, especially in high grades. Much of the coinage was melted and recoined at the time of the Union, and in any event the country was much poorer than England prior to the Union, with a consequent reduction in the amount of coinage circulating. Scottish coins are not yet collected extensively, and as Scotland takes its place more as a self determining nation in the years ahead, it may well be that prices will come to reflect the rarity of its coinage as collectors begin to recognise the potential of this fascinating field of study.

Because of the complex range of denominations in Scottish coinage, the listings are arranged primarily by reign, unlike in the rest of this catalogue.

Scotland: Charles II (1649 – 1685)

crowned at Scone 1st January 1651; restored 29th May 1660

Four Merks – Dollar – 53 Shillings and 4 Pence (later 56 Shillings)

During the period of the Commonwealth no coinage was struck specifically for Scotland. Some time after the restoration of Charles II and his return to London and coronation in 1661, Thomas Simon was commissioned to prepare dies for a new coinage. This included a gold 20 merk piece, although no specimens of this denomination appear to have been struck. The punches for the 4 merk coin were prepared in London by Thomas Simon and the actual dies manufactured at the Scottish mint, which had reopened in 1663. An Act of 24th March 1664 instructed Joachim Harder to prepare the dies, with the four-merk to weigh 21 deniers, 3 grains and 14 primes (i.e. 415.18 grains Troy, or 26.9 grams) and to be of 11 deniers fineness. Sir John Falconer was Warden of the Mint, and was succeeded in the post by his son of the same name; their initial F appears on some of the new coinage. The central area of the reverse of the 4 merks includes the value denoted as LIII 4, i.e. 53 shillings and 4 pence Scots.

In 1675, more modern machinery was imported from London, with punches prepared by John, Joseph and Philip Roettier. The 4 merk piece was redesigned, with the reverse Latin legend now referring separately to Scotland and England. The new coin was authorized by 'An Act anent the Coyne' of 25th February 1675, and was first struck in 1676; although it later became known as the dollar, the coin is referred to in the Act as the four-merk piece. The coinage from this period is generally referred to as the second coinage.

In early 1681 the value of the dollar was raised to 56 shillings; by this time the mark of value 53/4 no longer appeared on the reverse. During the following year, several high officials in the Mint were dismissed for malversation, and no further Charles II coinage was struck.

For the purpose of this catalogue, the 4 merks and dollar are treated as if one denomination, although of course all distinguishing details are itemized fully.

Denomination	Metal	Weight (grams)	Diameter (mm)	Rev. alignment
4 merks 1664 – 75	0.917 silver	25.8 – 27.8	39	varies
4 merks (dollar) 1676 – 82	0.917 silver	26.5 – 27.8	39	↓

Obverse 1   Head 1, right; CAROLVS II DEI GRA

Obverse 2   Head 2, left, F below, to left; same legend

Reverse 1   Cruciform shields of Scotland; quartered England/France; Scotland; Ireland; with LIII 4 at centre and interlinked 'C's in angles; MAG BRI FRA ET HIB REX (date)

Reverse 2   Cruciform shields of Scotland; England; France; Ireland; with interlinked 'C's at centre and thistles in angles; SCO ANG FR ET HIB REX (date)

Edge   plain

Obv. 1   Obv. 2

Rev. 1   Rev. 2

No.	Date	Features	Obv.	Rev.	VG	F	VF
SC24M-005	1664	thistle above head (obv)	1	1	170	280	900
SC24M-010	1664	thistle below head (obv)	1	1	500	800	2500
SC24M-015	1665	thistle below head (obv)	1	1	2000	3000	
SC24M-020	1670	thistle below head (obv)	1	1	140	240	800
SC24M-025	1670	F below head (obv)	1	1			
SC24M-030	1673	thistle below head (obv)	1	1	140	240	800
SC24M-035	1673	thistle below head (obv); 4 of value over horizontal 1 (rev)	1	1	140	240	800
SC24M-040	1674	F below head (obv)	1	1	120	200	650
SC24M-045	1674	4 of date over 3; F below head (obv)	1	1	180	300	900
SC24M-050	1674	F below head (obv); BR instead of BRI (rev)	1	1	250	450	1400
SC24M-055	1675	F below head (obv)	1	1	140	240	750
SC24M-060	1676	[1]	2	2	100	170	650
SC24M-065	1679		2	2	100	170	650
SC24M-070	1680		2	2	150	280	1000
SC24M-075	1681		2	2	120	200	700
SC24M-080	1682	[2]	2	2	90	140	500

1. Legend stops vary (obv and rev).
2. The 2 in the date is oddly shaped, resembling a reversed inverted 5.

The harp on reverse 2 may have 7, 8 or 9 strings

Two Merks – Half Dollar 26 Shillings and 8 Pence (later 28 Shillings)

Although specimens of the two merk coin were struck in 1664, the year after the reopening of the Scottish Mint, no further coins of this denomination were issued until 1670. In 1675, the coinage underwent a type change, and was struck using more sophisticated machinery, but the value of the new half dollar (as it was later termed) was equivalent to that of the old two merks. In 1680, the coin was revalued to twenty-eight shillings. No coinage was struck after 1682 because of dubious practices at the Scottish Mint. In that year the mint was closed, and many of its officials prosecuted for corruption.

Denomination	Metal	Weight (grams)	Diameter (mm)	Rev. alignment
2 merks 1664 – 75	0.917 silver	12.5 – 13.3	34	varies
2 merks (half dollar) 1675 – 81	0.917 silver	12.9 – 13.0	33 – 34	↓

Obverse 1   Head 1, right; CAROLVS II DEI GRATIA

Obverse 2   Head 2, left, F below, to left; same legend

Reverse 1   Cruciform shields of Scotland; quartered England/France; Scotland; Ireland; with XXVI 8 at centre, interlinked crowned 'C's in angles; MAG BRI FRA ET HIB REX (date)

Reverse 2   Cruciform shields of Scotland; England; France; Ireland; with interlinked 'C's at centre, thistles in angles; SCO ANG FR ET HIB REX (date)

Edge   plain

Obv. 1   Obv. 2

Rev. 1   Rev. 2

No.	Date	Features	Obv.	Rev.	VG	F	VF
SC22M-005	1664	thistle above head (obv)	1	1	130	210	700
SC22M-010	1664	thistle below head (obv)	1	1	200	350	1200
SC22M-015	1670	thistle below head (obv)	1	1	500	800	3000
SC22M-020	1673	thistle below head (obv)	1	1	90	150	500
SC22M-025	1674	thistle below head (obv)	1	1	190	320	1000
SC22M-030	1674	F below head (obv) [1]	1	1	170	280	900
SC22M-035	1675	F below head (obv) [2]	1	1	100	170	550
SC22M-040	1675	F below head (obv); BR instead of BRI (rev)	1	1	120	200	650
SC22M-045	1675	[3]	2	2	80	130	400
SC22M-050	1676		2	2	250	450	1500
SC22M-055	1681		2	2	120	200	600

1. Size of F varies (obv).
2. F below head is slightly larger than on previous dates (obv).
3. Struck only in November and December.

The thistle on the obverse varies in size and shape.

Merk – Quarter Dollar 13 Shillings and 4 Pence (later 14 Shillings)

The merk (obverses 1 and 2), and its equivalent quarter dollar (obverse 3), were struck almost every year from the reopening of the mint in 1663 to its closure in 1682. The coin is much more frequently encountered than the larger silver coins of this reign. Cardonnel mentions a piece dated 1667, but the existence of this date is doubtful.

The writer recently examined a specimen of the 1682 merk (quarter dollar) with 'Irish Arms at date', as it is usually catalogued, and it is obvious that this description of the variety requires some expansion. When the usual reverse die axis alignment is taken into account, it is found that the positions of the Arms and the central interlinked 'C's are correct. It is the outer legends and date (not the shields) which are rotated. Further research needs to be done on other 'rotated Arms' varieties in all denominations, taking into account the usual die axis alignment.

Denomination	Metal	Weight (grams)	Diameter (mm)	Rev. alignment
Merk 1664 – 75	0.917 silver	5.6 – 6.5	27 – 28	varies
Merk (quarter dollar) 1675 – 82	0.917 silver	6.4 – 6.6	26 – 27	↓

Obverse 1   Head 1, right, thistle below; CAROLVS II DEI GRA

Obverse 2   Head 2, right, slightly larger; same legend

Obverse 3   Head 3, left, F below; same legend

Reverse 1   Cruciform shields of Scotland; quartered England/France; Scotland; Ireland; with XIII 4 at centre, interlinked crowned 'C's in angles; MAG BRI FRA ET HIB REX (date)

Reverse 2   Cruciform shields of Scotland; England; France; Ireland; with interlinked 'C's at centre, thistles in angles; SCO ANG FR ET HIB REX (date)

Edge   plain

Obv. 2   Obv. 3

Rev. 1   Rev. 2

No.	Date	Features	Obv.	Rev.	VG	F	VF
SC21M-005	1664	small thistle (obv)	1	1	75	120	250
SC21M-010	1664	large thistle (obv)	1	1	85	140	320
SC21M-015	1665		1	1	120	200	450
SC21M-020	1666		1	1	150	250	600
SC21M-025	1668	[1]	1	1	120	200	450
SC21M-030	1669	[2]	1	1	70	100	200
SC21M-035	1669	no stops on obv.	1	1	120	180	350
SC21M-040	1669	Scottish Arms in second and fourth quarters (rev)	1	1	140	200	400

No.	Date	Features	Obv.	Rev.	VG	F	VF
SC21M-045	1670	[2]	1	1	75	120	250
SC21M-050	1671	[2]	1	1	70	100	200
SC21M-055	1672	thistle below head (obv) [2]	2	1	70	100	200
SC21M-060	1672	reversed 2 in date; thistle below head (obv)	2	1	150	220	450
SC21M-065	1673	thistle below head (obv) [3]	2	1	60	90	180
SC21M-070	1673	thistle below head (obv); BRA instead of BRI (rev) [3]	2	1	120	180	350
SC21M-075	1674	thistle below head (obv)	2	1	150	250	600
SC21M-080	1674	F below head (obv)	2	1	180	300	700
SC21M-085	1675	[4]	2	1	180	300	700
SC21M-090	1675	F below head (obv) [4]	2	1	120	170	350
SC21M-095	1675	F below head (obv); XII instead of XIII (rev) [4]	2	1	100	150	300
SC21M-100	1675	[5]	3	2	200	350	750
SC21M-105	1676		3	2	70	110	220
SC21M-110	1676	DRI instead of DEI (obv)	3	2	140	220	450
SC21M-115	1677		3	2	80	130	270
SC21M-120	1677	latter 7 over 6	3	2	80	130	270
SC21M-125	1678		3	2	300	500	1200
SC21M-130	1679		3	2	150	250	600
SC21M-135	1680		3	2	80	130	270
SC21M-140	1680	CAROLVS instead of CAROLVS (obv)	3	2	140	220	450
SC21M-145	1681		3	2	80	130	270
SC21M-150	1682		3	2	80	130	270
SC21M-155	1682	CAROLVS instead of CAROLVS (obv)	3	2	140	220	450
SC21M-160	1682	Irish shield at date (legends and date rotated anticlockwise by 90 degrees) (rev) [6]	3	2	140	220	450
SC21M-165	1682	CAROLVS instead of CAROLVS (obv); Irish shield at date (legends and date rotated anticlockwise by 90 degrees) (rev) [6]	3	2	400	750	

1. Struck only in August.
2. Legend stops vary; some have colon after date.
3. Date resembles 1675.
4. Last year of the merk issue; struck only in November and December.
5. Quarter dollar issue.
6. See remarks in introduction to merk section.

The harp on the reverse varies in size, shape, orientation, and number of strings.

Half Merk – Eighth Dollar
6 Shillings and 8 Pence
(later 7 Shillings)

The half merk was struck each year from (December) 1664 to 1673, and the series includes three major error varieties in which shields are transposed. The later type equivalent, the so-called eighth dollar, also includes an error shields transposition variety of 1680.

In the National Museum of Antiquities of Scotland there is a reverse die for an eighth-dollar of 1675, which coin is unknown today.

Denomination	Metal	Weight (grams)	Diameter (mm)	Rev. alignment
Half merk 1664 – 75	0.917 silver	2.6 – 3.4	23	varies
Half merk (eighth dollar) 1676 – 82	0.917 silver	3.2 – 3.3	22	↓

Obverse 1 Head 1, right, thistle below; CAROLVS II DEI GRA

Obverse 2 Head 2, left, F below; same legend

Reverse 1 Cruciform shields of Scotland; quartered England/France; Scotland; Ireland; with VI 8 at centre, interlinked crowned 'C's in angles; MAG BRI FRA ET HIB REX (date)

Reverse 2 Cruciform shields of Scotland; England; France; Ireland; with interlinked 'C's at centre, thistles in angles; SCO ANG FR ET HIB REX (date)

Edge plain

Obv. 1   Obv. 1   Obv. 2
1665 countermark
on 1664 coin

Rev. 1   Rev. 2   Rev. 2
shields transposed   reversed '2' in date

No.	Date	Features	Obv.	Rev.	VG	F	VF	EF
SC2HM-005	1664	[1]	1	1	60	100	300	
SC2HM-010	1664	1665 countermark behind head (obv)	1	1	90	150	450	
SC2HM-015	1665		1	1	55	90	250	
SC2HM-020	1665	shields of England/France and Ireland transposed (rev)	1	1	90	150	450	
SC2HM-025	1666		1	1	90	150	450	
SC2HM-030	1666	shields of England/France and Ireland transposed (rev)	1	1	130	220	700	
SC2HM-035	1667	[2]	1	1	90	150	450	
SC2HM-040	1668	[3]	1	1	60	100	300	
SC2HM-045	1669	[4]	1	1	30	50	150	400
SC2HM-050	1669	no stops on obv.	1	1	60	100	300	
SC2HM-055	1669	shields of Scotland in 2nd and 4th quarters	1	1	60	100	300	
SC2HM-060	1670	[4]	1	1	35	60	180	
SC2HM-065	1670	no stops on obv.	1	1	60	100	300	
SC2HM-070	1671	straight ribbon behind head (obv)	1	1	35	60	180	450
SC2HM-075	1671	curly ribbon behind head (obv)	1	1	35	60	180	450
SC2HM-080	1672		1	1	25	40	120	300
SC2HM-085	1673	[5]	1	1	60	100	300	
SC2HM-090	1675	F instead of thistle (obv)	1	1	30	50	150	400
SC2HM-095	1675	plain below head (obv)	1	1	60	100	300	
SC2HM-100	1676		2	2	30	50	150	400
SC2HM-105	1676	reverse 90 degrees to right	2	2	40	70	200	500
SC2HM-110	1677		2	2	30	50	150	400
SC2HM-115	1678	8 over 7	2	2	200	300		
SC2HM-120	1679		2	2	140	200		
SC2HM-125	1680	[6]	2	2	40	65	180	
SC2HM-130	1680	shields on reverse rotated by 180 degrees [6]	2	2	140	200		
SC2HM-135	1682	[7]	2	2	130	180		
SC2HM-140	1682	reversed 2 (or inverted 5) in date	2	2	180	270		

1. Struck only in December 1664.
2. Struck only in June and August.
3. Struck only in August.
4. Stops in obverse and reverse legends vary. Crown on 1669 coin varies (rev).

Notes continued

5. Crown varies (rev).
6. Some or all have a larger F below the head than is usual for this series (obv).
7. Some or all have 2 in date formed by reversed 5.

Denomination	Metal	Weight (grams)	Diameter (mm)	Rev. alignment
Bawbee	Copper	7.9 – 9.1	25	↓

Obverse 1   Head 1, left, F below; CAR II D G SCO ANG FR ET HIB REX

Obverse 2   Similar but R instead of REX

Obverse 3   Similar but legend reads CAR II D G SCO AN FR ET HIB R

Reverse 1   Crowned leaved thistle; NEMO ME IMPVNE LACESSET (date)

Edge   plain

Obv. 1	Obv. 3	Rev. 1

No.	Date	Features	Obv.	Rev.	F	VF	EF
SC2BB-005	1677		1	1	100	200	550
SC2BB-010	1677	AN (space) G instead of ANG (obv)	1	1	120	240	650
SC2BB-015	1677		2	1	160	350	1500
SC2BB-020	1677	[1]	3	1	80	160	450
SC2BB-025	1678		3	1	60	120	350
SC2BB-030	1679		3	1	45	90	250
SC2BB-035	1679	CAR H instead of CAR II (obv)	3	1	60	120	350
SC2BB-040	1679	SOC instead of SCO (obv)	3	1	100	200	600

1. The F on the obverse below the head is often poorly struck.

Quarter Merk – Sixteenth Dollar 3 Shillings and 4 Pence (later 3 Shillings and 6 Pence)

Although the 40 pence coin featured in the range of coinage specified in the remit to the Privy Council on 12th June 1661, in the event this denomination was never struck. The equivalent sixteenth dollar, authorised in February 1675 but not issued until 1677, was hence the only coin of the dollar series which did not have an equivalent in the old merk series. It must be remembered, however, that the nomenclature 'dollar' was not in general use until much later, and that all of the dollar denominated coins were known and authorised as merk coinage at the time. The coin would have been equivalent to a quarter of a merk.

It appears that the puncheons for the sixteenth-dollar were the only ones in the dollar series not prepared by the Roettier brothers.

Denomination	Metal	Weight (grams)	Diameter (mm)	Rev. alignment
Quarter merk (sixteenth dollar)	0.917 silver	1.6 – 1.7	17 – 18	↓

Obverse 1   Head 1, left, F below; CAROLVS II DEI GRA

Reverse 1   St. Andrew's Cross, with central crown; in angles thistle, rose, lis, harp; SCO ANG FRA ET HIB REX (date)

Edge   plain

Obv. 1	Rev. 1

No.	Date	Features	Obv.	Rev.	VG	F	VF	EF
SC2QM-005	1677		1	1	30	50	90	160
SC2QM-010	1678		1	1	160	250	450	
SC2QM-015	1678	8 over 7	1	1	140	220	400	
SC2QM-020	1679	9 over 7	1	1	180	280	500	
SC2QM-025	1680		1	1	140	220	400	
SC2QM-030	1680	80 over 79	1	1	180	300	550	
SC2QM-035	1681		1	1	25	45	80	140

Bawbee – 6 Pence

An Act of Privy of 27th February 1677 authorized the coining from 3000 stones weight of copper of issues of bawbees (six pence) together with a further issue of bodles (two pence) after the 1663 issue. The copper for this issue was obtained partly from Sweden. The coinage was ordered to be completed by May 1680, but this was subsequently brought forward to 10th February 1680.

The bawbee depicts a crowned leaved thistle, and was minted by the mill and screw method. The coins were issued for three consecutive years, and they vary considerably in weight.

The word 'bawbee' is said to have been derived from the French 'bas billon'. However, a 16th century mintmaster was Alexander Orrok of Sillebawby, and this may be considered a more likely contender for the derivation.

Turner – Bodle – 2 Pence

The name 'turner' is thought to have been derived from the French 'tournois'. The issue of turners which was minted from 31st July 1663 was ordered on 12th June 1661 to be coined from 3000 stones weight of pure copper, without any brass constituents, and to weigh 'one drop and a half', i.e. 44 grains Troy. These coins were of the design of those issued for the reign of Charles I, and the legend refers to the monarch as CAR rather than CAR II. However, the royal initials on the obverse have a small Roman numeral II above them and to the right. This was possibly intended as a mark of value (two pence), but this attribution is doubtful. The coins are undated, and are sometimes ascribed to Charles I, but are in fact an issue of Charles II.

Because of the late starting date of production, the original expiry date of the licence of June 1664 was extended to April 1665 for the first 2000 stones weight, and to June 1666 for the final 1000 stones. The dates were further extended up to 1st August 1668, when an order was made to stop production. However, what was not realised at the time was that the original 3000 stones had been completed by 1666. The total produced was over 8471 stones, totalling over 23 million pieces.

On 27th February 1677, a further issue of turners was authorised, to be minted by the mill and screw method over a period of three years, although very few exist dated 1679. The copper for this issue was obtained partly from Sweden. The obverse was radically redesigned, and depicts a sword and sceptre surmounted by a crown. The alternative name of bodle is rumoured to have been derived from Bothwell, said to be a Master of the Mint at this time, although in Cochran-Patrick's 'Records of the Coinage of Scotland', no person named Bothwell appears to have been connected with the Scottish Mint in any capacity.

Denomination	Metal	Weight (grams)	Diameter (mm)	Rev. alignment
Turner, undated (1663)	Copper	2.0 – 2.7	20 – 21	varies
Turner – Bodle 1677 – 79	Copper	2.6 – 2.8	19 – 20	varies

Obverse 1 Crowned CR, with II to right; CAR D G SCOT ANG FRA ET HIB R

Obverse 2 Crowned sword and sceptre; CAR II D G SCO ANG FRA ET HIB REX

Reverse 1 Thistle within circle; NEMO ME IMPVNE LACESSET

Reverse 2 Smaller thistle, no circle; same legend (date)

Edge plain

Obv. 1   Obv. 2   Rev. 1   Rev. 2

No.	Date	Features	Mintmark	Obv.	Rev.	F	VF	EF
SC2TN-005	(1663) [1]		pellet cross	1	1	10	20	60
SC2TN-010	(1663) [1]		rosette	1	1	10	20	60
SC2TN-015	(1663) [1]		lion rampant	1	1	18	40	110
SC2TN-020	(1663) [1]		cinquefoil	1	1	18	40	110
SC2TN-025	1677			2	2	20	40	120
SC2TN-030	1677	FBA instead of FRA (obv)		2	2	30	60	180
SC2TN-035	1677	IIIB instead of HIB (obv)		2	2	25	50	150
SC2TN-040	1677	REXI instead of REX (obv)		2	2	35	70	200
SC2TN-045	1677	NMEO instead of NEMO (rev)		2	2	25	50	150
SC2TN-050	1677	LAESSET instead of LACESSET (rev)		2	2	35	70	200
SC2TN-055	1677	LACSSET instead of LACESSET (rev)		2	2	35	70	200
SC2TN-060	1678			2	2	30	60	180
SC2TN-065	1678	FRAN instead of FRA (obv)		2	2	45	90	270
SC2TN-070	1679	[2]		2	2	150		

1. Undated.
2. 6 in date is larger than in previous years.

With the first type (Obv. 1/Rev. 1):

Early coins have a large T in the legend; later coins have a small T.

Early and late coins have a plain S in the legend; intermediate pieces have a Gothic S.

On very late pieces the top of the letter R is broken, resembling a K.

Several varieties of the mintmark occur.

Scotland: James VII (1685 – 1689)

60 Shillings

The sixty shilling piece of James VII is included in this catalogue as a numismatic curiosity rather than as an ordinary circulating coin, as only late strikings are known. An Act of Parliament of January 1686, however, authorized the issue of the sixty shilling piece 'to weigh tuenty one deniers, eighteen graines, ten prymes, eighteen seconds', and dies were prepared by Roettier, but no contemporarily struck coins were issued. Around 1827 or 1828, on the death of two old ladies in France, the last survivors of the Roettier family, the estate was found to include the dies of the James VII sixty shilling coin. A Mr. Cox bought them in partnership with a Frenchman. Cox brought the dies to England, but when he found how expensive it would be to have them cleaned and to strike impressions of the coinage, he sold them to a Mr. Mathew (aka Matthew) Young, of Tavistock Street, London. Young struck sixty of the coins in silver and three in gold, defaced the dies, and deposited them at the British Museum.

Denomination	Metal	Weight (grams)	Diameter (mm)	Rev. alignment
60 shillings	Silver	26.0 – 27.8	41	↑

Obverse 1 Head 1, right, 60 below; IACOBVS II DEI GRATIA

Reverse 1 Crowned quartered shield of arms within Collar of the Order of the Thistle; MAG BR FRA ET HIB REX 1688

Edge plain

Obv. 1   Rev. 1

No.	Date	Features	Obv.	Rev.	UNC
SJ760S-005	1688	[1]	1	1	1500
SJ760S-010	1688	struck in gold [2]	1	1	18000

1. Struck in 1828
2. Struck in 1828; weight 55.5 grams.

40 Shillings

As the sixty shilling 'coin' was not issued during the reign of James VII, the forty shilling piece is the highest denomination of the reign, no gold being struck. The forty shillings was the earliest Scottish coin to incorporate a legend around the edge. The issue was authorized by an Act of the Scottish Parliament of 14th June 1686, which also authorized other denominations, although some of these were not struck. During the previous three reigns, the value ratio of English to Scottish money had been 12 to 1. This was now adjusted to 13 and 2/45ths to 1. The standard of fineness

of silver for this reign was upgraded from 11 deniers (0.917) to 11 deniers 2 grains (0.924), a trace below the Sterling standard of 0.925. The title of the King on the obverse is that of James II of Great Britain.

The dies were prepared by John Roettier.

Denomination	Metal	Weight (grams)	Diameter (mm)	Rev. alignment
40 shillings	0.924 silver	18.1 – 18.5	37	↑

Obverse 1 Head 1, right, 40 below; IACOBVS II DEI GRATIA

Obverse 2 Similar but IACOBUS instead of IACOBVS

Reverse 1 Crowned quartered shield of Arms; MAG BRIT FRA ET HIB REX (date)

Edge (in relief) NEMO ME IMPUNE LACESSET ANNO REGNI (regnal date)

Obv. 1   Obv. 2

Rev. 1

No.	Date	Features	Regnal date	Obv.	Rev.	VG	F	VF	EF
SJ740S-005	1687		TERTIO	1	1	160	270	500	1200
SJ740S-010	1687		TERTIO	2	1	110	170	300	800
SJ740S-015	1687	LACESSIET instead of LACESSET (edge)	TERTIO	2	1	240	350	650	1600
SJ740S-020	1687		QVARTO	2	1	140	240	450	1100
SJ740S-025	1688		QVARTO	1	1	160	270	500	1200
SJ740S-030	1688		QVARTO	2	1	140	240	450	1100

10 Shillings

Apart from the 40 shilling pieces, the 10 shillings was the only coin struck for circulation in Scotland during the reign of James VII (the 60 shillings was a late striking of 1828), The 10 shilling coin was authorized by an Act of the Scottish Parliament of 14 June 1686, and examples were struck dated 1687 and 1688.

The dies for the coinage were engraved by John Roettier. The obverse titles of the king denote him as James II (of Great Britain).

Denomination	Metal	Weight (grams)	Diameter (mm)	Rev. alignment
10 shillings	0.924 silver	4.4 – 4.7	25 – 26	↑

Obverse 1 Head 1, right, 10 below; IACOBUS II DEI GRATIA

Reverse 1 Central St. Andrew's Cross including in its angles four shields with Arms of Scotland, England, France and Ireland; at four tips of cross are thistle, rose, lis and harp; MAG BR FRA ET HIB REX (date)

Edge milled (diagonally)

Obv. 1   Rev. 1

No.	Date	Features	Obv.	Rev.	VG	F	VF	EF
SJ710S-005	1687	[1]	1	1	60	90	170	400
SJ710S-010	1688	[1]	1	1	90	140	250	600
SJ710S-015	1688	unbarred A in FRA (rev)	1	1	100	150	280	700

1. Stops vary.

Scotland: William & Mary (1689 – 1694)

60 Shillings

Although all of the James VII sixty shilling pieces are late strikings, the issue of this denomination for William and Mary was carried into effect during the brief reign of the joint monarchs. Coins of two dates, 1691 and 1692, are known, although both of these share the same regnal edge date, TERTIO. This concurs with records which show that the 1691 piece could not have been struck before 22nd April 1692, as the puncheons were mislaid until that date.

The 1691 coin struck in copper is a curious piece. The two viable edge dates are SECUNDO and TERTIO, although only the latter is found on the regular coinage. The reason for the unusual edge legend, with its incongruous QUARTO regnal date, is a mystery.

Denomination	Metal	Weight (grams)	Diameter (mm)	Rev. alignment
60 Shillings	Silver	27.3 – 27.7	39	↑

Obverse 1　Heads 1, left, 60 below; GVLIELMVS ET MARIA DEI GRA

Reverse 1　Crowned quartered shield of Arms of Scotland; quartered England/France; Ireland; Scotland; with central escutcheon of Arms of Nassau, these including nine lozenges; MAG BR FR ET HIB REX ET REGINA (date)

Reverse 2　Similar but the harp is larger and differently ornamented

Edge　PROTEGIT ET ORNAT ANNO REGNI TERTIO

Obv. 1

Rev. 1

Rev. 2

No.	Date	Features	Obv.	Rev.	VG	F	VF	EF
SWM60S-005	1691	[1]	1	1	200	300	550	1200
SWM60S-010	1691	struck in copper [2]	1	1				
SWM60S-015	1692		1	1	140	200	400	900

No.	Date	Features	Obv.	Rev.	VG	F	VF	EF
SWM60S-020	1692		1	2	120	170	350	800

1. Struck in 1692.
2. Edge reads NEMO ME IMPUNE LACESS O REGNI QUARTO. The section reading ET ANN is missing.

40 Shillings

Unlike the limited issue of sixty shilling pieces, the forty shilling coinage was struck for each of the six years of the reign. The coins bear a lettered edge denoting the regnal year, and, with the exception of 1694, each date exists with two regnal years. This is possible because of the unusual way in which the regnal year is counted, from the date of accession rather than from the beginning of the calendar year. Strangely, the 1689 coinage predates the order of the Privy Council of September 1690 authorizing the issue, with the 1689 regnal dates duplicating those on the 1690 coinage.

Denomination	Metal	Weight (grams)	Diameter (mm)	Rev. alignment
40 shillings	0.924 silver	18.1 – 18.7	34 – 35	↑

Obverse 1　Heads 1, left, 40 below; GVLIELMVS ET MARIA DEI GRATIA

Reverse 1　Crowned quartered shield of Arms of Scotland; quartered England/France; Ireland; Scotland; with central escutcheon of Arms of Nassau (including lozenges unless stated); MAG BR FR ET HIB REX ET REGINA (date).

Edge　(in relief) PROTEGIT ET ORNAT ANNO REGNI (regnal date)

Obv. 1

Rev. 1

No.	Date	Features	Regnal date	Obv.	Rev.	VG	F	VF	EF
SWM40S-005	1689	[1]	PRIMO	1	1	150	220	350	900
SWM40S-010	1689	[1]	SECVNDO	1	1	150	220	350	900
SWM40S-015	1690		PRIMO	1	1	95	150	220	500
SWM40S-020	1690	[2]	SECVNDO	1	1	95	150	220	500
SWM40S-025	1691		SECVNDO	1	1	75	110	180	400
SWM40S-030	1691		TERTIO	1	1	75	110	180	400
SWM40S-035	1691	no lozenges in Dutch shield (rev)	TERTIO	1	1	95	150	220	500
SWM40S-040	1692		TERTIO	1	1	150	220	350	900

No.	Date	Features	Regnal date	Obv.	Rev.	VG	F	VF	EF
SWM40S-045	1692		QUARTO	1	1	80	120	190	420
SWM40S-050	1693		QUARTO	1	1	90	140	210	480
SWM40S-055	1693		QUINTO	1	1	90	140	210	480
SWM40S-060	1693	[3]	SIXTO	1	1	110	170	250	600
SWM40S-065	1693	no lozenges in Dutch shield (rev) [3]	SIXTO	1	1	100	150	230	550
SWM40S-070	1694	[3] [4]	SIXTO	1	1	110	170	250	600
SWM40S-075	1694	no lozenges in Dutch shield (rev) [3]	SIXTO	1	1	110	170	250	600

1. Struck in 1690.
2. Some or all have punctuation on edge more ornate than on 1690 PRIMO coin.
3. Regnal date SEXTO misspelt. Hoblyn reports SEXTO edge but existence doubtful.

The number of strings on the reverse harp varies, and the harp itself varies considerably in shape, size and orientation. In particular, it is much smaller from about 1693 onwards.

20 Shillings

Official sanction for the issue of a 20 shilling piece had first been granted in 1686 for the reign of James VII. However, no coins of this denomination had been struck by the time the king relinquished the throne, and no dies had been prepared for such an issue.

The Scottish Mint was closed at the beginning of the reign, and remained so until an order of the Privy Council of 26th September 1690 which authorized the new coinage. The dies were prepared in 1691 by James Clark, engraver to the Scottish Mint. Clark is usually referred to as Clerk, but several contemporary documents, including warrants to him to cut dies, refer to him as Clark. Although several early reference works refer to a 20 shilling coin dated 1691, no specimens of this date appear to be known today. The 1693 piece is recorded as having a mintage of 1,185, and the 1694 piece a mintage of 5,369; however, the 1694 coin is seldom encountered.

Denomination	Metal	Weight (grams)	Diameter (mm)	Rev. alignment
20 shillings	0.924 silver	9.1 – 9.3	30 – 31	↑

Obverse 1 Heads 1, left, 20 below; GVLIELMVS ET MARIA DEI GRATIA

Reverse 1 Crowned quartered shield of Arms of Scotland; quartered England/France; Ireland; Scotland; with central escutcheon of Arms of Nassau; MAG BR FR ET HIB REX ET REGINA (date)

Edge milled (diagonally)

Obv. 1   Rev. 1

No.	Date	Features	Obv.	Rev.	VG	F	VF	EF
SWM20S-005	1693	[1]	1	1	90	130	220	500
SWM20S-010	1694		1	1	400	800		

1. Obverse stops vary.

10 Shillings

When the Scottish Mint reopened in October 1690, at first only the forty- and ten-shilling pieces were struck, owing to a delay in the delivery of the punches for the other denominations. As with the forty shillings, some of the ten shillings were minted with the date 1689, but these are extremely rare.

The cruciform shield design of James VII was abandoned in favour of the quartered shield as used on the forty-shilling piece. The cruciform shields were retained on the English shilling, and thus there was now less likelihood of confusion between the two coins. At first, the shield was unusually small, but from 1691 onwards the design was modified so that the shield was very similar to that on the English half guinea. It has been suggested that the small shield was initially proposed for the five shilling coin.

Denomination	Metal	Weight (grams)	Diameter (mm)	Rev. alignment
10 shillings 1689 – 90	0.924 silver	4.5 – 4.6	24 – 25	↑ or ↓
10 shillings 1691 – 94	0.924 silver	4.5 – 4.6	24 – 25	↑

Obverse 1 Heads 1, left, 10 below; GVLIELMVS ET MARIA DEI GRATIA

Obverse 2 Similar but GRA instead of GRATIA

Reverse 1 English crown surmounting small quartered shield of Arms of Scotland; quartered England/France; Ireland; Scotland; with central escutcheon of Arms of Nassau; MAG BR FR ET HIB REX ET REGINA (date)

Reverse 2 Similar but shield is much larger, with Scottish crown; same legend (date)

Edge milled (diagonally)

Obv. 1   Obv. 2

Rev. 1   Rev. 2

No.	Date	Features	Obv.	Rev.	VG	F	VF	EF
SWM10S-005	1689		1	1	500			
SWM10S-010	1690		1	1	80	110	190	400
SWM10S-015	1690	0 over 9	1	1	90	120	210	450
SWM10S-020	1691	small '10' below heads, with I-type '1' (obv) [1]	1	2	60	90	150	300
SWM10S-025	1691	large '10' below heads, with J-type '1' (obv)	1	2	70	100	170	350

No.	Date	Features	Obv.	Rev.	VG	F	VF	EF
SWM10S-030	1691	small '10' below heads, with I-type '1' (obv); rev. ↓	2	2	80	110	190	400
SWM10S-035	1692	small '10' below heads, with I-type '1' (obv)	1	2	70	100	170	350
SWM10S-040	1692	large '10' below heads, with J-type '1' (obv)	1	2	70	100	170	350
SWM10S-045	1694	small '10' below heads, with I-type '1' (obv)	1	2	150	220	400	
SWM10S-050	1694	large '10' below heads, with J-type '1' (obv)	1	2	150	220	400	

1. Obverse stops vary.

The harp on the reverse varies in design and orientation.

5 Shillings

Although an order for the striking of five shilling coins had been made during the reign of James VII, it was not until William and Mary had ascended the throne that the coin was first issued. At the beginning of the reign the Scottish mint was closed, but Lord Cardross, the General of the Mint, had been authorized to receive the puncheons for the coinage. When the puncheons failed to appear, Lord Cardross complained of the delay, whereupon a search by the Lords of the Privy Council led to their being found in April 1692 sealed in their original box.

The reverse shield of the larger denomination is not used on the five shillings, and a simpler 'WM' monogram is substituted. Interestingly, the early ten shillings of 1689 and 1690 depict a small shield which may have been intended for the five shillings but abandoned as being too intricate for such a small coin.

On the 1691 coin the mark of value 'V' is on the reverse, whereas on the 1694 it is below the busts on the obverse.

Denomination	Metal	Weight (grams)	Diameter (mm)	Rev. alignment
5 shillings	0.924 silver	2.2 – 2.3	20 – 21	↑

Obverse 1   Heads 1, left; GVLIELMVS ET MARIA DEI GRA

Obverse 2   Similar but V below heads

Reverse 1   Crowned stylized WM monogram, V below; MAG BR FR ET HIB REX ET REG 1691

Reverse 2   Similar but no V below monogram; MAG BR FR ET HIB REX ET REGINA 1694

Edge   milled (diagonally)

| Obv. 1 | Obv. 2 | Rev. 1 | Rev. 2 |

No.	Date	Features	Obv.	Rev.	VG	F	VF
SWM5S-005	1691	1	1	1	150	250	750
SWM5S-010	1694		2	2	70	120	350
SWM5S-015	1694	GVLIELMⱯS instead of GVLIELMVS (obv)	2	2	100	160	500

1. Struck in 1692.

Bawbee – 6 Pence

No copper coins had been struck during the reign of James VII, but with the accession of William and Mary the issue of bawbees was resumed. Under an Act of June, 1686, the issue of copper coinage was restricted to bawbees and bodles, and an Act of Privy Council of August 1691 authorized an issue of bawbees from October of that year, to be coined (together with bodles) from 3000 stones weight of copper and from not more than 500 stones in any one year. When Mary died in 1694, the six-year contract continued to be valid for the issue of the subsequent reign. These were the last copper coins of Scotland.

The issue is similar to that for Charles II, but the thistle is markedly larger, and the obverse includes a mintmark above the head. The crown on the reverse is the Scottish type, unlike that on most of the silver coins.

Denomination	Metal	Weight (grams)	Diameter (mm)	Rev. alignment
Bawbee	Copper	8.1 – 9.0	25	varies

Obverse 1   Heads 1, left, mintmark at top; GVL ET MAR D G MAG BR FR ET HIB REX ET REGINA

Reverse 1   Crowned leaved thistle; NEMO ME IMPVNE LACESSET (date)

Edge   plain

| Obv. 1 | Rev. 1 |

No.	Date	Features	Mintmark	Obv.	Rev.	F	VF	EF
SWMBB-005	1691		Five pellets	1	1	60	120	350
SWMBB-010	1691	REX REGINA instead of REX ET REGINA (obv)	Five pellets	1	1	120	250	
SWMBB-015	1692		Five pellets	1	1	70	140	400
SWMBB-020	1692	ET 1692 REGINA instead of ET REGINA (obv)	Five pellets	1	1	120	250	
SWMBB-025	1692	1	Rosette	1	1	70	140	400
SWMBB-030	1692		Two opposed trefoils	1	1	80	150	450
SWMBB-035	1692		Star	1	1	70	140	400
SWMBB-040	1692		Lis	1	1	90	160	500
SWMBB-045	1693		Star	1	1	60	120	350
SWMBB-050	1693	3 over 2	Star	1	1	70	140	400
SWMBB-055	1694		Star	1	1	70	140	400
SWMBB-060	1694		Lis	1	1	70	140	400

1. The mintmark may be a leaved thistle.

Turner – Bodle – 2 Pence

Although no copper coins were struck during the reign of James VII, the striking of a twopence turner (or bodle, as it was now more commonly called) was resumed under the reign of William and Mary. The new six-year contract authorised the striking of bodles and bawbees, in the proportion of six bodles for each bawbee.

The obverse of the new issue bears the monogrammed initials of the King and Queen, while the reverse thistle is somewhat larger than that on the Charles II issue. Off-centre and double struck pieces are sometimes encountered.

Denomination	Metal	Weight (grams)	Diameter (mm)	Rev. alignment
Bodle – Turner 1691 – 93	Copper	2.4 – 2.8	20	↑
Bodle – Turner 1694	Copper	2.4 – 2.8	20	↓

Obverse 1 Crowned stylized 'WM' monogram; D G MAG BR FR ET HIB REX ET REGINA

Obverse 2 Similar but lettering smaller

Reverse 1 Crowned leaved thistle; NEMO ME IMPVNE LACESSET (date)

Reverse 2 Similar but IMPUNE instead of IMPVNE; all lettering is smaller

Edge plain

Obv. 1

Rev. 1

No.	Date	Features	Obv.	Rev.	F	VF	EF
SWMTN-005	1691	[1]	1	1	20	60	140
SWMTN-010	1692		1	1	15	40	100
SWMTN-015	1693		1	1	20	60	140
SWMTN-020	1694		1	1	15	40	100
SWMTN-025	1694	REGIN instead of REGINA (obv)	1	1	25	80	180
SWMTN-030	1694		2	2	30	90	220

1. Struck only from 1st October.

Scotland: William II (1694 – 1701)

Twelve Pounds – Pistole

The only gold coins of Scotland, the twelve and six pounds of William II, were struck using gold dust imported by the Darien Co. (The Scottish African Company) from the Central American colony of Darien. The company asked that its crest, a sun rising from the sea, should be placed on the coinage as an acknowledgement to themselves, and to the 'Rising Sun', the ship which had carried the gold. This request was granted, and the weight and fineness of the coins were fixed at a level which would provide a profit of about 10% for the company. On 6th January 1701, James Clark was ordered to prepare the puncheons. The order for the coins originally authorised an obverse legend beginning GVLIELMVS SECVNDVS, but the SECVNDVS was dropped so that it would correspond with the legend on the silver and copper coins.

On assaying the gold dust, the fineness was found to be somewhat below the standard claimed. The gold was refined, with the cost of this being charged to the company. The effect of this was to reduce its profit from 10% to about 6%.

The term 'pistole' often used for this coinage is somewhat of a misnomer. The coinage was authorised in pounds Scots, and was not intended for circulation abroad.

Denomination	Metal	Weight (grams)	Diameter (mm)	Rev. alignment
12 pounds 'pistole'	0.917 gold	6.8 – 6.9	24	↑

Obverse 1 Head 1, left; sun rising from sea below; GVLIELMVS DEI GRATIA

Reverse 1 Crowned quartered shield of Arms of Scotland; quartered England/France; Ireland; Scotland; with central escutcheon of Arms of Nassau, all dividing crowned W and crowned R; MAG BRIT FRA ET HIB REX 1701

Edge milled (diagonally)

Obv. 1

Rev. 1

No.	Date	Features	Obv.	Rev.	F	VF	EF
SW212P-005	1701		1	1	4500	8000	16000

Six Pounds – Half Pistole

The introduction to the twelve pounds applies in general to the six pounds also. The company crest omits the sea, however, owing to lack of space. The six pounds is rarer than the twelve pounds. It is not unusual to encounter this piece struck slightly off-centre.

Denomination	Metal	Weight (grams)	Diameter (mm)	Rev. alignment
6 pounds 'half pistole'	0.917 gold	3.4	19	↑

Obverse 1 Head 1, left; sun below; GVLIELMVS DEI GRATIA

Reverse 1 Crowned quartered shield of Arms of Scotland; quartered England/France; Ireland; Scotland; with central escutcheon of Arms of Nassau, all dividing crowned W and crowned R; MAG BRIT FRA ET HIB REX 1701

Edge milled (diagonally)

Obv. 1

Rev. 1

No.	Date	Features	Obv.	Rev.	F	VF	EF
SW26P-005	1701		1	1	3500	6000	12000

60 Shillings

Anderson, Snelling and Ruding mention a sixty shilling piece dated 1699, and bearing the regnal date VNDECIMO. Lindsay also refers to a piece of this date in 'a remote cabinet in the North of Scotland', supposed to be that of the Duke of Athole. However, no such coin was there when the Duke's cabinet was examined by Adam Black Richardson in 1883, nor is it mentioned in mint records. This coin is unknown today, and therefore no listing is included here, apart from the following brief description by Lindsay:

Obverse Head, laureate, 60 below

Reverse Arms; MAG BRIT FRA ET HIB REX 1699

Edge PROTEGIT ET ORNAT ANNO REGNI VNDECIMO

40 Shillings

After the death of Mary in 1694, William continued to rule alone. On 11th July 1695 a warrant was issued for the striking of 40 shilling pieces bearing the head of William II, but within hours a Proclamation of the Privy Council decreed that the value of the coin should be raised to 44 shillings. Sir William Denholme, Master of the Mint, protested that the value marked on the obverse should be amended, otherwise accounting procedures at the mint would be thrown into disarray. However, in June 1696 the order was reversed, and the coinage resumed its previous value.

An order of 10th December 1695 somewhat puzzlingly includes the information that the 40 shilling pieces had been 'milled' but were 'not yet past His Majesty's irons'.

The minor silver denominations of 1697 all possess a variety with inverted reverse axis, and it may be that the 40 shilling piece with this axis alignment also exists. Any evidence of this would be appreciated by the publishers.

Denomination	Metal	Weight (grams)	Diameter (mm)	Rev. alignment
40 (44) shillings	0.924 silver	18.0 – 18.5	34 – 35	↑

Obverse 1 Head 1, left, 40 below; GVLIELMVS DEI GRATIA

Reverse 1 Crowned quartered shield of Arms of Scotland; quartered England/France; Ireland; Scotland; with central escutcheon of Arms of Nassau (including lozenges unless stated); MAG BRIT FRA ET HIB REX (date).

Edge (in relief): PROTEGIT ET ORNAT ANNO REGNI (regnal date)

Obv. 1   Rev. 1

No.	Date	Features	Regnal date	Obv.	Rev.	VG	F	VF	EF
SW240S-005	1695	stops in obverse legend	SEPTIMO	1	1	80	120	200	450
SW240S-010	1695	no stops in obverse legend	SEPTIMO	1	1	90	140	230	500
SW240S-015	1695	no lozenges in Dutch shield (rev)	SEPTIMO	1	1	75	110	180	400
SW240S-020	1695		OCTAVO	1	1	80	120	200	450
SW240S-025	1696		OCTAVO	1	1	120	180	300	700
SW240S-030	1697		NONO	1	1	80	120	200	450
SW240S-035	1698		DECIMO	1	1	120	180	300	700
SW240S-040	1699		VNDECIMO	1	1	150	240	450	
SW240S-045	1700		VNDECIMO	1	1	1000	1500		
SW240S-050	1700		DUODECIMO	1	1	500	800		

The harp on the reverse varies in size, shape, orientation, and number of strings.

20 Shillings

After the death of Mary from smallpox in 1694, the 20 shilling coin continued to be minted bearing the new effigy of William alone, engraved by James Clark. In 1695, the value of the coin was raised by Proclamation to 22 shillings, but the value marked below the bust on the obverse remained at 20. In 1696, the coin was devalued back to the original 20 shillings.

Denomination	Metal	Weight (grams)	Diameter (mm)	Rev. alignment
20 (22) shillings	0.924 silver	9.1 – 9.3	30 – 31	↑

Obverse 1 Head 1, left, 20 below; GVLIELMVS DEI GRATIA

Reverse 1 Crowned quartered shield of Arms of Scotland; quartered England/France; Ireland; Scotland; with central escutcheon of Arms of Nassau; MAG BRIT FRA ET HIB REX (date)

Edge milled (diagonally)

Obv. 1   Rev. 1

No.	Date	Features	Obv.	Rev.	VG	F	VF	EF
SW220S-005	1695		1	1	60	100	200	400
SW220S-010	1696	[1]	1	1	60	100	200	
SW220S-015	1697		1	1	150	280	650	
SW220S-020	1697	reverse ↓			250	450	1000	
SW220S-025	1698	[2]	1	1	80	140	280	
SW220S-030	1698	8 over 7	1	1	100	180	400	
SW220S-035	1699		1	1	400	800	2000	

1. Occurs with and without stop after date.
2. Stop varieties may exist.

10 Shillings

On the death of Mary, the ten shillings continued with a similar reverse, and the obverse head of William alone. The legend bore no numeral after the name of the king; although he was William III of England and William II of Scotland, the King preferred his title of William I of Great Britain.

From the time of the original warrant for the coinage in July 1695 until June 1696, the ten shillings was revalued upwards by one shilling, although the value marked on the coinage below the head remained as '10' throughout.

Denomination	Metal	Weight (grams)	Diameter (mm)	Rev. alignment
10 (11) shillings	0.924 silver	4.4 – 4.6	23 – 24	↑

Obverse 1 Head 1, left, 10 below; GVLIELMVS DEI GRATIA

Reverse 1 Crown surmounting quartered shield of Arms of Scotland; quartered England/France; Ireland; Scotland; with central escutcheon of Arms of Nassau; MAG BRIT FRA ET HIB REX (date).

Edge milled (diagonally)

Obv. 1   Rev. 1

No.	Date	Features	Obv.	Rev.	VG	F	VF	EF
SW210S-005	1695		1	1	60	90	150	300
SW210S-010	1696		1	1	70	100	170	350
SW210S-015	1697		1	1	90	140	250	500
SW210S-020	1697	reverse ↓	1	1	110	180	350	700
SW210S-025	1698		1	1	110	180	350	700
SW210S-030	1698	8 over 7	1	1	90	140	210	550
SW210S-035	1699		1	1	180	300	450	1100

Variations in reverse punctuation exist for several dates.

5 Shillings

The five shillings continued to be minted after the death of Mary, bearing the head of William alone and with a different reverse, a crowned thistle. This denomination was struck for every year of the reign except 1698. This was somewhat unusual, as no other Scottish silver or copper coins were struck after 1699. Mint records for the period 1699–1702 appear to be missing. The piece dated 1702 is of special note: it is the only Scottish coin bearing this date, and not only does it bear a revised obverse legend, but it is sometimes claimed that this coin shares with the English fourpence the distinction of being a posthumous issue. However, it must be remembered that because the Scottish calendar switched to a January new year in 1600, the King died on 8th March 1702 (Scottish dating) rather than 1701 (English dating).

The mark of value changes on this series from the 'V' of William and Mary to the Roman '5'.

Denomination	Metal	Weight (grams)	Diameter (mm)	Rev. alignment
5 (5.5) shillings	0.924 silver	2.2 – 2.4	19 – 20	↑

Obverse 1 Head 1, left, 5 below; GVL D G MAG BR FR & HIB REX

Obverse 2 Similar but GVLIELMVS DEI GRATIA

Reverse 1 Crowned three-headed thistle; NEMO ME IMPVNE LACESSET (date)

Edge milled (diagonally)

Obv. 1	Obv. 2	Rev. 1

No.	Date	Features	Obv.	Rev.	VG	F	VF	EF
SW25S-005	1695		1	1	25	40	100	180
SW25S-010	1696	[1]	1	1	25	40	100	180
SW25S-015	1697	[1]	1	1	25	40	100	180
SW25S-020	1697	reverse ↓	1	1	35	55	140	250
SW25S-025	1699		1	1	80	120	300	600
SW25S-030	1700		1	1	40	60	150	300
SW25S-035	1701		1	1	150	240	600	1500
SW25S-040	1702		2	1	90	140	350	750

1. Punctuation varies.

Bawbee – 6 Pence

The issue of bawbees for the reign of William II was authorised under the unexpired part of the contract for William and Mary. The design of the reverse was almost identical to that for the previous reign, apart from the thistle leaves.

The bawbee and bodle of 1697 were the last copper coins of Scotland.

Denomination	Metal	Weight (grams)	Diameter (mm)	Rev. alignment
Bawbee	Copper	7.5 – 8.2	26	varies

Obverse 1 Head 1, left, mintmark at top; GVL D G MAG BR FR ET HIB REX

Obverse 2 Similar but head slightly different and legend reading BRIT FRA instead of BR FR

Reverse 1 Crowned leaved thistle; NEMO ME IMPVNE LACESSET (date)

Edge plain

Obv. 1	Obv. 2	Rev. 1

No.	Date	Features	Obv.	Rev.	F	VF	EF
SW2BB-005	1695		1	1	80	150	450
SW2BB-010	1695		2	1	100	200	600
SW2BB-015	1696		1	1	100	200	600
SW2BB-020	1696	stops are pellets on both sides	2	1	80	150	450
SW2BB-025	1696	stops are pellets (obv); annulets (rev)	2	1	80	150	450
SW2BB-030	1697		2	1	100	200	600

Turner – Bodle – 2 Pence

As with the bawbee, the contract for the production of bodles had not expired when Mary died in 1694. The bodle was thus struck under the terms of this contract for the years 1695 to 1697. The monogram on the reverse was replaced by a crowned sword and sceptre, and two different orientations of these items occur, as well as various obverse legend varieties.

The bodle and bawbee of 1697 were the last copper coins of Scotland.

Denomination	Metal	Weight (grams)	Diameter (mm)	Rev. alignment
Bodle – Turner	Copper	2.4 – 2.9	20	↑

Obverse 1 Crowned sword and sceptre disposed with acute and obtuse angles; GVLIELMVS D G MAG BRIT FRA ET HIB R

Obverse 2 Similar but legend ends BR FR ET HIB REX

Obverse 3 Similar but legend GVL D G MAG BRIT FRA ET HIB REX

Obverse 4 Similar but sword and sceptre at right angles; GVL D G MAG BR FR & HIB REX

Obverse 5 Similar but ET HIB REX instead of & HIB REX

Reverse 1 Crowned leaved thistle; NEMO ME IMPVNE LACESSET (date)

Reverse 2 Similar but a smaller thistle; same legend (date)

Edge plain

Obv. 1	Obv. 2	Obv. 5

Rev. 1	Rev. 2

No.	Date	Features	Obv.	Rev.	F	VF	EF
SW2TN-005	1695	[1]	1	1	25	75	170
SW2TN-010	1695	[1]	2	1	20	60	140
SW2TN-015	1695	[1]	3	1	30	90	200
SW2TN-020	1695	[1]	4	2	30	90	200
SW2TN-025	1695		5	2	20	60	140
SW2TN-030	1696	[1]	3	1	30	90	200
SW2TN-035	1696	[2]	4	2	30	90	200
SW2TN-040	1696		5	2	20	60	140
SW2TN-045	1697	[2]	5	2	25	75	170
SW2TN-050	1697	reverse ↓ [2]	5	2	35	100	240

1. With reverse stops.
2. Without reverse stops.

Scotland: Anne (1702 – 1714)

10 Shillings

No coinage of Anne was struck at the Scottish mint until 1705, and thereafter until the Act of Union only ten and five shillings were struck. These were the work of James Clark, engraver to the Scottish mint. A formal warrant to Clark was made in January of that year, and the mint was reopened in March.

Although at first glance the reverse appears to be identical to that used for the previous reign, there is one major difference; the central escutcheon bearing the Arms of Nassau is omitted. During 1706 the reverse legend REG becomes REGINA.

Denomination	Metal	Weight (grams)	Diameter (mm)	Rev. alignment
10 shillings	0.924 silver	4.5 – 4.6	24 – 25	↑

Obverse 1   Head 1, left, thistle on breast, 10 below; ANNA DEI GRATIA

Reverse 1   Crowned quartered shield of Arms of Scotland; quartered England/France; Ireland; Scotland; MAG BRIT FRA ET HIB REG (date)

Reverse 2   Similar but REGINA instead of REG

Edge   milled (diagonally)

Obv. 1   Rev. 1   Rev. 2

No.	Date	Features	Obv.	Rev.	VG	F	VF	EF
SA10S-005	1705		1	1	70	100	150	250
SA10S-010	1706		1	1	120	180	250	450
SA10S-015	1706		1	2	150	220	350	650

5 Shillings

James Clark engraved the five shillings of Anne, which was struck only for 1705 and 1706 prior to the Act of Union. The 1705 dated coins are notable for having four different obverse legends.

Denomination	Metal	Weight (grams)	Diameter (mm)	Rev. alignment
5 shillings	0.924 silver	2.2 – 2.5	19 – 20	↑

Obverse 1   Head 1, left, 5 below; ANNA DEI GRATIA

Obverse 2   Similar but ANNA D G M BR FR & HIB REG

Obverse 3   Similar but AN D G M BR FR & HIB REG

Obverse 4   Similar but AN D G MAG BR FR & HIB R

Reverse 1   Crowned three-headed thistle; NEMO ME IMPVNE LACESSET (date)

Reverse 2   Similar but IMPUNE instead of IMPVNE

Edge   milled (diagonally)

Obv. 1   Obv. 2

Obv. 3   Obv. 4

Rev. 1   Rev. 2

No.	Date	Features	Obv.	Rev.	VG	F	VF	EF
SA5S-005	1705		1	1	15	25	70	120
SA5S-010	1705		2	1	25	40	110	200
SA5S-015	1705	5 over 4	2	1	15	25	70	120
SA5S-020	1705		3	1	20	35	90	160
SA5S-025	1705	5 over 4	3	1	20	35	90	160
SA5S-030	1705	no stops on reverse	3	1	20	35	90	160
SA5S-035	1705		4	1	20	35	90	160
SA5S-040	1706		4	2	30	45	130	250

Several stop varieties exist in this series.

It is intended to include Post Union coins of the Edinburgh mint, together with other coins of Scottish interest, in the next issue of this catalogue.

Scotland: Patterns

'James VIII'

James Francis Edward was born in 1688 to James VII and his second wife, Mary of Modena. On his father's death in 1701, he assumed the title of James VIII and took part in an unsuccessful invasion of Scotland in 1708. On 29th August 1715, he issued a manifesto asserting his right to the crown, and on 16th January 1716 made an entrance into Dundee and thence to Scone, where he announced that his coronation would take place on 23rd January. The next month he fled to France. James died in Rome in January 1766.

The pattern coinage of the so-called James VIII was prepared by Norbert Roettier and is dated 1709 and 1716, the intention being that the coins should circulate following the capture of the throne. The coins known to exist were struck in 1828 by Mathew Young from the original dies, acquired no doubt as detailed under the entry for the James VII 60-shilling piece. The unique 1709 piece might be considered more as a U.K. pattern but is included because of its obvious Scottish connection. The legend carries the supposed British titles of James as James III.

Crown 1709

One example, designed by Norbert Roettier, is in the British Museum. In 1716, General George Hamilton wrote to James from Paris: 'I send a little box I got from M. Roettier — a crown designed for the English coin in 1709, and the impression of the crown piece that's to be now coined in Scotland.'

No.	Date	Denomination	Metal	Weight (grams)	Diameter (mm)	Rev. align.	Price
SJ8PTN-010	1709	Crown	Silver				

Obv.   Rev.

Obverse Head, right; IACOBVS III DEI GRATIA

Reverse Crowned oval shield of Arms of England; Scotland; France; Ireland; MAG BRI FRAN ET HIB REX 1709

Edge plain

Crown or 60 Shillings 1716

No.	Date	Denomination	Metal	Weight (grams)	Diameter (mm)	Rev. align.	Price
SJ8PTN-020	1716	Crown or 60 shillings	Silver	27.5	42	↓	1000
SJ8PTN-025	1716	Crown or 60 shillings	Gold				
SJ8PTN-030	1716	Crown or 60 shillings	Bronze				

No.	Date	Denomination	Metal	Weight (grams)	Diameter (mm)	Rev. align.	Price
SJ8PTN-035	1716	Crown or 60 shillings	White metal				

Obv.   Rev.

Obverse Head, right; IACOBVS VIII DEI GRATIA

Reverse Crowned quartered shield of Arms of Scotland; France/England quartered; Ireland; Scotland; SCOT ANGL FRAN ET HIB REX 1716

Edge plain

Guinea or shilling 1716

This piece has a reverse obviously designed for Scotland and yet it bears the English title of the intended king. The portrait appears to depict James as a young boy.

No.	Date	Denomination	Metal	Weight (grams)	Diameter (mm)	Rev. align.	Price
SJ8PTN-050	1716	Guinea or shilling	Silver	8.7	26	↓	600
SJ8PTN-055	1716	Guinea or shilling	Bronzed copper		26		

Obv.   Rev.

Obverse Head, left; IACOBUS TERTIUS

Reverse Four crowned cruciform shields of Scotland; Ireland; England; France; sceptres in angles; SCO AN FRA ET HIB REX 1716

Edge plain

Guinea or Shilling 1716

No.	Date	Denomination	Metal	Weight (grams)	Diameter (mm)	Rev. align.	Price
SJ8PTN-070	1716	Guinea or shilling	Gold	11.1	27		
SJ8PTN-075	1716	Guinea or shilling	Silver	6.9	27	↓	600
SJ8PTN-080	1716	Guinea or shilling	Bronze		27		

Obv.   Rev.

Obverse   Head, right; IACOBVS VIII DEI GRATIA

Reverse   Four crowned cruciform shields of Scotland; Ireland; England; France; thistle in centre and sceptres in angles; SCO AN FRA ET HIB REX 1716

Edge   plain

Scotland: Early 19th century countermarked dollars, etc.

As the 19th century began, there was an acute shortage of silver coinage in the United Kingdom. Although a reasonable quantity of shillings and sixpences had been issued in 1787, no crowns or halfcrowns had been struck for the United Kingdom since 1751. The situation had been remedied to some extent by the issue around 1797 of Spanish and Spanish American silver dollars countermarked with the head of George III, together with a limited number of minor coins similarly countermarked. In 1804 Bank of England dollars were overstruck on to the Spanish dollars, and this issue continued up to 1811, the coins bearing the date 1804.

During 1811, private traders in England issued their own shilling and sixpence tokens in silver which was often gleaned from melted down Spanish dollars. However, in Scotland, especially in the south of the country, it became fashionable to stamp the dollars themselves with countermarks of various enterprises, often incorporating a figure of value of around five shillings.

The idea of countermarking dollars had been put forward several times in the years before the idea was first carried out. In December 1803, a shopkeeper wrote to the Greenock Advertiser: 'The most proper method ... would be to recommend ... some of the most reputable merchants in town to stamp them payable at 4s 9d or 5s ...'. The same newspaper carried advertisements during 1816 giving notice that stamped dollars should be presented to their issuers for redemption forthwith.

The listings below, while not exhaustive, detail several of the most prominent countermarks, together with details of some of the coins on which they are struck (usually on the obverse unless stated). The valuation is for the most commonly found grade, countermark very fine, host coin fine.

Adelphi Cotton Works, Deanston, Perthshire

(same as Deanston Cotton Mill)

At the time of issue of the tokens the works were owned by Kirkman Finlay, who appointed James Smith as manager. The latter was a highly motivated individual who reorganized the mill and built a new village of Deanston.

Description of Countermark

Woolsack within circle, around which ADELPHI COTTON WORK (incuse) within border.

No.	Coin countermarked	£ (VF on F)
SCMK-010	FRANCE half ecu aux lauriers	500
SCMK-015	FRANCE half ecu au bandeau	700
SCMK-020	George III halfpenny	50

Alloa Colliery, Clackmannanshire

Description of Countermark

5/. (incuse) within circle, around which PAYABLE AT ALLOA COLLIERY (in relief) in border, all within circle.

No.	Coin countermarked	£ (VF on F)
SCMK-030	Forgery of Spanish American 8 reales	300

Ballindalloch Cotton Works, Stirlingshire

The Ballindalloch Cotton Works was founded in 1789 and operated until 1844. It is claimed to have been the first Scottish mill operated entirely with female labour.

Description of Countermark

5/ (in relief) around which BALLINDALLOCH COTTON WORKS (in relief) all within large circle.

No.	Coin countermarked	£ (VF on F)
SCMK-040	MEXICO 8 reales, Mexico City mint	1200

R. & G. Blair, Greenock Renfrewshire

Description of Countermark

4/6 (in relief) around which R & G BLAIR GREENOCK, all within oval.

No.	Coin countermarked	£ (VF on F)
SCMK-050	MEXICO 8 reales, Mexico City mint	1200

'D.C.': David Cummings or D. Campbell, Glasgow, Lanarkshire

Description of Countermark

Large incuse DC above 12-pointed rosette (countermark placed sideways so that the C is nearer the top of the head)

No.	Coin countermarked	£ (VF on F)
SCMK-060	MEXICO 8 reales, Mexico City mint	500

Catrine Cotton Works, Ayrshire

Description of Countermark

4/9 (in relief) in inner circle; CATRINE COTTON WORKS (in relief) No. (4 incuse digits) in outer ring.

No.	Coin countermarked	£ (VF on F)
SCMK-070	MEXICO 8 reales, Mexico City mint	800

Dalzell Farm, Lanarkshire

Archibald Hamilton of Dalzell Farm served in France between 1812 and 1814 and returned to Dalzell Farm after the surrender of Paris. It is probable that he brought back a number of French 5 franc pieces which form the host coins for this countermark.

Description of Countermark

PAYABLE AT DALZELL FARM (in relief) around border of circular countermark.

No.	Coin countermarked	£ (VF on F)
SCMK-080	Reverse of FRANCE 5 francs (Directory type)	400
SCMK-085	Reverse of FRANCE 5 francs (Napoleon type)	400

This countermark has been reported as having a mark of value 5/-in the centre, but it appears likely that the position of the 5 of the 5 francs reverse value gave rise to this.

Deanston Cotton Mill, Perthshire

(same as Adelphi Cotton Works)

Description of Countermark

5/ ' (in relief) within serrated octagon, around which DEANSTON COTTON MILL (in relief) in border, all within circle.

No.	Coin countermarked	£ (VF on F)
SCMK-100	MEXICO 8 reales, Mexico City mint	1200
SCMK-105	BOLIVIA 8 reales, Potosi mint with George III countermark in oval	1500
SCMK-110	PERU 8 reales, Lima mint with George III countermark in oval	1500

Galston Society, Ayrshire

The Gentleman's Magazine, volume 83, 1813, records that Lady Inglis patronized a local 'Dollar Society', formed on 1st January 1812, to provide relief to persons in want, with membership open to all who would 'subscribe the dollar'.

Description of Countermark

5s. No. 12 GALSTON SOCY (in relief) within circle.

No.	Coin countermarked	£ (VF on F)
SCMK-120	Charles II crown	2000
SCMK-125	MEXICO 8 reales, Mexico City mint	800

Andrew Gibson & Co., Lochwinnoch, Renfrewshire

The firm was a substantial enterprise comprising grocers, weavers and linen manufacturers.

Description of Countermark

5/. (in relief) within circle, around which A. GIBSON & Cᵒ LOCHWINNOCH (in relief) within border, all within circle.

No.	Coin countermarked	£ (VF on F)
SCMK-140	MEXICO 8 reales, Mexico City mint	600

Glasgow Bank, Glasgow, Lanarkshire

(The Glasgow Bank Company, affiliated to Morland, Ransom and Co., 56 Pall Mall, London)

The bank stood on the corner of Montrose Street and Ingram Street in Glasgow.

Description of Countermark

5/-(in relief) within circle, around which GLASGOW BANK (in relief) all within circle.

No.	Coin countermarked	£ (VF on F)
SCMK-150	MEXICO 8 reales, Mexico City mint	800

Description of Countermark

4/9 GLASGOW BANK (in relief) within circle.

No.	Coin countermarked	£ (VF on F)
SCMK-160	Penny 1797	500

Lanark Mills, Lanarkshire

The Lanark Mills were founded in 1783 and issued a prolific series of stamped dollars. The five shilling variety is probably the most often encountered Scottish countermark, around a hundred being

known. In 1799 the mills were bought by the social and educational reformer Robert Owen.

Description of Countermark

4/6 (incuse) within circle, around which PAYABLE AT LANARK MILLS (in relief) within border, all within circle.

No.	Coin countermarked	£ (VF on F)
SCMK-170	MEXICO 8 reales, Mexico City mint	600

A specimen is reported with an additional 'D' countermark 'at the right'.

Description of Countermark

4/9 (incuse) within circle, around which PAYABLE AT LANARK MILLS (in relief) within border, all within circle.

No.	Coin countermarked	£ (VF on F)
SCMK-180	MEXICO 8 reales, Mexico City mint	500

Description of Countermark

5/ (incuse) within circle, around which PAYABLE AT LANARK MILLS (in relief) within border, all within circle.

No.	Coin countermarked	£ (VF on F)
SCMK-190	FRANCE ecu	400
SCMK-195	MEXICO 8 reales, Mexico City mint	350
SCMK-200	MEXICO 8 reales, Mexico City mint; countermark reads LANAK instead of LANARK	1200

McFie, Lindsay & Co., Greenock, Renfrewshire

The firm were wholesale grocers located at 3 William Street, Greenock, and invented a salmon preservation process.

Description of Countermark

4/6 (in relief) within circle, around which MᶜFIE LINDSAY & COʸ GREENOCK (in relief) within border, all within circle.

No.	Coin countermarked	£ (VF on F)
SCMK-210	MEXICO 8 reales, Mexico City mint	800
SCMK-215	PERU 8 reales, Lima mint	900

A specimen is reported having an incuse 'S' under the 4 in the value. Further details, including what coin was counterstamped, are unavailable.

McGavin and Clarkson, Paisley, Renfrewshire

The firm manufactured textiles, and operated from premises at Sneddon Street, Paisley.

Description of Countermark

5/. (in relief) within circle, around which Mᶜ G & C PAISLEY (in relief), all within circle.

No.	Coin countermarked	£ (VF on F)
SCMK-230	MEXICO 8 reales, Mexico City mint	2000

Dugald McLachlan, merchant, Tobermory, Argyllshire

Description of Countermark

5/ (in relief) within circle, around which DUGᴰ MᶜLACHLAN MERCHT TOBERMORY (in relief), all within circle.

No.	Coin countermarked	£ (VF on F)
SCMK-240	FRANCE 5 francs	2000
SCMK-245	MEXICO 8 reales, Mexico City mint	700

The countermark is usually faintly struck.

J. Muir, Paisley, Renfrewshire

Description of Countermark

Obverse: 5/. (in relief) within circle, around which J. MUIR, Manufʳ PAISLEY (in relief) within border, all within circle.

Reverse: Prince of Wales plumes, including ICH DIEN on ribbon, all within circle.

Obv.   Rev.

No.	Coin countermarked	£ (VF on F)
SCMK-260	PERU 8 reales, Lima mint	400
SCMK-265	MEXICO 8 reales, Mexico City mint	

Rothsay Cotton Works, Buteshire

In the Gentleman's Magazine, volume 64, 1794, a Bachelor of Divinity noted that Roth(e)say was the first place in Scotland to have a cotton mill, and that 'dancing is the amusement of the younger, and newspapers and backgammon of the older inhabitants of Rothsay'.

Description of Countermark

4/6 1820 (in relief) within rope border, around which ROTHSAY COTTON WORKS (in relief), all within dotted border in circle.

No.	Coin countermarked	£ (VF on F)
SCMK-270	BOLIVIA 8 reales, Potosi mint	500
SCMK-275	MEXICO 8 reales, Mexico City mint	400
SCMK-280	MEXICO 8 reales, Zacatecas mint	400
SCMK-285	PERU 8 reales, Lima mint	500

Description of Countermark

2/6 (in relief) within circle, around which PAYABLE AT ROTHSAY MILLS (in relief), all within outer circle.

No.	Coin countermarked	£ (VF on F)
SCMK-300	Cut half of Spanish or Spanish American dollar	300

181

Thistle Bank, Glasgow, Lanarkshire

(affiliated to Smith, Payne and Co., George Street, Mansion House, City of London)

The Thistle Bank was founded in 1761 by Sir William Maxwell and James Ritchie and Co. It was absorbed into the Glasgow Union Bank in 1836, and subsequent acquisitions render it now as part of The Bank of Scotland.

See Appendix for documentation relating to this issue.

Description of Countermark

5/ (in relief) within circle, around which THISTLE BANK (in relief) all within circle.

No.	Coin countermarked	£ (VF on F)
SCMK-310	MEXICO 8 reales, Mexico City mint (with thistle in circle countermark on rev.)	700

Description of Countermark

4/9 (in relief) within circle, around which THISTLE BANK (in relief) all within circle.

Obv.   Rev.

No.	Coin countermarked	£ (VF on F)
SCMK-320	MEXICO 8 reales, Mexico City mint (with or without thistle in circle countermark on rev.)	350
SCMK-325	PERU 8 reales, Lima mint (with thistle in circle countermark on rev.)	400
SCMK-330	BOLIVIA 8 reales, Potosi mint (with thistle in circle countermark on rev.)	400
SCMK-335	GUATEMALA 8 reales, Nueva Guatemala mint (with thistle in circle countermark on rev.)	600
SCMK-340	Brass forgeries of 8 reales (with thistle in circle countermark on rev.)	200

Price of dollars in pence per ounce (low/high for year) as paid by the Bank of England (from returns made to The House of Commons)

Year	Low	High
1801	69	71
1802	63.5	70.5
1803	62.5	66
1804	60	67
1805	61	66
1806	65	66
1807	63	66
1808	63	64.5
1809	63	67
1810	65	69
1811	70.5	74
1812	73	80.5
1813	78	84.5
1814	63.5	83.5
1815	63	81
1816	58	63
1817	58	64
1818	61.5	66

Ecus and similar pieces

Ecus, the coins that never were...

With the economic union of the European States, there was a need for a unified currency. During the early part of the 1990s most people believed that it would be called the Ecu, but this was not to be. The EU decided to call the new currency the Euro instead.

Before the choice of name had been officially made, a number of countries and individuals struck many different medallic pieces which they labelled ecus. None of these pieces had any legal tender status but were made for collectors. Some purported to be patterns of what the currency might look like, but none had any official basis for this claim.

The pieces listed below were issued by the International Currency Bureau (ICB) and are included here for completeness. Prices reflect what is currently being charged in the numismatic market. They have become known as 'the coins that never were'.

R.L.

25 Ecu 1992

No.	Date	Denomination	Metal	Weight (grams)	Diameter (mm)	Rev. align.	Current Value
S25E-92A	1992	25 Ecu	Cupronickel	20.0	38	↑	8
S25E-92B	1992	25 Ecu	Cupronickel	40.0	38	↑	25
S25E-92C	1992	25 Ecu	Brass		38	↑	8
S25E-92D	1992	25 Ecu	Silver	23.0	38	↑	25
S25E-92E	1992	25 Ecu	Silver	46.0	38	↑	45
S25E-92F	1992	25 Ecu	Gold		38	↑	295

Obv.　　　　　Rev.

Obverse　Globe depicting Europe with 12-star border, flanked by Neptune and Europa; EUROPE EUROPA SCOTLAND

Reverse　Shield of Scotland and Unicorn on St. Andrew's Cross; TWENTY FIVE ECU 1992

Edge　plain

Gold Ecu 1992

No.	Date	Denomination	Metal	Weight (grams)	Diameter (mm)	Rev. align.	Current Value
SGE-92	1992	Gold Ecu	Gold	6.0	22	↑	125

Obverse　Globe depicting Europe with 12-star border, flanked by Neptune and Europa; EUROPE EUROPA SCOTLAND

Reverse　Shield of Scotland and Unicorn on St. Andrew's Cross; GOLD ECU 1992

Edge　plain

A companion gold half ecu piece of 1992 exists; details of this are not available at the time of going to press.

Silver Ecu 1992

'Silver Ecu' is a denomination and does not refer to the metal in which the piece is struck.

No.	Date	Denomination	Metal	Weight (grams)	Diameter (mm)	Rev. align.	Current Value
SSE-92A	1992	Silver Ecu	Cupronickel	20.0	38	↑	8
SSE-92B	1992	Silver Ecu	Cupronickel	40.0	38	↑	25
SSE-92C	1992	Silver Ecu	Brass		38	↑	8
SSE-92D	1992	Silver Ecu	Silver	23.0	38	↑	25
SSE-92E	1992	Silver Ecu	Silver	46.0	38	↑	45
SSE-92F	1992	Silver Ecu	Gold		38	↑	295

Obverse　Globe depicting Europe with 12-star border, flanked by Neptune and Europa; EUROPE EUROPA SCOTLAND

Reverse　Shield of Scotland and Unicorn on St. Andrew's Cross; SILVER ECU 1992

Edge　plain

Ecu 1992

No.	Date	Denomination	Metal	Weight (grams)	Diameter (mm)	Rev. align.	Current Value
SE-92A	1992	Ecu	Cupronickel	5.2	22.5	↑	1
SE-92B	1992	Ecu	Silver		22.5	↑	6
SE-92C	1992	Ecu	Gold		22.5	↑	95

Obv.　　　　　Rev.

Obverse　Globe depicting Europe with 12-star border, flanked by Neptune and Europa; EUROPE EUROPA SCOTLAND

Reverse　Shield of Scotland and Unicorn on St. Andrew's Cross; ONE ECU 1992

Edge　plain

Ecu 1995

No.	Date	Denomination	Metal	Weight (grams)	Diameter (mm)	Rev. align.	Current Value
SE-95A	1995	Ecu	Cupronickel	20.0	38	↑	12
SE-95B	1995	Ecu	Cupronickel	40.0	38	↑	25
SE-95C	1995	Ecu	Brass		38	↑	12
SE-95D	1995	Ecu	Silver	23.0	38	↑	25
SE-95E	1995	Ecu	Silver	46.0	38	↑	45
SE-95F	1995	Ecu	Gold		38	↑	295

Obverse   Globe depicting Europe with 12-star border, flanked by Neptune and Europa; EUROPE EUROPA SCOTLAND

Reverse   Flying Scotsman train (on adhesive paper disc); SCOTLAND 19 ECU 95

Edge   plain

Scotland: Mintage Information & Figures

In 1662, the Scottish Mint was located on the North side of Cowgate, a thoroughfare in Edinburgh, between Todrick's Wynd and Gray's Close. The Mint consisted of twelve 'work houses', which were known as:

1. The copper compting hous.
2. The gold melting hous.
3. The silver melting hous.
4. The compting hous.
5. The neling hous.
6. A roume vithin it.
7. The old printing hous.
8. The hors milne contening tuo roumes.
9. The justing hous.
10. The printing hous.
11. The great forge.
12. The litell forge.

Extract from 'Compt and Register'

Date	4 mk	2 mk	mk	1/2 mk	
1664	xr^1	xr^1	xr^1	xr^1	The 1/2 mk only printed in Dec.
1665	xr^2	xr^2	xr^2	xr^2	
1666	xr^2	xr^2	xr^2	xr^2	
1667			xr^3	xr^3	Mint only in op^n. in Jun and Aug
1668			xr^3	xr^3	Mint only in op^n. in Aug
1669	xr^1	xr^1	xr^1	xr^1	
1670	xr^1	xr^1	xr^1	xr^1	
1671			xr^1	xr^1	
1672			xr^1	xr^1	
1673	xr^2	xr^2	xr^1	xr^1	

The significance of the xr with suffix in this table is unclear.

Extract from 'Compt and Register', 1674

Moneth	Day	Fynnes	Species	Casts	od	st	pds	ounces	dr
Aprile	10th	11den 0gr	2M	0193	01	01	04	14	07
			1M	0168	03	02	01	02	00
			1/2 M	0197	00	00	05	05	09
					03	11	06	00	

Mintage figures

The following figures are taken from Mint records, but between 1664 and 1673 the figures are calculated from weights and may be misleading, as many coins were underweight. It should be noted that the figures are coins struck during the year in question, and not necessarily coins bearing that date.

Date	4-merk	2-merk	merk	half-merk	40-penny
1664	'see below'	'see below'	2,101	768	
1665	'see below'	'see below'	2,119	1,394	
1666	'see below'	'see below'	9,214	2,139	
1667	0	0	7,754	1,829	
1668	0	0	12,909	2,090	
1669	'see below'	'see below'	163,470	23,031	
1670	26,556	21,791	94,556	18,432	
1671	0	0	372,290	18,303	
1672	0	0	212,197	12,333	
1673	13,737	38,877	97,921	14,915	
1674	577	4,170	6,219	2,292	
1675 merk	4,083	23,119	87,947	17,824	
1675 dollar	0	2,379	5,700	1,411	
1676	2,368	1,383	199,669	40,047	
1677	0	0	109,490	31,853	16,577
1678	794	0	27,403	8,789	4,213
1679	7,679	0	60,975	16,490	1,469
1680	1,357	0	92,767	15,647	7,235
1681	5,917	1,961	148,748	16,101	5,465

The individual mintage figures for the 4-merk and 2-merk cannot be determined for the years 1664 to 1669, but the following are the combined 4-merk and 2-merk weights for individual years, when struck:

1664: 52st. 13lb. 9oz. 5dr.
1665: 18st. 12lb. 3oz. 15dr.
1666: 14st. 6lb. 12oz. 3dr.
1669: 61st. 3lb. 0oz. 0dr.

Salaries of Mint officers, 1686

Office	Salary in £ Scots
General of the Mint	3600
Master of the Mint	2400
Warden	1200
Assay Master	1200
Curator Warden	720
Sinker	600
Clerk	480
Master Smith	360
Clerk of the bullion	333.6s.8d

40 Shillings

Date	Mintage	Remarks
1691	39,244	Feb to May only
1692	18,376	23 Oct to 23 Dec only
1694	33,375	5 Jan to 5 Dec only
1695	10,564	Aug only
1697	11,822	Dec only
1698	15,904	3 Jan to 10 May only

20 Shillings

Date	Mintage	Remarks
1692	1,185	23 Oct to 23 Dec only
1694	5,369	5 Jan to 5 Dec only

10 Shillings

Date	Mintage	Remarks
1691	26,094	Feb to May only
1694	1,301	5 Jan to 5 Dec only
1698	9,030	3 Jan to 10 May only

5 Shillings

Date	Mintage	Remarks
1692	2,692	23 Oct to 23 Dec only
1694	3,496	5 Jan to 5 Dec only
1698	32,857	3 Jan to 10 May only

Coin brought into Edinburgh Mint to be melted and recoined following the Act of Union 1707

Date	Description	Value £.s.d
1707	Foreign money	132,080.17.0
1707	Milled Scottish money	96,856.13.9
1707	Hammered money	142,180. 0.0
1707	English money	40,000. 0.0
	Total of above	411,117.10.9
1708	Supplementary	375,000. 0.0
	Grand Total	786,117.10.9

Invoice relating to countermarked dollars

The Thistle Bank Co. 1803: Glasgow. To Robert Gray & Son

Septr. 2 Cash paid for a steel punch	2.6
Engraving Thistle Bank 4/6 on ditto	3.6
Engraving Thistle Bank 4/9 on ditto	3.6
Stamping 6000 dollars @ 2/6 per 1000	15.0
1804 Jan[y] 4 Engraving Thistle Bank 5/ on a steel punch	3.6
Novr 7th Received Payment JKC	1. 8.0

Ireland

The hammered coinage of Ireland

It is uncertain when Ireland first became inhabited but archaeology informs us that by 3500 BC farmers were clearing and cultivating the land. During this and later periods large tumuli, forts as well as standing stones were erected. Metal work was also important with gold, bronze, iron and lead being worked. The Romans never colonised Ireland and Christianity arrived in Ireland in the 5th century AD. During the late 8th century, the Vikings started to land in Ireland. They first just looted and pillaged in particular from the monasteries which had obtained some wealth as well as fine artwork, and they settled in certain areas of Ireland in particular Dublin. This was due to their poor land in their native Scandinavia however the Vikings never truly conquered Ireland but rather by the 12th century had learnt to live with the Irish. Some of their culture influenced the Irish, however their language and religion did not.

Coins were not struck in Ireland until 995 AD. Before this date Celtic gold ring money was produced and used as a form of exchange. These rings were first an incomplete ring of gold often with a twisted pattern. The dates of these 'rings' is uncertain but they are thought to be pre-Roman Celtic issues.

While the Romans did not land and colonise Ireland, Roman coins from traders did circulate in Ireland and have been found there. English Anglo-Saxon and Viking coins circulated during the 8th and 9th centuries and silver ingots also circulated as a form of currency. However most people in Ireland bartered and the main form of wealth during this period was cattle.

The hammered coinage of Ireland can be divided into two main periods. Firstly the Hiberno-Norse issues from 995 to 1150 AD. These issues were struck by the Scandinavian or Viking kings in Dublin. The second period consists of the Anglo-Irish coinage struck under the English monarchy.

The first Hiberno-Norse issues were struck in Dublin in 995 by the Scandinavian king Sihtric. These issues which were well struck in good quality silver were imitations in style and design of English Anglo-Saxon kings, in particular Aethelred II and Cnut. All these issues are very rare or extremely rare and must not be confused with the more common English issues.

The Hiberno-Norse coinage continued until 1150. However the weight and fineness of the issues was lowered during later issues. The style and quality of production also deteriorated and by 1060 the legends on the coins were blundered and meaningless. Many coins copied an English Anglo Saxon or Norman design however many issues were so blundered in design that they are difficult to distinguish a meaningful design. Most of these issues are extremely rare and it is probable that more varieties exist than we have listed. Many of these coins have been found in hoards in Scandinavian countries as well as the Baltic region and it is possible that some of these issues in particular the early issues which we have listed were not actually struck in Ireland.

By 1110 the coins had become so thin that they could not be pressed on both sides so these coins were impressed on one side only. These were known as bracteates; this style of coinage was sometimes issued in Europe.

In 1169 powerful Norman lords and knights invaded Ireland and carved territories for themselves. This worried Henry II of England who then visited Ireland to secure homage from his powerful subjects. He then negotiated with the Irish provincial rulers who had complained about the action of the Norman lords. The Irish provincial rulers submitted the land and control of the land to Henry II on condition that he would protect them from the Norman lords and knights who had invaded their land and so Henry II became king of Ireland. Henry II also received papal blessing on his new position.

In 1172 Henry II's son King John became Lord of Ireland and paid his first visit there in 1185. It was not a popular visit as Prince John showed the Irish nobles no respect and pulled their long beards for fun. Also the choice of many new Norman landowners was not popular and during this period the English monarchy had virtually no control of Ireland.

During this period there were several coinages struck. Firstly in 1185 a profile coinage was struck. These coins are halfpennies and it is thought they are attributed to John de Curcy who was Lord of Ulster. John de Curcy struck several issues from 1185 to 1205. He was Lord of Ulster and ruled as an independent Prince. He was eventually taken prisoner and his land was then ruled by Prince John.

King John issued two main coinages, the Dominus or Lord coinage which was issued while John was Lord of Ireland and the 'Rex' or king coinage, issued while John was king. Numerous mints were active during the Dominus coinage and produced halfpennies in some quantity although farthings are very rare. A 'moon' face bust of the king can be found on the obverse and a small cross with an annulet in each quarter on the reverse. The obverse legend consists of John's name and title, while the reverse bears the moneyer's name and an abbreviation for the mint. The moneyer was responsible not only for actually striking the coin but also for ensuring that it was of the correct weight and metal fineness. The inclusion of his details in the legend made him accountable for any sub-standard coins and this form of quality control created confidence in the new coinage. It is interesting to note in this context that the farthings of this issue were very small and do not include an obverse legend or royal title, the reverse still bears the moneyer's name, without a mint.

King John's 'Rex' coinage was struck between 1207 and 1211 and included pennies, halfpennies and farthings. The denominations are fairly similar in style, with a crowned bust of the king in a triangle on the obverse and a sun, moon and three stars in a triangle on the reverse of the penny and halfpenny and a star or starfoil in a triangle on the farthing. The obverse legend bears the king's title while the reverse has the moneyer's name and mint.

Henry III became king in 1216 but it was not until 1251 that coins were struck in his name, probably due to the large number that were in circulation from the previous reign.

In 1251 Richard de Haverhull was put in charge of the mint in Dublin with orders to make coins out of all the silver that was in the mint. Pennies were the only denomination struck bearing a crowned bust of Henry within a triangle on the obverse and a long cross with three pellets in each quarter on the reverse. The reverse design was identical to that of the English long cross pennies and both issues were designed so that they could be cut along the long cross to produce halfpennies and farthings. The royal title is found in the obverse legend while the reverse legend has the moneyer's name and mint. Various dies with minor differences were used for this issue and due to the coins' high silver content, many of them circulated in Europe. The mint was closed in 1254.

Edward I became king in 1272 and Richard Olof was placed in charge of the mint between 1276 and 1279. He struck a rare issue in the name of Henry III which was a copy of the previous reign.

With a population that was mainly illiterate it was considered important to retain a virtually identical style and only minor varieties differentiate the issues.

However, in 1279 Edward I decided to introduce a new coinage in Ireland as well as England. In Ireland the denominations were penny, halfpenny and farthing. These issues have the king's bust in a triangle on the obverse and a long cross on the reverse with three pellets in each quarter. The king's title can be found on the obverse while the reverse legend bears the name of the mint but, as in the English issues, the moneyer's name is omitted. Nevertheless, many minor varieties were introduced in these issues so that dies could still be attributed to a moneyer, should a problem arise.

Huge quantities of pennies were produced during this coinage and many circulated in England as well as in Northern Europe. Edward I's coinage was the envy of Europe and was heavily imitated in style in Germany and the Low Countries.

However this period of prosperity was followed by one of decline. From the reign of Edward II through to that of Henry VI, virtually no coins were struck in Ireland while the high quality issues of John, Henry III and Edward I were gradually exported out of the country as their silver content made them worth more than their face value. During this period the Black Death ravaged Ireland and brought poverty and unrest.

English and some Scottish coins circulated at the time. They were often very worn and clipped and it was not until the reign of Edward IV that coins were struck again in Ireland.

The main problem facing the authorities during the medieval and Tudor period was the rising price of silver. It resulted in coins being either melted down for profit or exported a few years after they had been struck because their silver content exceeded their face value.

By the beginning of Edward IV's reign the shortage of coinage in Ireland was acute. In 1460 the Anglo-Irish Parliament decided to strike a coinage with a silver content of less than its face value. It was hoped that this would stop the coins being melting down for profit or exported to Europe.

The issues of Edward IV are numerous and complex due mainly to the rising silver price. The face values of some denominations varied as did the silver content and copper coins were also introduced during this period. Many mints were active and many issues are fairly similar in design to the English ones, although they tend to be cruder in style.

No issues were minted bearing the name of Henry VI who ruled England in 1422 – 61 and 1470 – 71. It is interesting to note that some issues do not have the king's name, a decision probably dictated by the fact that the English War of the Roses made an allegiance to a particular monarch somewhat foolhardy, even though Ireland was ruled by Richard Duke of York, Lieutenant of Ireland.

Richard III struck groats and pennies during his reign. His second coinage is known as the three crowns coinage and is a non-portrait coinage. It shows the royal arms on the obverse and three crowns on the reverse. This style was also popular during the reign of Henry VII.

Richard III died at the battle of Bosworth and Henry VII of the house of Tudor became king of England and Ireland. This transfer of power produced a power vacuum in Ireland with Lambert Simnel and Gerald Earl of Kildare striking coins and trying to become rulers. Their attempts did not succeed and Henry VII became king of Ireland. Ireland was now not a prosperous country as it had been several centuries earlier and could help Henry VII little towards greater prosperity. During Henry VII's reign groats, halfgroats and pennies were struck. All issues are very crude in style with the three crowns coinage being struck during the early part of his reign and portrait coinage with a long cross on the reverse on most of his later coinage. All issues were struck at the Dublin or Waterford mints.

Henry VIII became king in 1509. Henry VIII believed in centralising monetary policy and in 1534 groats and halfgroats were struck in London and then exported to Ireland. These issues are known as the harp coinage. The obverse shows a crowned royal arms while the reverse a crowned harp dividing the initials of Henry (H) and his wife at that particular time. Due to the rising silver price and Henry's extravagant spending the silver content and weight of later issues was reduced and the value of the denomination was increased to sixpence from fourpence. The last harp issue of 1546 – 47 was struck in Bristol.

Henry VIII died in 1547 and his sickly son Edward VI became king at the age of ten. He was too young to rule and the Duke of Somerset who was Edward's uncle was his 'Protector' and he virtually ruled England as well as Ireland.

From 1547 to 1550 sixpences (sometimes referred to as groats), threepences, three halfpennies and three farthings were produced, bearing the elderly portrait of Henry VIII and bearing his name in the legend. This issue is known as the Posthumous issue of Henry VIII and all issues were struck in Dublin sometimes using Tower Mint obverse dies. These issues were of base metal of a low silver content and were unpopular.

In 1552 a dated base issue shilling with the bust of the boy king was produced. This issue had the mintmark harp which differentiates it from the more common English issues. Crude brass imitations of this coin were struck in Ireland and were known as bungals. They circulated in Connacht (Connaught) with a value of a penny each and can be classed as forgeries or tokens, however they were readily acceptable. It appears during this period there was a shortage of small coinage and English base pennies struck in York were exported to Ireland to help with the problem.

Edward VI died at the age of 16. Mary, Henry VIII's daughter and a devout Catholic became queen. While she reintroduced Catholicism in England she rarely interfered in Ireland however she did increase her power in Ireland by introducing more English settlers who founded plantations.

Mary's coinage can be divided into two: base issue coins which bear Mary's portrait, and coins of an even lower fineness which are dated and bear both the queen's bust and that of her husband, Philip of Spain. It is interesting to note during this period that all coins which were struck in England were struck in silver of a high fineness while in Ireland during the reign of Mary and her sister Elizabeth only base silver coins were struck with the exception of the 1561 fine silver coinage. This perhaps reflects the lack of interest the two monarchs had in Ireland. After all with gold and silver coming back from the Americas, Ireland economically had fairly little to offer England.

Mary died in 1558 and Elizabeth I became queen. During the first year of her reign base issue shillings and groats were struck, these issues show the bust of the queen on the obverse and a crowned harp on the reverse.

In 1561 a fine silver coinage of a shilling and groat was introduced, and no coins were then struck until 1601 – 02. This third coinage of 1601 – 02 was struck as emergency coinage to pay for the troops who were needed in Ireland during this period as unrest had broken out in the north of the country.

During Elizabeth's reign it was a time of unrest in Ireland, with private wars between earls and landowners and Elizabeth wanting more of the land to be controlled by English settlers and her profiteering from the developed land.

Elizabeth I died in 1603 and James VI of Scotland succeeded to the English throne as James I. A general amnesty was declared but the power and influence of the northern chiefs of Ireland had been curtailed by Elizabeth I's armies and much of the land, especially in the north, was now owned by new English settlers.

Silver shillings and sixpences were struck in London and shipped to Ireland. These coins had a high silver content and were of good style and design. They were smaller than the English issues and an Irish shilling was worth ninepence in England. All issues have a crowned king's bust on the obverse and a large crowned harp on the reverse.

As in England, there was a shortage of small change in Ireland so in 1613 copper farthings were manufactured under licence in England by Lord Harrington and they were used as legal tender in both countries. A harp can be found on the reverse of all issues reflecting the fact that they were to be issued in both countries.

James I died in 1625 and his son Charles I became king. The only coins issued during the early part of his reign were copper farthings which were produced in London under licence and exported to Ireland. These coins also circulated in England.

During this period large quantities of Scottish and European coins, in particular from Spain and Portugal circulated in Ireland due to the lack of Irish and English coinage. Due to the fighting and instability at the end of Elizabeth I's reign and English settlers arriving in Ireland, religious differences as well as unrest over land confiscation started the Great Rebellion in 1641. It started when two Protestant Lord Justices had prevented the Irish Parliament passing a Royal Bill to help alleviate Catholic grievances. It was a time when many people wanted many things and people fought not necessarily for the same reason. Many wanted revenge on the English plantation owners who had seized their land some forty years before, while others wanted Ireland free from the English. Huge numbers of English Protestant settlers were murdered and those that survived fled to fortified towns such as Londonderry. An army was sent from Scotland in 1642 to suppress the uprising however the civil war started in England that year and Lord Inchiquin was appointed by Charles I to command the Protestants.

In 1642 the Parliament of England passed the Adventurers Act to finance the reconquest of Ireland. This meant that by pledging Irish lands against bonds the reconquest of Ireland would be of economic interest to many individuals. Cromwell's troops landed in Ireland and eventually won. In 1652 an Act of settling Ireland was passed and was indirectly aimed at removing all land from the Catholics to Protestant English control. The rebellion had been at immense cost to Ireland. It is thought that during the ten years of war 600,000 people had been killed leaving a population of only 850,000.

The coinage of this period as one would expect is equally complicated with emergency coinage being made out of silver plates and many cities and towns producing their own coinage.

No coins were struck during the Commonwealth however tokens were issued by many traders and Ireland in 1653 was declared part of the Protectorate granting Ireland free trade with Scotland and England.

Ireland: Double Pistole

The gold double pistole was only struck during the Ormonde issue of Charles I. Equivalent in value to two French Louis d'or, it is known as 'weight' money because all that can be found on the coin is its weight value. The weight of the French Louis d'or was recognised throughout Europe.

Charles I   (1625 – 1649)

Ormonde Issue (1646)

Known as the Ormonde issue after the Earl of Ormonde who was the Lieutenant of Ireland, this issue just had its weight as a design and was often of slightly irregular size.

Collecting Hints

This issue is of the highest rarity.

Obverse   8 dw t.t. 14 gr

Reverse   As obverse.

IC1DP-005   ex. rare

Ireland: Pistole

The gold pistole was equivalent in value to the French Louis d'or and was struck during the Ormonde issue of Charles I. It is known as 'weight' money because all that can be found on the coin is its weight value. The weight of the French Louis d'or was recognised throughout Europe.

Charles I   (1625 – 1649)

Ormonde Issue (1646)

Known as the Ormonde issue after the Earl of Ormonde who was the Lieutenant of Ireland, this issue just had its weight as a design and coins were often of a slightly irregular size.

Collecting Hints

This issue is of the highest rarity.

Obverse   4dw t.t. 7 gr

Reverse   As obverse

IC1PS-005   ex. rare

Ireland: Crown

Silver crowns were only struck under Charles I and had a value of five shillings.

Charles I (1625 – 1649)

1642 Issue of the Great Rebellion

These coins were struck from irregular-sized pieces of plate. They were issued under an act that empowered Lord Inchiquin to take in silver plates at the Dublin mint and defer payment to the members of the public, who in turn received interest on the silver they gave. The plates were then cut up, weighed and marked with a value according to their weight. This issue was sometimes known as Inchiquin money. Coins can be of an irregular shape.

Collecting Hints

This issue is extremely rare and forgeries exist.

'19 dwt 8 gr' counterstamped on flan on both sides of the coin.

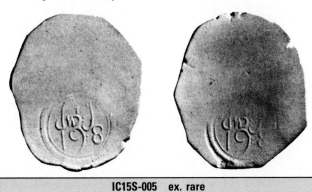

IC15S-005   ex. rare

Dublin Money (1643)

This is very much a continuation from the previous coinage and is known as Dublin money because it was struck there.

Collecting Hints

This issue is extremely rare and forgeries exist.

'VS' countermarked on both sides of the coin. Two sizes of countermark exist.

IC15S-010   ex. rare   Whytes sale Feb. 98: VF £2,400

Ormonde Issues
1643 – 1644 Issue

Known as Ormonde money after the Earl of Ormonde who was Lieutenant of Ireland in 1643, these crudely struck issues showed loyalty to the king by the crowned 'C.R.' on the obverse. As with the previous issue, these coins were struck from silver plates that were cut to the correct size, shape and weight.

Collecting Hints

While scarce, this issue is obtainable especially in the lower grades although coins are rarely found in better than Fine condition. Contemporary forgeries of base metal as well as 19th century forgeries exist.

Obverse   Crowned 'C.R.'.
Reverse   'VS'.

IC15S-015   VG £135   F £300   VF rare

1649 Issue

This issue was struck in 1649 after the execution of Charles I. Coins were struck in Dublin by James, Marquis of Ormonde who acknowledged Charles II as King of Ireland instead of Cromwell as Protector.

Collecting Hints

This issue is extremely rare.

Obverse Legend   CAR II D.G. MAG BRIT — Charles II by the grace of God King of Great Britain

Reverse Legend   FRA ET HYB REX F.D. — France and Ireland Defender of the faith

Obverse   Large crown within a circle.

Reverse   'VS' within a circle.

IC15S-020   ex. rare

Issues of Confederate Catholics
(1643 – 1644)

Rebel Money

Produced in imitation of Ormonde issues, these coins were probably struck in 1643 – 44 by the Confederate Catholics of Kilkenny. However, several numismatists consider that it is possible that this issue was struck in Dublin in 1648.

Collecting Hints

This issue is extremely rare.

Obverse   Large cross within circle, a pellet or star within margin.

Reverse   'VS' within circle.

IC15S-025   ex. rare   Whytes sale Feb. 98: F £1,200

Ireland: Halfcrown

Silver halfcrowns with a value of two shillings and sixpence were only struck during Charles I's reign.

Charles I   (1625 – 1649)

1642 Issue of the Great Rebellion

These coins were struck out of irregular-sized pieces of plate. They were issued under an act that empowered Lord Inchiquin to take in silver plate at the Dublin mint and defer payment to the members of the public, who in turn received interest on the silver they gave. The plates were then cut, weighed and marked with a value according to their weight. This issue was sometimes known as Inchiquin money.

Collecting Hints

This issue is extremely rare and forgeries exist.

'9DW tt 16 gr' counterstamped on flan on both sides of the coin.

IC1HC-005   ex. rare   Whytes sale Feb. 98: nr VF £1,600

Dublin Money (1643)

This is very much a continuation from the previous coinage and is known as Dublin money because it was struck there.

Collecting Hints

This issue is extremely rare and forgeries exist.

'II S VI D' counterstamped on flan on both sides of the coin.

IC1HC-010   ex. rare   Whytes sale Feb. 98: nr VF £1,800

Ormonde Issues

These issues are known as Ormonde money after the Earl of Ormonde who was Lieutenant of Ireland in 1643. They were crudely struck issues which showed loyalty to the king by the crowned 'C.R.' on the obverse. As with the previous issue, these coins were struck from silver plate that was cut to the correct size, shape and weight.

1643 – 1644

Collecting Hints

This issue is scarce but obtainable, although coins are rarely found in better than Fine condition.

Obverse   Crowned 'C.R.' in circle.
Reverse   'II S VI D' in circle.

IC1HC-015   VG £100   F £250   VF rare

1649

Struck in 1649 after the execution of Charles I, this issue was produced in Dublin by James, Marquis of Ormonde who acknowledged Charles II as King of Ireland and not Cromwell as Protector.

Collecting Hints

This issue is extremely rare.

Obverse Legend   CAR II D G MAG BRIT — Charles II by the grace of God King of Great Britain

Reverse Legend   FRA ET HYB REX FD — France and Ireland Defender of the faith

Obverse   Large crown within circle.

Reverse   'II S VI D' within circle.

IC1HC-020	ex. rare

Issues of the Confederate Catholics

Blacksmith's Halfcrown (1642?)

Struck at Kilkenny, this issue was very crude in both style and production and should not be confused with the more common English issues of the Tower mint, particularaly C1HC-055 and -060 which also have a mintmark harp on the reverse.

Collecting Hints

This issue is rare and crudely struck. When available, coins are in Fine or VF condition and often have weaknesses in the legend.

Obverse Legend CAROLUS D.G. MA BR FRA ET HI(B) REX — Charles by the grace of God King of Great Britain France and Ireland

Reverse Legend CHRISTO AUSPICE REGNO — I reign under the auspices of Christ

Obverse Crude king on horseback, a cross on the horse's housing; mintmark cross at the start of the legend.

Reverse Crude oval shield; mintmark harp at the start of the legend.

IC1HC-025	VG £250	F £400	VF £900

As previous, but no cross on horse's housing.

IC1HC-030	VG £300	F £600	VF £1300

Rebel Money (1643 – 1644)

Struck to imitate Ormonde issues, these coins were probably produced in 1643 – 44 by the Confederated Catholics at Kilkenny although several numismatists consider them to have been struck in Dublin in 1648.

Collecting Hints

This issue is extremely rare.

Obverse Cross within circle, a small star within margin.

Reverse 'II S VI D' within circle.

IC1HC-035	ex. rare

Ireland: Shilling

The billon shilling was introduced in Ireland with a value of twelve pence under Edward VI and was the only Irish issue to bear Edward's portrait. Although this early shilling was probably struck in London, it can be distinguished from the English issues (E6SH-030 to -085) by the mintmark harp. Also during Edward VI's reign, brass 'forgeries' of Edward VI shillings were struck in some quantity. Known as bungals, these coins circulated in Connacht and had a value of a penny although they were not official tender.

The denomination continued its somewhat shaky career under Elizabeth I, when English base issue shillings of Edward VI were sent to Ireland and had a value of sixpence or two pence farthing. From then on however, all future reigns that produced hammered coinage also struck shillings.

Edward VI   (1547 – 1553)

This is the first Irish coin to be dated.

Collecting Hints

This issue is very rare and it is important that it should not be confused with the much more common English issues (E6SH-030 to -085), which did not use the mintmark harp.

Obverse Legend   EDWARD VI D.G. AGL FRAN Z HB REX — Edward by the grace of God King of England France and Ireland

Reverse Legend   TIMOR DOMINI FONS VITE MDLII — The fear of God is the fountain of life 1552

Obverse   Crowned bust of the Boy King facing right; mintmark harp at the start of the legend.

Reverse   Arms in oval shield dividing 'E.R.'.

IE6SH-005   v. rare   Whytes sale Feb. 98: VF £1,300

Bungal Issue

While this issue is considered a forgery, it nevertheless circulated in Connacht with a value of one penny. The coins were struck in brass and, sometimes, copper.

Collecting Hints

These coins are fairly common but rarely found in better than VG condition.

As previous, but the obverse and reverse legends are sometimes blundered.

IE6SH-010   VG £40   F £100   VF rare

Mary   (1553 – 1554)

These two issues were struck in silver of 0.583 fineness and had a value of twelve pence.

Collecting Hints

The first issue is very rare, while the second is extremely so and forgeries of both exist.

Obverse Legend   MARIA D.G. ANG FRA Z HIB REGINA — Mary by the grace of God Queen of England France and Ireland

Reverse Legend   VERITAS TEMPORIS FILIA MDLIII — Truth the daughter of time 1553

Obverse   Crowned bust of the queen facing left.

Reverse   Crowned harp dividing small crowned 'MR'.

IMASH-005   v. rare

As previous, but reverse legend dated 'MDLIIII' (1554).

IMASH-010   ex. rare   Whytes sale Feb. 98: gd VF £1,900

Philip & Mary   (1554 – 1558)

This issue depicts the two facing busts of Philip and Mary and was struck in very low base silver of 0.250 fineness.

Collecting Hints

This issue is scarce in very low grades and rare in Fine or better condition. Coins are often poorly struck with cracked flans and weak legends and portraits.

Obverse Legend   PHILIP ET MARIA D.G. REX ET REGINA ANG(L) — Philip and Mary by the grace of God King and Queen of England

Reverse Legend POSVIMUS DEUM ADIUTOREM NOSTRUM — We have made God our helper

Obverse Facing busts of Mary and Philip, a crown above and the date (1555) below.

Reverse Crowned harp dividing crowned 'P' and 'M'; mintmark portcullis at the start of the legend.

IPMSH-005	VG £80	F £250	VF v. rare

Elizabeth I   (1558 – 1603)

Shillings were struck during three coinages of Elizabeth's reign with the first and third issues being of base silver and the second one of fine silver. Also, the first two were portrait issues while the third issue was non-portrait. And although all issues bear a harp on the reverse which easily differentiates them from the English ones (ELSH-005, -010, -015, -040 and -045), hoard evidence indicates that large quantities of English shillings in fact circulated in Ireland during this period.

Base Issue of 1558

Coins were struck in silver of 0.250 fineness.

Collecting Hints

This issue is scarce in poor or VG condition and rare in Fine or better. Coins are usually poorly struck with weak legends and portraits. Due to the poor metal content, flaking of the flan is not uncommon.

Obverse Legend ELIZABETH D.G. ANG FRA Z HIB REGINA (varieties exist) — Elizabeth by the grace of God Queen of England France and Ireland

Reverse Legend POSUI DEUM ADIUTOREM MEUM — I have made God my helper

Obverse Crowned bust of queen facing left; mintmark rose at the start of the legend.

Reverse Crowned harp dividing crowned 'E.R.'; mintmark rose at the start of the legend.

IELSH-005	VG £85	F £250	VF v. rare

Fine Issue of 1561

This issue was struck in silver of 0.916 fineness.

Collecting Hints

This is the scarcest of all three issues. Coins are usually found in VG to Fine condition, often badly creased with a weak portrait, and those in VF or better condition are rare.

Obverse Legend ELIZABETH D.G. A.F. ET HIBERNIE REGI (varieties exists) — Elizabeth by the grace of God Queen of England France and Ireland

Reverse Legend POSUI DEUM ADIUTOREM MEUM — I have made God my helper

Obverse Crowned bust of the queen facing left.

Reverse Crowned shield with three small harps on the shield dividing date (1561).

IELSH-010	VG £100	F £300	VF v. rare

Third Base Coinage (1601 – 1602)

Silver content of 0.250 fineness.

Collecting Hints

This issue is fairly common in low grades, but rare in better than Fine condition. It was poorly struck, often with weak legends and design as well as cracked flans.

Obverse Legend ELIZABETH D.G. ANG FR ET HIBER RE — Elizabeth by the grace of God Queen of England France and Ireland

Reverse Legend POSUI DEUM ADIUTOREM MEU — I have made God my helper

Obverse Royal shield; mintmark trefoil, star or martlet at the start of the legend.

Reverse Crowned harp; mintmarks as obverse, at the start of the legend.

IELSH-015	VG £50	F £150	VF rare

James I (1603 – 1625)

Silver shillings were struck during both of James' silver coinages. These issues, which are easily identified by a crowned harp on the reverse, were struck in London but were smaller than the English ones. In trade with England, these Irish issues had a value of ninepence.

Collecting Hints

All issues are fairly common, especially in the lower grades. Coins are often damaged and the king's bust is weakly struck on most of them. Coins in better than Fine condition are rare.

First Coinage (1603 – 1604)

Obverse Legend   IACOBUS D.G. ANG SCO FR A ET HIB REX — James by the grace of God King of England Scotland France and Ireland

Reverse Legend   EXURGAT DEUS DISSIPENTUR INIMICI — Let God arise and His enemies be scattered

Obverse   Crowned bust of king facing right with a square-cut beard; mintmark bell at the start of the legend.

Reverse   Crowned harp; mintmark bell at the start of the legend.

| IJ1SH-005 | VG £35 | F £80 | VF £300 |

As previous, but the king has a pointed beard; mintmark bell or martlet at the start of the legends.

| IJ1SH-010 | VG £35 | F £90 | VF £325 |

Second Coinage (1604 – 1607)

Obverse Legend   IACOBUS D.G. MAG BRIT FRA ET HIB REX — James by the grace of God King of Great Britain France and Ireland

Reverse Legend   HENRICUS ROSAS REGNA IACOBUS — Henry (united) the roses James the kingdoms

Obverse   Crowned bust of king with long square-cut beard; mintmark martlet, rose or escallop at the start of the legend.

Reverse   Crowned harp; mintmarks as obverse.

| IJ1SH-015 | VG £35 | F £90 | VF £325 |

Obverse Legend   As previous.

Reverse Legend   As previous.

Obverse   As previous, but king has longer, bushier beard and his clothing is less ornate; mintmark rose or escallop at the start of the legend.

Reverse   Crowned harp; mintmarks as obverse.

| IJ1SH-020 | VG £45 | F £120 | VF rare |

Charles I (1625 – 1649)

1642 Issue of the Great Rebellion

These issues were struck out of irregular-sized pieces of plate. They were issued under an act that empowered Lord Inchiquin to take in silver plate at the Dublin mint and defer payment to the members of the public, who in turn received interest on the silver they gave. The plates were then cut up and weighed and marked with a value according to their weight. This issue was sometimes known as Inchiquin money.

Collecting Hints

This issue is extremely rare and forgeries exist.

'3DWT 21 GR' countermarked on the flan on both sides of the coin.

| IC1SH-005 | ex. rare |

Ormonde Issue (1643 – 1644)

These issues are known as Ormonde money after the Lord of Ormonde who was Lieutenant of Ireland in 1643. They were crudely struck issues which showed loyalty to the king by the crowned 'C.R.' on the obverse. As with the previous issue, the coins were struck from silver plate that had been cut to the correct size, shape and weight.

Collecting Hints

This issue, while scarce, is obtainable but rarely found in better than Fine condition.

Obverse   Crowned 'C.R.'.

Reverse   'XII D' (the coin's value of twelve pence).

| IC1SH-010 | VG £65 | F £160 | VF rare |

Cities of Refuge – Cork

Of the four Munster towns (Bandon, Kinsale, Youghal and Cork) that held out against the armies of the confederated Catholics, Cork was the only one to strike shillings.

Collecting Hints

This issue is very rare and forgeries exist.

Obverse CORK 1647
Reverse XII

IC1SH-015   v. rare

Ireland: Ninepence

The silver ninepence was only struck under Charles I, during the coinage of the Great Rebellion.

Charles I (1625 – 1649)

1642 Issue of the Great Rebellion

These coins were struck out of irregular-sized pieces of plate. They were issued under an act that empowered Lord Inchiquin to take in silver plate at the Dublin mint and defer payment to the public who received interest on the silver they gave. The plates were then cut up and weighed and marked with a value according to their weight. This issue was sometimes known as Inchiquin money.

Collecting Hints

This issue is extremely rare and forgeries do exist.

'2 DWT 20 GR' counterstamped on flan on both sides of the coin.

IC19D-005	ex. rare

Obverse   As previous.
Reverse   Nine annulets.

IC19D-010	ex. rare

Ireland: Sixpence

The sixpence was introduced during the reign of Elizabeth I although groats with a value of six pence had been struck under both Henry VIII and Edward VI (see under groats, p.215 and p.216). Apart from Elizabeth, James I and Charles I also produced sixpences.

Elizabeth I   (1558 – 1603)

Sixpences were struck at the end of Elizabeth's reign during the base coinage of 1601 – 02. This was a non-portrait issue, struck in silver of 0.250 fineness.

Collecting Hints

This issue is fairly common especially in the lower grades. Coins were usually weakly and badly struck and are rarely found in better than Fine condition.

Obverse Legend   ELIZABETH D.G. ANG FR ET HIBER RE — Elizabeth by the grace of God Queen of England France and Ireland

Reverse Legend   POSUI DEUM ADIVITOREM MEU — I have made God my helper

Obverse   Royal arms; mintmark trefoil star or martlet at the start of the legend.

Reverse   Crown over harp; mintmark star, trefoil or martlet at the start of the legend.

IEL6D-005	VG £50	F £125	VF £400

James I   (1603 – 1625)

The sixpence was struck during both of James' silver coinages. All issues were produced in London so as to provide the realm with a uniform currency, but the Irish sixpence was smaller than its English counterpart and had a value in England of four and a half pence. It is easily identified by a large crowned harp found on the reverse and was struck in good quality silver of 0.925 fineness.

Collecting Hints

This issue is fairly common, especially in the lower grades. Coins are often found creased or damaged and undoubtedly saw considerable circulation. Examples in VF condition are rare.

First Coinage (1603 – 1604)

Obverse Legend   IACOBUS D.G. ANG SCO FRA ET HIB REX — James by the grace of God King of England Scotland France and Ireland

Reverse Legend   TUEATUR UNITA DEUS — May God guard the united (kingdoms)

Obverse   Crowned bust of the king facing right; mintmark bell or martlet at the start of the legend.

Reverse   Crowned harp; mintmark as obverse.

IJ16D-005	VG £35	F £70	VF £250

Second Coinage (1604 – 1607)

Obverse Legend   IACOBUS D.G. MAG BRIT FRA ET HI REX — James by the grace of God King of Great Britain France and Ireland

Reverse Legend   As previous.

Obverse   Crowned bust of the king facing right; mintmark martlet, rose or escallop at the start of the legend.

Reverse   Crowned harp; mintmark martlet, rose or escallop at the start of the legend.

IJ16D-010	VG £40	F £80	VF £280

Charles I   (1625 – 1649)

1642 Issue of the Great Rebellion

These coins were struck out of irregular-sized pieces of plate. They were issued under an act that empowered Lord Inchiquin to take in silver plate at the Dublin mint and defer payment to the members of the public, who in turn received interest on the silver they gave. The plates were then cut up and weighed and marked with a value according to their weight. This issue was sometimes known as Inchiquin money.

Collecting Hints

These issues are extremely rare and forgeries exist.

'1 DWT. 22 GR' stamped on the flan on both sides of the coin.

IC16D-005	ex. rare

Obverse   '1 DWT. 22 GR' stamped on the flan.

Reverse   Six annulets.

IC16D-010	ex. rare

Ormonde Issue (1643 – 1644)

These issues are known as Ormonde money after the Earl of Ormonde who was Lieutenant of Ireland in 1643. They were crudely
struck issues which showed loyalty to the king by the crowned
'C.R.' on the obverse. As with the previous issue, these coins were
struck from silver plates that were cut to the correct size, shape
and weight.

Collecting Hints

This issue, while scarce, is obtainable, usually in Fine
condition.

Obverse Crowned 'C.R.'.

Reverse VI D.

IC16D-015	VG £60	F £125	VF £300

Cities of Refuge – Cork (1647)

Of the four Munster towns (Bandon, Kinsale, Youghal and Cork)
that held out against the armies of the Confederated Catholics,
Cork was the only one to strike sixpences.

Collecting Hints

This issue is very rare and forgeries exist.

Obverse Cork 1647

Reverse VI

IC16D-020	v. rare

Ireland: Groat

The groat was first introduced in Ireland in 1460 under Edward IV and had a value of fourpence. The word itself is derived from the French 'gros' and the Italian 'grosso', meaning great or thick, and France was the first European country to successfully introduce a groat-sized coin in 1260, the *gros tournois*. In England, although Edward I struck groats in small quantities, it was not until the fourteenth century that Edward III issued groats in large quantities. At first, many of these issues circulated in Ireland, a practice that was facilitated by the fact that the coins were worth their silver value. However, under Edward IV, the need for a more steady supply grew and large quantities of groats were produced locally.

Edward IV   (1461 – 1483)

Edward's first issue, known as the anonymous issue, does not bear the king's name, probably because it was considered undiplomatic to name a ruling monarch in view of the civil war between Lancastrians and Yorkists raging in England at the time. The omission was rectified in subsequent issues of which there are a number of varieties. Edward's Irish groats had about two thirds of the value of their English counterparts due to the sharp rise in the price of silver throughout Europe which, in Ireland, led first to a reduction in the weight of the coins and then, in the Fourth Coinage, to the doubling of the groat's face value to eight pence.

Several mints struck groats during Edward's reign but all bear the mint's name in the reverse legend, preceded by CIVITAS or VILLA (city or town). Below we list the town names with the most common reverse legends, although it is important to remember that varieties in the spelling exist.

Cork	CIVITAS CORCAGIE
Drogheda	VILLA DE DROGEDA
Dublin	CIVITAS DUBLINIE
Limerick	CIVITAS LIMIRICI
Trim	VILLA DE TRIM
Waterford	CIVITAS WATERFORD
Wexford	VILLA WEISFOR

First (Anonymous) Coinage (1460 – 1463)

Collecting Hints

This issue is rare, especially in better than Fine condition.

Dublin Mint

Obverse Legend   None.

Reverse Legend   CIVITAS DUBLINIE — City of Dublin

Obverse   Large crown in tressure of ten arcs, a trefoil of pellets at each end of the tressure.

Reverse   Long cross with three pellets in each quarter and sometimes an annulet in two of the quarters.

IE44D-005	VG £250	F £700	VF rare

As previous, but a tressure of nine arcs.

IE44D-010	VG £225	F £600	VF rare

As previous, but a small cross in three top angles of the tressure.

IE44D-015	VG £225	F £600	VF rare

As IE44D-010, but eight arcs in tressure with small suns in each angle.

IE44D-020	VG £250	F £700	VF rare

As previous, but the arc of the tressure is fleured, suns or rosettes in the angles.

IE44D-025	VG £250	F £700	VF rare

As previous, but a large rosette in each angle of the tressure.

IE44D-030	VG £350	F £900	VF rare

Second ('Crown') Coinage (1463 – 1465)

Collecting Hints

This issue is very rare in any grade.

Dublin Mint

Obverse Legend   EDWARDUS DI GRA DNS HYBERNIE — Edward by the grace of God Lord of Ireland

Outer Reverse Legend   POSUI DEUM ADIUTOREM MEU(M) — I have made God my helper

Inner Reverse Legend CIVITAS DUBLINIE — City of Dublin

Obverse A large crown in tressure, annulets in spandrel of the tressure; mintmark rose or cross pattée at the start of the legend.

Reverse Long cross with three pellets in each quarter.

IE44D-035 v. rare

Waterford Mint

Obverse Legend As previous.

Outer Reverse Legend As previous.

Inner Reverse Legend CIVITAS WATERFORD — City of Waterford

Obverse As previous, but pellets in spandrels of the tressure ; mintmark cross at the start of the legend.

Reverse As previous.

IE44D-040 v. rare

As previous, but annulets in spandrels of tressure, saltires by crown.

IE44D-045 v. rare

Third (Small Cross on Rose/Radiant Sun) Coinage (1465 – 1467)

Collecting Hints

This issue is very rare.

Dublin Mint

Obverse Legend EDWARDUS DEI GRA DNS HYBERNI(E) — Edward by the grace of God Lord of Ireland

Outer Reverse Legend POSUI DEUM ADIUTOREM MEU(M) — I have made God my helper

Inner Reverse Legend CIVITAS DUBLINIE — City of Dublin

Obverse Small cross in the centre of a large rose.

Reverse Radiant sun.

IE44D-050 v. rare

Fourth (Rose on Sun) Coinage (1467 – 1470)

During the fourth coinage the groat was struck with two values. One denomination had a value of eight pence and was known as the double groat, while the other had a value of four pence and was known as the groat. The sizes of these two issues differed to correspond with their face value.

Collecting Hints

All issues are very rare or, in some cases, extremely rare.

Double Groat of Eightpence
Dublin Mint

Obverse Legend EDWARDUS DEI GRA DNS HYBERN — Edward by the grace of God Lord of Ireland

Reverse Legend CIVITAS DUBLINIE — City of Dublin

Obverse Crowned bust of the king in fleured tressure; mintmark rose at the start of the legend.

Reverse Rose at the centre of a large radiant sun, small roses divide the words in the legend.

IE44D-055 v. rare

As previous, but unfleured tressure in the obverse.

IE44D-060 v. rare

Drogheda Mint

As IE44D-055, except that the reverse legend reads VILLA DE DROGHEDA — Town of Drogheda.

IE44D-065 ex. rare

Trim Mint

Obverse Legend As IE44D-055.

Reverse Legend VILLA DE TRIM — Town of Trim

Obverse As IE44D-055, but two pellets over the king's crown and below his bust.

Reverse As IE44D-055.

IE44D-070 ex. rare

Groat of Fourpence
Dublin Mint

Obverse Legend EDWARD DI GRA DNS HIBERN — Edward by the grace of God Lord of Ireland

Reverse Legend CIVITAS DUBLINIE — City of Dublin

Obverse   Crowned bust of the king in unfleured tressure; mintmark rose at the start of the legend.

Reverse   Rose at the centre of a large radiant sun, small roses divide the words in the legend.

IE44D-075	ex. rare

Drogheda Mint

As previous, except that the reverse legend reads VILLA DE DROGHEDA — Town of Drogheda.

IE44D-080	ex. rare

Trim Mint

Obverse Legend   As IE44D-075.

Reverse Legend   VILLA DE TRIM — Town of Trim

Obverse   As IE44D-075, but pellets over the king's crown and below his bust.

Reverse   As IE44D-075.

IE44D-085	ex. rare

Fifth (Heavy 'Cross & Pellet') Coinage (1470 – 1473?)

These issues are fairly similar to Edward's English issues (E46D-005 to -180), except for the mint names in the inner reverse legend (see list on p.205). By the Royal Act of 1470, coinage of the previous issue was reduced to half its original value.

> # Collecting Hints
>
> The Dublin issues are scarce but obtainable, while the other mints tend to be harder to obtain and several issues are extremely rare. Coins are often found clipped and most are usually available in VG to Fine condition with VF specimens being rare. Contemporary forgeries of low metal content and rather crude style exist. These issues are cruder in style than the English ones.

Dublin Mint

Obverse Legend   EDWARDUS DEI GRA DNS HIBERNIE — Edward by the grace of God Lord of Ireland

Outer Reverse Legend   POSUI DEUM ADIUTOREM MEUM — I have made God my helper

Inner Reverse Legend   CIVITAS DUBLINIE — City of Dublin

Obverse   Crowned bust of the king in tressure.

Reverse   Long cross with three pellets in each quarter.

IE44D-090	VG £65	F £150	VF £500

As previous, but a pellet in one or three of the lower spandrels of the tressure.

IE44D-095	VG £65	F £150	VF £500

As previous, but a pellet also to the right of the crown.

IE44D-100	VG £90	F £200	VF £650

As IE44D-090, but a star on either side of the crown.

IE44D-105	VG £110	F £200	VF £750

As IE44D-090, but a 'G' (initial of the mintmaster Germyn Lynch) on the king's breast.

IE44D-110	VG £90	F £200	VF £650

Drogheda Mint

Obverse Legend   As IE44D-090.

Outer Reverse Legend   As IE44D-090.

Inner Reverse Legend   VILLA DE DROGHEDA — Town of Drogheda

Obverse   Crowned bust of the king within a tressure, three pellets on some points of the tressure and a cross below the bust.

Reverse   Long cross with three pellets in each quarter.

IE44D-115	VG £125	F £300	VF £800

As previous, but the tressure is fleured.

IE44D-120	VG £90	F £200	VF £650

As previous, but no cross below the bust.

| IE44D-125 | VG £80 | F £180 | VF £550 |

As previous, but a pellet below the bust.

| IE44D-130 | VG £90 | F £200 | VF £650 |

Limerick Mint

Obverse Legend   As IE44D-090.

Outer Reverse Legend   As IE44D-090.

Inner Reverse Legend   CIVITAS LIMIRICI — City of Limerick

Obverse   Crowned bust of the king with a tressure.

Reverse   Long cross with three pellets in each quarter.

| IE44D-135   ex. rare |

Trim Mint

As previous, but the inner reverse legend reads VILLA DE TRIM — Town of Trim.

| IE44D-140 | VG £125 | F £300 | VF rare |

Waterford Mint

As IE44D-135, but the inner reverse legend reads CIVITAS WATERFORD — City of Waterford.

| IE44D-145 | VG £100 | F £250 | VF £800 |

As previous, but crosses on either side of the king's neck.

| IE44D-150 | VG £100 | F £250 | VF £800 |

As IE44D-145, but a 'V' on the king's breast.

| IE44D-155 | VG £100 | F £250 | VF £800 |

As IE44D-150, but a sideways 'W' on the king's breast, crosses or saltires on either side of the neck.

| IE44D-160 | VG £100 | F £250 | VF £800 |

Cork Mint

This issue is crude in style.

Obverse Legend   As IE44D-090.

Outer Reverse Legend   As IE44D-090.

Inner Reverse Legend   CIVITAS CORCAGIE — City of Cork

Obverse   Crowned bust of the king within a tressure, a rosette on either side of his neck.

Reverse   Long cross with three pellets in each quarter.

| IE44D-165   ex. rare |

As previous, but a cross on either side of the king's neck on the obverse.

| IE44D-170   ex. rare |

Sixth (Light 'Cross & Pellets') Coinage (1473 – 1478?)

This issue is fairly similar to the previous coinage although the weight of the coins was reduced by about a quarter. Several issues used the dies from the previous coinage, making correct identification of coins in low grades difficult. Collectors should refer to the previous coinage when identifying an issue, paying particular attention to any marks or letters which have been noted on the coin.

Collecting Hints

Some issues are fairly common, while several varieties and mints are rare. Coins are usually available in VG to Fine condition and are often clipped and poorly struck. Contemporary forgeries of crude style and low fineness silver exist for some issues. Coins in VF or better condition are difficult to obtain.

Dublin Mint

Obverse Legend   EDWARDUS DEI GRA DNS HYBERNIE — Edward by the grace of God Lord of Ireland

Outer Reverse Legend   POSUI DEUM ADIUTOREM MEUM — I have made God my helper

Inner Reverse Legend   CIVITAS DUBLINIE — City of Dublin

Obverse   Crowned bust of the king within tressure, the mintmaster Germyn Lynch's initial 'G' below the bust.

Reverse   Long cross with three pellets in each quarter or three pellets in two of the quarters and two pellets and a rosette in the other two.

| IE44D-175 | VG £50 | F £120 | VF £375 |

As previous, but annulets in two spandrels of the tressure.

| IE44D-180 | VG £60 | F £120 | VF £375 |

As previous, but crosses by the king's neck.

| IE44D-185 | VG £90 | F £200 | VF £600 |

As IE44D-180, but annulets, sometimes in two spandrels, by the king's neck and no crosses.

| IE44D-190 | VG £50 | F £100 | VF £350 |

As IE44D-175, but pellets in some spandrels of the tressure.

| IE44D-195 | VG £50 | F £100 | VF £350 |

As IE44D-175, but an 'I' on the king's breast.

| IE44D-200 | VG £100 | F £300 | VF rare |

In the nineteenth century, one issue was noted with an English title obverse legend. This is possibly a forgery or a mule with an English obverse die.

Drogheda Mint

Obverse Legend   As previous.

Outer Reverse Legend   As previous.

Inner Reverse Legend   VILLA DE DROGHEDA — Town of Drogheda

Obverse   Crowned bust of the king within a tressure, a 'G' below the bust and annulets in two spandrels of the tressure.

Reverse   As previous.

| IE44D-205 | VG £60 | F £120 | VF £350 |

As previous, but an annulet on either side of the king's neck.

| IE44D-210 | VG £100 | F £200 | VF £600 |

As previous, but a trefoil by the king's breast.

| IE44D-215 | VG £125 | F £300 | VF rare |

As IE44D-205, but no marks apart from a 'G' on the king's breast on the obverse. There is also an extra pellet in two of the quarters on the reverse.

| IE44D-220 | ex. rare |

Limerick Mint

Obverse Legend   As previous.

Outer Reverse Legend   As previous.

Inner Reverse Legend   CIVITAS LIMIRICI or LIMERICI — City of Limerick

Obverse   Crowned bust of the king within a tressure, an 'L' on his breast and crosses, a saltire or quatrefoil on either side of his neck.

Reverse   Long cross with three pellets in each quarter.

| IE44D-225 | VG £100 | F £225 | VF £600 |

As previous, but a rosette or cinquefoil either side of the king's neck.

| IE44D-230 | VG £100 | F £225 | VF £600 |

Trim Mint

Obverse Legend   As previous.

Outer Reverse Legend   As previous.

Inner Reverse Legend   VILLA DE TRIM — Town of Trim

Obverse   Crowned bust of the king within a tressure.

Reverse   As previous.

| IE44D-235 | VG £100 | F £225 | VF £600 |

As previous, but pellets in some spandrels of the tressure and/or over the crown.

| IE44D-240 | VG £100 | F £225 | VF £600 |

As IE44D-235, but a pellet on either side of the king's neck.

| IE44D-245 | ex. rare |

As IE44D-235, but a 'B' on the king's breast.

| IE44D-250 | ex. rare |

Waterford Mint

Obverse Legend   As previous.

Outer Reverse Legend   As previous.

Inner Reverse Legend   CIVITAS WATERFORD — City of Waterford

Obverse Crowned bust of the king within a tressure, a rosette on either side of his neck.

Reverse Long cross with three pellets in each quarter.

IE44D-255	VG £100	F £225	VF £600

As previous, but a cross or saltire either side of the king's neck.

IE44D-260	VG £60	F £130	VF £325

As IE44D-225, but a 'V' on the king's breast and no rosettes.

IE44D-265	VG £80	F £160	VF £350

As previous, but a 'G' on the king's breast.

IE44D-270	VG £60	F £130	VF £325

One issue for Waterford exists weighing some 50% more than regular issues with annulets at the king's neck and a crowned leopard at the end of the obverse legend. Due to this coin's irregular weight, it is probably correct to class it as a pattern. It is extremely rare.

Cork Mint

Obverse Legend As previous.

Outer Reverse Legend As previous.

Inner Reverse Legend CIVITAS CORCAGIE — City of Cork

Obverse Crowned bust of the king within a tressure, all of crude style.

Reverse Long cross with three pellets in each quarter.

IE44D-275	ex. rare

As previous, but a pellet on either side of the king's neck.

IE44D-280	ex. rare

Wexford Mint

Obverse Legend As previous.

Outer Reverse Legend As previous.

Inner Reverse Legend VILLA WEISFOR or WEIXFOR — Town of Wexford

Obverse Crowned bust of the king within a tressure, all of crude style.

Reverse Long cross with three pellets in each quarter.

IE44D-285	ex. rare

It is possible that groats were also struck in Youghal, Kinsale and Killmallock but none are known to exist.

Seventh (Sun & Rose) Coinage (1478 – 1483)

This issue had a value of fourpence and was struck in Dublin and Drogheda. The inner reverse legend bears the mint name.

> # Collecting Hints
> This issue is very rare in any grade.

Dublin Mint

Varieties exist in the position and size of the sun and rose on the obverse.

Obverse Legend EDWARDUS DEI GRA HIBERNA (varieties exist) — Edward by the grace of God King of Ireland or EDWARDUS DEI GRA REX AGL FRAE D — Edward by the grace of God King of England France

Outer Reverse Legend POSUI DEUM ADIUTORE(M) MEU(M) — I have made God my helper

Inner Reverse Legend CIVITAS DUBLINIE — City of Dublin

Obverse Crowned bust of the king with a sun and rose of varying size alternating at the crown and neck.

Reverse Long cross with a rose in the centre.

IE44D-290	v. rare

Drogheda Mint

As previous, except that the inner reverse legend reads VILLA DE DROGHEDA — Town of Drogheda.

IE44D-295	v. rare

While no groats were struck in the name of Edward V, it is

possible that coins from Edward IV's seventh coinage were struck during his reign.

Richard III   (1483 – 1485)

Two issues of groats were struck during Richard's short reign. The first was very much like the previous ones of Edward IV and one variety uses an altered die from that reign. The second issue is known as the 'three crowns' coinage due to its reverse design, which was also popular under Henry VII. The main difference between the two reigns lies in the obverse legends.

First Coinage (1483)

Collecting Hints

This issue is very rare in any grade.

Drogheda Mint

Obverse Legend   RICARDUS DEI GRA DNS HYB(E) — Richard by the grace of God Lord of Ireland

Outer Reverse Legend   POSUI DEUM ADIUTOREM MEU(M) — I have made God my helper

Inner Reverse Legend   VILLA DROGHEDA — Town of Drogheda

Obverse   Crowned bust of the king in tressure, a sun and a rose alternating at the crown and neck.

Reverse   Long cross with a rose in the centre.

IR34D-005   ex. rare

Altered dies from IE44D-295 with RIC over EDW in the obverse legend.

IR34D-010   ex. rare

Second (Three Crowns) Coinage (1483 – 1485)

Collecting Hints

The Dublin issue is very rare while the Waterford one is extremely rare. Both issues are crudely struck and the Dublin issue is rarely found in better than Fine condition.

Dublin Mint

Obverse Legend   RICAR REX ANGL FRAN(C) — Richard King of England France

Reverse Legend   DOMINUS HYBERNIE — Lord of Ireland

Obverse   Royal arms over long cross with pellet ends.

Reverse   Three crowns over a cross with pellet ends.

IR34D-015   VG £150   F £450   VF rare

Waterford Mint

Obverse Legend   RICARDUS DEI GRAIA REX — Richard by the grace of God King

Reverse Legend   CIVITAS WAT(T)ERFOORD (varieties exist) — City of Waterford

Obverse   Royal arms within a tressure over a long cross with pellet ends.

Reverse   Three crowns within a tressure over a long cross with pellet ends.

IR34D-020   ex. rare

Henry VII   (1485 – 1509)

A large variety of groats was struck during the reign of Henry VII. The first issues were very much continuations from Richard's three crowns coinage, while the later issues have a front-facing crowned portrait on the obverse and a long cross on the reverse. All are very crude in style and even though the portrait issues could at first glance be confused with English issues (H74D-005 to -050), they are of inferior style and production.

Early Three Crowns Issue (1485 – 1487)

Collecting Hints

These issues while scarce are obtainable, especially in lower grades. Coins are often clipped with weaknesses in legend and are rarely found in better that Fine condition.

Dublin Mint

Obverse Legend   REX ANGLIE FRANC(IE) — King of England France

Reverse Legend   DOMINUS HYBERNIE — Lord of Ireland

Obverse   Royal shield over long cross, three pellets at the end of the cross.

Reverse   Three crowns over long cross, three pellets at the end of the cross.

IH74D-005   VG £60   F £140   VF £350

As previous, but the obverse legend also reads DOMINUS HYBERNIE.

IH74D-010	VG £60	F £140	VF £350

Obverse Legend   REX ANGLIE FRANCIE — King of England France

Reverse Legend   ET REX HYBERNIE — And King of Ireland

Obverse & Reverse   As previous.

IH74D-015	VG £80	F £200	VF £500

Waterford Mint

Obverse Legend   HENRICUS DI GRACIA REX — Henry by the grace of God King

Reverse Legend   CIVITAS WATERFOR(D) — City of Waterford

Obverse   Royal arms over cross with three pellets at the ends, all within a quatrefoil.

Reverse   Three crowns with an 'H' below over a cross with pellet ends, two lis by the central crown, all within a tressure with trefoils on the points of the tressure.

IH74D-020	VG £60	F £140	VF £350

As previous, but omitting lis by central crown.

IH74D-025	VG £60	F £140	VF £350

As previous, but royal arms not within a quatrefoil, annulets at cross's ends.

IH74D-030	ex. rare

As IH74D-020, but three annulets at cross's ends sometimes with crosses or mullets in lower angles of quatrefoil.

IH74D-035	VG £60	F £140	VF £350

As previous, but stars by lower reverse crown.

IH74D-040	VG £80	F £200	VF £500

Three Crowns Issue of Lambert Simnel (1487)

Lambert Simnel was crowned in Dublin in 1487. He was a usurper and known as the pretender who took advantage of the power vacuum left after the War of the Roses.

Collecting Hints

All issues are extremely rare and struck in the name of EDWARDUS.

Dublin Mint

Obverse Legend   EDWARDUS REX ANGL FRANC (varieties exist) — Edward King of England France

Reverse Legend   ET REX HYBERNIE — And King of Ireland

Obverse   Royal shield over long cross, three pellets at each cross's end.

Reverse   Long cross over three crowns, three pellets at cross's ends.

IH74D-045	ex. rare

As previous, but the reverse legend reads DEMINUS HYBERNIE — Lord of Ireland; the obverse legend is similar to the previous one.

IH74D-050	ex. rare

Waterford Mint

Obverse Legend   As previous.

Reverse Legend   CIVITAS WATERFORD — City of Waterford

Obverse   Royal arms over long cross in quatrefoil, three annulets at cross's end.

Reverse   Three crowns over long cross, three annulets at cross's ends, the crowns within a tressure and a reversed 'E' below the lower crown.

IH74D-055	ex. rare

Obverse   The IH74D-020 obverse die.

Reverse   As previous.

IH74D-060	ex. rare

Obverse   As IH74D-055.

Reverse   The IH74D-020 reverse die.

IH74D-065	ex. rare

It is probable that other mules exist. All of which will be extremely rare.

Three Crowns Issue of Geraldin (1487)

The Fitzgeralds of Kildare were a powerful family who took control for a brief period after Lambert Simnel's abortive attempt to win the crown. The arms of the Earl can be found beside the royal shield.

Collecting Hints

These issues are rare and rarely found in better than Fine condition.

Obverse Legend   REX ANGLIE (Z) FRANC(IE) — King of England (and) France

Reverse Legend   DOMINUS YBERNIE (varieties exist) — Lord of Ireland

Obverse   Long cross over royal shield, three annulets at the cross's ends, saltire cross either side of the shield.

Reverse   Three crowns with an 'H' below, all within a tressure and over a cross with three annulets at each end.

IH74D-070   VG £100   F £225   VF £500

As previous, but no 'H' below crowns.

IH74D-075   VG £100   F £225   VF £500

As previous, but muled with reverse of IH74D-035.

IH74D-080   ex. rare

Late Three Crowns Issue (1488 – 1490)

Collecting Hints

These issues, which were struck in Dublin, are rare but obtainable. Coins were struck from crude dies and are usually clipped. They are rarely found in better than Fine condition.

Obverse Legend   HENRICUS REX AN — Henry King of England

Reverse Legend   DOMINUS VBERNIE — Lord of Ireland

Obverse   Royal shield over long cross with three annulets at each end.

Reverse   Three crowns over long cross, three annulets at the end of each end, an 'H' below the crown.

IH74D-085   VG £100   F £300   VF rare

As previous, but the obverse legend reads REX ANGLIE Z FRANC — King of England and France.

IH74D-090   VG £80   F £200   VF rare

As previous, but the obverse legend reads DOMINOS VBERNIE — Lord of Ireland.

IH74D-095   VG £80   F £200   VF rare

Obverse Legend   HENRICUS REX AN — Henry King of England

Reverse Legend   CIVITAS DUBLIN(IE) — City of Dublin

Obverse   As previous.

Reverse   As previous, but upper crown is arched.

IH74D-100   VG £150   F £350   VF rare

Late Portrait Issue (1496 – 1505)

This issue appears strikingly similar in style to Henry's more common English issues (H74D-005 to -050), with a front-facing crowned bust of the king on the obverse and a long cross with three pellets in each quarter on the reverse. These coins however are much cruder than the English ones and collectors should pay particular attention to the inner reverse legend which reads CIVITAS DUBLINIE (minor varieties) on the Irish issues. This issue was struck at the Dublin mint only.

Collecting Hints

These issues are obtainable but scarce and usually found clipped in VG to Fine condition. Coins are rarely found in VF condition and some varieties appear to be made of silver of a low fineness.

Obverse Legend   HENRICUS DI GRA DNS HYBERNIE (varieties exist) — Henry by the grace of God Lord of Ireland

Outer Reverse Legend   POSUI DEUM ADIVTOREM MEU — I have made God my helper

Inner Reverse Legend   CIVITAS DUBLINIE — City of Dublin

Obverse   Large crowned bust of the king with open crown, within a fleured tressure.

Reverse   Long cross with three pellets within each quarter.

IH74D-105   VG £60   F £150   VF rare

As previous, but a smaller bust of the king.

| IH74D-110 | VG £60 | F £150 | VF rare |

As IH74D-105, but the outer reverse legend reads PROVERBO ADIVTORIUM — I will provide help.

| IH74D-115 | VG £80 | F £200 | VF rare |

Legends   As previous.
Obverse   As IH74D-110.
Reverse   As IH74D-110.

| IH74D-120 | VG £80 | F £200 | VF rare |

Obverse Legend   As previous.
Reverse Legends   As IH74D-105.
Obverse   Bust of front-facing king wearing an arched crown, all within a tressure which is broken by the crown.
Reverse   As previous.

| IH74D-125 | VG £80 | F £200 | VF rare |

As previous, but reverse legend as IH74D-115.

| IH74D-130 | VG £100 | F £250 | VF rare |

Obverse Legend   As previous.
Reverse Legends   As IH74D-105.
Obverse   Large crowned bust of the king wearing an arched crown, a trefoil at some points of the tressure.
Reverse   Long cross, three pellets in each quarter, an 'H' in the centre of the cross.

| IH74D-135 | VG £80 | F £200 | VF rare |

As previous, but annulets on either side of the crown and neck.

| IH74D-140 | VG £125 | F £300 | VF rare |

Obverse Legend   As previous.
Reverse Legends   As previous.
Obverse   King wearing an open crown within a plain tressure, saltires on either side of the neck.
Reverse   Long cross with three pellets in each quarter.

| IH74D-145 | VG £80 | F £200 | VF rare |

As previous, but saltires at points of tressure only.

| IH74D-150 | VG £80 | F £200 | VF rare |

Obverse Legend   As previous.
Reverse Legends   As previous.
Obverse   Bust of the king front-facing wearing an open crown not within a tressure, a cross on either side of crown.
Reverse   Long cross with three pellets in each quarter.

| IH74D-155 | VG £80 | F £200 | VF rare |

As previous, but a rosette on either side of the crown.

| IH74D-160 | VG £100 | F £250 | VF rare |

As IH74D-155, but no marks by the crown, a rosette in the centre of the reverse cross.

| IH74D-165 | VG £100 | F £250 | VF rare |

Obverse Legend   As previous.
Outer Reverse Legend   As previous.
Inner Reverse Legend   CIVITAS or SIVITAS DUBLIN(IE) — City of Dublin
Obverse   Facing bust of the king wearing a flat crown.
Reverse   Long cross with three pellets in each quarter.

| IH74D-170 | VG £60 | F £180 | VF rare |

Henry VIII   (1509 – 1547)

No coins were struck in Ireland for the first twenty-six years of Henry's reign although from 1534 onwards groats were being struck in London and Bristol and shipped to Ireland, because Henry was in favour of central control of the money supply. These groats, which had a value of either four or six pence, were known as harp groats as a large crowned harp can be found on the reverse. Some harp groats are found with a small countermark of four annulets which was possibly done in later years to reduce their value from sixpence to fourpence. It should be noted that Edward VI also produced groats in Henry VIII's name with Henry's bust on the obverse; they had a value of sixpence and are listed here under Edward.

Collecting Hints

Most issues are fairly common and found in all grades, usually undamaged in VG to VF condition.

First Coinage (1534 – 1540)

London Mint

Obverse Legend HENRIC VIII D.G.R. AGL Z (minor varieties exist) — Henry VIII by the grace of God King of England and

Reverse Legend FRANCE DOMINUS HIBERNIE — France Lord of Ireland

Obverse Crowned arms; mintmark crown at the start of the legend.

Reverse Crown over large harp dividing a crowned 'H' (for Henry) and 'A' (for Anne Boleyn); a mintmark crown at the start of the legend.

| IH84D-005 | VG £30 | F £60 | VF £150 |

As previous, but the initials 'H' and 'I' (for Jane Seymour) on either side of the harp.

| IH84D-010 | VG £30 | F £60 | VF £150 |

As previous, but the initials 'H' and 'K' (for Katherine Howard) on either side of the harp.

| IH84D-015 | VG £35 | F £70 | VF £170 |

As previous, but 'HR' (HENRICUS REX) on either side of the harp.

| IH84D-020 | VG £30 | F £60 | VF £150 |

Second Coinage (1540 – 1542)

London Mint

Obverse Legend As previous.

Reverse Legend As previous.

Obverse As previous, but mintmark trefoil at the start of the legend.

Reverse As previous, 'HR' on either side of the harp; mintmark trefoil at the start of the legend.

| IH84D-025 | VG £30 | F £60 | VF £150 |

As previous, but obverse legend omits the 'VIII'.

| IH84D-030 | VG £35 | F £75 | VF £170 |

Obverse Legend As IH84D-025.

Reverse Legend FRANCE ET HIBERNIE REX — France King of Ireland

Obverse As previous.

Reverse As previous.

| IH84D-035 | VG £35 | F £75 | VF £170 |

Third Coinage (1543)

London Mint

This issue had a silver content of 0.833.

As previous, but mintmark rose at the start of the obverse and reverse legends.

| IH84D-040 | VG £35 | F £75 | VF £170 |

Fourth Coinage (1544)

London Mint

The value of this groat was sixpence although its silver content was reduced to 0.666.

As previous, but mintmark lis at the start of the obverse and reverse legends.

| IH84D-045 | VG £50 | F £100 | VF £250 |

Fifth Coinage (1544 – 1546)

London Mint

The value of this groat was sixpence and its silver content further reduced to 0.500.

As previous, except that the reverse legend reads FRANCE ET HIBERNIE REX S — France King of Ireland (?)S.

| IH84D-050 | VG £50 | F £100 | VF £250 |

As previous, but the reverse legend reads FRANCE ET HIBERNIE REX 37 — France King of Ireland 37, indicating that it was the thirty seventh year of Henry's reign (i.e. 1545)

IH84D-055	VG £70	F £150	VF £350

Sixth Coinage (1546 – 1547)

Bristol Mint

These coins were struck by the Bristol mintmaster William Sharrington. They had a value of sixpence and were struck in silver of 0.250 fineness

Obverse Legend HENRIC 8 D.G. ANGL FRANC — Henry VIII by the grace of God of England France

Reverse Legend WS ET HIBERNIE REX 38 — WS (William Sharrington's initials) and Ireland King 38 (thirty-eighth year of Henry's reign, i.e. 1546)

Obverse As previous.

Reverse As previous.

IH84D-060	VG £120	F £300	VF £700

As previous, but omits the '38' at the end of the legend.

IH84D-065	VG £70	F £150	VF £350

Countermarked Issues

As any of the previous, but countermarked with four annulets on the reverse, usually in the field.

IH84D-070	VG £200	F £400	VF rare

Edward VI   (1547 – 1553)

Henry VIII Posthumous Issue (1547 – 1550)

No groats were struck in Edward's name but coins bearing Henry VIII's portrait and title were struck in Dublin, sometimes using English-made dies. These issues are very similar to the English ones (H84D-060 to -115), the main difference being the reverse legend which reads CIVITAS DUBLINIE — City of Dublin for the Irish issues. The value of these issues was sixpence but they were known as groats and have therefore been included here. All issues were struck of a low metal fineness between 0.250 and 0.333.

It is probable that IH84D-065 was struck during this period.

Collecting Hints

While scarce, these issues are obtainable, especially in the lower grades. Coins tend to be poorly struck and are often rather dull in colour due to their low metal content but they should never be cleaned.

Obverse Legend HENRIC 8 D.G. AGL FRA Z HIB REX (varieties exist) — Henry VIII by the grace of God King of England France and Ireland

Reverse Legend CIVITAS DUBLINIE — City of Dublin

Obverse Crowned bust of the king of Tower mint style.

Reverse Arms over cross; mintmark harp, 'P' or boars head at the start of the legend.

IE64D-005	VG £60	F £150	VF £450

As previous, but the obverse bears a crude large crowned bust of the king (Dublin dies).

IE64D-010	VG £60	F £150	VF £450

As previous, but a crude small crowned bust of the king on the obverse (Dublin dies).

IE64D-015	VG £60	F £150	VF £450

As previous, but smaller bust of the king facing half right on the obverse (Tower mint style).

| IE64D-020 | VG £50 | F £140 | VF £400 |

Mary (1553 – 1554)

During Mary's short reign groats were struck with a value of fourpence and a silver content of 0.583 fineness. A large harp on the reverse of the coin differentiates this issue from the more common English one (MA4D-005), which has the royal shield on the reverse.

Collecting Hints

This issue is very rare and Victorian forgeries are known to exist. Also, dated coins similar to this issue are considered forgeries of unknown origin.

Obverse Legend　MARIA D.G. ANG FRA Z HIB REGI — Mary by the grace of God Queen of England France and Ireland

Reverse Legend　VERITAS TEMPORIS FILIA — Truth is the daughter of time

Obverse　Crowned bust of the queen facing left; mintmark lis after 'MARIA'.

Reverse　Crown over harp dividing crowned 'M.R.'.

| IMA4D-005 | ex. rare |

Philip & Mary (1554 – 1558)

Together with the shilling of this issue, the groat of Philip and Mary is the first Irish coin to be dated using Arabic numerals, not Roman. It was struck in very base silver of about 0.250 fineness. All issues bear the busts of the king and queen facing each other on the obverse and a crowned harp on the reverse. By contrast, contemporary English sixpences have an obverse similar to the Irish groat, but bear a shield on the reverse and are made of fine silver.

Collecting Hints

These issues are fairly common especially in the low grades. They were often weakly struck, with unclear portraits so coins with clear dates and strong portraits are desirable.

Obverse Legend　PHILIP ET MARIA D.G. REX ET REGINA AN — Philip and Mary by the grace of God King and Queen of England

Reverse Legend　POSVIMUS DEUM ADIUTOREM NOSTRUM — We have made God our helper

Obverse　Two busts facing each other with a crown above, dividing the date (1555).

Reverse　Crown over harp dividing crowned 'P' and 'M'; mintmark portcullis or rose at the start of the legend.

| IPM4D-005 | VG £40 | F £90 | VF £300 |

As previous, but dated 1556; mintmark portcullis only.

| IPM4D-010 | rare |

As previous, dated 1556; mintmark rose.

| IPM4D-015 | VG £40 | F £90 | VF £300 |

As previous, but dated 1557 or 1553 (die error); mintmark rose.

| IPM4D-020 | VG £40 | F £85 | VF £280 |

As previous, but dated 1558; mintmark rose often on both sides of the coin.

| IPM4D-025 | VG £50 | F £100 | VF £325 |

Elizabeth I (1558 – 1603)

The groat with a value of fourpence was struck during the first two coinages of Elizabeth's reign. The first issue is the base issue of 1558 with coins being struck in silver of 0.250 fineness. The second issue is the fine silver issue made of silver of 0.916 fineness. Both issues have a harp design on the reverse which easily differentiates them from contemporary English groats.

Coinage of 1558

Collecting Hints

This base issue while scarce is obtainable especially in the lower grades. It is often poorly struck with much of the detail weak.

Obverse Legend   ELIZABETH D.G. ANG FRA Z HIB REGINA (varieties exist) — Elizabeth by the grace of God Queen of England France and Ireland

Reverse Legend   POSUI DEUM ADIVTOREM MEUM — I have made God my helper

Obverse   Small crowned bust of the queen facing left, no inner circle; mintmark rose at the start of the legend.

Reverse   Crown over harp dividing crowned 'E.R.'; mintmark rose at the start of the legend.

| IEL4D-005 | VG £60 | F £150 | VF £400 |

Coinage of 1561

Collecting Hints

This issue is rare in any grade.

Obverse Legend   ELIZABETH D.G. A F Z HIBERNIE RE(GI) — Elizabeth by the grace of God Queen of England France and Ireland

Reverse Legend   POSUI DEUM ADIUTOREM MEUM — I have made God my helper

Obverse   Crowned bust of the queen facing left; mintmark harp at the start of the legend.

Reverse   Crown over three harps dividing date (1561).

| IEL4D-010 | VG £150 | F £450 | VF rare |

Charles I   (1625 – 1649)

1642 Issue of the Great Rebellion

This issue was struck out of irregular-sized pieces of plate. Coins were issued under an act that empowered Lord Inchiquin to take in silver plate at the Dublin mint and defer payment to the members of the public, who in turn received interest on the silver they gave. The plates were then cut up and weighed and marked with a value according to their weight. This issue is sometimes known as Inchiquin money.

Collecting Hints

This issue is extremely rare and a variety of forgeries of these issues exist.

Obverse   Countermark of '1DWT 6GR'.
Reverse   As obverse.

| IC14D-005 ex. rare |

Obverse   As previous.
Reverse   Four annulets.

| IC14D-010 ex. rare |

Ormonde Issue (1643 – 1644)

These issues are known as Ormonde money after the Earl of Ormonde who was Lieutenant of Ireland in 1643. They were crudely struck but showed loyalty to the king by the crowned 'C.R.' on the obverse. As with the previous issue, these coins were struck from silver plates that were cut to the correct size and shape.

Collecting Hints

This issue is fairly common and usually found in Fine condition.

Obverse   Crown over 'C.R.'.
Reverse   A 'D' above 'IIII' (four pence).

| IC14D-015 | VG £40 | F £100 | VF £250 |

Ireland: Threepence

The threepence complemented the sixpence and was part of a new denomination structure which eventually replaced the halfgroat. The denomination was introduced under Edward VI although the coins bear the ageing bust of Henry VIII and his title in the legend on the obverse. These coins are often called twopences as some were struck with twopence obverse dies from English issues (H82D-100 to -150). They can also be confused with English issues sometimes, but their reverse legend reads CIVITAS DUBLINIE — City of Dublin. Threepences were also struck during later reigns.

Edward VI   (1547 – 1553)

Henry VIII Posthumous Issue (1547 – 1550)

> ## Collecting Hints
>
> These coins are very scarce and difficult to obtain in better than Fine condition.

Obverse Legend   HENRIC 8 D.G. AG. FR Z HIB REX — Henry VIII by the grace of God King of England France and Ireland

Reverse Legend   CIVITAS DUBLINIE — City of Dublin

Obverse   Crowned front-facing bust of king of early Tower mint style.

Reverse   Shield over cross; mintmark boar's head, harp, sun, or 'P' at the start of the legend.

IE63D-005	VG £60	F £150	VF rare

As previous, but slightly cruder bust using Irish-made obverse and reverse dies.

IE63D-010	VG £80	F £150	VF rare

As previous, but late Tower mint style of bust.

IE63D-015	VG £60	F £150	VF rare

Elizabeth I   (1558 – 1603)

Under Elizabeth non-portrait base silver threepences were struck during the third base coinage of 1601 – 02.

Base Issue (1601 – 1602)

> ## Collecting Hints
>
> This issue is rare and rarely found in better than Fine condition, often with cracked flans and weak legends.

Obverse Legend   ELIZABETH D.G. AN FR ET HIBER RE — Elizabeth by the grace of God Queen of England France and Ireland

Reverse Legend   POSUI DEU ADIUTOREM MEU — I have made God my helper

Obverse   Royal arms; mintmark trefoil star or martlet at the start of the legend

Reverse   Crowned harp; mintmarks as obverse

IEL3D-005	VG £100	F £250	VF rare

Charles I   (1625 – 1649)

1642 Issue of the Great Rebellion

This issue was struck out of irregular-sized pieces of plate. It was issued under an act that empowered Lord Inchiquin to take in silver plate at the Dublin mint and defer payment to the members of the public, who in turn received interest on the silver they gave. The plates were then cut, weighed and marked with a value according to their weight. This issue was sometimes known as Inchiquin money.

> ## Collecting Hints
>
> This issue is extremely rare and forgeries exist.

Obverse   '23 GR' in circle.

Reverse   Three annulets.

IC13D-005 ex. rare	

Ormonde Issue (1643 – 1644)

This issue is known as Ormonde money after the Earl of Ormonde who was Lieutenant of Ireland in 1643. It was crudely struck and showed loyalty to the king by the crowned 'C.R.' on the obverse. As with the previous issue, these coins were struck from silver plates that had been cut to the correct size, shape and weight.

Collecting Hints

This issue is fairly common and usually found in Fine condition.

Obverse   Crowned 'C.R.'.

Reverse   'III D'

IC13D-010 VG £45 F £100 VF £250			

Ireland: Halfgroat

The Irish halfgroat was introduced into circulation during the second crown coinage of Edward IV (1463 – 65) as part of a new denomination structure which included the groat. However, in all reigns, the halfgroat is much scarcer than the groat or penny and was never struck in large quantities. Sometimes it was not struck at all for some coinages or issues. Although the silver fineness of the Irish halfgroats varied, all issues had a value of twopence. The mint's name can be found in the inner reverse legend.

Edward IV   (1461 – 1483)

Second (Crown) Coinage (1463 – 1465)

Collecting Hints

This issue is extremely rare.

Dublin Mint

Obverse Legend   EDWARDUS DI GRA DNS HYBERNIE — Edward by the grace of God Lord of Ireland

Outer Reverse Legend   POSUI DEUM ADIUTOREM MEU(M) — I have made God my helper

Inner Reverse Legend   CIVITAS DUBLINIE — City of Dublin

Obverse   Crown in tressure.

Reverse   Long cross with three pellets in each quarter.

IE42D-005   ex. rare

Fourth (Rose on Sun) Coinage (1467 – 1470)

Collecting Hints

These issues are extremely rare.

Dublin Mint

Obverse Legend   EDWARD D.G. D. HYBER — Edward by the grace of God Lord of Ireland

Reverse Legend   CIVITAS DUBLIN — City of Dublin

Obverse   Crowned front-facing bust of king.

Reverse   Rose at the centre of a large sun.

IE42D-010   ex. rare

As previous, but crosses by neck on the obverse.

IE42D-015   ex. rare

Trim Mint

Obverse Legend   EDWARDUS DI GRA DNS HYBE — Edward by the grace of God Lord of Ireland

Reverse Legend   VILLA DE TRIM — Town of Trim

Obverse   As IE42D-010.

Reverse   As IE42D-010.

IE42D-020   ex. rare

As previous, but two pellets over crown.

IE42D-025   ex. rare

Fifth (Heavy 'Cross & Pellet') Coinage (1470 – 1473)

These issues are fairly similar in style to the much more common English issues (E42D-005 to -185) and collectors should pay particular attention to the inner reverse legend, which gives the mint's name in both the English and Irish issues.

Collecting Hints

These issues are either very rare or extremely rare and difficult to obtain in any condition.

Dublin Mint

Obverse Legend   EDWARD D. GRA DNS. HBERNIE — Edward by the grace of God Lord of Ireland

Outer Reverse Legend   POSUI DEUM ADIVTOR MEU(M) — I have made God my helper

Inner Reverse Legend   CIVITAS DUBLINI — City of Dublin

Obverse   Crowned front-facing bust of the king with an annulet on either side of his neck.

Reverse   Long cross with three pellets in each quarter.

IE42D-030   ex. rare

As previous, but no annulets. Pellets over crown and below bust.

IE42D-035   v. rare

As previous, but pellets in each angle of tressure too.

IE42D-040   ex. rare

Galway Mint

Obverse Legend   As previous.

Outer Reverse Legend   As previous.

Inner Reverse Legend   VILLA GALWEY — Town of Galway

Obverse   Crowned front-facing bust of the king within a tressure that is fleured.

Reverse   As previous.

IE42D-045   ex. rare

Trim Mint

Obverse Legend   As previous.

Outer Reverse Legend   As previous.

Inner Reverse Legend   VILLA DE TRIM — Town of Trim

Obverse   Crowned front-facing bust of the king with two pellets over the crown.

Reverse   As previous.

IE42D-050   ex. rare

Sixth (Light 'Cross & Pellets') Coinage (1473 – 1478)

This coinage is very much a continuation from the previous one, and again collectors should pay particular attention to the mint name in the inner reverse legend to avoid confusion with the much more common English issues (E42D-005 to -185). A nineteenth century source also notes a specimen from Trim mint; it is uncertain, although probable, that such a coin exists.

Collecting Hints

All issues are extremely rare.

Dublin Mint

Obverse Legend   EDWARD DI GRA DNS HYBER — Edward by the grace of God Lord of Ireland

Outer Reverse Legend   POSUI DEUM ADIVTOR MEU — I have made God my helper

Inner Reverse Legend   CIVITAS DUBLIN — City of Dublin

Obverse   Crowned front-facing bust of the king.

Reverse   Long cross with three pellets in each quarter.

IE42D-055   ex. rare

As previous, but an annulet either side of the neck.

IE42D-060   ex. rare

Drogheda Mint

Obverse Legend   As previous.

Outer Reverse Legend   As previous.

Inner Reverse Legend   VILLA DE DROGHEDA — Town of Drogheda

Obverse   As IE42D-055.

Reverse   As previous.

IE42D-065   ex. rare

Limerick Mint

Obverse Legend   As previous.

Outer Reverse Legend   As previous.

Inner Reverse Legend   CIVITAS LIMIRICI — Town of Limerick

Obverse   Crowned front-facing bust of the king with an 'L' on his breast and rosette on either side of his neck.

Reverse   Long cross with three pellets in two of the quarters and two pellets and a rosette in the other two.

IE42D-070   ex. rare

As previous, but no 'L' on the king's breast.

IE42D-075   ex. rare

Waterford Mint

Obverse Legend   As previous.

Outer Reverse Legend   As previous.

Inner Reverse Legend   CIVITAS WATERFO — City of Waterford

Obverse   Crowned front-facing bust of the king.

Reverse   Long cross with three pellets in each quarter.

IE42D-080   ex. rare

Wexford Mint

Obverse Legend   As previous, often blundered.

Outer Reverse Legend   As previous, often blundered.

Inner Reverse Legend   CIVITAS WEISFOR — Town of Wexford

Obverse   As previous.

Reverse   As previous.

IE42D-085   ex. rare

No halfgroats were struck during Richard III's reign.

Henry VII   (1485 – 1509)

Silver halfgroats with a value of twopence were struck during most of Henry's coinages. Two basic types exist: the three crowns issues named after their reverse design, and the late portrait issues which are fairly similar to the previous reign with a crowned front-facing bust of the king. They were all struck in Dublin.

Early Three Crowns Issue (1485 – 1487)

Collecting Hints

This issue is rare in any grade.

Obverse Legend   REX ANGLIE FRANCIE — King of England France

Reverse Legend   DOMINUS HIBERNIE — Lord of Ireland

Obverse   Royal shield over cross with three pellets at the end.

Reverse   Three crowns over a cross.

IH72D-005   VG £80   F £200   VF rare

As previous, but a lis below the crown.

IH72D-010   ex. rare

Three Crowns Issue of Geraldine (1487)

The Fitzgeralds of Kildare were a powerful family who for a brief period took control after Lambert Simnel's abortive attempt to win the crown.

Collecting Hints

This issue is extremely rare.

Obverse Legend   REX ANGLIE FRANCIE — King of England France

Reverse Legend   DOMINOS VRERNIE — Lord of Ireland

Obverse   Royal arms over cross with three annulets at each end of the cross and Fitzgerald arms on either side of the shield.

Reverse   Three crowns over long cross with three annulets at the ends of the cross.

IH72D-015   ex. rare

Obverse Legend   DOMINOS VRERNIE — Lord of Ireland

Reverse Legend   DOMINOS VRERNIE — Lord of Ireland

Obverse   As previous.

Reverse   As previous.

IH72D-020   ex. rare

Late Three Crowns Issue (1488 – 1490)

Collecting Hints

All of these issues are fairly rare and rarely found in better than Fine condition, often clipped with weak legends.

Obverse Legend   REX ANGLIE Z FRANCIE — King of England and France

Reverse Legend   DOMINOS VBERNIE — Lord of Ireland

Obverse   Royal shield over long cross with pellets ends.

Reverse   Three crowns over long cross with annulet ends, an 'H' below the crowns.

IH72D-025   VG £100   F £250   VF rare

As previous, but no 'H' below the crowns.

IH72D-030   VG £100   F £250   VF rare

As previous, but crosses with annulet ends on both sides of the coin.

IH72D-035   VG £125   F £300   VF rare

Obverse Legend   DOMINOS VBERNIE — Lord of Ireland

Reverse Legend   As previous.

Obverse   As previous.

Reverse   As previous, but an 'H' below the crowns.

IH72D-040   VG £150   F £350   VF rare

As previous, but no 'H' on the reverse.

IH72D-045   VG £150   F £350   VF rare

Obverse Legend   REX ANGLIE — King of England

Reverse Legend   CIVITAS DUBLINIE — City of Dublin

Obverse   As IH72D-035.

Reverse   As previous.

| IH72D-050 | VG £110 | F £275 | VF rare |

Obverse Legend HENRICUS DI ORAI — Henry of (?) or HENRIC DOM OBAR — Henry Lord of (?)

Reverse Legend CIVITAS DUBLINIE — City of Dublin

Obverse As previous.

Reverse As previous, but an 'H' below the crowns.

| IH72D-055 | VG £150 | F £350 | VF rare |

Late Portrait Issue (1496 – 1505)

This issue must not be confused with the much more common English issues (H72D-005 to -070). Collectors should pay particular attention to the reverse inner legend where the mint name is to be found. This issue is also fairly similar to those of Edward IV. The main difference is the style of bust and crown.

Obverse Legend HENRIC DEI GR REX ANGL FR. — Henry by the grace of God King of England France

Outer Reverse Legend POSUI DEUM ADIVTOR MEU — I have made God my helper

Inner Reverse Legend CIVITAS DVXLIN (varieties exist) — City of Dublin

Obverse Front-facing bust of king wearing arched crown. The bust is breaking the tressure.

Reverse Long cross with three pellets in each quarter.

| IH72D-060 | ex. rare |

As previous, but the king's bust is within a fleured tressure, a 'V' on the king's breast.

| IH72D-065 | ex. rare |

As previous, but the 'V' below the bust is inverted.

| IH72D-070 | ex. rare |

Henry VIII (1509 – 1547)

Halfgroats were only struck during Henry VIII's first coinage which is known as the harp coinage because of its reverse design. The denomination complemented the groat, which was produced in large quantities at the time, and was struck in London and shipped out to Ireland as part of a policy intended to keep central control of finances.

Obverse Legend HENRIC (VIII) or (8) D.G.R. AGL Z — Henry VIII by the grace of God King of England and

Reverse Legend FRANCE DOMINUS HEBERNIE — France Lord of Ireland

Obverse Crowned arms; mintmark crown at the start of the legend.

Reverse Crown over harp, crowned 'H.A.' (for Henry and Anne Boleyn) divided by the harp; mintmark crown at the start of the legend.

| IH82D-005 | VG £150 | F £350 | VF rare |

As previous, but the initials are 'H.I.' for Henry and Jane Seymour.

| IH82D-010 | ex. rare |

As previous, but the initials are 'H.K.' for Henry and Katherine Howard.

| IH82D-015 | ex. rare | Whytes sale Feb. 98: VF £1,900 |

Threepences with Henry's portrait and title were struck during Edward VI's reign and are often confused with halfgroats. For further details see p.219, under threepence.

Mary (1553 – 1554)

This issue, struck in silver of 0.583 fineness, bears a portrait of Mary on the obverse and a large harp on the reverse. An issue without the crown above the harp is considered a forgery.

Obverse Legend   MARIA D.G.A. FR Z HIB REGI — Mary by the grace of God Queen of England France and Ireland

Reverse Legend   VERITAS TEMPORIS FILIA — Truth is the daughter of time

Obverse   Crowned bust of the queen facing left.

Reverse   Harp with crown above, dividing crowned 'M.R.'.

IMA2D-005   ex. rare

Charles I   (1625 – 1649)

A halfgroat was produced as part of the Ormonde issue, which derived its name from the Earl of Ormonde, Lieutenant of Ireland during this period. Exhibiting loyalty to the king by the crowned 'C.R.' (CAROLUS REX) on their obverse, these coins were crudely struck. They were made from silver plates that were cut to size in accordance to the required weight, then stamped with the value 'II' (twopence) on the reverse.

Ormonde Issue (1643 – 1644)

Collecting Hints

This denomination is actually quite rare. Collectors who just want an example of the reign should perhaps consider a sixpence, groat or threepence.

Obverse   Crowned 'C.R.'.

Reverse   Small 'D' over 'II'.

IC12D-005   rare

Ireland: Three Halfpence

This denomination was struck under Edward VI, but is known as the Henry VIII posthumous coinage as it bears Henry's bust and title. In some catalogues it is referred to as a penny because it is possible that the obverse was struck using London penny dies. It is also very similar to the English issues H81D-070 to -105, apart from the reverse legend which gives the Dublin mint name.

Edward VI   (1547 – 1553)

Henry VIII Posthumous Issue (1547 – 1550)

> ## Collecting Hints
>
> This issue is scarce and difficult to obtain; it is rare in better than Fine condition.

Obverse Legend   H. D.G. ROSA SINE SPINE — Henry by the grace of God a rose without a thorn

Reverse Legend   CIVITAS DUBLIN(IE) — City of Dublin

Obverse   Large bust of the king, front-facing and wearing crown.

Reverse   Cross over royal shield.

IE63HD-005	VG £60	F £200	VF rare

As previous, but a smaller, neater bust of king.

IE63HD-010	VG £50	F £160	VF rare

Ireland: Penny – Hiberno-Norse Coinage

The penny, or sterling as it is sometimes known, was introduced in Ireland by the Vikings in 995. Before then it is likely that English and Scandinavian issues had circulated, together with Arabic and Byzantine gold and silver coins. The first pennies which were struck between 995 and 1150 are known as Hiberno-Norse issues. Many of them imitated the style of English and Scandinavian issues and it is possible that some of the issues listed in the Hiberno-Norse section were struck in Scandinavia. Poor legends and crude style make many issues difficult to identify. When a particular issue has been copied or looks similar to an English one, this has been noted and collectors may want to refer to an English Catalogue to check the identification. Although Hiberno-Norse coins are difficult to obtain, they tend to be found in hoards so the condition available to collectors is fairly high.

In 1169, the Anglo Norman conquest of Ireland began and it was not until the reign of King John that pennies to an English king were struck. Henry III, Edward I and Edward IV all produced pennies in large quantities, but the penny was no longer an important denomination during later reigns. At the end of Elizabeth I's reign, copper pennies were struck in some quantity mainly to pay English troops stationed in Ireland.

Imitations of Aethelred II & Cnut Issues of 995 – 1020

These issues are imitations of English pennies of Aethelred II and Cnut. They are all rare and should not be confused with their much more common English counterparts. The main difference between the two issues lies in the legends which, for most Irish issues of this period, include the king's name SIHTRIC on the obverse and the details of Dublin mint on the reverse (DIFLMEI, DIFLME, DLFME or DLFM, with numerous minor varieties). Coins sometimes have blundered legends and it is possible that some of these issues were struck in Scandinavia.

Collecting Hints

All issues are very rare, but more specimens have come on to the market in recent years. Coins are usually in the higher grades as most have come from hoards.

Mints & Moneyers

The mint and moneyer's name can be found on the reverse of the coin, the moneyer's name is followed by the mint name which is usually abbreviated due to lack of space. Below we list the moneyers' names and mint abreviations. It is important to note that other abbreviations and moneyers' names possibly exist.

Dublin:

DIFL(I)N, DIFLMN, DIIFLIINE, DNE, DNI, DY, DYFELI, DYFLIM, DYFLIMO, DYFLN, HHO, IDFIII, IFIM, IIDYIII, IIIO, IN, NIO

Moneyers:

AELFELN, ASCETEL, CAR, EDRIC, EIOMNS, EOLE, FAENEMIN, FAEREMIN, FASTOLF, GODRIC, GOLDSTEGN, LIOELF, LIOGOLF, NDREMIN, NIRIN, RIN-

GULF, SIEL, SIULF, SIULT, STENG, STIREIN, ULFIAT, WULFGER, WULFIG/ While all issues of this period were probably struck in Dublin, reverse legends with other mint names can be found. These are copies of English issues and were not struck at the English mints but probably in Dublin.

All of the 'English' issues are extremely rare and many are unique. We have noted in the issues which coins had these reverse legends. However it is possible more issues exist.

Mint	Abbreviation	Moneyer(s)
Chester	LEIG, LEIC, LEGICES	ELEWNE
		PULSIGE
Cricklade	GROI	AETHERNIE
Derby	DEOR or DEOL	GODWINE
		OSGOT
Exeter	EAXE	EDWINE
Ipswich	GIPES	GIODRIC
Leicester	LERCS(?)	WULSIG
Lincoln	LII	OSGOT
		STEINBIT
London	LUND or LUNDRMO	AELRINE
		EMIRNIE
		GIOTHMAN
		LYFING
		THGDOAN
Oxford	OX	WULFWINE
Shrewsbury	SCROI	AEFLRHEH
Stamford	SAND(?)	GODERIC
		GODLEOW
uncertain	ENMD	ERMINIE
uncertain	MN	NDOMNREIL
uncertain	RINI	BYRHTIOD
Watchet	PECI	SIGERIC
Wilton	PILT	GODWINE
Winchester	PINTS or PINI	BYRHTMAER
		GODWINE
York	EOFR or EFORE	ARTHUR
		EADRIL
		STEORGER
		UNULF

Aethelred II Crux Type (995 – 1000)

The obverse and reverse designs for these issues (IHN1D-005 to -015) are the same, differences lie in the legends.

Obverse Legend SINTRCRE DYFLI or DYFLNMO — Sihtric King of Dublin

Reverse Legend Moneyer's name followed by DYFEHI (many varieties) — Dublin

Obverse Left-facing bust holding a sceptre.

Reverse Short cross with the letters 'C R U X' in each quarter.

IHN1D-005	F —	VF £1,500	EF £3,000

As previous, but the reverse legend bears an English moneyer and mint name, usually EFORE — York or PECI — Watchet.

IHN1D-010   F —   VF £1,800   EF £3,500

As IHN1D-005, but the obverse legend reads AEDELRED RE ANGN (varieties exist) — Aethelred King of England.

IHN1D-015   F —   VF £1,500   EF £3,000

Aethelred II Long Cross Type (1000 – 1010)

The obverse and reverse designs for these issues (IHN1D-020 to -065) are the same, differences lie in the legends. It should be noted that two issues (IHN1D-045 and IHN1D-050) were attributed in Victorian times to Donald King of Monaghan, although there is no historical evidence to support this.

Obverse Legend   SIHTRIC RE DYFLIN — Sihtric King of Dublin

Reverse Legend   DYFLNIEIMIIU or DYFLI (with moneyer's name) — Dublin

Obverse   Left-facing bust, no sceptre.

Reverse   Long voided cross, no pellets in the angles of the cross.

IHN1D-020   F —   VF £1,000   EF £2,000

As previous, but the reverse legend usually bears an English moneyer and mint name, DEOR or DEOL (Derby), LIII (Lincoln), LUND (London) or EOFR (York).

IHN1D-025   F —   VF £1,200   EF £2,500

Obverse Legend   SIHTRIC CUNVNC — Sihtric (?)

Reverse Legend   Not Dublin mint, usually English mints: PINTS — Winchester or LUND — London

Obverse & Reverse   As IHN1D-020.

IHN1D-030 ex. rare

Obverse Legend   AEDELRED REX (varieties exist) — King Aethelred

Reverse Legend   Moneyer's name followed by DYFLI, DYEN or DYIH — Dublin

Obverse & Reverse   As IHN1D-020.

IHN1D-035   F —   VF £1,000   EF £2,000

As previous, but the reverse legend bears the details not of Dublin but usually of an English mint: LEIG — Chester, LHC — Lincoln, LUND — London, PINI — Winchester, GROI — Cricklade.

IHN1D-040   F —   VF £1,400   EF £2,800

Obverse Legend   DYMN ROE MNEGNI — uncertain

Reverse Legend   Moneyer's name followed by DERMNO or DYNROE (many varieties) — Dublin

Obverse & Reverse   As IHN1D-020.

IHN1D-045   F —   VF £1,400   EF £2,800

As previous, but the reverse legend does not bear Dublin's details but usually London's — LUND.

IHN1D-050   F —   VF £1,500   EF £3,000

As IHN1D-045, except that the obverse legend reads OGSEN HEA MELNEM — uncertain.

IHN1D-055   ex. rare

As IHN1D-045, except that the obverse legend reads SISIG RE ANGLSIO — Sihtric King of England.

IHN1D-060	ex. rare

Obverse Legend   Blundered legend

Reverse Legend   Moneyer's name followed by STAN — Stanford

Obverse   Right-facing bust.

Reverse   As previous.

IHN1D-065	ex. rare

Aethelred II Helmet Type (1004 – 1010)

Obverse Legend   SIHTRIC RE DUF — Sihtric King of Dublin

Reverse Legend   Moneyer's name followed by DYFLINR or DYFLI — Dublin

Obverse   Helmeted bust.

Reverse   Long cross over ornamental square.

IHN1D-070	F —	VF £3,000	EF £5,000

Obverse Legend   AEDELRED REX (varieties) — King Aethelred

Reverse Legend   Moneyer's name followed by DYFLI or DYM — Dublin

Obverse & Reverse   As previous.

IHN1D-075	F —	VF £2,000	EF £4,000

As previous, but the reverse legend bears the details not of Dublin mint but usually York — EO, Ipswich — GIPE or Exeter — EAXE. It is possible that this issue is a Scandinavian imitation of an Hiberno-Norse coin.

IHN1D-080	ex. rare

Aethelred II Small Cross Coinage (1010 – 1016)

Obverse Legend   SIHTRERE DYFLI — Sihtric King of Dublin

Reverse Legend   Moneyer's name followed by DM or DYFIN or DYFLIMO (many varieties) — Dublin

Obverse   Left-facing bust.

Reverse   Small cross within inner circle.

IHN1D-085	F —	VF £2,000	EF £4,000

As previous, but the reverse legend does not bear Dublin's detail, instead the moneyer's name is usually followed by the details of an English mint: LEIC — Chester or LUNDR — London (many varieties).

IHN1D-090	F —	VF £2,500	EF £4,500

Obverse Legend   AEDELRED AIO — Aethelred of England

Reverse Legend   Moneyer's name followed by DYFL — Dublin

Obverse & Reverse   As previous.

IHN1D-095	F —	VF £2,500	EF £4,500

As previous, but the reverse legend does not bear the details of Dublin mint, but LUNDRIN — London, SCROI — Shrewsbury, or LEGICES — Chester.

IHN1D-100	F —	VF £3,000	EF £5,000

Cnut Quatrefoil Issues (1016 – 1020)

Obverse Legend   SIHTRIC DYELMO — Sihtric of Dublin

Reverse Legend   Moneyer's name followed by DND or OND — Dublin

Obverse   Left-facing bust within a quatrefoil.

Reverse   Long cross with two crescents in each quarter.

IHN1D-105	F —	VF £4,000	EF £6,000

Obverse Legend   CNUT REX ANGLORUM — Cnut King of the English

Reverse Legend   Moneyer's name followed by DYF (many varieties) — Dublin

Obverse & Reverse   As previous.

| IHN1D-110 | F — | VF £2,000 | EF £4,000 |

Late Long Cross Issues (1015 – 1035)

These issues are very much a continuation of the imitation issues of Aethelred II's long cross coinage, although they are smaller in size and often have blundered legends. The early issues have a pellet at each end of the reverse cross which may help collectors distinguish them from these later ones. Coins with blundered legends tend to be lighter in weight than un-blundered issues.

Collecting Hints

All issues are rare and some are extremely rare but, because many of these coins have been found in hoards, they tend to be in the higher grades.

Obverse Legend SIHTRECRE DYFLM (many minor varieties exist) — Sihtric King of Dublin

Reverse Legend Moneyer's name followed by DYF(LI) — Dublin

Obverse Cruder left-facing bust with a cross or pellet(s) behind the head.

Reverse Long cross with a pellet in each quarter.

| IHN1D-115 | F £300 | VF £800 | EF £1,600 |

As previous, but details of an English mint instead of Dublin in the reverse legend.

| IHN1D-120 | ex. rare |

Obverse Legend AEDERLREDRE AIG — Aethelred King of England

Reverse Legend Moneyer's name followed by DYFLI — Dublin

Obverse & Reverse As previous.

| IHN1D-125 | ex. rare |

The following issues (IHN1D-130 to -165) tend to be more blundered than the previous ones.

As IHN1D-115, but very crude in style.

| IHN1D-130 | F £250 | VF £500 | EF £1,000 |

As IHN1D-130, but an inverted crozier behind the king's head.

| IHN1D-135 | F £300 | VF £600 | EF £1,200 |

As IHN1D-130, but an 'E' on the neck and in one of the reverse quarters.

| IHN1D-140 | F £250 | VF £500 | EF £1,000 |

As IHN1D-130, but a triquetra in a quarter of the reverse.

| IHN1D-145 | F £250 | VF £500 | EF £1,000 |

As IHN1D-130, but spiral and millrind symbols on the reverse.

| IHN1D-150 | F £350 | VF £750 | EF £1,500 |

As IHN1D-130, but a hand behind the neck.

| IHN1D-155 | F £350 | VF £750 | EF £1,500 |

As IHN1D-130, but a hand in one reverse quarter.

| IHN1D-160 | ex. rare |

Long Cross & Hand Coinage (1035 – 1060)

These issues are very much a continuation from the previous ones, with the bust of Aethelred II on the obverse and a long cross on the reverse; one or more hands can be found in the design. Coins are very crude in style and the legends so blundered that they are mostly rendered meaningless, and have therefore not been listed here.

Collecting Hints

These coins are usually found in Fine to VF condition, although sometimes damaged with cracked or clipped flans. Coins in higher grades tend to have been found in hoards. As with all Hiberno-Norse coins, these issues are fairly difficult to obtain.

Obverse Left-facing bust.

Reverse Long cross with a hand in two of the quarters.

| IHN1D-165 | VG — | F £500 | VF £1,000 |

Obverse As previous, but with a hand in front of the face, touching the nose.

Reverse As previous, but sometimes just one hand in the quarters.

IHN1D-170 VG — F £500 VF £1,000

As previous, but the hand on the obverse is on the neck.

IHN1D-175 VG — F £500 VF £1,000

The following two issues (IHN1D-180 and -185) tend to be slightly smaller in size than previous ones. Many varieties exist, particularly in the design of the bust and many issues are very crude in style.

Obverse Left-facing bust, sometimes with pellet(s) in front of face or behind bust.

Reverse Long cross with a crude hand in two quarters.

IHN1D-180 VG £85 F £225 VF £500

As previous, but a cross of four pellets on or behind the head. Sometimes there is also an extra pellet or a pellet in annulet in the remaining reverse quarters.

IHN1D-185 VG £125 F £300 VF £700

Obverse Left-facing bust, usually with four pellets on the neck.

Reverse Long cross with a hand and an 'S' in a quarter.

IHN1D-190 VG £100 F £250 VF £500

Scratched Die Coins (1060 – 1065)

These very crude issues have the reverse die part-punched and part-engraved. As with the previous issue these coins have a blundered legend, which has therefore not been listed. The first issue is not to be confused with previous issues as it is much cruder in style.

Collecting Hints

All issues are rare or very rare.

Obverse Left-facing bust with several pellets on and around it.

Reverse Long cross with a crude hand and cross in two of the angles and pellets in the other two.

IHN1D-195 VG — F £600 VF £1,250

As previous, but right-facing bust.

IHN1D-200 v. rare

Obverse Front-facing bust wearing a helmet, triple lines make up the moustache and beard.

Reverse As previous, but varieties of symbols exist.

IHN1D-205 VG — F £1,000 VF £2,000

As previous, but different symbols of very crude style on the reverse.

IHN1D-210 VG — F £1,000 VF £2,000

Imitations of Late Anglo Saxon, Norman & European Coins

These issues are crude imitations of coins of other reigns and countries. All of them are very crude in style and rarely circulated in England as they were underweight. Virtually all have blundered legends, a feature that should help collectors distinguish a Hiberno-Norse immitation from an original coin with unblundered legends.

Collecting Hints

All issues are rare and many are extremely rare. Most issues are badly struck, using poorly made dies so resulting in very crude issues. Coins are sometimes found cracked or chipped.

Aethelred II Type Issues

Obverse Crude left-facing bust.

Reverse Short cross with 'C R U X' in the quarters.

IHN1D-215   ex. rare

Obverse   Crude left-facing bust with a cross or hand on it.
Reverse   Long cross with pellets, annulet and anchor in the angles.

IHN1D-220   VG —   F £600   VF £1,200

Obverse   Left-facing bust with a crozier in front.
Reverse   Long cross with a comb, pellets and annulets in the angles.

IHN1D-225   VG —   F £700   VF £1,400

This issue, IHN1D-230, should not be confused with IHN1D-180 or -185 as it is much cruder.

Obverse   Very crude left-facing bust.
Reverse   Long cross with two crude hands in two of the angles.

IHN1D-230   VG —   F £400   VF £800

Obverse   Very crude left-facing bust.
Reverse   Long cross with two crosses in the angles.

IHN1D-235   VG —   F £600   VF £1,200

Obverse   Right-facing bust, a cross on the neck and three pellets in front of the face.
Reverse   Long cross with two anchors, a pellet and an annulet(?) in the quarters.

IHN1D-240   VG —   F £1,000   VF £2,000

Obverse   Crude horse with cross above (similar to Aethelred II 'Agnus Dei' type).
Reverse   Cross to lettering, an 'E' in two quarters, a cross in two quarters.

IHN1D-245   ex. rare

Obverse   Crude horse with cross above (similar to Aethelred II 'Agnus Dei' type).
Reverse   Cross with curved sides, an annulet in the centre.

IHN1D-250   ex. rare

Obverse   Crude horse with two hands above.
Reverse   Cross to lettering, an anchor in one angle.

IHN1D-255   ex. rare

Cnut Type Issues

Obverse   Right-facing bust, sometimes with pellets in front of the face.
Reverse   Short cross with nothing in the quarters (Cnut reverse).

IHN1D-260   v. rare

Obverse   Left-facing bust, sometimes with pellets in front of the face.
Reverse   Short cross with nothing in the quarters (Cnut reverse).

IHN1D-265   v. rare

Obverse   Complicated design with an annulet or cross in the centre of four(?) croziers in saltire.
Reverse   Annulet in the centre of a short cross (similar to Cnut Short Cross issue).

IHN1D-270   ex. rare

Harthacnut Type Issues

Obverse   Left-facing bust, sometimes with pellets in front of the face.
Reverse   A jewel cross (Harthacnut reverse).

IHN1D-275   ex. rare

As previous, but right-facing bust.

IHN1D-280   ex. rare

Obverse   Complicated design with an annulet or cross in the centre of four(?) croziers in saltire.

Reverse   Jewel cross in the centre (similar to Harthancnut Jewel Cross issue).

IHN1D-285   ex. rare

Edward the Confessor Type Issues

Obverse   Left-facing bust, sometimes with pellets in front of the face.

Reverse   Large expanding cross (Edward the Confessor reverse).

IHN1D-290   ex. rare

Obverse   As previous.

Reverse   Voided cross with three crescents at each end (Edward the Confessor reverse).

IHN1D-295   ex. rare

Obverse   Left-facing bust.

Reverse   Small cross (Edward the Confessor reverse).

IHN1D-300   v. rare

Obverse   Right-facing bust with a crozier in front of the face.

Reverse   Small cross within a circle (Edward the Confessor reverse).

IHN1D-305   v. rare

Obverse   Right-facing bust.

Reverse   Hammer cross (Edward the Confessor type).

IHN1D-310   ex. rare

Harold II Type Issues

Obverse   Left-facing bust with a cross in front of it.

Reverse   A word in the centre, often blundered (Harold II PAX type).

IHN1D-315   ex. rare

As previous, but a bird above and below the central word on the reverse, which is usually very badly blundered (Harold II type).

IHN1D-320   ex. rare

Obverse   Right-facing bust with a cross on it.

Reverse   A word in the centre, often blundered (Harold II PAX type).

IHN1D-325   ex. rare

Obverse   Crude bust with flat top, uncrowned head with no hair.

Reverse   A word crudely blundered in a central box with a pellet above and below (similar to Harold II PAX penny).

IHN1D-330   ex. rare

William I Type Issues

Obverse   Bust facing either right or left.

Reverse   Cross fleury with an annulet in the centre (William I reverse).

IHN1D-335   ex. rare

Obverse   Left-facing bust.

Reverse   Cross voided with an annulet in the centre and a pellet between two crescents at the end of each limb.

IHN1D-340   ex. rare

Obverse   Crude, left-facing bust.

Reverse   Cross botonnée over quadrilateral with incurved sides and an annulet in the centre (William I type).

IHN1D-345   ex. rare

Obverse   As previous.

Reverse   Cross pattée with an annulet containing one letter of 'PAXS' (peace) in each angle (William I type).

IHN1D-350   ex. rare

Obverse   Small bust with round head and realistic hair, two hands held by the neck.

Reverse   Cross voided with an annulet in the centre and a pellet between two crescents at the end of each limb (similar to William I Bonnet type).

IHN1D-355   ex. rare

Obverse   Front-facing bust wearing a triangular helmet with two pillars on either side (similar to William I Canopy type).

Reverse   Three crude birds.

IHN1D-360   ex. rare

Obverse   Front-facing bust with a sceptre(?) on either side (similar to William I Two Sceptre type).

Reverse   Cross in quatrefoil (similar to William II type).

IHN1D-365   ex. rare

Obverse   As previous.

Reverse   Crude bird with a cross above.

IHN1D-370   ex. rare

Obverse   Front-facing bust with a star on either side (similar to William I Two Stars issue).

Reverse   Long cross with a hand(?) in one angle.

IHN1D-375   ex. rare

Obverse   As previous.

Reverse   Long cross with an annulet containing one letter of PAXS (peace) in each angle (similar to William I Pax type).

IHN1D-380   ex. rare

Obverse   Crowned bust facing right or left.

Reverse   Cross fleury with an annulet in the centre (similar to William I Right Profile type).

IHN1D-385   ex. rare

Obverse   Complicated design with an annulet or cross in the centre of four(?) croziers in saltire.

Reverse   Double quadrilateral with incurved sides, fleur at the angles, annulet in the centre (similar to William I Canopy type).

IHN1D-390   ex. rare

William II Type Issues

Obverse   Left-facing bust.

Reverse   Cross pattée over a cross fleury (William II type).

IHN1D-395   ex. rare

Obverse   Front-facing bust.

Reverse   Cross in quatrefoil (similar to William II Cross in Quatrefoil type).

IHN1D-400   ex. rare

Non-attributed Issues

Obverse   Left-facing bust with three pellets on the neck.

Reverse   Small cross with triple pellet ends.

IHN1D-405   v. rare

Obverse   Left-facing bust with a cross on the neck.

Reverse   Short voided cross with small crosses at the ends.

IHN1D-410   ex. rare

Obverse   Left-facing bust.

Reverse   A bow-like cross with a small cross and pellets in the centre.

IHN1D-415   ex. rare

Obverse   Crude, left-facing bust.

Reverse   Cross crosslet over Celtic cross, pellets in the Celtic cross.

IHN1D-420   ex. rare

Obverse   Left-facing bust.

Reverse   Three birds of crude style.

IHN1D-425   VG —   F £1,000   VF £2,000

Obverse   As previous.

Reverse   Small cross in the centre with a trefoil of pellets and/or small crosses around it.

IHN1D-430   VG —   F £1,000   VF £2,000

Obverse   Very crude bust facing right.

Reverse   Cross to lettering, two joined annulets with pellet centre in two of the angles, a cross in the other two.

IHN1D-435   VG —   F £1,000   VF £2,000

Obverse   Crude bust with flat top, uncrowned head with no hair.

Reverse   Long cross with a comb in two of the quarters.

IHN1D-440   ex. rare

As previous, but pellet or pellets in annulets in the reverse quarters. A variety of designs exists.

IHN1D-445 ex. rare

Obverse Crude bust with flat top, uncrowned head with no hair.

Reverse Small cross surrounded by four pellets.

IHN1D-450 ex. rare

Obverse Crude front-facing head with a beard and cross above the eyebrows.

Reverse A crude hand in the centre, a crude bird in each quarter (varieties exist).

IHN1D-455 ex. rare

Obverse Front-facing bust with a pellet on either side and a cross above.

Reverse Two crosses.

IHN1D-460 ex. rare

Obverse A cross to lettering, a bar in two of the quarters.

Reverse Crude cross, a letter(?) in each quarter.

IHN1D-465 ex. rare

Obverse Complicated design with an annulet or cross in the centre of four(?) croziers in saltire.

Reverse Long cross with one pellet in two of the quarters and three pellets in the other two.

IHN1D-470 ex. rare

Degraded Imitations of Long Cross Coins (1095 – 1100)

These issues are cruder copies of previous issues. They are extremely crude in style and lighter in weight than the issues they imitate. Once more, the legends are totally blundered and have not been listed.

Collecting Hints

The first issue is scarce but obtainable and usually found in Fine to VF condition. The following two issues are rare.

Obverse Crude left-facing bust with a crozier in front of the face.

Reverse Long cross with a pellet in two of the angles and a sceptre in the other two.

IHN1D-475 VG £80 F £200 VF £400

Obverse As previous.

Reverse Long cross with a sceptre in two of the angles and a cross in the other two.

IHN1D-480 v. rare

As IHN1D-475 but the bust is facing right.

IHN1D-485 v. rare

Semi-Bracteate & Bracteate Issues (1110 – 1150)

During the first half of the twelfth century the flans of the coins were becoming so thin that the design could not be struck in the usual way showing an obverse and a reverse. The bracteate issues have a design impressed on one side only, thus giving a raised design on one side and an inverted version of the raised design on the other side. Semi-bracteates were struck this way on both sides, resulting in a rather poor definition on each side. None of the issues had legends.

Collecting Hints

All these issues are very rare or even extremely rare. Due to the thinness of the flan, they are usually found damaged and tend to be ugly in appearance.

Semi-Bracteates Issues

Obverse Crude bust.

Reverse Long cross with a sceptre in each angle.

IHN1D-490 ex. rare

Obverse As previous.

Reverse Long cross within a quatrefoil.

IHN1D-495 v. rare

Obverse As previous.
Reverse Plain cross with cross bottoné in the quarters.

IHN1D-500   v. rare

Bracteates Issues

Obverse Voided cross with pellets in the void and a sceptre and pellets in the quarters.

IHN1D-505   ex. rare

Obverse Plain cross with an annulet in the centre and quatrefoils or trefoils(?) (varieties exist) in the quarters.

IHN1D-510   ex. rare

Obverse Plain cross and quatrefoil.

IHN1D-515   ex. rare

Obverse Voided cross, pellets or quatrefoils (varieties exist) in the quarters.

IHN1D-520   ex. rare

Obverse Cross pommée in quatrefoil.

IHN1D-525   ex. rare

Obverse Cross with trefoils in the angles.

IHN1D-530   ex. rare

Obverse Cross with a lis in each angle.

IHN1D-535   ex. rare

Obverse Cross potent with annulets in the angles.

IHN1D-540   ex. rare

Obverse Hammer cross over a quatrefoil.

IHN1D-545   ex. rare

Obverse Short cross pommée over long cross.

IHN1D-550   ex. rare

Obverse Small cross within inner circle with a sceptre in two of the angles and two Is in the other two.

IHN1D-555   ex. rare

Obverse Cross pattée with a pellet in each angle.

IHN1D-560   ex. rare

Obverse Small cross pommée in inner circle.

IHN1D-565   ex. rare

Obverse Cross fleury in inner circle with two annulets in two of the quarters and a crescent and pellets in the other two.

IHN1D-570   ex. rare

Obverse Cross pommée with sceptres in each angle.

IHN1D-575   ex. rare

Obverse Double cross pommée over hammer cross.

IHN1D-580   ex. rare

Obverse Cross over quatrefoil with a pellet in each quarter.

IHN1D-585   ex. rare

Obverse   Cross fleury over long cross.

IHN1D-590   ex. rare

Obverse   Long cross with a man's head in each quarter.

IHN1D-595   ex. rare

Obverse   Long cross with a head in each of two quarters and a cross in the other two.

IHN1D-600   ex. rare

Ireland: Penny – Anglo-Irish Issues

John as King of Ireland (1199 – 1216)

Rex Coinage (1207 – 1211)

This coinage is sometimes known as the 'Rex' (King) coinage, because it was struck when John was King, not Lord, of Ireland. Although only halfpennies and farthings had been struck during his earlier coinages, the penny was the main denomination of his main coinage as king and it was struck at Dublin, Limerick and Waterford.

All issues of John, Henry III and Edward I bear the bust of the king in a triangle, easily differentiating them from English issues which all have a circle instead.

The moneyer and mint name can be found in the reverse legend. Below we list the moneyers names and the mint abbreviations as found on the coins.

Mint	Abbreviation	Moneyers
Dublin	DIVE	Iohan
		Roberd
		Wilelm P.
		Willem
Limerick	LIME	Wace
		Willem
Waterford	WAT	Willem

Collecting Hints

The Dublin issues are fairly common, especially those of the moneyer Roberd. Coins are usually found in Fine condition but VF examples are not uncommon. Limerick and Waterford coins are fairly rare and difficult to obtain. All mints circulated in England and it is not uncommon for them to be found there.

Dublin Mint

Obverse Legend   IOHANNE(S) REX — King John

Reverse Legend   Moneyer's name and mint; by far the most common moneyer's name is ROBERD.

Obverse   Bust of the king holding a sceptre in a triangle.

Reverse   Sun, moon and three stars in a triangle.

IJH1D-005	VG £30	F £65	VF £150

Limerick Mint

As previous, but with the details of Limerick mint on the reverse legend.

IJH1D-010	VG £60	F £150	VF rare

Waterford Mint

As previous, but with the details of Waterford mint on the reverse legend.

IJH1D-015	VG £60	F £150	VF rare

Henry III   (1216 – 1272)

In 1251, dies were sent from London to strike coins at the Dublin mint where Roger de Haverhull was put in charge and only two moneyers, Ricard and Davi, struck the coins. Large quantities were struck, but the mint was closed in 1254.

The obverse depicts the king's bust in a triangle, while the reverse is virtually identical to the English long cross issues which had recently been introduced in England (1247). They have a long cross which goes to the edge of the coin with three pellets in each quarter, the moneyer's name and mint (Dublin) can be found in the legend. Although only pennies were struck during this period, coins could legally be cut along the long cross to produce half-pennies and farthings.

These issues were popular and because of their high silver content (0.925 silver) they circulated in England and parts of Europe. The style was in fact copied in Germany so, if the legends of a coin are different from the ones we have listed, it could be a German issue.

Collecting Hints

This issue is fairly common and usually found in Fine condition although coins in VF are not uncommon.

Obverse Legend   HENRICUS REX III — King Henry III

Reverse Legend   Moneyer's name DAVI or RICARD ON DIVELI or DIVE (Dublin)

Obverse   King holding sceptre, a cinquefoil to the right of the bust, all within a voided triangle.

Reverse   Long cross with three pellets in each quarter.

IH31D-005	VG £25	F £50	VF £90

As previous, but the king's bust is in a single triangle.

IH31D-010	VG £25	F £50	VF £90

As previous, but a sexfoil to the right of the king's neck and a small triangle below the central fleur of the crown.

IH31D-015	VG £40	F £70	VF £140

As previous, but a small star by the head of the king's sceptre.

IH31D-020	VG £50	F £110	VF £225

As IH31D-015, but a double band to the king's crown.

IH31D-025	VG £55	F £120	VF £250

The following four issues (IH31D-030 to -045) are of coarser and cruder style than the previous ones.

Obverse Legend   As previous.

Reverse Legend   As previous.

Obverse   Crowned bust of the king in a triangle holding a sceptre, a cinquefoil to the right of his neck, the crown's pellets are not joined to the band.

Reverse   As previous.

IH31D-030	VG £30	F £60	VF £100

As previous, but the band of the crown is jewelled with pellets.

IH31D-035	VG £60	F £125	VF £250

As previous, but three curls on either side of the king's head instead of two.

IH31D-040	VG £60	F £125	VF £250

As previous, but the king's shoulders are showing.

IH31D-045	VG £60	F £125	VF £250

Edward I   (1272 – 1307)

Two coinages were produced in Ireland during this period. The first coinage was struck in Dublin and constitutes a continuation from the coinage of Henry III although cruder in style. It bears Henry's name on the obverse and the name of the moneyer (RI-CARD) and mint on the reverse. However, unlike the issues of Henry III, these issues have realistic hair.

The second coinage was introduced in 1279. All dies were made in London, where coin production was being centralised, and minor marks differentiated issues so a coin could be linked to a die and moneyer. The moneyer's name was not placed on the coins, although the mint name was. The obverse bears the king's bust in a triangle which easily differentiates it from English issues which have a circle instead. The reverse shows a long cross with three pellets in each quarter and the mint name in the legend. The mints are as follows:

Cork — CIVITAS CORCAGIE or CORCACIE
Dublin — CIVITAS DUBLINIE
Waterford — CIVITAS WATERFOR

Many coins can be found with legends which are badly blundered or not as previously listed. The blundered legends tend to be contemporary forgeries while those with legible legends (often of English mints) are continental imitations. Due to their high silver content and correct weight, these coins were popular throughout England and Europe where they were readily accepted by merchants.

First Coinage (1276 – 1279)

Collecting Hints

This issue is rare.

Obverse Legend   HENRICVS REX III — King Henry III

Reverse Legend   RICARD ON DIVE — Richard of Dublin

Obverse   Crude bust of the king holding a sceptre in a triangle, the king has realistic hair made up of numerous strokes. Roman 'V' in lettering.

Reverse   Long cross with three pellets in each quarter.

IE11D-005	rare

As previous, but a Lombardic 'U' in HENRICUS and DIUE.

IE11D-010	rare	Whytes sale Feb. 98: gd F £1,150

Second Coinage (1279 – 1302)

Collecting Hints

Dublin and Waterford coins are common and found in all grades from Fair to VF. Many issues have been found in hoards throughout Europe showing how extensively they circulated. Issues of Cork are extremely rare.

Dublin Mint

1279 – 1284 Issue

Obverse Legend   EDWR ANGL DNS HYB — Edward King of England Lord of Ireland

Reverse Legend   CIVITAS DUBLINIE — City of Dublin

Obverse   Crowned bust of the king within a triangle, a trefoil of pellets on the king's breast.

Reverse   Long cross with three pellets in each quarter.

IE11D-015   VG £20   F £40   VF £80

As previous, but a pellet at the start of the obverse legend.

IE11D-020   VG £20   F £40   VF £80

As previous, but a small cross at the start of the obverse legend.

IE11D-025   VG £22   F £45   VF £90

1294 Issue

Obverse Legend   As previous.

Reverse Legend   As previous.

Obverse   As IE11D-015, but a rosette on the king's breast.

Reverse   As previous.

IE11D-030   v. rare

1295 Issue

Obverse Legend   As previous.

Reverse Legend   As previous.

Obverse   As IE11D-015, but a pellet in each angle of the triangle.

Reverse   As previous.

IE11D-035   ex. rare   Whytes sale Feb. 98: VF £800

1297 – 1302 Issue

Obverse Legend   As previous.

Reverse Legend   As previous.

Obverse   As IE11D-015, but a pellet below the bust, also the lettering of the legend is small in size.

Reverse   As previous, but the lettering of the legend is large in size.

IE11D-040   VG £22   F £45   VF £90

As previous, but a pellet at the start of the obverse legend.

IE11D-045   VG £25   F £60   VF £120

As IE11D-040, but small size lettering on both obverse and reverse.

IE11D-050   VG £25   F £60   VF £120

As previous, but oblong pellet below the bust, large or small lettering.

IE11D-055   v. rare

As previous, but no pellet below the bust.

IE11D-060   ex. rare

Waterford Mint
1279 – 1284 Issue

Obverse Legend   As previous.

Reverse Legend   CIVITAS WATERFOR — City of Waterford

Obverse   Crowned bust of the king within a triangle, trefoil of pellets on the king's breast and a pellet at the start of the legend.

Reverse   Long cross with three pellets in each quarter.

IE11D-065   VG £20   F £40   VF £80

1294 Issue

Obverse Legend   As previous, but irregular sized lettering.

Reverse Legend   As previous, but irregular sized lettering.

Obverse   As previous, but a rosette on the king's breast.

Reverse   As previous.

IE11D-070   v. rare

Cork Mint

1295 Issue

Obverse Legend   As previous.

Reverse Legend   CIVITAS CORCAGIE or CORCACIE — City of Cork

Obverse   Crowned bust of the king within a triangle, a pellet in each angle of the triangle.

Reverse   As previous.

IE11D-075   ex. rare

With the exception of Edward III's extremely rare halfpenny issue, no coins were produced again in Ireland until the early part of the fifteenth century when Henry VI struck pennies that are also extremely rare. In fact it was not until Edward IV that coins were produced again in any quantity on the island. From the reign of Edward II to that of Henry VI, large quantities of English and Scottish coins circulated in Ireland. English coins tended to be worth more than Irish ones, and an English halfgroat would have probably had a value of threepence in Ireland. Many of the coins produced during the reigns of John, Henry III and Edward I had been traded abroad and were either circulating in Europe or being melted down when their metal content was higher than their face value, as often happened.

Henry VI   (1422 – 1461)

1425 – 1426 Issue

In 1425 Henry VI's Anglo-Irish parliament authorised the production of pennies in Dublin similar in style to the English annulet issue. This issue, which is of the highest rarity and bears the Dublin mint name (CIVITAS DUBLINIE) on the reverse, should not be confused with the common English issue (see *Coincraft's Standard Catalogue of English & UK Coins*, H61D-005 to -030).

Collecting Hints

This issue is of the highest rarity.

Obverse Legend   HENRICUS DNS HIBNIE — Henry Lord of Ireland

Reverse Legend   CIVITAS DUBLINIE — City of Dublin

Obverse   Front-facing crowned bust of the king, a star to the right of the bust and an annulet at the end of the legend.

Reverse   Long cross with three pellets in each quarter and an annulet after CIVI in legend.

IH61D-005   ex. rare

Edward IV   (1461 – 1483)

During Edward's reign, large quantities of pennies were struck in a total of seven coinages. The styles of these coinages is diverse and collecting hints are given for each. One problem with virtually all coinages is the fact that the legends are unclear due to poor striking or clipping, and collectors will have to look for various marks or styles to help them identify an issue.

First (Anonymous) Coinage (1460 – 1463)

This issue does not bear the king's name in the legend, probably because it was considered un-diplomatic to name a ruling monarch in view of the civil war raging between the Lancastrians and Yorkists in England at the time.

Collecting Hints

These issues are very rare or extremely rare.

Dublin Mint

Obverse Legend   None.

Reverse Legend   CIVITAS DUBLIN — City of Dublin

Obverse   Large crown in tressure of nine arcs.

Reverse   Long cross with three pellets in each quarter, an annulet in two quarters.

IE41D-005   v. rare

As previous, but crosses in angles of tressure and sometimes no annulets on the reverse.

IE41D-010   v. rare

As previous, but a saltire below the crown.

IE41D-015   ex. rare

As previous, but the crown is in a tressure of eight arcs and there are annulets in two quarters of the reverse.

IE41D-020   ex. rare

As previous, but the crown is not in a tressure.

IE41D-025   v. rare

Waterford Mint

Obverse Legend   None.

Reverse Legend   CIVITAS WATER — City of Waterford

Obverse   Cross in tressure of fleured arcs.

Reverse   Long cross with three pellets in each quarter.

IE41D-030   ex. rare

Second (Crown) Coinage (1463 – 1465)

Collecting Hints

This issue is extremely rare.

Dublin Mint

Obverse Legend   EDWARD DI G DNS HYB — Edward by the grace of God Lord of Ireland

Reverse Legend   CIVITAS DUBLIN — City of Dublin

Obverse   Crown within a circle.

Reverse   Long cross with three pellets in each quarter.

IE41D-035   ex. rare

Waterford Mint

Obverse Legend   None.

Reverse Legend   CIVITAS WATERFOR or WATFORD — City of Waterford

Obverse & Reverse   As previous.

IE41D-040   ex. rare

Third (Small Cross on Rose/Radiant Sun) Coinage (1465 – 1467?)

Collecting Hints

This issue is extremely rare.

Dublin Mint

Obverse Legend   EDW D.G. DNS HYBERN — Edward by the grace of God Lord of Ireland

Reverse Legend   CIVITAS DUBLINIE — City of Dublin

Obverse   Large rose with cross in the centre.

Reverse   Sun with a pellet in an annulet in the centre.

IE41D-045   ex. rare

Fourth (Rose on Sun) Coinage (1467 – 1470)

Collecting Hints

This issue is extremely rare.

Dublin Mint

Obverse Legend   EDWARD D.G. DN (HYBER) (varieties exist) — Edward by the grace of God Lord

Reverse Legend   CIVITAS DUBLINI — City of Dublin

Obverse   Crowned front-facing bust of the king.

Reverse   Rose at the centre of a radiant sun.

IE41D-050   ex. rare

Drogheda Mint

Obverse Legend   As previous.

Reverse Legend   VILLA DE DROGH — Town of Drogheda

Obverse Reverse   As previous.

IE41D-055   ex. rare

Fifth (Heavy 'Cross & Pellet') Coinage (1470 – 1473?)

The issues for the next three coinages are fairly similar in style. The obverse shows a crowned facing bust of the king and the reverse a long cross, often with three pellets in each quarter. Numerous mints were active and the mint name is in the reverse legend although most coins are found with the legends non-existent or unclear. There are, however, many marks on the coins which should help in the identification of an issue, often by a process of elimination. But, to add to the collector's difficulties, it should be noted that large quantities of forgeries of pennies of this period exist. It is thought most were made in England and are of a fairly low silver content. Most of these forgeries have illegible legends and do not have the marks which help identify the Irish issues. Many coins are in such poor condition that they will never be correctly identified.

Collecting Hints

While Dublin and Waterford issues are scarce, the issues of Galway and Limerick are very rare. Coins are rarely found unclipped or in better than Fine condition.

Dublin Mint

Obverse Legend   EDWARD DI GR DNS HYBE (varieties exist) — Edward by the grace of God Lord of Ireland

Reverse Legend   CIVITAS DUBLIN(IE) — City of Dublin

Obverse   Crowned front-facing bust of the king.

Reverse   Long cross with three pellets in each quarter, sometimes small pellets in two quarters.

IE41D-060   VG £35   F £75   VF -

As previous, but pellets over the crown.

IE41D-065   VG £35   F £75   VF -

As IE41D-060, but a cross on either side of the king's neck.

IE41D-070   VG £40   F £85   VF -

Waterford Mint

Obverse Legend   As previous.

Reverse Legend   CIVITAS WAT(ER)FOR — City of Waterford

Obverse   Crowned front-facing bust of the king, two crosses on either side of his neck and a pellet on either side of his crown.

Reverse   Long cross with three pellets in each quarter.

IE41D-075   VG £40   F £85   VF -

Galway Mint

Obverse Legend   As previous.

Reverse Legend   VILLA DE GALWAY — Town of Galway

Obverse   Crowned bust of the king.

Reverse   Long cross with three pellets in each quarter.

IE41D-080   ex. rare

Limerick Mint

Obverse Legend   As previous.

Reverse Legend   CIVITAS LIMIRICI — City of Limerick

Obverse   As previous.

Reverse   As previous.

IE41D-085   v. rare

Sixth (Light 'Cross & Pellets') Coinage (1473 – 1478?)

Large quantities of pennies were struck during the sixth coinage at a total of six mints, whose names can be found on the reverse and in fact constitute the entire reverse legend. They read as follows:

CIVITAS CORCAGIE — City of Cork
CIVITAS DUBLIN — City of Dublin
CIVITAS LIMIRICI — City of Limerick
CIVITAS WATERFORD or WATFOR — City of Waterford
VILLA DE DROGHEDA — Town of Drogheda
VILLA DE TRIM — Town of Trim

However, most issues are very badly clipped or struck on small flans and the entire legend is often missing which can make identification difficult and, in some cases, even impossible. Although most issues bear certain marks which can help differentiate them, large quantities of contemporary forgeries were struck in England, possibly at a slightly earlier date, and these coins can quite easily be confused with the Irish issues even if they tend to be of a much lower silver content. There are some coins that it is impossible to identify correctly.

Collecting Hints

Most issues, with the exception of the Cork mint, are fairly common. Coins with full legends are extremely rare and worth considerably more than the prices listed.

Dublin Mint

Obverse Legend   EDWAR DI GR DNS HYBE or EDWARD DI GR DNS IBERNIE — Edward by the grace of God Lord of Ireland or EDWARD REX ANG Z FR — Edward King of England and France

243

Reverse Legend   CIVITAS DUBLIN — City of Dublin
Obverse   Crowned front-facing bust of the king.
Reverse   Plain long cross with three pellets in each quarter.

IE41D-090   VG £20   F £40   VF £100

As previous, but quatrefoil in the centre of the reverse cross.

IE41D-095   VG £25   F £50   VF £120

As IE41D-095, but a 'D' in the centre of the reverse cross.

IE41D-100   VG £25   F £50   VF £120

As IE41D-090, but a saltire on either side of the king's neck on the obverse.

IE41D-105   VG £20   F £40   VF £100

As previous, but a saltire also to the right of the king's crown on the obverse; plain cross on reverse.

IE41D-110   VG £30   F £70   VF £150

As IE41D-090, but a pellet on either side of the king's neck on the obverse.

IE41D-115   VG £20   F £40   VF £100

As previous, but a quatrefoil in the centre of the reverse cross.

IE41D-120   VG £20   F £40   VF £100

As previous, but a mullet on either side of the king's neck on the obverse.

IE41D-125   VG £20   F £40   VF £100

As previous, but the mullets are by the crown instead of the neck.

IE41D-130   VG £20   F £40   VF £100

Drogheda Mint

Obverse Legend   As previous.
Reverse Legend   VILLA DE DROGHEDA — Town of Drogheda
Obverse   Crowned front-facing bust of the king.
Reverse   Long cross with three pellets in each quarter.

IE41D-135   VG £20   F £40   VF £100

As previous, but a quatrefoil in the centre of the reverse cross.

IE41D-140   VG £20   F £40   VF £100

As IE41D-135, but a small rose in the centre of the reverse cross.

IE41D-145   VG £20   F £40   VF £100

As IE41D-135, but a cross on either side of the king's neck.

IE41D-150   VG £30   F £70   VF £160

As previous, but a pellet on either side of the king's neck.

IE41D-155   VG £25   F £50   VF £120

As previous, but a quatrefoil in the centre of the reverse cross, also pellets are sometimes found on either side of the crown on the obverse.

IE41D-160   VG £30   F £70   VF £160

As previous, but plain reverse cross and pellets and rosettes on either side of the king's neck on the obverse.

IE41D-165   VG £30   F £70   VF £160

As previous, but a saltire by the side of the king's crown on the obverse and a small rose in the centre of the reverse cross.

IE41D-170   VG £30   F £70   VF £160

Limerick Mint

Obverse Legend   As previous.
Reverse Legend   CIVITAS LIMIRICI — City of Limerick
Obverse   Crowned front-facing bust of the king, a rosette or cinquefoil on either side of his neck.
Reverse   Long cross with three pellets in each quarter.

| IE41D-175 | VG £40 | F £80 | VF £180 |

As previous, but crosses on either side of the king's neck on the obverse.

| IE41D-180 | VG £50 | F £100 | VF £225 |

Waterford Mint

Obverse Legend As previous.

Reverse Legend CIVITAS WATERFORD or WATFOR — City of Waterford

Obverse Crowned front-facing bust of the king.

Reverse Long cross with three pellets in each quarter.

| IE41D-185 | VG £20 | F £40 | VF £100 |

As previous, but an annulet on either side of the king's neck.

| IE41D-190 | VG £40 | F £80 | VF £180 |

As IE41D-190, but a quatrefoil in the centre of the reverse cross.

| IE41D-195 | VG £40 | F £80 | VF £180 |

As IE41D-185, but a pellet on either side of the king's neck on the obverse.

| IE41D-200 | VG £40 | F £80 | VF £180 |

As previous, but crosses by the neck and crown on the obverse.

| IE41D-205 | VG £40 | F £80 | VF £180 |

As previous, but crosses by the king's neck and a quatrefoil in the centre of the reverse cross.

| IE41D-210 | VG £25 | F £50 | VF £120 |

Trim Mint

Obverse Legend As previous.

Reverse Legend VILLA DE TRIM — Town of Trim

Obverse Crowned front-facing bust of the king.

Reverse Long cross with three pellets in each quarter.

| IE41D-215 | VG £40 | F £90 | VF rare |

As previous, but a pellet on either side of the king's bust.

| IE41D-220 | VG £50 | F £110 | VF rare |

As previous, but a quatrefoil in the centre of the reverse cross.

| IE41D-225 | VG £40 | F £80 | VF £180 |

As IE41D-215, but a quatrefoil in the centre of the reverse cross.

| IE41D-230 | VG £50 | F £110 | VF rare |

Cork Mint

Obverse Legend As previous.

Reverse Legend CIVITAS CORCAGIE — City of Cork

Obverse Crowned front-facing bust of the king, a pellet on either side of the crown.

Reverse Long cross with three pellets in each quarter.

| IE41D-235 | ex. rare |

As previous, but the king has a large head.

| IE41D-240 | ex. rare |

Seventh (Sun & Roses) Coinage (1478 – 1483)

These issues were struck at the Dublin mint and all have a sun and roses in the design. They depict a crowned front-facing bust of the king on the obverse and a long cross with a rose in the centre on the reverse.

Collecting Hints

These issues are scarce and difficult to obtain. Coins are usually found in the lower grades, clipped and with much of the legends missing.

Obverse Legend EDWARD REX ANGL Z FRANC (varieties exist) — Edward King of England and France

Reverse Legend CIVITAS DUBLIN — City of Dublin

Obverse Crowned front-facing bust of the king with a sun and rose on either side of the neck.

Reverse Long cross with a small rose in the centre, a rose and two suns or a sun and two roses alternating in the angles.

| IE41D-245 | VG £100 | F £200 | VF rare |

As previous, but large symbols on the obverse.

| IE41D-250 | VG £120 | F £250 | VF rare |

As IE41D-245, but large rose in centre of reverse cross, and no marks in the quarters.

IE41D-255	VG £150	F £300	VF rare

As previous, but without symbols by the crown.

IE41D-260	ex. rare

Richard III   (1483 – 1485)

Pennies were struck for both issues of Richard III.

First Coinage (1483 – 1485?)

> ## Collecting Hints
>
> This issue is extremely rare.

Drogheda Mint

Obverse Legend RICARDUS DEI GRA DNS HYB — Richard by the grace of God Lord of Ireland

Reverse Legend VILLA DROGHEDA — Town of Drogheda

Obverse Crude, front-facing crowned bust of the king, a sun and rose alternating at the crown and neck; mintmark rose at the start of the legend.

Reverse Large rose at the centre of a long cross.

IR31D-005	ex. rare

Second (Cross & Pellet) Coinage (1483 – 1485?)

> ## Collecting Hints
>
> These two issues are extremely rare.

Dublin Mint

Obverse Legend RICARD DNS HYB — Richard Lord of Ireland

Reverse Legend CIVITAS DUBLIN — City of Dublin

Obverse Crowned front-facing bust of the king, an annulet on either side of his neck.

Reverse Long cross with quatrefoils in the centre and three pellets in each angle.

IR31D-010	ex. rare

Waterford Mint

Obverse Legend As previous.

Reverse Legend CIVITAS WATERFORD — City of Waterford

Obverse & Reverse As previous.

IR31D-015	ex. rare

Henry VII   (1485 – 1509)

Silver pennies were struck during the three crowns coinages and the portrait issues of Henry VII but in very low numbers, probably because there were enough pennies in circulation from Edward IV's issues. All issues were struck at the Dublin mint.

> ## Collecting Hints
>
> All issues are fairly crude in style and usually found in the lower grades; they are all very rare or extremely rare.

Early Three Crowns Issue (1485 – 1487)

Obverse Legend REX ANGLIE FRANC — King of England France

Reverse Legend DOMINUS VRERNI — Lord of Ireland

Obverse Arms of England over a cross.

Reverse Three crowns over a cross.

IH71D-005	v. rare

Late Three Crowns Issue (1488 – 1490)

Obverse Legend REX ANGLIE (Z FRANC) — King of England and France

Reverse Legend DOMINOS VRERNIE — Lord of Ireland

Obverse Arms of England.

Reverse Three crowns with an 'H' below.

IH71D-010	v. rare

As previous, but both obverse and reverse legends read DOMINOS VRERNIE — Lord of Ireland.

IH71D-015	ex. rare

Obverse Legend HENRICUS REX AN — Henry King of England

Reverse Legend CIVITAS DUBLIN — City of Dublin

Obverse As previous.

Reverse As previous, but omits the 'H'.

IH71D-020	v. rare

Early Portrait Issue (dates uncertain)

Obverse Legend HENRICU REX ANGLIE — Henry King of England

Reverse Legend CIVITAS DUBLIN — City of Dublin

Obverse Neat crowned bust of the king, saltire at the start of the legend.

Reverse Long cross with a large rose in the centre.

IH71D-025	ex. rare

Late Portrait Issue (1496 – 1505)

It is uncertain if the obverse legends of the following four types will ever be known because all available examples are so poor.

Obverse Legend   uncertain

Reverse Legend   CIVITAS DUBLINIE — City of Dublin

Obverse   Crowned bust of the king, the crown has a high arch.

Reverse   Long cross with splitting ends, three pellets in each quarter.

IH71D-030	ex. rare

As previous, but a pellet on either side of the king's bust.

IH71D-035	ex. rare

Obverse Legend   uncertain

Reverse Legend   CIVITAS DUBLIN — City of Dublin

Obverse   Large crown over an 'H'.

Reverse   Long cross with three pellets in each quarter.

IH71D-040	ex. rare

Obverse Legend   uncertain

Reverse Legend   CIVITAS DUBLIN(IE) — City of Dublin

Obverse   Front-facing bust of the king wearing a flat crown made up of three annulets.

Reverse   Long cross with three pellets in each quarter.

IH71D-045	ex. rare

Mary   (1553 – 1558)

This issue was struck in silver of 0.583 fineness.

Collecting Hints

This issue is extremely rare and, as high quality Victorian copies exist, collectors should beware when purchasing a coin.

Obverse Legend   M.D.G. ROSA SINE SPIN — Mary by the grace of God a rose without a thorn

Reverse Legend   VERITAS TEMPORIS FELIA — Truth is the daughter of time

Obverse   Crowned bust of the queen facing left.

Reverse   Crown over harp dividing crowned 'M.R.'.

IMA1D-005	ex. rare

Philip & Mary   (1554 – 1558)

While no pennies were produced in Ireland, base issue pennies struck in England were exported to Ireland for circulation. They have a large rose in the obverse and the royal shield in the reverse (see *Coincraft's Standard Catalogue of English & UK coins*, PM1D-010).

Elizabeth I   (1558 – 1603)

Non-portrait copper pennies were struck in 1601 and 1602 and could be considered emergency issues as they were produced to pay the troops stationed in Ireland at the time.

Collecting Hints

While the undated issue is extremely rare, the two dated issues are fairly common, especially in the lower grades. Many coins are poorly struck and show weaknesses in the design and legend.

Obverse Legend   ELIZABETH D.G. AN FR ET HIBER RE — Elizabeth by the grace of God Queen of England France and Ireland

Reverse Legend   POSUI DEU ADIUTOREM MEU — I have made God my helper

Obverse   Royal shield dividing 'E.R.'; mintmark trefoil or star at the start of the legend.

Reverse   Crown over harp, dividing the date (1601); mintmarks as obverse.

IEL1D-005	VG £15	F £30	VF £90

As previous, but dated 1602; mintmark martlet at the start of the legend.

IEL1D-010	VG £15	F £35	VF £100

As previous, dated 1602, mintmark martlet but the obverse is struck from the threepence die.

IEL1D-015	ex. rare

As previous, but undated; mintmark star at the start of the legend. Struck from the threepence dies.

IEL1D-020 ex. rare

No pennies were struck during the reigns of James I or Charles I.

Ireland: Three Farthings

Three farthings were struck during Edward VI's reign but bear the portrait and legend of his father Henry VIII and are thus known as the posthumous issue. They should not to be confused with Henry's English third coinage halfpenny (H8HD-045 to -075), although it is probable that the obverse die of the English halfpenny was used to strike the Irish obverse. The main difference between the two issues is the reverse legend which, for the Irish coins, gives Dublin mint's details. In some publications this Irish issue is referred to as a halfpenny.

Edward VI   (1547 – 1553)

Henry VIII Posthumous Issue (1547 – 1550)

Collecting Hints

This issue is very rare, especially in better than Fine condition.

Obverse Legend   H.D.G. ROSA SINE SP — Henry by the grace of God a rose without a thorn

Reverse Legend   CIVITAS DUBLIN(IE) — City of Dublin

Obverse   Crowned front-facing bust of king.

Reverse   Long cross with three pellets in each quarter.

IE63F-005   v. rare

Ireland: Halfpenny

The silver halfpenny was first struck in Ireland by John de Curcy, Lord of Ulster, around 1185. It was not until 1190 however that halfpennies were struck in large quantities when John, the youngest son of Henry II, was Lord of Ireland and produced the 'Dominus' or Lord coinage. Several of the later monarchs also produced halfpennies.

John de Curcy Lord of Ulster (c.1185 – 1205)

These issues are very crude in style. It is possible that the first issue, which bears the moneyer's name on the reverse, was struck in Dublin.

First Issue (1185)

Obverse Legend   IOHANNES — John

Reverse Legend   Moneyer's name: ELIS, RAUL, BLUNT or ROGER

Obverse   Bust of John de Curcy.

Reverse   Cross potent with a lis in each quarter.

IJCHD-005   ex. rare

St Patrick Issue (1185 – 1205)

This issue was probably struck in Downpatrick.

Obverse Legend   PATRICUS — Patrick

Reverse Legend   IOHS DE CURCI — John de Curcy

Obverse   A crozier, a cross in the field.

Reverse   A cross, annulets with a pellet at the end of each cross limb, a pellet in each quarter.

IJCHD-010   unique

John as Lord of Ireland (1172 – 1199)

Dominus Coinage (1190 – 1199)

As no pennies were struck during this period, the halfpenny was the main and most important denomination in circulation. It is known as the Dominus coinage because the obverse legend bears John's title of Lord (DOMINUS) of Ireland. The obverse shows a moon faced bust of the king while the reverse has a short cross with an annulet in each quarter. The names of the moneyer and the mint are abbreviated in the reverse legend, as listed below. The moneyer is listed first, followed by the mint which is usually abbreviated.

Mint	Abbreviation	Moneyers
Carrickfergus	CRAC, CRAF, CRAGFEUR	Roberd
		Salmo
		Thomas
Downpatrick	DUNO	Thomas
Dublin	DWE, DVVE, DW, DVV	Adam
		Huge
		Nicholas
		Norman
		Rodberd
		Tomas
		Turgod
		Willelm
Kilkenny	KIL, KEN	Andreh
		Simund
		Waltex
Limerick	LIM	Siward
Waterford	WATER, WATE, WA, VVA	Davi
		Gefrei
		Geifri
		Marcus
		Robert
		Walter
		Willelm
		Willelmus
		Willmus

Dublin Mint

Class 1A
Obverse Legend IOHANNES DOMIN YBER — John Lord of Ireland
Reverse Legend Mint and moneyer's name (see above for details).
Obverse Large flan, front-facing bust of the king.
Reverse Large flan, small cross potent, an annulet in each quarter.

> IJHHD-005   VG £50   F £100   VF £300

Class 1B
Obverse Legend IOHANNES DOM — Lord John
Reverse Legend Mint and moneyer's name (see above for details).
Obverse As previous, but small flan.
Reverse As previous, but small flan.

> IJHHD-010   VG £35   F £60   VF £150

Class 1C
As IJHHD-010, except that the obverse legend reads IOHANNES DE MO — John of Mortain, because John was Count of Mortain.

> IJHHD-015   VG £50   F £100   VF £250

Class 2
As IJHHD-010, except that the reverse bears a small cross pommée in the centre with an annulet in each quarter.

> IJHHD-020   VG £35   F £60   VF £150

Waterford Mint
As IJHHD-010 (class 1B), except that the reverse legend bears Waterford's mint and moneyer names.

> IJHHD-025   VG £40   F £90   VF £300

As IJHHD-015 (class 1C), except that the reverse legend bears Waterford's mint and moneyer names.

> IJHHD-030   VG £60   F £150   VF £450

Obverse Legend IOHANNES COMI — Lord John

Reverse Legend Mint and moneyer's name (see above).
Obverse As IJHHD-010.
Reverse As IJHHD-010.

> IJHHD-035   VG £60   F £150   VF £450

As IJHHD-010, with Waterford's mint details, except that the obverse legend reads IOHANNES DOM or DNS (varieties exist).

> IJHHD-040   VG £60   F £120   VF £280

Kilkenny Mint
As IJHHD-010 (class 1B), except that the reverse legend bears the Kilkenny mint and moneyer names.

> IJHHD-045   v. rare

Limerick Mint
Obverse Legend IOHANNES DOMI — Lord John
Reverse Legend LIM SIWARD (Limerick mint and moneyers' name)
Obverse As IJHHD-010.
Reverse As IJHHD-010.

> IJHHD-050   rare

As previous, but the reverse bears a small cross pommée in the centre with an annulet in each quarter (as IJHHD-020, class 2).

> IJHHD-055   rare

Carrickfergus Mint
As IJHHD-010 (class 1B), except that the reverse legend bears the Carrickfergus mint and moneyer names.

> IJHHD-060   v. rare

As IJHHD-020 (class 2), except that the reverse legend bears the Carrickfergus mint and moneyer names.

> IJHHD-065   v. rare

As previous, except that the obverse legend reads CAPUT IONIS PEGIS — The head of King John

> IJHHD-070   v. rare

Downpatrick Mint

Obverse Legend CAPUT IOHANIS PEG — The head of King John

Reverse Legend DUNO THOMAS (Downpatrick mint and moneyers' name)

Obverse As IJHHD-020.

Reverse As IJHHD-020.

IJHHD-075	v. rare

It is possible that IJHHD-070 and IJHHD-075 were struck when John was king.

John as King of Ireland (1199 – 1216)

Rex Coinage (1207 – 1211)

John also struck halfpennies when he was King of Ireland, in what is known as the Rex (king) coinage (1207 – 11). All issues bear the king's bust within a triangle on the obverse and, on the reverse, the mint name and moneyer in the legend outside a triangle that has a moon, a cross and star inside. Three mints were active during this coinage: Dublin, Limerick and Waterford.

Collecting Hints

These issues are scarce and difficult to obtain, with coins rarely found in better than Fine condition.

Dublin Mint

Obverse Legend IOHAN REX — King John

Reverse Legend ROBERD or WILLEM ON D(IVE) — Roberd or Willem of Dublin

Obverse Crowned front-facing bust of the king within a triangle.

Reverse Cross moon and stars within a triangle.

IJHHD-080	VG £40	F £90	VF £250

Limerick Mint

As previous, but the reverse legend reads WILLEM or WACE ON LI — Willem or Wace of Limerick.

IJHHD-085	VG £60	F £150	VF rare

Waterford Mint

As previous, but the reverse legend reads WILLEM VA — Willem of Waterford.

IJHHD-090	rare

Henry III (1216 – 1272)

No halfpennies were struck under Henry III, but long cross pennies were legally cut to produce both halfpennies and farthings. These coins are fairly common and circulated in England as well as in Ireland. In fact, one of the reasons for the long cross on the reverse of the penny was precisely so that coins could be cut accurately into halves and quarters.

Edward I (1272 – 1307)

Halfpennies were struck in some quantity during the reign of Edward I. All issues bear a crowned bust of the king within a triangle on the obverse and a long cross with three pellets in each quarter on the reverse. The king's name and title are found on the obverse while the mint name (but no moneyer's name) are found on the reverse. Dublin, Waterford and Cork all struck halfpennies during this period.

Collecting Hints

Most Dublin and Waterford issues are fairly common and usually found in Fine condition. However, they are often weakly struck and show ghosting where the design of one side can be found on the other due to the rather thin flan used. Issues of Cork are very rare.

Dublin Mint

Obverse Legend EDW R ANGL DNS HYB — Edward King of England Lord of Ireland

Reverse Legend CIVITAS DUBLINE — City of Dublin

Obverse Crowned front-facing bust of the king, no pellets in the legend.

Reverse Long cross with three pellets in each quarter.

IE1HD-005	VG £35	F £75	VF £200

As previous, but a pellet before the king's name, Lombardic or Roman 'E' at the start of the legend.

IE1HD-010	VG £35	F £75	VF £200

As previous, but a rosette on the king's breast.

IE1HD-015	ex. rare

As IE1HD-010, but with a Lombardic 'N', square 'E' and scroll-tailed 'R' in the legends.

IE1HD-020	VG £35	F £75	VF £200

As previous, but a pellet on the king's breast.

IE1HD-025	VG £40	F £85	VF £225

Waterford Mint

As IE1HD-005, except that the reverse legend reads CIVITAS VATERFOR (or WATERFOR) — City of Waterford.

IE1HD-030	VG £40	F £85	VF £225

As previous, but a pellet before the king's name.

IE1HD-035	VG £40	F £85	VF £225

As IE1HD-020, but with Waterford mint details, also the king's bust is slightly different with a curved neckline.

IE1HD-040	ex. rare

Cork Mint

As IE1HD-040, but the reverse legend reads CIVITAS CORCACIE — City of Cork.

IE1HD-045	ex. rare

No halfpennies were struck again in any quantity until the reign of Edward IV, although English coins circulated in Ireland during this period.

Edward III (1327 – 1377)

Coinage of 1339 – 1340

The main difference between this issue and those of Edward I is in the obverse legend.

Collecting Hints

This issue is extremely rare.

Obverse Legend EDWARDUS REX — King Edward

Reverse Legend CIVITAS DUBLINIE — City of Dublin

Obverse Crowned front-facing bust of the king within a triangle, a star at the start of the legend.

Reverse Long cross with three pellets in each quarter.

IE3HD-005	ex. rare

Edward IV (1461 – 1483)

Halfpennies were struck during the heavy coinage (1470–73) but only in Dublin. Some nineteenth century reference works list additional varieties. It is however probable that such issues are actually clipped pennies or contemporary forgeries.

Heavy Coinage (1470 – 1473)

Collecting Hints

This issue is extremely rare.

Obverse Legend EDWARD D.G. DNS HYBER (?) — Edward by the grace of God Lord of Ireland

Reverse Legend CIVITAS DUBLIN — City of Dublin

Obverse Crowned front-facing bust of the king.

Reverse Long cross with three pellets in each quarter.

IE4HD-005	ex. rare

Henry VII (1485 – 1509)

Halfpennies were struck during the three crowns early coinages of Henry's reign, but only at the Dublin mint. It is a non-portrait issue and known as the three crowns coinage because of the reverse design.

Collecting Hints

This issue is extremely rare.

Obverse Legend REX ANGLIE — King of England

Reverse Legend DOMINUS YRERNI — Lord of Ireland

Obverse Royal shield over cross.

Reverse Three crowns over cross.

IH7HD-005	ex. rare

Elizabeth I (1558 – 1603)

Copper halfpennies were struck at the end of Elizabeth's reign; they were dated and complemented the larger penny.

Obverse Legend   ELIZABETH D.G. AN FR ET HIBER RE — Elizabeth by the grace of God Queen of England France and Ireland

Reverse Legend   POSUI DEUM ADIUTOREM MEU — I have made God my helper

Obverse   Royal shield dividing 'E.R.'; mintmark trefoil or star at the start of the legend.

Reverse   Crown over harp dividing the date (1601); mintmark as obverse.

IELHD-005	VG £25	F £50	VF £150

As previous, but dated 1602; mintmark martlet at the start of the legends.

IELHD-010	v. rare

No halfpennies were struck during the reign of James I.

Charles I   (1625 – 1649)

Issues of the Confederated Catholics

Kilkenny Issue

In 1642, the Irish Catholics remained loyal to Charles I and set up their own council, the Catholic Confederacy, in Kilkenny where they produced halfpennies and farthings using a total of 4,000 lbs of copper. Some coins have been counterstamped to confirm their authenticity and, possibly, so that they could be circulated more widely. The size of these coins varies considerably.

Obverse Legend   CAROLUS D.G. MAG BRI — Charles by the grace of God King of Great Britain

Reverse Legend   FRA ET HIB REX — France and Ireland

Obverse   Crown over two sceptres.

Reverse   Crown over harp dividing 'C.R.'.

IC1HD-005	VG £100	F £200	VF rare

As previous, but no 'C.R.' on the reverse.

IC1HD-010	v. rare

As IC1HD-005, but countermarked with a castle over 'K' on either the obverse or the reverse.

IC1HD-015	v. rare

As previous, but counterstamped with a rosette.

IC1HD-020	v. rare

Cities of Refuge – Cork

Of the four Munster towns (Bandon, Kinsale, Youghal and Cork) that held out against the armies of the Confederated Catholics, Cork was the only one to strike halfpennies. All issues were struck in copper. It should also be noted that numerous European copper coins the size of a halfpenny were counterstamped with 'CORK' and it is possible that most of them are forgeries, although this is not certain.

Collecting Hints

This issue is extremely rare.

Obverse 'CORK' within a dotted circle.

Reverse A castle within a circle of pellets.

IC1HD-025   ex. rare

These countermarked issues are possibly forgeries or struck as 'later' token issues.

Ireland: Farthing

With a value of a quarter of a penny, the farthing was introduced under John de Curcy. The early issues were made of silver, while the later ones were often made of base metal.

John de Curcy Lord of Ulster (c.1185 – 1205)

John de Curcy became Prince of most of Down and Antrim in 1177 with the help of his private army. He was eventually outlawed by King John and taken prisoner.

First Issue (1185 – 1195)

Downpatrick Mint

Obverse Legend   PATRICI — Patrick

Reverse Legend   GOAN D CURCI — John de Curcy

Obverse   Cross pattée a pellet in each quarter.

Reverse   Voided cross.

> **IJCFA-005   ex. rare**

Anonymous Issue (1195 – 1205)

Downpatrick Mint

Obverse Legend   DE DUNO — Of Downpatrick

Reverse Legend   PATRICII — Patrick

Obverse   Cross potent with crescent in each angle.

Reverse   Voided cross.

> **IJCFA-010   ex. rare**

Carrickfergus Mint

Obverse Legend   CRAJ — Carrickjergus

Reverse Legend   PATRICII — Patrick

Obverse   Cross.

Reverse   Voided cross (varieties of cross exist).

> **IJCFA-015   ex. rare**

John as Lord of Ireland (1172 – 1199)

Dominus Coinage (1190 – 1199)

These very small and crude issues were struck while Prince John was Lord of Ireland. Although they bear neither the prince's name nor the mint's name, the coins do have the moneyer's name on the reverse.

Dublin Mint

Obverse Legend   None.

Reverse Legend   Moneyer's name (ADAM, NICO, NORM, ROBD or TOMA).

Obverse   Mascle shaped cross with trefoils at the corners.

Reverse   Moneyer's name in the angles of a cross.

> **IJHFA-005   ex. rare**

Waterford Mint

As previous, but the moneyer's name is MARC, WALT or GEFR.

> **IJHFA-010   ex. rare**

Limerick Mint

As previous, but the moneyer's name is SIWA.

> **IJHFA-015   ex. rare**

John as King of Ireland (1199 – 1216)

Third (Rex) Coinage (1207 – 1211)

This issue is often known as the Rex (king) issue, as it was struck when John was king of England.

Dublin Mint

Obverse Legend IOHAN REX — King John

Reverse Legend Moneyer's name (ROBERD or WILLEM).

Obverse The king's bust within a triangle, the legend around the triangle.

Reverse A starfish within a triangle, the moneyer's name around the triangle.

IJHFA-020   ex. rare

Henry III   (1216 – 1272)

Although pennies were the only coins struck during Henry III's long reign, they bore a long cross on the reverse and were thus legally cut into halves or quarters to produce halfpennies and farthings.

Edward I   (1272 – 1307)

Farthings were struck during the reign of Edward I at the Dublin and Waterford mints. These issues complemented the larger denominations of halfpenny and penny in style and design.

Collecting Hints

These issues used to be very rare but, thanks to metal detectors, they have become more common with many coins being found in England where they had also circulated. Coins can be found in all grades but some are struck off centre, sometimes on flans of irregular shape. Care should be taken when handling these coins as they are prone to breaking and chipping.

Dublin Mint

Obverse Legend ERA NGLIE — Edward King of England

Reverse Legend CIVITAS DUBLINI — City of Dublin

Obverse Crowned bust of king within a triangle.

Reverse Long cross with three pellets in each quarter.

IE1FA-005   VG £50   F £125   VF £300

As previous, but the obverse legend reads EDWARDUS REX — King Edward.

IE1FA-010   v. rare

Waterford Mint

Obverse Legend ERANGLIE — Edward England

Reverse Legend CIVITAS WATERFOR — City of Waterford

Obverse As previous.

Reverse As previous.

IE1FA-015   VG £100   F £225   VF £500

No farthings were struck again until the reign of Edward IV although English coins circulated during this period.

Edward IV (1461 – 1483)

Billon and copper farthings were struck at Dublin during the early part of Edward IV's reign.

Billon issue (1462)

Collecting Hints

This issue is extremely rare.

1462 Issue

Obverse Legend None

Reverse Legend CIVITAS DUBLINIE — City of Dublin

Obverse Crown in the centre with alternate suns and roses around it.

Reverse Cross, a sun between the 'S' and 'D' of the legend.

IE4FA-005   ex. rare

Copper issue

Collecting Hints

These issues are very rare.

1463 – 1465 Issue

Obverse Legend PATRICIUS — Patrick

Reverse Legend SALVATOR — Saviour

Obverse Saint wearing mitre.

Reverse Long cross with rose and sun in alternate angles.

IE4FA-010   v. rare

1467 – 1470 Issue

Obverse Legend EDWARDUS DNS HYBER (or HYBERNI) — Edward Lord of Ireland

Reverse Legend CIVITAS DUBLINI — City of Dublin

Obverse Shield with three crowns, three pellets around the shield.

Reverse Long cross over a sun, with a rose in the centre.

IE4FA-015	v. rare

James I (1603 – 1625)

In 1613, farthings were struck in England by Lord Harrington under licence from the king. These issues depict a harp on the reverse and were designed for circulation in Ireland as well as England, even though this was not confirmed by the Irish Parliament until 1622. There is no doubt that these issues of Lord Harrington as well as the later issues of the Duke of Lennox who took over the licence on Lord Harrington's death circulated widely in Ireland as did the Richmond and Maltravers issues of the reign of Charles I.

Collecting Hints

James I farthings are fairly common, usually obtainable in Fine or VF condition, with coins in EF condition being not uncommon. In the last twenty years many of these coins have been found in the River Thames making them more common.

Harrington Issues

Mintmarks
The mintmark is found between the sceptres or on the bands of the crown on the obverse, and sometimes on the reverse at the start of the legend.

The following mintmarks can be found: cinquefoil, martlet, crescent, millrind, cross saltire, mullet, ermine, pellet, lis, trefoil, A, B, C, D, F, S and L.

Tin Surface Issue

These issues originally had a surface of tin which served two purposes. Firstly, to make counterfeiting more difficult; secondly, to make the coins look like silver and, therefore, more acceptable. Issues with original tin showing are more valuable than issues without and coins in VF or better condition must have a full tin surface to command the values stated here. These small Harringtons are on a 12.25 mm flan.

Obverse Legend IACO DG MAG BRIT — James by the grace of God King of Great Britain

Reverse Legend (continued from the obverse legend) FRA ET HIB REX — France and Ireland

Obverse Two sceptres through a crown.

Reverse Crowned harp.

J1FA-005	VG £15	F £30	VF £60	EF £100

As previous, but central jewel on circlet of crown.

J1FA-010	VG £20	F £40	VF £70	EF £110

Larger Size Issue

This issue is larger (15 mm flan) and the coin surface was not tin washed. From now on no other issues were washed in tin.

As previous, but crowned harp is reversed.

J1FA-015	VG £8	F £20	VF £35	EF £65

Lennox Issue

This issue can be easily differentiated by referring to the obverse legends. The Lennox obverse legend starts at the top, or bottom of the coin while the Harrington issue has the legend starting before the top of the coin. All Lennox issues are of the new larger size (15 mm flan).

Mintmarks
Lion passant, annulet, lion rampant, ball, 3 lis, bell, mascle, coronet, quatrefoil, crescent, rose, star, stirrup, dagger, thistle head, eagle's head, trefoil, flower, triangle, grapes, tun, woolpack, fusil, cross fleury, cross fourchée.

Legends As previous.

Obverse Crown with sceptres in centre; no mintmark. The legend starts at the top of the coin.

Reverse Crowned harp; mintmark at start of legend.

J1FA-020	VG £6	F £18	VF £35	EF £60

As previous, but mintmark both sides.

J1FA-025	VG £6	F £18	VF £35	EF £60

As previous, but mintmark on obverse only.

J1FA-030	VG £6	F £18	VF £35	EF £60

As previous, but larger crowns on obverse and reverse.

| J1FA-035 | VG £6 | F £18 | VF £35 | EF £60 |

This issue is oval, the legends start at the bottom of the coin and there is a mintmark on both sides.

Obverse Legend   As previous; mintmark cross pattée.

Reverse Legend   As previous; mintmark cross pattée.

Obverse   As previous, with long sceptres.

Reverse   As previous.

| J1FA-040 | VG £20 | F £45 | VF £80 |

Charles I   (1625 – 1649)

These issues were struck in London but designed for circulation in England and Ireland and bear a harp on the reverse. They are known as Richmond farthings because they were struck under licence by the Duchess of Richmond who received the licence after the death of the Duke of Lennox. In 1634 another farthing patent was issued to Lord Maltravers. Rose farthings which were struck in England also legally circulated in Ireland.

Collecting Hints

These issues are fairly common and found in all grades. Many have been found over the last twenty years in the river Thames and because of the acids in the river are often bright in colour. Large quantities of forgeries were produced during this period. The forgeries tend to have blundered legends with poor design to the crown and harp. They are often irregular in shape with excess metal outside the legends.

Mintmarks of Royal & Maltravers Issues 1625 – 1642

A, fusil, two fusil, annulet, gauntlet, annulet with pellet centre, halberd, bell, harp, book, heart, cinquefoil, horseshoe, crescent, leaf, cross calvary, lion passant, cross patonce, lion rampant, cross pattée, lis, cross fitchée, martlet, cross saltire, nautilus, cross with pellets in angles, quatrefoil, dagger, rose, ermine, shield, estoile, spearhead, estoile pierced, three lis, eye, tower, fish hook, trefoil, fleece, woolpack, fusil, woolpack over annulet, mascle, demi lis.

Richmond or Royal Issues

This issue is an altered die from James I's Lennox issue (J1FA-030).

Obverse Legend   CARO (over IACO) D.G. MAG BRI — Charles by the grace of God King of Great Britain

Reverse Legend   FRA ET HIB REX — France and Ireland

Obverse   Crown with two sceptres; mintmark above crown.

Reverse   Crown over harp; no mintmark.

| C1FA-005 | VG £5 | F £18 | VF £30 | EF £50 |

As previous, but new die with the king's name spelt CARA; mintmark on obverse.

| C1FA-010 | VG £40 | F £90 | VF £180 | EF ex. rare |

As previous, but new die with the king's name spelt CARO.

| C1FA-015 | VG £5 | F £18 | VF £30 | EF £50 |

The next four issues (C1FA-020 to -035) have apostrophe stops in the legend instead of single stops.

As previous, but the harp on the reverse has an eagle's head.

| C1FA-020 | VG £5 | F £18 | VF £30 | EF £50 |

As previous, but the harp is beaded.

| C1FA-025 | VG £5 | F £18 | VF £30 | EF £50 |

As previous, but the harp is scroll fronted with five jewels.

| C1FA-030 | VG £10 | F £25 | VF £40 | EF £60 |

As previous, but with seven jewels.

| C1FA-035 | VG £5 | F £18 | VF £30 | EF £50 |

Transitional Issue

This issue is fairly similar to the previous one, however, it has a double arched crown on both sides as used for the Maltravers issue.

| C1FA-040 | VG £25 | F £30 | VF £60 | EF £100 |

Maltravers Issues

This issue is easily identified because it has inner circles on the obverse and reverse.

Obverse Legend CAROLUS D.G. MAG BR — Charles by the grace of God King of Great Britain

Reverse Legend FRAN ET HIB REX — France and Ireland

Obverse Crown with two sceptres in inner circles; mintmark at the start of the legend.

Reverse Harp with crown above; no mintmark.

| C1FA-045 | VG £8 | F £25 | VF £40 | EF £60 |

As previous, but mintmark on both sides of the coin.

| C1FA-050 | VG £5 | F £18 | VF £30 | EF £50 |

As previous, but different mintmark on either side of the coin (i.e. muled).

| C1FA-055 | VG £5 | F £18 | VF £30 | EF £50 |

Oval Issues

These reasonably scarce issues are quite similar to the last ones of James I. In fact Charles I's first issue actually uses the James I die. However, the king's name has been altered from IACO to CARO. These issues are oval and, in all cases, the legend starts at the bottom of the coin.

Obverse Legend CARO (over IACO) DG MAG BRI — Charles by the grace of God King of Great Britain

Reverse Legend FRA ET HIB REX — France and Ireland

Obverse Crown with two long sceptres; mintmark on both sides. The king's name is over that of James I, this being an altered die from the previous reign.

Reverse Crown and harp.

| C1FA-060 | VG £15 | F £30 | VF £50 | EF £100 |

As previous, but mintmark on obverse only.

| C1FA-065 | VG £12 | F £25 | VF £45 | EF £90 |

Maltravers Oval Issue

Maltravers oval type, with king's full name but no inner circles. Note the double-arched crown which makes this a Maltravers issue.

Obverse Legend CAROLUS DG MAG BRIT — Charles by the grace of God King of Great Britain

Reverse Legend FRAN ET HIB REX — France and Ireland

Obverse Crown and sceptre; mintmark both sides.

Reverse Harp and crown.

| C1FA-070 | VG £15 | F £30 | VF £60 | EF £100 |

It is important to note that varieties exist in the legends of all the previous issues. When identifying a coin collectors should refer to the number of arches on the crown, to the point where the legend starts and to any inner circles or stops in the legend.

Rose Farthing

These issues are smaller and thicker than the previous ones. They are made of copper, with a brass plug in the coin to deter forgers. On many coins of poorer condition the plug has fallen out, leaving a rather unsightly gap. The obverse of the coin has a crown with two sceptres. The reverse a crowned rose, hence the name Rose farthing.

Mintmarks

crescent, martlet, cross pattée, mullet, lis, crescent

Obverse Legend CAROLUS D G MAG BRIT — Charles by the grace of God King of Great Britain

Reverse Legend FRAN ET HIB REX — France and Ireland

Obverse Double-arched crown with small sceptres in inner circle.

Reverse Double rose within inner circle.

| C1FA-075 | VG £10 | F £20 | VF £30 | EF £40 |

As previous, but the sceptres on the obverse just break the inner circle.

| C1FA-080 | VG £8 | F £16 | VF £24 | EF £34 |

As previous, but the sceptres almost reach the outer circle.

| C1FA-085 | VG £6 | F £14 | VF £22 | EF £32 |

As previous, but the obverse legend reads CAROLUS DG. MAG BRI.

| C1FA-090 | VG £15 | F £30 | VF £42 | EF £55 |

As previous, but muled with the next issue: the obverse has a double-arched crown, the reverse a single-arched crown.

| C1FA-095 | VG £8 | F £16 | VF £24 | EF £34 |

Obverse Legend   CAROLU(S) D G. MAG BRI — Charles by the grace of God King of Great Britain

Reverse Legend   FRA ET HIB REX — France and Ireland

Obverse   Single-arched crown over two sceptres.

Reverse   Single plain rose with crown above.

| C1FA-100 | VG £6 | F £14 | VF £22 | EF £32 |

As previous, but with sceptres below the crown and the king's name in the obverse legend shortened to CAROLU.

| C1FA-105 | VG £20 | F £50 | VF £100 | EF — |

Issues of the Confederate Catholics
(1642 – 1643)

Kilkenny Issue

In 1642, the Irish Catholics remained loyal to Charles I and set up their own council, the Catholic Confederacy, in Kilkenny. There they produced Kilkenny halfpennies and farthings using a total of 4,000 lbs of copper.

Collecting Hints

Despite the large numbers of coins struck, the farthing is rare and rarely found in better than Fine condition. These coins were badly produced, often with very weak legends. Coins with very crude legends and style are contemporary forgeries and less valuable, albeit interesting.

Obverse Legend   CARO D.G. MAG BRI — Charles by the grace of God (King) of Great Britain

Reverse Legend   FRA ET HIB REX — France and Ireland

Obverse   Crown and two sceptres.

Reverse   Crowned harp.

| IC1FA-005 | VG £150 | F £300 | VF v. rare |

Cities of Refuge

The four Munster towns of Bandon, Kinsale, Youghal and Cork held out against the armies of the Confederated Catholics. Each town produced farthings, in either copper or brass.

Collecting Hints

All of these issues are extremely rare.

Bandon (1646 – 1647)

This issue is irregular in shape and struck in copper.

Obverse Legend   None

Reverse Legend   None

Obverse   'B.B.' within a circle of pellets.

Reverse   Three castles within a circle of pellets.

| IC1FA-010 | ex. rare |

261

Cork (1647)

This issue is square in shape and struck in copper.

Obverse Legend   None

Reverse Legend   None

Obverse   'CORK' or 'CORKE' within a circle of pellets.

Reverse   A castle.

IC1FA-015   ex. rare

Kinsale (1647)

This issue is square in shape and struck in copper.

Obverse Legend   None

Reverse Legend   None

Obverse   'K.S.' within a circle of pellets.

Reverse   A chequered shield.

IC1FA-020   ex. rare

Youghal (1646)

These issues were usually struck in brass.

Square Issues

Obverse Legend   None

Reverse Legend   None

Obverse   'YT' above date (1646), a bird facing left above 'YT'.

Reverse   A galley enclosed within a double linear circle.

IC1FA-025   ex. rare

Obverse   As previous, but no date.

Reverse   A galley.

IC1FA-030   ex. rare

Obverse   'YT' above date (1646).

Reverse   Galley enclosed in a double linear circle.

IC1FA-035   ex. rare

Obverse   Date (1646) above 'YT', a bird facing right.

Reverse   As previous.

IC1FA-040   ex. rare

Obverse   Date (1646) below 'YT', a branch above 'YT'.

Reverse   As previous.

IC1FA-045   ex. rare

Obverse   'YT' within a circle of pellets.

Reverse   A galley on shield enclosed by a circle of triangular dots.

IC1FA-050   ex. rare

Obverse   'YT' in an elaborate circle enclosed by a circle of small triangles.

Reverse   A shield bearing a galley within a circle of triangles.

IC1FA-055   ex. rare

Round Issue

Obverse   'YT' within a circle of pellets.

Reverse   A fish surrounded by a circle of pellets.

IC1FA-060   ex. rare

Ireland: Half Farthing

The half farthing is the smallest denomination ever issued in Ireland and was struck in copper and only produced during the reign of Edward IV.

Edward IV   (1461 – 1483)

Issue of 1460 – 1461

Collecting Hints

This issue is rare and sometimes referred to as a Patrick from the coin's legend, which bears the name of Ireland's patron saint. Coins are rarely found in better than Fine condition.

Obverse Legend   PATRIK — Patrick

Reverse Legend   None.

Obverse   Legend divided by a branch, a crown in the centre.

Reverse   Large cross.

IE4HF-005   VG £250   F £500   VF rare

As previous, but a 'P' in an angle of the reverse cross.

IE4HF-010   ex. rare

Issue of 1463 – 1465

Collecting Hints

This issue is extremely rare.

Obverse Legend   None.

Reverse Legend   None.

Obverse   A crown.

Reverse   Large cross, a pellet in each quarter.

IE4HF-015   ex. rare

The milled coinage of Ireland

The milled coinage of Ireland began during the reign of Charles II who, after his restoration, granted a patent to Sir Thomas Armstrong in 1660 to coin farthings 'by engines'. This was, however, an ill-fated beginning, as the Chief Governor of Ireland prohibited the issue, and few were struck.

The next attempt to produce a coinage was even more unsuccessful. On 28th April 1662, a patent was granted to Sir Thomas Vyner, Robert Vyner and David Bellingham to produce groats, threepences, twopences, pennies and halfpennies in silver. Under the terms of the patent, the King was to receive twelve pence out of every pound weight of silver coined. For some reason, Sir Thomas Vyner was ordered in November of the same year to surrender the patent in order for it to be cancelled. It is possible that the patentees, on consideration, had decided that the venture would not be sufficiently profitable.

Around this period unofficial tokens proliferated, even though various proclamations sought to outlaw them. Somewhat ironically, and to some extent no doubt because of their relatively high value, many people were reluctant to accept the previously universally tendered Mexican pillar dollars because the proclamation of 29th January 1660 had not included them. Because of this, a further proclamation was issued by the Duke of Ormond, the Lord Lieutenant, on 19th September 1662 ordering that the dollars should be deemed to have been included in the first proclamation and that they should circulate at four shillings and ninepence (and the smaller pieces pro rata) provided that they weighed at least 17 pennyweights.

For several years, tokens continued to circulate in large quantities, and during 1673 it became so profitable to export currency that a proclamation was issued on 28th July which made it clear that previous statutes prohibiting such exports would be rigorously enforced; other quantities exported would need a licence, with the exception of amounts needed for reasonable expenses. All of the official searchers at the ports were ordered to be vigilant in upholding the law. However, even this failed to stop the outflow of coinage from Ireland, and in 1674, in correspondence between the Lord Lieutenant and Lord Ranelagh, it was suggested that Ireland should be provided with farthings of the same weight and fineness as those which had been issued in England since 1672, and that copper should be imported from Sweden for the purpose. However, nothing came of the proposal.

On 26 July 1675, a further proclamation was issued prohibiting the export of money out of Ireland, with the further incentive to the searchers that they should receive a commission on any amount that they discovered.

In 1677, the Lord Lieutenant and Council of Ireland learned that some merchants had brought into Ireland some Dutch silver coins known as New Lion dollars dated 1674, 75 and 76, and that they had successfully put them into circulation at a rate of four shillings and ninepence, whereas their intrinsic worth was about three shillings and fourpence. Consequently, a proclamation was issued on 9th April giving notice that no person was by law required to accept these coins.

At this time, the St. Patrick pieces and the Dublin halfpenny may have gone some way to alleviating the shortage of small change prior to the introduction of a regular issue of official coinage. However, it is by no means certain that the St. Patrick pieces were denominated at a halfpenny and a farthing.

The patent granted to Sir Thomas Armstrong in 1660 to coin farthings for a period of 21 years had never been properly implemented, and in 1680, his son, Sir William Armstrong, together with Colonel George Legg, petitioned the King and were granted a further patent to coin halfpence. The coins produced under this patent were the first regular issued of milled coinage worthy of the name; they were struck each year from 1680 to 1684 to an excellent standard. The patent had, however, been assigned to John Knox on 7th June 1680 for the sum of £1500.

In 1683, because of confusion as to the exact equivalent values of various foreign gold and silver coins, a proclamation was issued on 6th June to declare the current values. Such information had been available hitherto, but the documentation was out of print, and the publication of the proclamation meant that virtually all of the required rates were now available in one listing. The proclamation also stipulated the characteristics of the weights to be used to verify the coins, and that they should be manufactured by Henry Paris and John Cuthbeard (aka Cuthbert) of Dublin.

In February 1685 (1684 old style calendar) Charles II died, and his brother was proclaimed King as James II. Shortly afterwards, John Knox, to whom Armstrong and Legg had assigned their patent for coining halfpence, petitioned the King to grant a new patent to produce coinage for James II. This was granted, and the new coins were minted in each year from 1685 to 1688, although those of 1687 are rare.

In December 1688, the King abdicated and retired to France, but on 24th March 1689 (1688 old style calendar) James landed in Dublin in an attempt to recover his crown. The unusual coinage produced by him during this escapade is the subject of a separate section in this catalogue.

On 14th June 1690, King William III landed at Carrickfergus and on 1st July defeated James's army at the Battle of the Boyne, subsequently encamping at Finglas, near Dublin. From this camp on 10th July he issued a proclamation to demonetize the gunmoney issues of James 'to the value of the standard of the like copper money formerly current in this Kingdom', begging the question as to what copper money ever circulated in Ireland which resembled gunmoney! Nevertheless, the crown and the large halfcrown were reduced to one penny; the small halfcrown to three-farthings; the shilling and the sixpence to one farthing. On 23rd February 1691 (1690 old style calendar) a proclamation declared that, after the 26th of that month, gunmoney coins were to cease to have any value whatsoever.

It seems probable that the King now renewed the patent to produce halfpennies. This had been sold by John Knox to Colonel Roger Moore, and coins dated 1692, 1693 and 1694 were struck prior to the death of Mary in December 1694.

During 1695, exporting of gold and silver from Ireland again became a problem. The value of these metals abroad had increased markedly, and on 29th May a proclamation raised the values accordingly. The gold pistole became equivalent to 21 shillings, a ducatoon six shillings and eightpence and a Mexican pillar dollar five shillings and fourpence, but the somewhat similar Peruvian dollar was rated only at four shillings and tenpence. Although the proclamation did not mention English coins, it may be assumed that they also saw an equivalent rise in Ireland; the guinea, for example, passed for 26 shillings.

The halfpenny of the type issued for William and Mary was struck in 1696 for William III ruling alone, but during 1697 many forgeries of Irish halfpence were imported into northern Ireland from Scotland, to such an extent that most of the pieces in circulation were counterfeit. On 13th August a proclamation forbade the importation of false money under pain of imprisonment. Another problem was the manufacture in Ireland of counterfeit gold and silver coins, and it was decreed that such counterfeit pieces could be tendered only if cut through the middle or defaced so that they could not be confused with genuine coins. On 21st February 1698 (1697 old style calendar) Paris and Cuthbeard, the official makers of money-weights, were removed from their posts for unprofessional work, and Vincent Kidder of Dublin was authorized to be the sole manufacturer.

Later in 1698 there was a considerable problem with counterfeiting in England following the Great Recoinage, and the increasing severity of the penalties in England led many of the perpetrators to flee to Ireland, where they continued their practices.

On 2nd June 1701, foreign coins in Ireland were reduced in value; the gold pistole became eighteen shillings and sixpence, and the Mexican pillar dollar four shillings and ninepence. Again, English coinage was not specified, but Simon considered that the guinea was reduced from 26 to 23 shillings.

During the reign of Anne, no coinage was struck for Ireland but some alterations were made to the values in Ireland of foreign coinage. In particular, in 1714 the new gold French Louis was rendered current at one pound and two shillings, and the new silver Louis at five shillings and sixpence.

The lack of coinage struck specifically for Ireland continued through the early years of the reign of George I, such that by 1722 many manufacturers were paying their employees with tallies or card tokens signed with an undertaking that they would later be exchanged for money; counterfeit coins known as raps proliferated, usually of greatly inferior quality. During that year the King gave to his mistress, the Duchess of Kendal. a patent for the manufacture of copper money for Ireland which she sold to a William Wood for £10,000.

William Wood was born in July, 1671, and became a successful businessman, owning mines in the West of England; the patent he acquired had a term of 14 years, and gave him the sole right to produce halfpence and farthings to a total weight not exceeding 360 tons, to be coined as 100 tons in the first year, and up to 20 tons in each of the successive 13 years. For this privilege Wood had to pay £1000 per year. The metal to be used was fine British copper which, when heated red hot, would spread thinly under the hammer.

At an early stage it must have occurred to Wood that producing coins strictly according to the terms of the patent would result in a minimal profit. Accordingly, he decided that it was necessary to reduce the weight of the coins somewhat, and began to strike them in London in January 1723 (1722 old style calendar). The London Post of 14th January reported: 'William Wood of Wolverhampton, having a patent for 14 years for coining farthings and halfpence for Ireland, and halfpence, pence and twopence for all His Majesty's dominions in America, hath erected a building in Phoenix Street, Brown's Gardens, near the Seven Dials, for the American coinage, and another in the City of Bristol for Irish coinage. 'The same journal reported on 18th January: 'Wood began his coinage for Ireland on Monday last at the Seven Dials' (the Seven Dials was, and is, a monument in the centre of a junction where seven streets meet). Later in 1723 his Bristol mint came into operation; this possessed the largest copper smelting works in Britain, and records show a total for 1722 and 1723 of £13,480 in halfpence and £1,086 in farthings.

The Wood coinage was struck to an excellent standard, arguably the best struck and most attractively designed as yet produced for Ireland. The dies were engraved by Lammas, Harold and Standbroke ('Old Harold'), of Tottenham Court Road, London. Leake,

writing in 1726, remarks that the coins have 'on one side the King's head like the guinea, but more resembling His Majesty, and a much handsomer coin than the English halfpenny'. However, they were unpopular in Ireland, to a large extent because of rumour and misrepresentations put around in several quarters. Unfortunately, Wood rose to the bait, and most unwisely replied on one occasion that he 'would cram his brass down their throats' (i.e. the Irish). Naturally, this was not well perceived in the Emerald Isle.

Dean Jonathan Swift, the celebrated writer, who played a substantial part in the demise of William Wood, was a disappointed cleric and politician with a considerable axe to grind. He hated the English ministry, and was living at the Deanery of St. Patrick's in Dublin during the issue of Wood's coinage. In an attempt to embarrass the Government, Swift launched a campaign against Wood and his coinage by means of a series of letters, including allegations such as that Wood had entered into a secret agreement with the Duchess of Kendal in order to acquire his patent, and that the Duchess was continuing to benefit from profits made from the issuance of substandard coinage.

As so frequently happens, much of the mud stuck. Wood surrendered the patent on 18th August 1724, and died in August 1730. His epitaph in Fog's Journal on 29th August 1730 read:

> Here lies Master Wood
> Who did what he could,
> Whitehaven by tricks to environ
> But his glass is run out,
> Who made such a rout
> With his halfpence and making of iron.

On 22nd January 1725 a proclamation legalized the 'new gold of Portugal' (i.e. the four escudos) at £4 sterling, and the smaller pieces pro rata.

As George II came to the throne in 1727, the coinage was in a sorry state. The Wood issue had been rejected by the populace, and there was no coinage worthy of the name except for foreign pieces. Manufacturers who employed workmen were often forced to continue their employment until their wages totalled a gold double pistole which the employees had to change as best they could, for example at an alehouse, and even then they frequently had to pay ten pence or a shilling for this privilege. Tokens of silver and copper were privately issued by traders in Belfast, Armagh, Portadown, etc. James Maculla, a Dublin brazier, proposed to issue tokens for distribution throughout Ireland at 48 pieces to the pound weight, netting him a 16% profit. Dean Swift disapproved of the idea, and proposed issuing tokens having a greater intrinsic value than Maculla's, to be issued by a society of ten gentlemen, of whom he was one.

Calls came for the establishment of a mint in Ireland. An anonymous writer, in a tract entitled 'A scheme of the money matters of Ireland', published in Dublin in 1729, observed: 'Poor, unhappy Ireland must for ever suffer, unless the collective body of the nation, her Parliament, which must for ever be supposed to be best acquainted with her true interests and wants, interposes in her favour, and shews His Majesty and his ministers how greatly they are deceived, and how heavily all the affairs of this unfortunate forlorn country languish and droop, for want of a well registered cash, and a mint that may from time to time support it. There is not, perhaps, any one thing that could create so good an understanding between England and Ireland as the establishment of a mint here.' This writer also published a list of the condition of what silver coinage could be found: £100 in sixpences had worn by £10.17s.5d; in shillings by £8.10s.0d; in halfcrowns by £3.7s.7d; and in crowns by £2.17s.1d.

A directive of 1736 called for a 'proper agent' to contract for fifty tons of copper to be delivered to the Tower of London. This was coined into halfpennies and farthings for Ireland at the Tower, the first consignment being sent over to Ireland in April 1737. A proclamation of 6th May 1737 declared the coins to be valid as currency, stating that the coinage should be legal tender up to sixpence in any single payment, but only then if the recipient found the new issue acceptable.

The first contract for this coinage was completed by 26th January 1739; the second contract of March 1741 was for one hundred tons, and was completed by November 1749; an April 1750 contract of fifty tons was partially filled (39 tons, 400 lbs) by 31st July 1753; a September 1760 contract for 50 tons was completed by April 1762, and two further contracts for halfpennies only, and for 50 tons each, were dated 1766 and 1769. Ireland was at last well endowed with copper coinage; George III had ascended the throne in 1760, and Ireland had acquired much of his coinage before England had minted a single copper piece for this reign. The situation regarding silver was less happy; James Simon had written in 1749: 'What silver is now left is some English money, not worth melting, shilling pieces hardly worth nine pence or ten pence, and sixpenny pieces not worth a groat.'

The British shilling of 1763 struck in London is worth a mention here, although its low mintage precludes any serious consideration as a contender to alleviate the silver shortage. The coin was struck for distribution amongst the citizens of Dublin on the occasion of the first public appearance of Hugh, Earl of Northumberland, as Lord Lieutenant of Ireland. Legend has it that £100 face value were struck, but doubts exist about this. Certainly, the coins were hoarded rather than used as currency, as the extant specimens are encountered more often in very fine or extremely fine than in fine condition.

Halfpennies of George III were struck until 1782, but subsequently no coins of any description were coined for Ireland up to the end of the century. Counterfeits were everywhere. By 1800, the country was again desperate for currency. Banks outside Dublin were allowed to issue notes of below £1 provided that they were payable in Bank of Ireland notes. 'Silver notes' issued by traders circulated, especially in the south of Ireland, supposedly redeemable for silver but in all probability well in excess of the amount of silver available. Merchants issued IOUs which were often redeemable only by doing further business with the trader.

It is appropriate at this point to consider the cost of everyday items in Ireland at the time, as shown below:

Year	Wheat per bushel	Horse	Cow	Hen	Butter per pound	Cheese per pound	Ale per gallon
1675	4/6d	£5/10s	£2/17s	1/3d	4½d	2d	8d
1700	4/9½d						10d
1720	4/4½d						1s
1740	3/8d	£10	£7/7s	1/6d	9d	3½d	1s
1760	3/10d	£14	£7	1/10d	10d	5½d	1/2d
1780	4/5½d						
1795	7/10d	£19	£16/8s	1/6d	11½d	5d	1/2¾d

On 1st January 1801, the Union of Great Britain and Ireland was enacted, but there was no immediate improvement in the coinage situation. Rogers Ruding, writing in 1840, recalled that at the turn of the century the silver coinage was in 'a wretched state', with 21 shillings face value being worth intrinsically nine shillings. Crown-size pieces and halfcrowns disappeared for 18 months, and sixpences were virtually non-existent. The copper coinage was in a somewhat better state, but most of it was 'cammacs', which were counterfeit halfpennies made by a person of that name who owned a number of copper mines. In the south of Ireland silver notes continued to flourish. Even government offices accepted counterfeits, and the army paid their troops with them. However, in March 1804 the Post Office decided to make a stand and announced that henceforth it would reject all counterfeit coinage. Such an announcement has a surreal quality when viewed in a modern context.

On 1st April 1804, the Bank of Ireland, by arrangement with the Government, began to accept counterfeit silver coins at a rate of five shillings (later 4 shillings and 6 pence) per ounce for between 50 and 200 pieces. Larger amounts were accepted for assaying at the current rate of about six shillings per ounce of pure silver. Also in 1804, the six shilling silver bank token was issued by the Bank of Ireland, following the prohibition of notes below one pound. These pieces were restruck from Spanish and Spanish American eight real pieces at Matthew Boulton's Soho mint in Birmingham, and were identical in size and weight to the Bank of England dollars of the same year. They were issued at six shillings face value because if lower it would have been profitable to export them. In 1805 – 06 the Soho mint struck pennies, halfpennies and farthings of excellent quality for Ireland, and the Bank of Ireland issued silver tokens for ten and five pence, followed by a thirty pence token in 1808. The silver pieces engraved by Pingo were not of good workmanship, and also suffered from metal flaws, but the 1813 issue of silver ten pence were by Thomas Wyon and were better executed.

In 1809, a motion in the House of Commons sought to equalize the currency between Great Britain and Ireland, but it was not passed. After George IV ascended the throne, the two currencies were equalized in 1821, but there was no immediate move to stop the coining of Irish currency, and on 5th July 1822, an Order in Council provided for the striking of pence, halfpence and farthings. The farthing was not issued, but proofs or patterns dated 1823 exist. On 27th June 1825, an Act provided 'for the assimilation of the currency and monies of account throughout the United Kingdom of Great Britain and Ireland.' pointing out that 'the silver coin which represents a shilling of the money of Great Britain is paid and accepted and taken as representing one shilling and one penny of the currency of Ireland.' On 26th December 1825 a proclamation announced the complete assimilation of the currencies from 5th January 1826. Copper coins were specially dealt with in a proclamation dated 30th January 1826, providing for acceptance of the new British copper coinage. On 12th July 1826, Irish copper coins were demonetized.

A fascinating insight into the situation at the time comes from the 1826 diary of one Amhlaoibh O Suilleabhain, who wrote: 'There is no longer any difference between the silver sixpenny-piece and the bronze, each is now worth six pence whereas, before the 5th January 1826, the silver sixpence was worth six and a half pence. Similarly, the eight-testoon piece is worth only a bare half-crown, and the former thirteen-pence only a bare shilling or twelve-pence. The five-penny pieces, the ten-penny pieces, the Irish half-crown (or thirty-pence piece) and the six shilling pieces have all disappeared. They would be accepted now only at half-price.'

No further coinage for Ireland was struck until the inception of the Irish Free State.

Ireland: Six Shillings Bank Token

George III (1760 – 1820)

At the beginning of the nineteenth century, silver coinage of Britain and other countries such as Spain and Spanish America circulated in Ireland. The acute shortage of such coin in readable condition necessitated urgent action. In 1804, at Matthew Boulton's Soho mint in Birmingham, England, there were struck both the Bank of England dollar and its Irish sister coin, the Bank of Ireland six shillings token. Both bear the same laureated portrait of George III. Permission from the Privy Council was obtained by the Bank of Ireland to issue this coinage, which was overstruck on old Spanish and Spanish American eight real pieces. The status of the piece was 'semi-official', being strictly speaking a token for the sum of six shillings rather than a fully legal tender coin. The equivalent value to the British five shilling token at a ratio of 13:12 would have been five shillings and five pence Irish, and the token was fixed at six shillings to prevent its being exported for profit. The design was by C. H. Küchler, whose initials appear on the truncation on the obverse, and as 'K' on the reverse.

Contemporary counterfeits exist. These were often made by soldering wafer-thin surfaces obtained from genuine pieces on to brass blanks, and then applying a silver collar to the edge to hide the brass. These pieces can be deceptive and are usually of around the correct weight, but often the underlying brass shows through as dark patches in a number of places.

Obv. 1　　　　　　　　Obv. 3

Obv. 3 detail　　　　　　Rev. 1

Denomination	Metal	Weight (grams)	Diameter (mm)	Rev. alignment
6 shillings Bank Token	Silver	26 – 28	40 – 41	↑

Obverse 1　Head 1, right, C.H.K (with stops) on truncation; GEORGIUS III DEI GRATIA REX (stop after REX); top right leaf of wreath points to left hand side of 'E'

Obverse 2　As obverse 1 but C.H.K. reads CHK (no stops)

Obverse 3　As obverse 1 but leaf points to centre of 'E'

Obverse 4　As obverse 3 but no stop after REX

Obverse 5　As obverse 1 but leaf points to right hand side of 'E'

Reverse 1　Hibernia seated, facing left, holding palm branch, with left arm resting on harp; BANK OF IRELAND TOKEN. In exergue: 1804 SIX SHILLINGS

Edge　plain

No.	Date	Features	Obv.	Rev.	F	VF	EF	UNC
IG36S-005	1804		1	1	100	180	450	750
IG36S-010	1804	PROOF in copper	1	1				500
IG36S-015	1804	PROOF in gilt copper or gilt silver [1]	1	1				600
IG36S-020	1804		2	1	130	240	550	950
IG36S-025	1804		3	1	120	220	500	850
IG36S-030	1804	PROOF in copper	3	1				500
IG36S-035	1804		4	1	110	200	480	800
IG36S-040	1804	PROOF in copper	4	1				500
IG36S-045	1804		5	1	130	240	550	950
IG36S-050	1804	PROOF	5	1				1200
IG36S-055	1804	PROOF in copper	5	1				600
IG36S-060	1804	PROOF in gilt copper	5	1				700
IG36S-065	1804	PROOF in gilt silver	5	1				1000

1. A specimen in the British Museum weighs 24.1 grams.

Ireland: Thirty Pence Bank Token

George III   (1760 – 1820)

This token was struck as part of the series issued by the Bank of Ireland to alleviate the acute shortage of regal silver coinage in the early nineteenth century. It was, like the six shillings, a 'semi-official' token, not a true legal tender coin. The word 'Irish' on the reverse refers to the currency of 'pence-Irish' rather than being intended to denote the country of issue. At the time, 13 pence-Irish were equivalent to one British shilling.

Like the six shilling token, the thirty pence-Irish token depicted the laureate head of George III, with a seated Hibernia on the reverse. The date, however, appeared on the obverse rather than in the reverse exergue. This innovation appeared some years before it was used on British silver coins, and was possibly inspired by the obverse dating of British copper coins a few years earlier, or of Spanish and Spanish-American silver coins. The design was by Lewis Pingo.

This series often appears with haymarking or serious metal flaws. Counterfeits cast in lead and other base metals exist. The obverse of this coin did not stand up at all well to heavy wear, whereas the reverse of worn pieces often exhibits relatively good detail.

Denomination	Metal	Weight (grams)	Diameter (mm)	Rev. alignment
30 pence – Irish Bank Token	Silver	12.4 – 12.5	32.5	↑

Obverse 1   Head 1, right; GEORGIVS III DEI GRATIA REX 1808

Reverse 1   Hibernia seated, facing left, holding palm branch, with left arm resting on harp; BANK TOKEN (harp top points between O and K). In exergue: XXX PENCE IRISH

Reverse 2   Similar but harp top points to O

Edge   milled (diagonally)

Obv. 1   Rev. 2

No.	Date	Features	Obv.	Rev.	F	VF	EF	UNC
IG330D-005	1808		1	1	30	75	180	280
IG330D-010	1808		1	2	40	100	250	380

Ireland: Shilling

George III   (1760 – 1820)

Although not strictly speaking an Irish coin, the so-called 'North-umberland' shilling of 1763 is included in this catalogue because of its Irish connotations. The coin was distributed in Dublin by the Earl of Northumberland on his appointment as Lord Lieutenant of Ireland. The portrait was designed by Richard Yeo, with the reverse based on the current standard design for the British shilling. The coins were struck in London, and almost certainly more were issued than the official 2,000 figure. Northumberland shillings were hoarded rather than spent, and occur more often in very fine or extremely fine than fair or fine condition.

Denomination	Metal	Weight (grams)	Diameter (mm)	Rev. alignment
Shilling	Silver	6.0	26	↓

Obverse 1   Head 1, right; GEORGIVS III DEI GRATIA

Reverse 1   Cruciform shields around star, plain in angles; M B F ET H REX F D B ET L D S R I A T ET E 1763

Edge   milled

Obv. 1

Rev. 1

No.	Date	Features	Obv.	Rev.	F	VF	EF	UNC
G3SH-005	1763	1	1	1	180	300	500	650

1. The number allocated to this piece is that from *Coincraft's Standard Catalogue of English & UK Coins.*

Ireland: 10 Pence Bank Token
5 Pence Bank Token

George III (1760 – 1820)

At the beginning of the 19th century there were no silver coins in circulation which were struck specifically for Ireland. Those silver coins which did circulate were mainly from Britain, Spain and Spanish America, and they were generally in a very sorry state. Many of the low denomination silver pieces were British shillings and sixpences, worn as thin as hammered silver coins, with no trace of designs but countermarked with initials of various tradesmen; these were known as 'slap tokens'.

To alleviate the situation, in 1805 the Bank of Ireland issued silver token denominations of ten pence and five pence. These were considered to be too small to portray the Hibernia reverse used on the six shilling token (and later on the 30 pence), and a legend detailing the denomination was used instead. The 1805 and 1806 coins were designed by Lewis Pingo, and the 1813 tenpence by Thomas Wyon, the obverse for this date being the same as for the British pattern ninepence of 1812. The five pence was intended to be equivalent to one-thirteenth of a pillar dollar, with the ten pence at two-thirteenths. Counterfeiting statutes were extended to cover these pieces.

At the end of 1805, the workers at the mint altered the date of the 5 pence token to 1806 without realising that the Act authorizing the issue had stipulated that the date should be 1805 on all of the issue. Both of the tokens were withdrawn in 1817 when the new English coinage was introduced.

These denominations are not difficult to find in extremely fine condition. However, with the exception of the 1813 ten pence, the quality of striking of the head of the monarch is often poor. In grading such pieces, an attempt should be made to gauge how much actual wear has been sustained rather than simply using overall appearance as a basis.

Many cast base metal counterfeits exist.

10 Pence Bank Token

Denomination	Metal	Weight (grams)	Diameter (mm)	Rev. alignment
10 pence – Irish Bank Token 1805 – 06	0.89 Silver	4.1	22.5	↑
10 pence – Irish Bank Token 1813	0.89 Silver	3.5 – 3.6	22	↑

Obverse 1 Head 1, right; GEORGIVS III DEI GRATIA

Obverse 2 Head 2, right; GEORGIUS III DEI GRATIA REX

Reverse 1 (in six lines) BANK TOKEN TEN PENCE IRISH (date)

Reverse 2 (in five lines) BANK TOKEN 10 PENCE IRISH 1813 within ornamentation of shamrocks and leaves

Edge (1805–06) milled (diagonally); (1813) plain

Obv. 1   Obv. 2

Rev. 1   Rev. 2

No.	Date	Features	Obv.	Rev.	F	VF	EF	UNC
IG310D-005	1805	first laurel leaf under E of DEI (obv)	1	1	12	30	90	140
IG310D-010	1805	first laurel leaf under D of DEI (obv)	1	1	10	25	75	120
IG310D-015	1806		1	1	15	35	110	180
IG310D-020	1813	[1]	2	2	8	20	55	80
IG310D-025	1813	PROOF	2	2				250

1. Position of 10 relative to shamrock leaves varies (rev).

5 Pence Bank Token

Denomination	Metal	Weight (grams)	Diameter (mm)	Rev. alignment
5 pence – Irish Bank Token	Silver	2.1	18.5	↑

Obverse 1 Head 1, right; GEORGIVS III DEI GRATIA

Reverse 1 (in six lines) BANK TOKEN FIVE PENCE IRISH (date)

Edge milled (diagonally)

Obv. 1   Rev. 1

No.	Date	Features	Obv.	Rev.	F	VF	EF	UNC
IG35D-005	1805		1	1	10	25	65	90
IG35D-010	1806	[1]	1	1	15	40	110	180

1. Issue was technically not legal tender; alteration of date to 1806 contravened the authorizing Act.

Ireland: Penny

George III   (1760 – 1820)

At the beginning of the nineteenth century, copper and lead tokens circulated extensively in Ireland in lieu of official currency, but very few of these were denominated at one penny. The first regal penny was issued in 1805, designed by Küchler and struck by Boulton at the Soho mint in Birmingham. It resembled in many ways the British penny of 1806 and 1807, and shared a common designer and place of minting. The halfpennies of the late eighteenth century had been extensively counterfeited, ironically mainly in Birmingham, but the Soho issue of 1805 was much more difficult to copy on account of its excellent strike and the engrailed edge.

This issue is not too difficult to find in collectable condition. The slightly concave strike ensured that even after considerable circulation much of the design was still evident.

Denomination	Metal	Weight (grams)	Diameter (mm)	Rev. alignment
Penny	Copper	17.2 – 17.6	34	↓

Obverse 1   Head 1, right; GEORGIUS III D G REX

Obverse BR   Britannia facing left, holding olive branch and trident; BRITANNIA (reverse of British penny 1806 – 07)

Reverse 1   Crowned harp; HIBERNIA 1805

Edge   milled diagonally in centre; remainder plain. Restrikes with edge plain exist for some pieces

Obv. 1

Rev. 1

No.	Date	Features	Obv.	Rev.	F	VF	EF	UNC
IG31D-005	1805		1	1	6	18	50	120
IG31D-010	1805	PROOF [1]	1	1				120
IG31D-015	1805	bronzed PROOF [1]	1	1				120
IG31D-020	1805	gilt PROOF [1][2]	1	1				150
IG31D-025	1805	PROOF in silver [1]	1	1				800
IG31D-030	1805	PROOF in gold [1]	1	1				
IG31D-035	1805	bronzed PROOF [3]	BR	1				1000

1. Some or all may be struck at a later date.
2. Issued in circular metal shell.
3. At least one specimen has a faultily applied milled edge.

George IV   (1820 – 1830)

Although U.K. silver coinage had been generally introduced in 1817, the absence of regularly minted U.K. copper coins in the subsequent few years resulted in a need for an issue of regal Irish copper during this reign. The legal tender status lasted only until 12th July 1826; the new U.K. copper coinage of George IV had been introduced as legal tender on 13 January of that year.

The obverse was designed by Pistrucci, and engraved by William Wyon. The reverse was designed and engraved by Wyon. The coins are often said to have been struck at the Soho mint, Birmingham, by Matthew Boulton, but Dolley has produced convincing evidence that they were struck at the Royal Mint, quite apart from the fact that Boulton died in 1809!

The field on the George IV penny was not concave as on the George III piece, and thus it sustained circulation wear rather more easily. However, it is not too difficult to obtain coins in attractive very fine or extremely fine.

A number of forgeries exist.

Denomination	Metal	Weight (grams)	Diameter (mm)	Rev. alignment
Penny	Copper	16.3 – 17.7	33	↓

Obverse 1   Head 1, left; GEORGIUS IV D G REX

Reverse 1   Crowned harp; HIBERNIA (date)

Reverse 2   Britannia seated left, plain exergue below; BRITANNIA (reverse of Ionian Islands 2 oboli 1819)

Edge   plain

Obv. 1

Rev. 1

Rev. 2

No.	Date	Features	Obv.	Rev.	F	VF	EF	UNC
IG41D-005	1822		1	1	6	18	45	110
IG41D-010	1822	PROOF	1	1				200
IG41D-015	1822	PROOF on thick flan [1]	1	1				1000
IG41D-020	1822	bronzed PROOF	1	1				250
IG41D-025	1823		1	1	6	20	50	120
IG41D-030	1823	PROOF	1	1				170
IG41D-035	1823	bronzed PROOF	1	1				250
IG41D-005	none	[2]	1	2	600	1000		

1. Weight 18.9 grams.
2. Undated error mule.

Ireland: Halfpenny

Charles II (1660 – 1685)

'St. Patrick's' Issue

Some mystery is attached to the St. Patrick's issue of halfpennies and farthings, and no records about their origins survive. As the pieces were undated, doubt exists as to the exact date of issue. Simon states that they were struck in 1643, but Dr. Aquilla Smith and Evelyn considered that they were issued between 1660 and 1680. Nelson surmised, possibly somewhat improbably, that a figure '8' beneath the kneeling figure of King David indicated that the issue date was 1678, and stated categorically that the pieces were struck in Dublin. The coins certainly circulated in the Isle of Man in 1679, as an Act of Tynwald (The Man Parliament) on 24th June 1679 demonetized them as from 1st January 1680 (1679 old style calendar). Thereafter they circulated to some extent in the State of New Jersey (U.S.A.), having been imported into that territory in November 1681 by a Mark Newby, an Irish immigrant. A local Act of 1682 legalized their circulation in New Jersey.

The design of the kneeling figure, usually held to be King David, is almost identical, except for the harp, to an engraving illustrating the 'Eikon Basilike' and representing King Charles I. The coins usually occur with a brass plug impressed into the reverse of the flan. The plug is counterstamped with a crown, and unconfirmed reports exist of specimens in brass with a copper plug. It has been suggested that the brass plug is instead a layer which has been dropped on to the heated copper immediately before striking, and that the brass or yellow metal may have been obtained from a consecrated source.

William S. Ogden (BNJ III, 1906) suggested that the legend ECCE GREX is in fact ECCE C. REX (behold King Charles) and pointed out that on Irish coins of the period C and G are almost indistinguishable.

The obverse/reverse notation for the St, Patrick issues in this catalogue is that suggested by the numismatic historian Michael Dolley, and is opposite to that used in some reference works.

Denomination	Metal	Weight (grams)	Diameter (mm)	Rev. alignment
Halfpenny or token	Copper with brass plug	7.8 – 9.7	28	↑

Obverse 1 King David kneeling, playing harp, crown above; FLOREAT REX

Reverse 1 St. Patrick preaching to disciples; shield with arms of Dublin; ECCE GREX

Edge milled

Obv. 1

Rev. 1

No.	Date	Features	Obv.	Rev.	VG	F	VF
IC2HD-005	none		1	1	80	150	400
IC2HD-010	none	FLORE AT T REX instead of FLOREAT REX (obv)	1	1	160	300	1000
IC2HD-015	none	star in obv. legend	1	1	160	300	1000
IC2HD-020	none	star in obv. legend; edge plain	1	1	240	400	1400
IC2HD-025	none	PROOF (?) in silver	1	1	350	500	1000
IC2HD-030	none	star in obv. legend; PROOF (?) in silver [1]	1	1	500	700	1500

1. One specimen in worn condition weighs 11.4 grams.

The harp on the obverse has been noted with 14, 16 and 17 strings. Variations in punctuation exist (obv. and rev.).

The Dublin Halfpenny

This piece was probably issued by Dublin Corporation and may be regarded therefore as being more in the nature of a token; however, like the St. Patrick pieces, it seems to have circulated generally as a coin, but is now extremely rare. Issued in 1679, just before the advent of the regal coinage, it would have met a considerable demand for small change which was then virtually non-existent.

Denomination	Metal	Weight (grams)	Diameter (mm)	Rev. alignment
Halfpenny	Copper	10.2 – 12.4	29	↑

Obverse 1 Crowned harp; LONG LIVE THE KING

Reverse 1 Arms of Dublin; THE DVBLIN HALFEPENNIE 1679

Edge milled (perpendicularly or diagonally)

Obv. 1

Rev. 1

No.	Date	Features	Obv.	Rev.	VG	F	VF	EF
IC2HD-050	1679		1	1				

Regal Issue

In 1660, Charles II had granted a patent to Sir Thomas Armstrong for coining copper farthings for a period of 21 years. However, Sir Thomas had been unable to 'obtayne allowance from the chiefe governor of Ireland to issue the said farthing tokens', and in consequence very few were struck.

The period was notable for the virtual non-existence in Ireland of currency suitable for use as low denomination change. Simon noted that this was especially true during the period 1667 to 1677. Brass and copper tokens proliferated, and proclamations in 1661 and 1673 sought to prohibit them, with restrictions also being imposed in 1673 on the export of money and plate from Ireland. In 1662, a patent was granted to Messrs. Vyner and Bellingham to establish a Mint Office in Dublin and to coin silver groats, threepences, half groats, pennies and halfpennies; however, the enterprise was never put into effect. A minute of the Privy Council of 14th November 1662 records that Sir Thomas Vyner was ordered to surrender the patent to be cancelled.

In 1680, shortly before the expiry of the patent to Sir Thomas Armstrong, and after his death, his son, Sir William Armstrong, made a representation that, since his father had laid out capital expenses and had not been allowed to fulfil the terms of the patent, he (Sir William) should be granted a similar patent. As a result, the King issued a patent on 18th May 1680 to Sir William and to Colonel George Legg on payment of £16.13.4 per annum (payable in instalments on 24th June and 25th December) to coin halfpennies at a weight of 110 grains for a period of 21 years. This coinage was confirmed as lawful by a Proclamation on 19th July 1680 by the Lord Lieutenant (the Duke of Ormonde) which also prohibited counterfeiting of the coins. However, the Proclamation also restricted the legal tender limit of the coins to five shillings per one hundred pounds, and required the patentees to redeem these coins if required at the rate of 20 shillings of gold or silver for every 21 shillings of halfpence surrendered.

The coins were struck 'en medaille' unlike the English coinage of the period, and circulated as legal tender in the Isle of Man as farthings.

The quality of striking of this issue was superior to that of the St. Patrick coinage, and fine condition pieces are often bold enough to display the main features of the design well. Very fine or better specimens are not too difficult to obtain.

Denomination	Metal	Weight (grams)	Diameter (mm)	Rev. alignment
Halfpenny	Copper	6.8 – 7.7	26	↑

The earlier dates appear generally to weigh slightly more than the later ones.

Obverse 1 Head 1, right; CAROLVS II DEI GRATIA (large lettering)

Obverse 2 Similar but small lettering

Reverse 1 Crowned harp flanked by divided date; MAG BR FRA ET HIB REX (large lettering)

Reverse 2 Similar but small lettering

Edge milled (perpendicularly or diagonally)

Obv. 1   Obv. 2

Rev. 1   Rev. 2

No.	Date	Features	Obv.	Rev.	F	VF	EF
IC2HD-102	1680	cross after CAROLVS and DEI (obv)	1	1	100	250	
IC2HD-105	1680	pellet after CAROLVS and DEI (obv)	1	1	35	110	280
IC2HD-110	1680	GARTIA instead of GRATIA (obv)	1	1	120	250	
IC2HD-115	1680	PROOF in silver [1]	1	1	500	800	
IC2HD-120	1681		1	1	30	100	250
IC2HD-125	1681		2	2	150		
IC2HD-130	1681	PROOF in silver [2]	2	2	500	800	
IC2HD-135	1682		1	1	40	150	
IC2HD-140	1682		2	2	20	75	180
IC2HD-145	1683		2	2	20	75	180
IC2HD-150	1683	MAG BR FRA larger than ET HIB REX (rev)	2	2	25	95	220
IC2HD-155	1684		2	2	80	300	

1. A specimen in the British Museum weighs 10.4 grams and has a diameter of 28mm.
2. Two specimens in the British Museum weigh 7.6 and 8.4 grams.

The harp on the reverse has been noted with between 12 and 17 strings. The variation may be the result of an internal coding system at the mint.

James II (1685 – 1688)

Regal Issue

The patent issued by Charles II to Sir Thomas Armstrong and George Legg was transferred by a Deed of Assignment to Sir John Knox, Lord Mayor of Dublin, and under this was issued a series of halfpennies from 1685 to 1688 prior to the King's flight to France. These coins are of a similar type to those issued under Charles II, and are the only regal coinage struck for Ireland during this reign.

Denomination	Metal	Weight (grams)	Diameter (mm)	Rev. alignment
Halfpenny	Copper	6.6 – 8.4	26	↑

Obverse 1 Head 1, left; IACOBVS II DEI GRATIA

Reverse 1 Crowned harp flanked by divided date; MAG BR FRA ET HIB REX

Edge milled (perpendicularly or diagonally), partially milled or plain

Obv. 1   Rev. 1

No.	Date	Features	Obv.	Rev.	F	VF	EF
IJ2HD-005	1685		1	1	20	80	190
IJ2HD-010	1685	PROOF in pewter	1	1			
IJ2HD-015	1686		1	1	20	75	180
IJ2HD-020	1687		1	1	500		
IJ2HD-025	1688		1	1	45	150	500

The harp on the reverse has been noted with between 12 and 16 strings. The variation may be the result of an internal coding system at the mint.

William & Mary (1688 – 1694)

The general design of halfpenny of the two previous reigns was continued from 1692 to 1694 for the reign of William and Mary.

This series was the only coinage of this reign specifically struck for Ireland. It should be mentioned that at this time James II gunmoney had been devalued, and circulated at values of between one penny and one farthing. Batty, Thorburn, Simon and others refer to currency halfpennies of 1690 and 1691, but these seem to be non-existent today; Batty noted a specimen of 1691 with thirteen harp strings and a flaw through the harp, so it is possible that at least this date was struck. No proofs were struck for this reign.

The series is well struck, but fine condition specimens do not show the portraits to advantage, and very fine pieces should be sought. Some pieces appear to have been cast or struck on cast flans.

Denomination	Metal	Weight (grams)	Diameter (mm)	Rev. alignment
Halfpenny	Copper	6.4 – 7.5	25 – 26	↑

Obverse 1   Head 1, right; GVLIELMVS ET MARIA DEI GRATIA

Reverse 1   Crowned harp flanked by divided date; MAG BR FRA ET HIB REX ET REGINA

Edge   milled (diagonally)

Obv. 1   Rev. 1

No.	Date	Features	Obv.	Rev.	F	VF	EF
IWMHD-005	1692		1	1	35	110	280
IWMHD-010	1692	each A in GRATIA is unbarred (obv)	1	1	50	160	400
IWMHD-015	1692	GVLIELMVS instead of GVLIELMVS (obv) [1]	1	1	70	200	500
IWMHD-020	1693		1	1	20	70	170
IWMHD-025	1693	edge plain	1	1	30	100	250
IWMHD-030	1693	struck on thick flan [2]	1	1			
IWMHD-035	1694		1	1	35	110	280

1. This coin, in the Ulster Museum, has a heavy die flaw obscuring the date, and a harp with 14 strings. W. A. Seaby conjectured that the date was 1692 by arguing that the rarity of 14-string 1692 coins signifies that the issue from this die was discarded because of the date flaw.
2. This piece, in the British Museum, weighs 9.2 grams and has a faintly milled edge. It has many differences from the normal coinage and, in the opinion of the writer, it is a forgery.

The harp on the reverse has been noted with between 12 and 18 strings. The variation may be the result of an internal coding system at the mint.

William III   (1694 – 1701)

After the death of Mary from smallpox in December 1694, the halfpenny was minted for William III only in 1696. There are two principal types of bust, draped and undraped. Some legend variations also occur. The quantities of halfpenny were not sufficient to meet demand, and Simon reported that during 1697 only forgeries circulated in the northern part of Ireland, these having been imported from Scotland.

The William III halfpenny is somewhat scarcer than its predecessors, especially in higher grades. However, a specimen in at least very fine condition should be sought, as much obverse detail is missing on lower grade coins.

Denomination	Metal	Weight (grams)	Diameter (mm)	Rev. alignment
Halfpenny	Copper	6.7 – 6.8	26	↑

Obverse 1   Head 1, draped, right; GVLIELMVS III DEI GRA (head faces III)

Obverse 2   Head 2, very different and undraped, right; GVLIELMVS III DEI GRATIA (III behind head)

Reverse 1   Crowned harp flanked by divided date; MAG BR FRA ET HIB REX

Reverse 2   Similar but legend reads MAG BRI FRA ET HIB REX

Edge   milled (diagonally)

Obv. 1   Obv. 2

Rev. 1   Rev. 2

No.	Date	Features	Obv.	Rev.	F	VF	EF
IW3HD-005	1696		1	1	18	60	150
IW3HD-010	1696	GWLIELMVS instead of GVLIELMVS (obv)	1	1	30	100	250
IW3HD-015	1696	PROOF in silver [1]	1	1	300	500	
IW3HD-020	1696		1	2	24	80	200
IW3HD-025	1696	PROOF in silver [2]	1	2	400	600	
IW3HD-030	1696		2	1	200		
IW3HD-035	1696	PROOF in silver	2	1	1500		

1. A specimen in the British Museum weighs 5.8 grams. This coin is struck on a slightly thinner flan than the ordinary coin.
2. Occasionally found gilt.

The harp on the reverse has been noted with between 10 and 14 strings. The variation may be the result of an internal coding system at the mint.

George I   (1727 – 1760)

William Wood issue

No Irish money was struck during the reign of Anne, but in 1722 the Duchess of Kendal, the mistress of George I, was granted a patent to strike copper coins for Ireland. She sold this patent to William Wood, a landowner from the Midlands, for £10,000. The coins, halfpennies and farthings, were initially struck in London in January 1723 (1722 old style calendar), and later in Bristol. The terms of the patent were somewhat stringent in respect of the weights of the coinage, so much so that little profit would be made after all costs were taken into account. A degree of weight latitude was therefore exercised, resulting in some accusations of fraud directed towards Wood (see Introduction to Milled Coinage of Ireland). Consequently, the coins were not popular, although undoubtedly they were of excellent workmanship, probably superior to any seen in Ireland hitherto, except for the wide discrepancies of weight. It is recorded that the dies were engraved by 'Old Harold', of Tottenham Court Road, London. The coinage was first struck a short distance away at Phoenix Street, Seven Dials, just off Charing Cross Road.

In 1725 Wood agreed to renounce the patent in consideration of a pension of £3000 a year. The coinage was withdrawn and sent to the American colonies where it circulated with other coinage struck by Wood.

The coins of this series are well struck, and a fine condition specimen will be satisfactory for many collectors. Metal flaws are sometimes noticeable.

Denomination	Metal	Weight (grams)	Diameter (mm)	Rev. alignment
Halfpenny	Copper	6.2 – 7.9	27 – 28	↓

Obverse 1 Head 1, right; GEORGIUS DEI GRATIA REX

Obverse 2 Head 2, right, slightly different; same legend

Reverse 1 Hibernia, facing left playing a harp before her; HIBERNIA 1722

Reverse 2 Hibernia, facing left, with left hand resting on harp to her left; right hand holds a palm branch; HIBERNIA (date)

Edge plain

Obv. 1

Obv. 2

Rev. 1

Rev. 2

No.	Date	Features	Obv.	Rev.	F	VF	EF	UNC
IG1HD-005	1722		1	1	40	100	250	400
IG1HD-010	1722	PROOF	1	1				1200
IG1HD-015	1722	PROOF in silver	1	1				1400
IG1HD-020	1722		1	2	40	100	250	400
IG1HD-025	1722	latter 2 inverted	1	2	80	200		
IG1HD-030	1722	PROOF	1	2				1400
IG1HD-035	1723	[1]	2	2	20	50	150	250
IG1HD-040	1723	3 over 2 [1]	2	2	35	80	250	400
IG1HD-045	1723	each R on obv. is over B [1]	2	2	35	80	250	400
IG1HD-050	1723	PROOF [1]	2	2				800
IG1HD-055	1723	PROOF in silver [1]	2	2				1200
IG1HD-060	1724	[1]	2	2	40	100	250	400
IG1HD-065	1724	PROOF [1]	2	2				1000

1. Punctuation varieties exist; alignment of palm branch with respect to HIBERNIA varies (rev).

The harp on the reverse has been noted with between 7 and 12 strings. The variation may be the result of an internal coding system at the mint.

George II (1727 – 1760)

The withdrawal of the William Wood coinage resulted in a drastic shortage of copper coin in Ireland. Although British halfpennies were struck for the new reign from 1729, it was not until 1736 that Irish coinage was issued. Prior to this, token coinage had been privately struck in various places in Ireland, notably by James Maculla, a brazier in Dublin. In 1736, it was ordered that 50 tons of copper should be coined at the Tower of London. It was stipulated that the copper must be of such fineness that, when heated red hot, would spread thin under the hammer without cracking. The first of the minted coins were sent over to Ireland in April, 1737, samples were subsequently assayed and a Proclamation of 6th May 1737 validated them. In the initial contract five-sixth of the copper was to be struck into halfpennies, and one-sixth into farthings. In March, 1741 a second contract was signed for 100 tons, the resultant coinage being delivered until 1749. A third contract in April 1750 was for 50 tons, and records show that up to 31st July 1753, 39 tons and 4 cwt. had been delivered. The final contract, in 1760 and for 50 tons, was completed in 1762, even though by that time the King was dead. When the first of the new coinage was issued, the previously circulating tokens were prohibited. Public cynicism, justified or not, about the William Wood debacle was still in evidence. It was therefore decreed that profits from the new coinage would be paid into the Irish revenue account. Controversy arose from another quarter, however, as the omission of 'Dei Gratia' on the obverse resulted in considerable disapproval. The anonymously written 'Queries relating to the new halfpence addressed to all the good people of Ireland', published in 1737, was devoted entirely to adverse criticism of the new coin. Amongst the 35 queries raised in the tract were: 'whether every reason, urged by the honest drapier against that scoundrell Wood's brass, will not hold as strongly against the present new coined halfpence?' 'Who advised the coinage and importation of these pernicious halfpence?' 'Whether there does not already appear among us several different sorts of them, and some much more adulterate than others?'

The series is well struck, although perhaps not as attractive or as well defined as Woods's coinage. A fine or very fine specimen will be suitable for most purposes.

Denomination	Metal	Weight (grams)	Diameter (mm)	Rev. alignment
Halfpenny 1736 – 37	Copper	7.8 – 8.2	27 – 28	↓
Halfpenny 1738 – 60	Copper	8.6 – 9.0	27 – 28	↓

Obverse 1 Head 1, left; GEORGIUS II REX

Obverse 2 Similar but larger and thicker lettering

Obverse 3 Similar but GEORGIVS II REX

Obverse 4 Head 2, older with broader truncation, left; same legend

Reverse 1 Crowned harp; HIBERNIA (date)

Edge plain

Obv. 1   Obv. 3

Obv. 4   Rev. 1

No.	Date	Features	Obv.	Rev.	F	VF	EF	UNC
IG2HD-005	1736		1	1	10	45	120	220
IG2HD-010	1736	PROOF	1	1				250
IG2HD-015	1736	PROOF in silver [1]	1	1				500
IG2HD-020	1737		1	1	8	35	100	180
IG2HD-025	1737	PROOF	1	1				250
IG2HD-030	1738		1	1	8	35	100	180
IG2HD-035	1741		2	1	8	35	95	170
IG2HD-040	1742	[2]	2	1	8	35	95	170
IG2HD-045	1743		2	1	10	40	110	200
IG2HD-050	1744		2	1	10	40	110	200
IG2HD-055	1744	latter 4 over 3	2	1	8	35	95	170
IG2HD-060	1746		2	1	10	40	110	200
IG2HD-065	1747		3	1	8	35	95	170
IG2HD-070	1748		3	1	8	35	95	170
IG2HD-075	1749		3	1	8	35	95	170
IG2HD-080	1750		3	1	8	35	95	170
IG2HD-085	1751	[3]	3	1	8	35	95	170
IG2HD-090	1752		3	1	8	35	95	170
IG2HD-095	1752	PROOF	3	1				250
IG2HD-100	1753		3	1	10	40	110	200
IG2HD-105	1755		3	1	18	75	200	400
IG2HD-110	1760	[4]	4	1	8	30	85	150
IG2HD-115	1760	PROOF	4	1				220

1. Two specimens in the British Museum weigh 10.4 and 10.9 grams.
2. A somewhat similar pattern occurs.
3. Colour of copper varies markedly.
4. Issued posthumously in 1762; many forgeries exist.

George III (1760 – 1820)

'Voce Populi' issue

As George III ascended the throne, there was a noticeable shortage of copper coinage in Ireland. The last regal coinage had been issued in 1755, and the 1760 regal issue of George II was not issued in the country until 1762. To meet the shortage, several sources issued promissory tokens, most notable of which were those produced by Roche (or Roach), a button manufacturer, of South King Street, Dublin. These have become known as the 'Voce Populi' (Voice of the People) tokens, on account of the legend on the obverse. The head on the obverse does not resemble that of George III, and its appearance resembles that of a younger representation of the exiled James III, who was by then 72 years old. However, Pamphlet No. 428 in the Harleian Library states that 'The Irish halfpence, Voce Populi, 1760, were struck in two different dies, in consequence of the delay they suffered in the receipt of a coinage from England; the head is that of Hely Hutchinson, afterwards Provost of Dublin College'.

Some of the pieces bear the letter 'P' on the obverse. The reason for this is unclear, as no records appear to have survived which relate directly to the striking of this issue.

The series displays a considerable number of varieties, including about ten markedly different portraits. Some pieces have two small crosses behind the harp, and some two roses; some have a cross after VOCE, some a rose or point; on some, the globe on which Hibernia is sitting is missing. Since this catalogue deals principally with regular coinage, the intricacies of this token coinage are not dealt with here in detail, but the main features are summarized. The series is included in the coinage listings rather than as tokens because they are usually considered as coins and collected as such, despite the fact that the issue did not receive official sanction.

The Voce Populi tokens are usually encountered somewhat crudely struck, and this should be taken into account when grading the pieces. Wide variations in size and weight are common.

Denomination	Metal	Weight (grams)	Diameter (mm)	Rev. alignment
'Halfpenny' token	Copper	6.0 – 8.8	25 – 29	↓

Obverse 1   Head 1, right; VOCE POPULI

Reverse 1   Hibernia seated on globe, with harp; HIBERNIA. In exergue: 1760

Edge   plain

Obv. 1   Obv. 1   Rev. 1
                (two varieties)

No.	Date	Features	Obv.	Rev.	VG	F	VF	EF
IG3HD-005	1760	[1]	1	1	35	60	120	400

1. Many varieties exist; isolated letter P may be present on obverse or reverse, e.g before or below head; VOCE may read VOOE.

Regal Issue

The regal halfpenny coinage of George III falls into two distinct categories: the eighteenth century pieces struck in London, and the 1805 issue struck at the Soho Mint, Birmingham. The London issue closely resembles the George II regal coinage in style, and was struck as a result of two contracts: one in 1766 for 50 tons, and a second in 1769 for the same amount. No farthings were struck, and the quantities of halfpennies issued were barely enough to rectify the shortage of copper coinage but proved sufficient to curtail the output of unofficial tokens until 1782. Thereafter, despite a statute of 1783 prohibiting the importation of unofficial pieces, a great many token halfpennies circulated in Ireland. In particular, the issue known as 'Cronebane', struck in 1789 by the Irish Mining Company, was very prevalent. From 1790 to 1795, tokens such as these formed almost exclusively the copper currency in Ireland.

Many clever forgeries exist of the eighteenth century coinage. However, the issue of 1805 was much more difficult to counterfeit with its sharp strike and engrailed edge. It is interesting to include a specimen of one of the contemporary forgeries in a collection, otherwise a very fine specimen of both types of regal coinage will normally be acceptable. The field of the 1805 issue is somewhat concave; this preserved the main design to some extent during circulation, particularly on the reverse.

Denomination	Metal	Weight (grams)	Diameter (mm)	Rev. alignment
Halfpenny 1766 – 82	Copper	8.1 – 9.0	29	↓
Halfpenny 1805	Copper	8.7 – 8.9	29	↓

Obverse 1   Head 1, right; GEORGIVS III REX

Obverse 2   Head 2, slightly larger, right; same legend

Obverse 3   Head 3, larger, with profuse hair, right; same legend

Obverse 4   Head 4, small, laureate and draped, right; GEORGIUS III D G REX

Reverse 1   Crowned harp; HIBERNIA (date)

Reverse 2   Redesigned crowned harp; HIBERNIA 1805

Edge   (1766–1782): plain; (1805): milled diagonally around central section only; remainder plain

Obv. 1   Obv. 2   Obv. 3

Obv. 4   Rev. 1   Rev. 2

Denomination	Metal	Weight (grams)	Diameter (mm)	Rev. alignment
Halfpenny	Copper	8.3 – 8.8	27	↓

Obverse 1 Head 1, left; GEORGIUS IV D G REX

Reverse 1 Crowned harp; HIBERNIA (date)

Edge plain

Obv. 1   Rev. 1

No.	Date	Features	Obv.	Rev.	F	VF	EF	UNC
IG4HD-005	1822		1	1	5	15	35	75
IG4HD-010	1822	PROOF	1	1				150
IG4HD-015	1822	bronzed PROOF	1	1				150
IG4HD-020	1823		1	1	5	15	35	75
IG4HD-025	1823	PROOF	1	1				140

No.	Date	Features	Obv.	Rev.	F	VF	EF	UNC
IG3HD-055	1766	[1]	1	1	10	50	140	240
IG3HD-060	1766	PROOF	1	1				250
IG3HD-065	1769	[1]	1	1	10	50	140	240
IG3HD-070	1769	[2]	2	1	12	55	150	270
IG3HD-075	1774	PROOF	3	1				300
IG3HD-080	1775		3	1	10	50	150	260
IG3HD-085	1775	PROOF	3	1				250
IG3HD-090	1775	PROOF on thick flan; reverse ↑ [3]	3	1				1200
IG3HD-095	1776		3	1	25	120	400	700
IG3HD-100	1781		3	1	8	35	100	170
IG3HD-105	1781	PROOF	3	1				400
IG3HD-110	1782		3	1	8	35	100	170
IG3HD-115	1782	reverse ↑	3	1	20	70	180	300
IG3HD-120	1782	PROOF	3	1				250
IG3HD-125	1805		4	2	5	14	35	85
IG3HD-130	1805	PROOF	4	2				120
IG3HD-135	1805	bronzed PROOF	4	2				120
IG3HD-140	1805	bronzed PROOF; plain edge [4]	4	2				200
IG3HD-145	1805	gilt PROOF [5]	4	2				150
IG3HD-150	1805	gilt PROOF on thick flan	4	2				500
IG3HD-155	1805	PROOF in silver [6]	4	2				600
IG3HD-160	1805	PROOF in gold [6]	4	2				
IG3HD-165	1805	PROOF in gold; plain edge [6]	4	2				

1. Alignment of head and spacing of REX vary (obv).
2. Possibly a pattern.
3. Two specimens in the British Museum weigh 10.2 and 11.5 grams.
4. A specimen in the British Museum weighs 9.7 grams.
5. Some or all issued in circular metal shell.
6. Struck at a later date.

Coins dated 1783 are almost certainly all counterfeit.

George IV   (1820 – 1830)

Despite the 1800 Act of Union, at the turn of the century there was no sign of a total unification of the British and Irish monetary systems, and it was accepted that coinage would continue to be struck specifically for Ireland. British coins did circulate, however, but no British halfpennies were struck between 1808 and 1824. It was therefore considered necessary to strike a further Irish issue of this denomination in 1822 and 1823. These had an obverse designed by Pistrucci and engraved by William Wyon. The reverse was designed and engraved by Wyon, and the coins were struck at the Royal Mint (see entry for the George IV penny). They remained legal tender only until 12th July 1826, six months after the introduction of British coinage.

Ireland: Farthing

Charles II   (1660 – 1685)

Regal Issue

On 14th December 1660, Charles II granted a 21-year patent to Sir Thomas Armstrong to coin 'such a quantity of farthing tokens of copper as might be conveniently issued during the said term amongst His Majesty's subjects in Ireland'. The coins were to depict on one side two sceptres crossing a diadem, and on the other side a harp, with a legend originally authorized as CAROLUS SECUNDUS MAGNAE BRITANNIAE, FRANCIAE ET HIBERNIAE REX, with a privy mark. They were to weigh 20 grains or more, and to be made 'by engines'. For the privilege of coining the issue, Armstrong was to pay sixteen pounds thirteen shillings and fourpence yearly, in two instalments, on the 24th June and the 25th December. If any payment was overdue by more than 30 days, the patent would lapse.

A proclamation of 17th August 1661 prohibited the making of private tokens throughout Ireland, and it was subsequently noted that this was drafted too widely, and included the Armstrong issue. It was therefore necessary to legalize these with another proclamation. Ironically, however, after all of this preparation, the Chief Governor of Ireland decided to prohibit the issue, and very few were struck.

The presence of a capital R on the band of the crown on the obverse has led to speculation that the dies were engraved by Thomas Rawlins. Presumably, however, the letter might indicate REX.

Denomination	Metal	Weight (grams)	Diameter (mm)	Rev. alignment
Farthing	Copper	1.9 – 2.0	17 – 18	↓

Obverse 1   Two sceptres in saltire through crown, within beaded circle; CAROLVS II D G M B

Reverse 1   Crowned harp, partly within beaded circle; FRA ET HIB REX; mintmark plume

Edge   plain

Obv. 1   Rev. 1

No.	Date	Features	Obv.	Rev.	VG	F	VF
IC2FA-005	None		1	1	25	50	150
IC2FA-010	None	reverse ↑	1	1	35	60	200
IC2FA-015	None	silver PROOF	1	1			

'St. Patrick's' issue

The origins and date of the St. Patrick's issue of coinage are unclear; see the entry under the St. Patrick's halfpenny for more details. The legend may be intended to signify a wish for peace, with the reptiles representing rebels and the evils brought by them. The coinage is generally encountered in about fine condition. The weight range is very wide.

Denomination	Metal	Weight (grams)	Diameter (mm)	Rev. alignment
Farthing or token	Copper with brass plug	5.0 – 7.1	24 – 25	↑

Obverse 1   King David playing harp, crown above; FLOREAT REX

Reverse 1   St. Patrick holding in left hand a double cross, with right hand driving away reptiles; cathedral to right; QVIESCAT PLEBS

Edge   milled

Obv. 1   Rev. 1

No.	Date	Features	Obv.	Rev.	VG	F	VF
IC2FA-055	none		1	1	45	80	150
IC2FA-060	none	stars in legend (obv)	1	1	65	100	200
IC2FA-065	none	stars in legend (obv); PROOF in silver [1]	1	1	600	800	1200
IC2FA-070	none	stars in legend (obv); PROOF in gold	1	1			
IC2FA-075	none	martlet below king (obv)	1	1	150	250	500
IC2FA-080	none	annulet below king (obv)	1	1	130	220	420
IC2FA-085	none	annulets and martlet below king (obv)	1	1	150	250	500

1. Weight 6.7 – 7.4 grams.

Many small differences to the ground on the obverse occur. Variations in punctuation exist (obv. and rev.).

George I   (1727 – 1760)

William Wood issue

Farthings dated 1722, 1723, and 1724 were struck by William Wood under the terms of the patent bought from the Duchess of Kendal, as described in the halfpenny section.

The coins are very well struck and of good craftsmanship. Metal flaws are sometimes encountered.

Denomination	Metal	Weight (grams)	Diameter (mm)	Rev. alignment
Farthing 1722	Copper	3.6 – 4.1	22	↑
Farthing 1723 – 24	Copper	3.6 – 4.1	22	↓

Obverse 1   Head 1, right; GEORGIUS D G REX

Obverse 2   Similar but GEORGIUS DEI GRATIA REX

Reverse 1   Hibernia, facing left playing a harp before her; HIBERNIA 1722

Reverse 2   Hibernia, facing left, with left hand resting on harp to her left; right hand holds a palm branch; HIBERNIA (date)

Edge   plain

Obv. 1   Obv. 2

Rev. 1   Rev. 2

Obv. 1   Obv. 3

Rev. 1   Rev. 2

No.	Date	Features	Obv.	Rev.	F	VF	EF	UNC
IG1FA-005	1722		1	1	180	450	1000	
IG1FA-010	1723	colon before REX (obv)	1	2	65	150	350	600
IG1FA-015	1723	no colon before REX (obv)	1	2	90	200		
IG1FA-020	1723		2	2	30	70	180	300
IG1FA-025	1723	PROOF	2	2				1000
IG1FA-030	1723	PROOF in silver [1]	2	2				1500
IG1FA-035	1724	stop after date (rev)	2	2	40	90	240	450
IG1FA-040	1724	no stop after date (rev)	2	2	60	130	350	
IG1FA-045	1724	PROOF in silver	2	2				1500

1. A specimen in the British Museum weighs 4.6 grams.

No.	Date	Features	Obv.	Rev.	F	VF	EF	UNC
IG2FA-005	1737		1	1	20	70	180	350
IG2FA-010	1737	PROOF	1	1				250
IG2FA-015	1737	PROOF in silver	1	1				500
IG2FA-020	1738		1	1	15	50	130	250
IG2FA-025	1744	[1]	2	2	15	50	130	250
IG2FA-030	1760	[2]	3	2	8	22	50	100

1. Many forgeries exist.
2. Issued posthumously in 1762 until April.

The harp on the reverse has been noted with between 9 and 11 strings. The variation may be the result of an internal coding system at the mint.

George II (1727 – 1760)

Farthings were struck at the Tower of London from 1737 to alleviate the shortage of copper coinage, which persisted despite the widespread use of tokens in the early part of the reign. The unpopularity and subsequent withdrawal of the William Wood coinage had exacerbated the situation.

The new issue of farthings was accepted by the public and was more popular than the Woods's issue, although the omission of DEI GRATIA on the obverse was much commented upon.

See under 'Halfpenny' for details of the contracts for copper coinage effected during this reign.

The series is attractive and well struck, although the finish is possibly not as good as on the Woods farthing. A very fine specimen should be acceptable for most collectors.

Denomination	Metal	Weight (grams)	Diameter (mm)	Rev. alignment
Farthing	Copper	3.9 – 4.6	22 – 23	↓

Obverse 1   Head 1, left; GEORGIUS II REX

Obverse 2   Similar but larger lettering

Obverse 3   Head 2, older, with broader truncation; GEORGIVS II REX

Reverse 1   Crowned harp; HIBERNIA (date)

Reverse 2   Similar but larger lettering

Edge   plain

George III (1760 – 1820)

'Voce Populi' issue

In addition to the generally circulated Voce Populi halfpenny issue, a very small quantity of farthings was struck. It is possible that these were patterns for a series which was not issued. Two types exist, with slightly different busts.

Denomination	Metal	Weight (grams)	Diameter (mm)	Rev. alignment
'Farthing' token	Copper	4.0 – 4.2	21 – 22	↓

Obverse 1   Head 1, right, truncation is looped at left; VOCE POPULI

Obverse 2   Similar but truncation is not looped; same legend

Reverse 1   Hibernia, seated, with harp; HIBERNIA. In exergue: 1760

Edge   plain

Obv. 1   Obv. 2   Rev. 1

No.	Date	Features	Obv.	Rev.	VG	F	VF
IG3FA-005	1760	[1]	1	1	150	250	800
IG3FA-010	1760	[1]	2	1	600	1000	

1. Varieties exist.

Regal Issue

No farthings were struck to accompany the series of halfpennies from 1766 to 1782, and the first issue of this denomination was that of 1806, one year after the halfpenny of similar design was struck. The coinage was struck at the Soho mint in Birmingham, and bears some resemblance to the 1806 and 1807 British farthings struck at the same mint.

The field of the 1806 farthing is slightly concave, and consequently the main design was to some extent protected from circulation wear. Specimens are normally encountered in fine to very fine condition rather than in poorer grades.

Dolley has pointed out that the presence or absence of a stop after HIBERNIA on the reverse is the easiest way of distinguishing original early proofs both from currency pieces and from restrikes, these early proofs lacking the stop. This is of such significance that two reverses have been allocated in the tables to facilitate identification.

Denomination	Metal	Weight (grams)	Diameter (mm)	Rev. alignment
Farthing	Copper	4.3 – 4.4	21	↓

Obverse 1 Head 1, right; GEORGIUS III D G REX

Reverse 1 Crowned harp; HIBERNIA 1806 (with stop after HIBERNIA)

Reverse 2 Similar but without stop after HIBERNIA

Edge engrailed in groove

Obv. 1

Rev. 1

No.	Date	Features	Obv.	Rev.	F	VF	EF	UNC
IG3FA-055	1806		1	1	3	8	16	35
IG3FA-060	1806	PROOF	1	2				100
IG3FA-065	1806	bronzed PROOF	1	2				100
IG3FA-070	1806	gilt PROOF	1	2				150
IG3FA-075	1806	gilt PROOF on thin flan	1	2				250
IG3FA-080	1806	bronzed PROOF [1]	1	1				80
IG3FA-085	1806	gilt PROOF; edge plain [1] [2]	1	1				120
IG3FA-090	1806	PROOF in silver; edge plain [1]	1	1				250
IG3FA-095	1806	PROOF in gold [1]	1	1				

1. Struck at a later date.
2. A specimen in the British Museum weighs 5.6 grams.

George IV   (1820 – 1830)

For the 1822 farthing of George IV, see the pattern section, p.283.

Ireland: Patterns

This listing represents a selection only.

George I   (1714 – 1727)

1722

Listed below are two of several patterns of the Woods coinage; the reverse of the first piece bears some resemblance to the first reverse of the 1722 halfpenny.

No.	Date	Denomination	Metal	Weight (grams)	Diameter (mm)	Rev. align.	Price
IG1PTN-020	1722	Halfpenny	Copper	7.3 – 7.8	27 – 28	↓	1500

Obv.   Rev.

Obverse   Head, right; GEORGIVS D G REX

Reverse   Hibernia playing harp and looking backwards to a rock mass; HIBERNIAE 1722

Edge   plain

1724

No.	Date	Denomination	Metal	Weight (grams)	Diameter (mm)	Rev. align.	Price
IG1PTN-040	1724	Halfpenny	Copper	8.3	30	↓	

Obv.   Rev.

Obverse   Head, right; GEORGIUS DEI GRATIA REX

Reverse   Hibernia, facing left, leaning on a harp and holding palm branch; HIBERNIA 1724

Edge   plain

George II   (1727 – 1760)

1742

This piece is found with numerous flaws, and it is considered that the dies broke after a few examples had been struck.

No.	Date	Denomination	Metal	Weight (grams)	Diameter (mm)	Rev. align.	Price
IG2PTN-020	1742	Halfpenny	Copper	8.6	30		

Obv.   Rev.

Obverse   Head with profuse hair, left; GEORGIUS II REX

Reverse   Crowned harp; HIBERNIA 1742

Edge   plain

George III   (1760 – 1820)

1773

No.	Date	Denomination	Metal	Weight (grams)	Diameter (mm)	Rev. align.	Price
IG3PTN-020	1773	Halfpenny	Copper	8.7 – 10.1	28 – 29	↑	1000

Obv.   Rev.

Obverse   Head, right; GEORGIVS III REX

Reverse   Crowned harp; HIBERNIA 1773

Edge   plain

1789

In 1789, William Mossop (1751 – 1805), a Dublin jeweller, designed and executed a pattern penny with a classical design of Britannia and Hibernia hand in hand. Mossop called the piece the 'Union Penny', and it is said that six examples were struck before the reverse die broke; two were presented to George III, and the design met with the king's approval.

In the Hutchins sale of 18th December 1792, an example appears as Lot 44, which was sold for £3.4.0. The catalogue notes: 'Pattern piece struck in Dublin, 1789; the dies are broke and none of them to be had'.

It is possible that more than six pieces exist, and that a few have plain edges.

No.	Date	Denomination	Metal	Weight (grams)	Diameter (mm)	Rev. align.	Price
IG3PTN-040	1789	Penny	Bronze	23.9 – 25.7	32	↑	6000

Obv.   Rev.

Obverse Head, right, harp below; GEORGIVS III REX

Reverse Britannia and Hibernia hand in hand, with lion and harp; CONCORDIA

Edge milled (but see above)

1813

Thomas Wyon, junior prepared the die for the reverse of this pattern penny, which uses (with minor modifications) the obverse of the Ceylon 2 stuivers.

No.	Date	Denomination	Metal	Weight (grams)	Diameter (mm)	Rev. align.	Price
IG3PTN-060	1813	Penny	Copper	19.0 – 19.1	33 – 34	↓	1500

Obv.   Rev.

Obverse Head, right; GEORGIUS III D G BRITANNIARUM REX

Reverse Crowned harp; HIBERNIA 1813

Edge milled diagonally in centre; remainder plain

1813

This pattern uses virtually the same reverse as the previous piece (there are very minor differences), with the obverse of the Demerara and Essequibo 1 stuiver.

No.	Date	Denomination	Metal	Weight (grams)	Diameter (mm)	Rev. align.	Price
IG3PTN-080	1813	Penny	Copper	17.7 – 17.9	33	↓	1500

Obv.   Rev.

Obverse Head, right; GEORGIUS III D G REX

Reverse Crowned harp; HIBERNIA 1813

Edge milled diagonally in centre; remainder plain

George IV   (1820 – 1830)

1822

This pattern uses the Pistrucci obverse as used on the currency pieces. The reverse, by Thomas Wyon, junior, is similar to the 1813 pattern. The adopted design resembles it to a large extent, although the crown on the pattern is much smaller.

No.	Date	Denomination	Metal	Weight (grams)	Diameter (mm)	Rev. align.	Price
IG4PTN-020	1822	Penny	Copper	17.1	33		2000

Obv.   Rev.

Obverse Head, left; GEORGIUS IV D G REX

Reverse Crowned harp; HIBERNIA 1822

Edge plain

1822

The pattern farthing is the companion piece to the currency penny and halfpenny, and the reverse exhibits the similar large crown. Six pieces are said to have been struck, but more may exist.

No.	Date	Denomination	Metal	Weight (grams)	Diameter (mm)	Rev. align.	Price
IG4PTN-040	1822	Farthing	Copper	4.3	21	↓	1500

Obv.   Rev.

Obverse Head, left; GEORGIUS IV D G REX

Reverse Crowned harp; HIBERNIA 1822

Edge plain

283

Ireland: 'James II' emergency coinage

James II landed in Ireland at Kinsale from France on 12th March 1689 (1688 old style calendar) with about 5,000 French troops in an attempt to regain his throne, and made his public entry into Dublin on 24th March. At the outset, he needed some form of currency with which to pay his army, but for some time previously large quantities of gold and silver coinage had been sent by Protestants to England for safe keeping, as they feared that James's pro-Catholic stance would jeopardise their position. On the day following his entry into Dublin, the first day of the year 1689 of the old calendar, he issued a proclamation raising the current values of all English and foreign gold and silver coinage by about 20 and 8½ per cent respectively. For example, the French gold pistole was revalued at 19 shillings, the guinea at 24 shillings, the Spanish and Mexican eight reales at 6 shillings and 3 pence and the crown at 5 shillings and 5 pence. The French 3 sous piece, very convenient for paying soldiers, although worth only about a penny-halfpenny, was raised by proclamation on 4th May to threepence-halfpenny. However, the entire scheme failed, and he solved his problem in an innovative manner, reputedly suggested by a Quaker, William Bromfield, one of the commissioners of the mint, and a trusted ally of James. On the 18th June 1689 sixpences were ordered to be struck from 'copper and brass' obtained from old cannon and various other sources, and on 27th June half-crowns and shillings were also ordered to be struck: 'We have ordered a further quantity of copper and brass money to be coyned, to pass currant in this Our Kingdom, during our pleasure, in twelve-penny pieces and half-crown pieces, each piece of the said twelve penny pieces having of one side the Effigies or figure of Our head, with this inscription round, Jacobus II Dei Gratia, and upon the other side, the stamp or impression of cross Scepters and a Crown between J.R. with XII above the month wherein they are coyned below, with this inscription round; and each of the said half-crown pieces to be marked and stamped as the said twelve penny pieces, only that on the said half-crown pieces in stead of XII shall be marked XXX, each of the said pieces to be of the metal of copper and brass'. The counterfeit of all pieces was declared to be high treason, and informers were to be rewarded. Refusal to accept the new money would (with some exceptions) engender penalties. The commissioners of the mint would issue 20 shillings and 6 pence of brass money for every 20 shillings of gold and silver exchanged.

The halfcrowns, shillings and sixpences struck by James were to be dated with the month of issue as well as the year, and the well-intentioned aim was to redeem these with good silver coin when the king was back on his throne. This redemption would be carried out in the order, month by month, in which the original coins had been issued. The Proclamation of James II made at Dublin on 18th June 1689 directs: 'Whereas we have caused the said copper and brass money to be made currant money for present necessity, and therefore do not intend that the same shall continue for any long time. We do, by this our Royal Proclamation, promise and engage to all our subjects here that as soon as the said money shall be decried and made null, that we shall thereupon receive from all and every our subjects within this kingdom such proportion of the said money as shall be, and remain in their respective hands at the time shall be decried and made null; and at the same time either allow for the same to them the value thereof, at the rates aforesaid, out of what rent, duties or debts, they respectively shall owe to us, or to make them full satisfaction

for the same according to the rates aforesaid, in gold or silver of the currant coyne of this kingdom'.

An order from James II to Justin Lord Viscount Mount Cashel strikingly confirms the story that, at least in part, the coins were struck from the metal from old cannons: 'Our will and pleasure is that you forthwith deliver to the commissioners of the Mint those two brass canons now lying in the court of this our castle marked &c. weighing &c. and for soe doeing this shall be your warrant. Given at our Court at Dublin Castle this eleventh day of July 1689 and in the fifth year of our reign'.

James laid aside the patent granted four years earlier and currently assigned to Sir John Knox, and gave an order to seize Knox's engines and tools; he then set up mints at 27 Capel Street, Dublin (also the birthplace of Thomas Sheridan, the father of Richard Brinsley Sheridan), and in the Deanery House in Limerick, which was better placed to receive consignments of copper from France than was Dublin. In the first, there were two presses, known as the James Press and the Duchess. However, the Dublin press proved to be somewhat slow, and on 1st July 1689 the commissioners were ordered to 'consult what is fit to be done to advance the coinage', Their recommendation was to employ shift working so that both presses in Dublin could be worked around the clock. The officers appointed were: six commissioners, two secretaries, four comptrollers, two wardens, a treasurer, four tellers, four feeders, eight labourers at the fly, two porters, a messenger, two doorkeepers and a storekeeper. Each party worked for twelve hours continuously, and the presses never stopped.

As more coins were produced, brass became in short supply, and its value increased. Colles, in his diary, observed: '...made the Irish to wonder that England had more silver and gold than Ireland brass.' There was much cynical anti-Catholic comment about the coinage from Protestants. Typical were: 'Their brass imaginary coin made only valuable by the magic of their priests'; 'It circulates more than silver, for those that have it are very uneasy until they dispose of it.'

It is interesting at this point to note the cost of various items during this period. A proclamation of 27th September 1689 laid down the following maximum prices at which goods could be sold in Dublin:

Largest men's shoes ... 4 shillings
Women's shoes ... 2 shillings and 6 pence
Candles ... 3½ pence per pound weight
Soap ... 3 pence per pound weight
Cheese ... 2½ pence per pound weight
Bacon ... 2½ pence per pound weight
Beef ... three farthings per pound weight
Mutton, Veal, Pork ... 1 penny per pound weight
Wheat ... 15 shillings per barrel
Beer ... 17 shillings per barrel
Ale ... 15 shillings per barrel

The term 'brass money' was used in Ireland at the time as a derogatory description of the new coinage, but it is difficult to determine when the term 'gun money' was first coined, so to speak. The term 'gunn mettle' was used in correspondence between the Commissioners of the Mint and their agents who collected metal, as in the letter from Walter Plunkett, the sole Commissioner at LImerick to John Trindar, one of the Dublin Commissioners on 4th January 1690 (1689 old style calendar) that he had sent 'six thousand six hundred weight of gunn mettle, six hundred a quarter, and two pounds of fine pewter, and they will be eleven or twelve days a-goeing, because the roads are very deep'. The term 'gun money' was used in a sale catalogue of 1764 of the 'Musaeum Thoresbyanum' in London.

On 28th March 1690, a proclamation authorized the striking of pennies and halfpennies of 'white mixed metal' (pewter) with a central plug of 'Prince's metal' (brass), 'each piece of the said penny pieces about the bigness of one shilling', and from 21st April 1690, with gun metal in short supply, the halfcrowns were reduced in diameter from 32mm to 27mm. Crowns of diameter 34mm, not bearing the month of issue, were authorized to be current as from 21st April 1690. These coins were also to be of 'white mixed metal' and to have a 'Prince's Metal' plug through the flan, and a lettered edge. Unlike the smaller coinage, the crown was not to bear the month of issue. Severe penalties were threatened for anyone refusing to accept the crown pieces. In the event, very few, if any, of the pewter crowns were issued but a bag of 150 pieces (another source says 5,000 pieces) was found in the Treasury in Dublin after James had left Ireland.

Two proclamations of 15th June 1690 dictated that all halfcrowns struck before May 1690 should be called in and exchanged for the new smaller type, and that crowns should now also be struck in gun metal, made from the halfcrowns now being reclaimed, although this fact was not mentioned in the proclamations, which decreed: 'We have for weighty reasons ... thought fit to call in all the halfcrown pieces of copper and brass money which appear by the stamp upon them to have been coyned within this our kingdom before the month of May last' (Sixth Proclamation) and 'We have ordered a quantity of copper and brass to be coyned into crown pieces' (Seventh Proclamation). Some of the halfcrowns were simply restamped as crowns, while others were melted down and recoined. Another proclamation of the same date rendered it illegal, under pain of death, to pay more than 30 shillings in gunmoney for a French gold pistole, or more than 38 shillings for a guinea, or more than 7 shillings and sixpence for a silver crown. Other coins were listed pro rata. Furthermore, counterfeiting was confirmed to continue to be high treason, with import and export forbidden. Reissuing the halfcrowns and crowns gave a nominal value to gun metal of £22,400 per ton.

The Dublin mint was captured in July, 1690, but James's adherents held the mint at Limerick under siege until as late as October 1691. Any pieces dated after July 1690 were struck at Limerick; however, doubt has been cast on the authenticity of some pieces dated after July, including at least one in the British Museum.

Following the Battle of the Boyne, almost the first thing that the victorious King William did was to issue a proclamation from his camp at Finglas, near Dublin, on 10th July 1690 to deal the final ignominy to James's 'money'. The gunmoney crowns and large halfcrowns were to be redeemed at one penny, the smaller halfcrown at three farthings, the large shilling at a halfpenny, and the sixpence and small shilling at one farthing, all 'the value of copper money formerly currant in the Kingdom'. The pewter pence were relatively generously valued at a halfpenny, with the pewter halfpenny at a farthing. The halfcrowns and shillings circulated unofficially on the Isle of Man as halfpennies and farthings respectively, owing to the scarcity of small change on the island.

It is significant that the pewter crowns were not mentioned in the proclamation redeeming the coinage, and lends credence to the theory that these pieces did not enter circulation. It is probable that around this time the patent previously held by Knox was confirmed to Roger Moore to allow the conventional coinage to continue under William and Mary.

On 23rd February 1692, a proclamation totally abolished the value of gunmoney, bringing this unhappy chapter to an end.

When considering the dates on gunmoney, it must be remembered that the year changeover occurred at that time on March 25th; hence January and February 1689 fell after December 1689, while March 1689 and March 1690 are different parts of the same month.

The dies for the gunmoney issue were probably engraved by Roettier, whose family were intimately associated with the Stuart cause. In view of the conditions in which the coins were issued, the existence of contemporary gold and silver proofs would seem unlikely, to say the least. Common sense would dictate that such pieces were struck later than the ordinary issues.

Crown

A proclamation of 21st April 1690 decreed that 'We have ordered a certain quantity of white mixed metal to be coyned in Crownpieces, each piece of the said Crown-pieces having on the one side Our Effigies or figure on horseback, with this inscription round JAC II DEI GRA MAG BRI FRA & HIB REX, and on the other side having a piece of Princes Metal fixed in the middle, with the stamp or impression of the crown, surrounded with the arms of England, Scotland, France and Ireland, with this inscription round, Christo Victore triumpho, Anno Dom 1690, and round about the edge of each such piece having this inscription, Melioris Tessera Fati Anno Regni Sexto; all which pieces of money so coyned, we have thought fit, by the advice of our Privy Council to make current money within this Our Kingdom ...'

Crowns in 'white mixed metal' (pewter) did not enter general circulation, and it was only following the proclamations of 15th June 1690 that this denomination came into use; this issue was in gun metal, and the crowns were in fact restamped large halfcrowns. The proclamations dated above withdrew the halfcrowns from circulation and authorized the crowns, but did not mention that the halfcrown flans would be reused as crowns.

Denomination	Metal	Weight (grams)	Diameter (mm)	Rev. alignment
Crown	Gun metal	10 – 16	31 – 32	↑
Crown	Pewter with brass plug	15 – 19	34	↑
Crown	Others	See tables	32 – 34	↑

Obverse 1   King, wearing breastplate, on horseback (front of horse's head vertical; tail is mostly straight down), sword drawn, facing left; IAC II DEI GRA MAG BRI FRA ET HIB REX (legend starts to right of king's head; slanting sword points to E of REX)

Obverse 2   Similar but king and horse are thinner, lettering is smaller, legend starts to left of king's head, and almost vertical sword points between REX and IAC

Obverse 3   Similar but king is without breastplate, horse's head is drawn back, tail is markedly more curved and sword is vertical

Reverse 1   Cruciform shields of Ireland, England, Scotland, France around central crown; CHRISTO VICTORE TRIVMPHO ANO DOM 1690, with horizontal lines above ANO DOM (French shield divides T and O of VICTORE)

Reverse 2   Similar but French shield divides O and R of VICTORE

Reverse 3   Similar to reverse 1 but no horizontal lines above ANO DOM

Reverse 4   Similar to reverse 2 but no horizontal lines above ANO DOM

Reverse 5   Similar to Reverse 1 but legend reads TRIUMPHO instead of TRIVMPHO

Edge   (gun metal issue) ornamentation of triple row of leaves; (pewter issue) MELIORIS TESSERA FATI ANNO REGNI SEXTO; (others: see tables)

Several minor design differences occur. In particular, on the obverse the groundline varies considerably. On the reverse the position of the horizontal lines above ANO DOM varies.

Obv. 3   Rev. 1

Rev. 2   Rev. 5

Gun metal issues

No.	Date	Features	Obv.	Rev.	VG	F	VF	EF
IECR-005	1690		1	1	80	130	250	700
IECR-010	1690		1	2	150	250		
IECR-015	1690	[1]	2	1	25	50	100	300
IECR-020	1690	[2]	2	2	40	80	160	500
IECR-025	1690	reverse 90 degrees to left	2	4	120	200		
IECR-030	1690		3	1	20	40	90	280
IECR-035	1690	reverse ↓	3	1	40	80	160	500
IECR-040	1690	reverse 90 degrees to left	3	1	40	80	160	500
IECR-045	1690	RIX instead of REX (obv)	3	1	120	200		
IECR-050	1690		3	2	40	80	160	500
IECR-055	1690	reverse 90 degrees to right	3	2	60	120	240	700
IECR-060	1690	RIX instead of REX (obv)	3	2	120	200		
IECR-065	1690	struck on thick flan [3]	3	3	500	800		
IECR-070	1690		3	4	150	250		

1. Some examples exhibit major reverse flaws.
2. On some specimens, the sword on the obverse slants slightly and points to X of REX.
3. A specimen in the British Museum weighs 16.9 grams.

Pewter issues

No.	Date	Features	Obv.	Rev.	VG	F	VF	EF
IECR-105	1690		3	2	400	600	1500	
IECR-110	1690	without plug in flan	3	2	1000	1500		

Issues in other metals

No.	Date	Features	Obv.	Rev.	VG	F	VF	EF
IECR-155	1690	struck in gold; edge plain [1]	3	1				
IECR-160	1690	struck in gold; edge reads MLIORIS TESSERA FATI [2]	3	5				
IECR-165	1690	struck in silver; edge plain [3]	3	1	2000	3000		
IECR-170	1690	struck in silver; edge reads MLIORIS TESSERA FATI [4]	3	5	1000	1400	2000	3500

No.	Date	Features	Obv.	Rev.	VG	F	VF	EF
IECR-175	1690	struck in copper; edge as gun metal issue	3	1	200	400		
IECR-180	1690	struck in copper; edge plain	3	5	500	800		

1. A specimen in the British Museum weighs 27.5 grams.
2. A specimen in the British Museum weighs 36.2 grams; note spelling of MLIORIS; regnal year missing.
3. A specimen in the British Museum weighs 19.6 grams.
4. Note spelling of MLIORIS; regnal year missing.

Halfcrown

Denomination	Metal	Weight (grams)	Diameter (mm)	Rev. alignment
Halfcrown Obv 1/Rev 1	Gun metal	11.9 – 16.8	31 – 32	↑
Halfcrown Obv 2/Rev 2	Gun metal	6.7 – 12.7	27	↑

Obverse 1 Head 1, left, extending from top to bottom of flan; IACOBVS II DEI GRATIA

Obverse 2 Similar but smaller size, even after allowing for smaller flan size; the truncation is almost straight

Reverse 1 Crown and four sceptres, flanked by scripted IR; XXX above crown, (month) below; MAG BR FRA ET HIB REX (date)

Reverse 2 Similar but smaller size

Edge (obv 1/rev 1) ornamentation of triple row of leaves

(obv 2/rev 2) milled (diagonally) or ornamentation of double row of leaves

Obv. 1   Obv. 2

Rev. 1   Rev. 2

No.	Date*	Features	Obv.	Rev.	VG	F	VF	EF
IEHC-005	1689 July		1	1	25	45	130	400
IEHC-010	1689 July	small and less garnished IR (rev)	1	1	50	90	250	
IEHC-015	1689 Aug		1	1	15	25	70	250
IEHC-020	1689 Aug.		1	1	15	25	70	250
IEHC-025	1689 Aug:		1	1	15	25	70	250
IEHC-030	1689 Aug¹		1	1	15	25	70	250
IEHC-035	1689 Aug¹:		1	1	15	25	70	250
IEHC-040	1689 Aug¹:	outer legend and date rotated around rim by 180 degrees [1]	1	1	30	50	140	700
IEHC-045	1689 Aug	struck in silver [2]	1	1				2000
IEHC-050	1689 Sepr		1	1	15	25	70	250
IEHC-055	1689 Sepr	no stops on obverse	1	1	25	45	130	400

No.	Date*	Features	Obv.	Rev.	VG	F	VF	EF
IEHC-060	1689 Sepr:		1	1	15	25	70	250
IEHC-065	1689 Sepr		1	1	15	25	70	250
IEHC-070	1689 Sepr.		1	1	15	25	70	250
IEHC-075	1689 Sepr:		1	1	15	25	70	250
IEHC-080	1689 Sept:		1	1	15	25	70	250
IEHC-085	1689 Septr.		1	1	20	35	85	300
IEHC-090	1689 Sept:		1	1	15	25	70	250
IEHC-095	1689 Sep	struck in silver [2]	1	1				2000
IEHC-100	1689 Oct:		1	1	15	25	65	220
IEHC-105	1689 Octr.		1	1	15	25	65	220
IEHC-110	1689 OCT		1	1	15	25	65	220
IEHC-115	1689 OCT.		1	1	15	25	65	220
IEHC-120	1689 OCT:		1	1	15	25	65	220
IEHC-125	1689 OCTR		1	1	15	25	65	220
IEHC-130	1689 OCTR.	[3]	1	1	15	25	65	220
IEHC-135	1689 8r	[4]	1	1	35	60	150	500
IEHC-140	1689 8BER	[4]	1	1	35	60	150	500
IEHC-145	1689 8BER.	[4]	1	1	35	60	150	500
IEHC-150	1689 Nov.		1	1	15	25	65	220
IEHC-155	1689 Nov:		1	1	15	25	65	220
IEHC-160	1689 Novr.		1	1	15	25	65	220
IEHC-165	1689 Nov	struck in silver [2]	1	1				2000
IEHC-170	1689 Dec.		1	1	15	25	65	220
IEHC-175	1689 Dec:		1	1	15	25	65	220
IEHC-180	1689 Decr.		1	1	15	25	65	220
IEHC-185	1689 10r	[5]	1	1	35	60	150	500
IEHC-190	1689 10r.	[5]	1	1	35	60	150	500
IEHC-195	1689 Jan		1	1	15	25	65	220
IEHC-200	1689 Jan [7]	edge plain	1	1	25	45	120	400
IEHC-205	1689 Jan.		1	1	15	25	65	220
IEHC-210	1689 Jan:		1	1	15	25	65	220
IEHC-215	1689 jan		1	1	15	25	65	220
IEHC-220	1689 Jav		1	1	15	25	65	220
IEHC-225	1689 Jan [7]	struck in silver	1	1				2000
IEHC-230	1689 Feb		1	1	15	25	65	220
IEHC-235	1689 Feb.		1	1	15	25	65	220
IEHC-240	1689 Feb:		1	1	15	25	65	220
IEHC-245	1689 Feb:	struck in silver [6]	1	1				2000
IEHC-250	1689 Mar	[7]	1	1	20	35	80	280
IEHC-255	1689 Mar.	[7]	1	1	20	35	80	280
IEHC-260	1689 Mar:	[7] [8]	1	1	20	35	80	280
IEHC-265	1689 Mar:		1	1	20	35	80	280
IEHC-270	1689 Mar:	struck in silver [9]	1	1				2000
IEHC-275	1690 Mar:		1	1	25	40	90	320
IEHC-280	1690 Mar:	[7]	1	1	25	40	90	320
IEHC-285	1690 Mar:	MAO instead of MAG (rev)	1	1	60	100	250	
IEHC-290	1690 Mar	struck in silver [2]	1	1				2000
IEHC-295	1690 Apr.		1	1	15	25	65	220
IEHC-300	1690 Apr.	struck in silver [10]	1	1				1500
IEHC-305	1690 Apr.	struck in gold [11]	1	1				9000
IEHC-310	1690 Apr:		1	1	15	25	65	220
IEHC-315	1690 Apr:	[7]	1	1	15	25	65	220
IEHC-320	1690 Apr:	[7]	1	1	15	25	65	220
IEHC-325	1690 Apr:		2	2	60	100		
IEHC-330	1690 May		1	1	10	15	45	130
IEHC-335	1690 May:		1	1	10	15	45	130
IEHC-340	1690 May	rev. ↓	1	1	15	25	60	200
IEHC-345	1690 may		2	2	10	15	45	130
IEHC-350	1690 May		2	2	10	15	45	130
IEHC-355	1690 May	[7]	2	2	10	15	45	130
IEHC-360	1690 May	FR . A instead of FRA (rev) [7]	2	2	15	25	60	200
IEHC-365	1690 May.	[7]	2	2	10	15	45	130
IEHC-370	1690 May.	struck on thick flan [7]	2	2	30	45	120	
IEHC-375	1690 May	cinquefoil stops on rev. [2]	2	2	50	80	200	
IEHC-380	1690 May	struck in tin [2]	2	2				800
IEHC-385	1690 May.	struck in silver [7] [12]	2	2			600	1000
IEHC-390	1690 May	struck in gold [13]	2	2				6000
IEHC-395	1690 Jun		2	2	15	25	70	250
IEHC-400	1690 June		2	2	15	25	70	250
IEHC-405	1690 June.		2	2	15	25	70	250
IEHC-410	1690 Jnue.	[14]	2	2	30	50	150	600
IEHC-415	1690 July		2	2	20	35	80	280
IEHC-420	1690 July	reverse 90 degrees to right	2	2	30	50	120	400
IEHC-425	1690 Iuly		2	2	20	35	80	280
IEHC-430	1690 Aug:	[15]	2	2	30	50	150	600
IEHC-435	1690 Sept:	[16]	2	2				

No.	Date*	Features	Obv.	Rev.	VG	F	VF	EF
IEHC-440	1690 Oct:	[15]	2	2	150	200		

*and abbreviated month as on coin, with following punctuation
1. Usually inaccurately referred to as 'crown and sceptres reversed'; the date appears to read Aug ¹: 6891.
2. Month style and punctuation not available.
3. A specimen in the British Museum weighs 18.3 grams.
4. October.
5. December.
6. One specimen weighs 16.9 grams.
7. Initial letter of month is in script; others for this month are plain.
8. A specimen in the British Museum weighs 19.2 grams.
9. Two specimens weigh 15.7 and 16.5 grams.
10. Two specimens weigh 16.6 and 17.5 grams.
11. A specimen in the British Museum weighs 23.6 grams.
12. A specimen in the British Museum weighs 10.4 grams.
13. Two specimens in the British Museum weigh 14.9 and 16.9 grams.
14. June misspelt.
15. Struck at Limerick following capture of Dublin mint.
16. May not exist except as forgeries. At least one piece appears to have been tooled from an August coin.

Apart from the date/month punctuations listed, many other varieties of legend punctuation occur.

Coins struck in metals other than gun metal have been variously described as proofs or patterns. When one considers that gun-money was struck in war conditions at a time when even gun metal was scarce, it appears probable that these pieces were struck at a later date.

Shilling

Small size shillings are sometimes catalogued as sixpences by auctioneers, even including leading auction houses. The item to check is the 'XII' on the reverse.

The 'IR' on the reverse is much more ornate on the small size pieces than on the larger size; presumably this was changed intentionally to avoid confusion with the sixpence, even though the bust of James is different.

Denomination	Metal	Weight (grams)	Diameter (mm)	Rev. alignment
Shilling Obv 1/Rev 1	Gun metal	4.7 – 9.9	24 – 27	↑
Shilling Obv 2/Rev 2	Gun metal	4.3 – 6.8	22 – 24	↑

Obv 1/Rev 1: The heaviest tend to be dated March 1689; the lightest April 1690.

Obverse 1 Head 1, left; IACOBVS II DEI GRATIA

Obverse 2 Head 2, left, much smaller (even after allowing for smaller flan); the hair of James does not drape along the truncation; same legend

Reverse 1 Crown and four sceptres, flanked by scripted IR; XII above crown, (month) below; MAG BR FRA ET HIB REX (date)

Reverse 2 Similar but on a smaller flan; the IR is more ornate

Edge milled (diagonally)

Obv. 1   Obv. 1 castle below head   Obv. 2

Rev. 1   Rev. 2

No.	Date*	Features	Obv.	Rev.	VG	F	VF	EF
IESH-005	1689 July	stops on obverse	1	1	12	20	60	160
IESH-010	1689 July	struck in silver; stops on obverse	1	1				750
IESH-015	1689 July	no stops on obverse	1	1	15	25	75	200
IESH-020	1689 July.		1	1	12	20	60	160
IESH-025	1689 July.	half of milling missing	1	1	15	25	75	200
IESH-030	1689 Aug		1	1	12	20	60	160
IESH-035	1689 Aug.		1	1	12	20	60	160
IESH-040	1689 Aug:		1	1	12	20	60	160
IESH-045	1689 Augᵗ		1	1	12	20	60	160
IESH-050	1689 Augᵗ	struck in copper; edge plain	1	1	60	100	250	
IESH-055	1689 Augᵗ.		1	1	12	20	60	160
IESH-060	1689 Augᵗ:		1	1	12	20	60	160
IESH-065	1689 Augt:		1	1	12	20	60	160
IESH-070	1689 Augᵗ	struck in silver [1]	1	1				750
IESH-075	1689 Sep:		1	1	10	15	45	130
IESH-080	1689 SEPR.		1	1	10	15	45	130
IESH-085	1689 Sepʳ		1	1	10	15	45	130
IESH-090	1689 Sepʳ.		1	1	10	15	45	130
IESH-095	1689 Sepʳ:		1	1	10	15	45	130
IESH-100	1689 Sept.		1	1	10	15	45	130
IESH-105	1689 Septᵗ.		1	1	10	15	45	130
IESH-110	1689 Septr.		1	1	10	15	45	130
IESH-115	1689 Sept	struck in silver [2]	1	1				750
IESH-120	1689 Oct		1	1	10	15	45	130
IESH-125	1689 Oct.		1	1	10	15	45	130
IESH-130	1689 Oct:		1	1	10	15	45	130
IESH-135	1689 OCT		1	1	10	15	45	130
IESH-140	1689 OCT.	stops on obverse	1	1	10	15	45	130
IESH-145	1689 OCT.	no stops on obverse	1	1	15	22	65	180
IESH-150	1689 OCT.	FI instead of ET (rev)	1	1	30	50	150	
IESH-155	1689 OCTᴿ		1	1	15	22	65	180
IESH-160	1689 OCTʳ		1	1	15	22	65	180
IESH-165	1689 OCTʳ.		1	1	15	22	65	180
IESH-170	1689 8 BER [3]		1	1	45	70	200	
IESH-175	1689 8 BEʳ. [3]		1	1	45	70	200	
IESH-180	1689 8 BR [3]		1	1	45	70	200	
IESH-185	1689 8 br. [3]		1	1	45	70	200	
IESH-190	1689 NOV		1	1	12	20	60	170
IESH-195	1689 Nov		1	1	12	20	60	170
IESH-200	1689 Nov:		1	1	12	20	60	170
IESH-205	1689 Novr:		1	1	12	20	60	170
IESH-210	1689 Nov [4]		1	1	12	20	60	170
IESH-215	1689 Nov. [4]		1	1	12	20	60	170
IESH-220	1689 Nov: [4]		1	1	12	20	60	170
IESH-225	1689 novʳ:		1	1	12	20	60	170
IESH-230	1689 9 [5]		1	1	18	30	80	200
IESH-235	1689 9ʳ [5]		1	1	18	30	80	200
IESH-240	1689 9ʳ	castle with two towers under head (obv) [5]	1	1	300	450	1200	
IESH-245	1689 9ʳ	castle with two towers under head (obv) [5]	1	1	200	300	800	
IESH-250	1689 Dec		1	1	10	15	45	130
IESH-255	1689 Dec.		1	1	10	15	45	130
IESH-260	1689 Dec:		1	1	10	15	45	130
IESH-265	1689 Decʳ.		1	1	10	15	45	130
IESH-270	1689 10 [6]		1	1	15	22	65	180
IESH-275	1689 10ʳ [6]		1	1	15	22	65	180
IESH-280	1689 10ʳ	reverse ↓ [6]	1	1	20	30	90	240
IESH-285	1689 Jan		1	1	10	15	45	130
IESH-290	1689 Jan	edge perpendicularly milled [7]	1	1	25	40	120	300

No.	Date*	Features	Obv.	Rev.	VG	F	VF	EF
IESH-295	1689 Jan	reverse 90 degrees to left	1	1	15	22	60	200
IESH-300	1689 Jan	no stops on reverse; ERA EI instead of FRA ET (rev)	1	1	30	50	150	350
IESH-305	1689 Jan.		1	1	10	15	45	130
IESH-310	1689 Jan.	ERA instead of FRA (rev)	1	1	25	40	120	300
IESH-315	1689 Jan:		1	1	10	15	45	130
IESH-320	1689 Jan:	'a' in Jan reversed (rev)	1	1	80	120	300	
IESH-325	1689 Jan:	struck in silver	1	1				750
IESH-330	1689 Jan:	struck in silver; 'a' in Jan reversed (rev)	1	1				1500
IESH-335	1689 Feb		1	1	10	15	45	130
IESH-340	1689 Feb	reverse ↓	1	1	15	22	60	200
IESH-345	1689 Feb.		1	1	10	15	45	130
IESH-350	1689 Feb:		1	1	10	15	45	130
IESH-355	1689 Feb:	reverse 90 degrees to left	1	1	15	22	60	200
IESH-360	1689 Feb:	struck in silver [8]	1	1				750
IESH-365	1689 Mar		1	1	12	18	50	150
IESH-370	1689 Mar	reverse ↓	1	1	18	28	75	220
IESH-375	1689 Mar:		1	1	12	18	50	150
IESH-380	1689 Mar:	struck on thick flan	1	1	30	50	150	
IESH-385	1689 Mar [4]		1	1	12	18	50	150
IESH-390	1689 Mar. [4]		1	1	12	18	50	150
IESH-395	1689 Mar:	struck in silver	1	1				600
IESH-400	1690 Mar		1	1	12	18	50	150
IESH-405	1690 Mar:		1	1	12	18	50	150
IESH-410	1690 Mar: [9]		1	1	12	18	50	150
IESH-415	1690 Mar	no stops on reverse [2]	1	1	16	24	70	200
IESH-420	1689 Mar.	struck in silver [4]	1	1		150	400	700
IESH-425	1689 Mar:	struck in silver [10]	1	1		400	700	1000
IESH-430	1690 Mar.	struck in gold [11]	1	1				5000
IESH-435	1690 Apr.		1	1	12	18	50	150
IESH-440	1690 Apr:		1	1	12	18	50	150
IESH-445	1690 Apr	struck in silver	1	1				700
IESH-450	1690 Apr	struck in gold [2]	1	1				5000
IESH-455	1690 Apr [12]		2	2	18	25	75	220
IESH-460	1690 apr		2	2	18	25	75	220
IESH-465	1690 May [12]		2	2	12	18	50	150
IESH-470	1690 May	reverse ↓ [12]	2	2	18	25	75	220
IESH-475	1690 May. [12]		2	2	12	18	50	150
IESH-480	1690 May.	GRATA instead of GRATIA (obv) [12]	2	2	24	35	100	250
IESH-485	1690 MAY [12]		2	2	12	18	50	150
IESH-490	1690 MAY	ERA instead of FRA (rev) [12]	2	2	24	35	100	250
IESH-495	1690 May	struck in silver [13]	2	2			400	700
IESH-500	1690 May	struck in gold [14]	2	2		2000	3500	5000
IESH-505	1690 May.	struck in gold [10]	2	2		2000	3500	5000
IESH-510	1690 may		2	2	12	18	50	150
IESH-515	1690 June		2	2	12	18	50	150
IESH-520	1690 June.		2	2	12	18	50	150
IESH-525	1690 June.	with pewter plug	2	2	100	150		
IESH-530	1690 Junc	struck on thin flan [15]	2	2	60	100		
IESH-535	1690 June	struck in silver [16]	2	2				700
IESH-540	1690 June	struck in gold [17]	2	2				5000
IESH-545	1690 July [18]		2	2				
IESH-550	1690 Augᵗ: [19]		2	2	600	1000		
IESH-555	1690 Sep: [20]		2	2	150	250		

* and abbreviated month as on coin, with following punctuation
1. One specimen weighs 9.7 grams.
2. Month style and punctuation not available.
3. October.
4. Initial letter of month is in script; others for this month are plain.
5. November.
6. December.
7. Several minor design differences from normal on obverse and reverse.
8. A specimen in the British Museum weighs 6.4 grams.
9. On some coins a flaw on the reverse appears to make the date read 1699.
10. One specimen weighs 7.2 grams.
11. Two specimens in the British Museum weigh 7.5 and 7.9 grams.
12. Stops vary in shape. A large hoard of shillings dated May 1690 was found near Rathcormuck.
13. Two specimen weigh 3.8 and 4.0 grams.
14. One specimen weighs 8.3 grams.
15. Note mis-spelling of month.
16. A specimen in the British Museum weighs 5.9 grams.

Notes continued
17. A specimen in the British Museum weighs 6.1 grams.
18. May not exist except as forgeries.
19. May not exist; specimens with obv. 1 and rev. 1 (large flan) have the date on the coin retooled from 1689. The final 0 of the date is too small and high up; it is formed from the loop of the 9.
20. Struck at Limerick following capture of Dublin mint.

Apart from the date/month punctuations listed, many other varieties of legend punctuation occur.

Coins struck in metals other than gun metal have been variously described as proofs or patterns. When one considers that gun-money was struck in war conditions at a time when even gun metal was scarce, it appears probable that these pieces were struck at a later date.

Sixpence

Denomination	Metal	Weight (grams)	Diameter (mm)	Rev. alignment
Sixpence Obv 1/Rev 1	Gun metal	2.6 – 4.2	20	↑

The heaviest tend to be dated Sep 1689; the lightest June 1689.

Obverse 1   Head 1, left; IACOBVS II DEI GRATIA

Reverse 1   Crown and four sceptres, flanked by scripted IR; VI above crown, (month) below; MAG BR FRA ET HIB REX (date)

Edge   milled (diagonally)

Obv. 1   Rev. 1

No.	Date*	Features	Obv.	Rev.	VG	F	VF	EF
IE6D-005	1689 June		1	1	14	20	60	180
IE6D-010	1689 June.		1	1	14	20	60	180
IE6D-015	1689 Jvne		1	1	14	20	60	180
IE6D-020	1689 Jvne.		1	1	14	20	60	180
IE6D-025	1689 July		1	1	14	20	60	180
IE6D-030	1689 July	wide date	1	1	14	20	60	180
IE6D-035	1689 July.		1	1	14	20	60	180
IE6D-040	1689 July	struck in silver	1	1				600
IE6D-045	1689 Aug		1	1	14	20	60	180
IE6D-050	1689 Aug:	edge plain	1	1	20	35	90	270
IE6D-055	1689 Augt.		1	1	14	20	60	180
IE6D-060	1689 Augᵗ		1	1	14	20	60	180
IE6D-065	1689 Aug	FR instead of FRA (rev)	1	1	25	40	120	350
IE6D-070	1689 Aug	struck in silver	1	1				600
IE6D-075	1689 Sep		1	1	14	20	60	180
IE6D-080	1689 Sep	struck in copper; edge plain	1	1	50	90	200	
IE6D-085	1689 Sepr		1	1	14	20	60	180
IE6D-090	1689 Sepʳ		1	1	14	20	60	180
IE6D-095	1689 Sepʳ:		1	1	14	20	60	180
IE6D-100	1689 Sept	struck in silver [1]	1	1				600
IE6D-105	1689 7ber	[2]	1	1	40	60	180	500
IE6D-110	1689 Oct:	[3]	1	1				
IE6D-115	1689 Nov		1	1	14	20	60	180
IE6D-120	1689 Nov.		1	1	14	20	60	180
IE6D-125	1689 Nov:		1	1	14	20	60	180
IE6D-130	1689 Dec.		1	1	14	20	60	180
IE6D-135	1689 Dec:		1	1	14	20	60	180
IE6D-140	1689 Jan	stops on reverse	1	1	14	20	60	180
IE6D-145	1689 Jan	no stops on reverse	1	1	22	35	100	280
IE6D-150	1689 Jan.		1	1	14	20	60	180
IE6D-155	1689 Jan:		1	1	14	20	60	180
IE6D-160	1689 Jan	struck in silver	1	1				600
IE6D-165	1689 Jan:	struck in silver	1	1				600
IE6D-170	1689 Jan	struck in gold	1	1				6000

No.	Date*	Features	Obv.	Rev.	VG	F	VF	EF
IE6D-175	1689 Jan	struck in gold over James II half guinea [4]	1	1				8000
IE6D-180	1689 Feb		1	1	16	24	75	220
IE6D-185	1689 Feb:		1	1	16	24	75	220
IE6D-190	1689 Feb.	struck in silver	1	1				400
IE6D-195	1689 Feb:	struck in silver	1	1				500
IE6D-200	1689 Feb	struck in gold [5]	1	1				6000
IE6D-205	1689 Feb.	struck in gold [6]	1	1				6000
IE6D-210	1689 Mar:	[3]	1	1				
IE6D-215	1690 Mar:	[3]	1	1				
IE6D-220	1690 Apr	[3]	1	1				
IE6D-225	1690 apr:	[3]	1	1				
IE6D-230	1690 May		1	1	24	40	100	350
IE6D-235	1690 May.		1	1	24	40	100	350
IE6D-240	1690 May:	struck on thick flan; edge plain	1	1	50	90	200	
IE6D-245	1690 May	struck in gold	1	1				8000
IE6D-250	1690 June:	[7]	1	1				
IE6D-255	1690 June	struck in gold	1	1				8000

* and abbreviated month as on coin, with following punctuation
1. Month style and punctuation not available.
2. September.
3. May not exist except as forgeries. Hardinge reported in 1874 that the James Press struck no sixpences throughout October 1689.
4. A specimen weighs 4.0 grams.
5. A specimen weighs 5.2 grams.
6. A specimen in the British Museum weighs 5.0 grams.
7. This unique piece in the British Museum appears to have the date retooled from 1689, but is included as a curiosity.

Apart from the date/month punctuations listed, many other varieties of legend punctuation occur.

Sixpences dated October 1690 are considered to be concoctions.

Coins struck in metals other than gun metal have been variously described as proofs or patterns. When one considers that gun-money was struck in war conditions at a time when even gun metal was scarce, it appears probable that these pieces were struck at a later date.

Groat

The obverse is from the die for the sixpence obverse. Although normally stated to be in pewter, the British Museum specimen appears to be in copper.

Denomination	Metal	Weight (grams)	Diameter (mm)	Rev. alignment
Groat	Copper (or pewter?)	3.3 – 3.5	20 – 21	↑

Obverse 1   Head 1, left; IACOBVS II DEI GRATIA

Reverse 1   Crowned harp, flanked by II each side; MAG BR FRA ET HIB REX 1689

Edge   milled (diagonally)

Obv. 1   Rev. 1

No.	Date	Features	Obv.	Rev.	VG	F	VF	EF
IE4D-005	1689		1	1	300	500	1200	4000

Penny

Denomination	Metal	Weight (grams)	Diameter (mm)	Rev. alignment
Penny Obv 1/Rev 1	Pewter with brass or copper plug on reverse	7.0 – 7.7	25 – 26	↑
Penny Obv 2/Rev 2	Pewter with brass or copper plug	6.2 – 7.4	25	↑

Obverse 1   Head 1, left; IACOBVS II DEI GRATIA

Obverse 2   Head 2, smaller, left; 1ᴰ behind head; same legend

Reverse 1   Crowned harp, (date) above; MAG BR FRA ET HIB REX

Reverse 2   Somewhat similar harp but flanked by divided date 16 90 below; same legend

Edge   milled (diagonally)

Obv. 1

Obv. 2

Rev. 1

Rev. 2

No.	Date	Features	Obv.	Rev.	VG	F	VF
IE1D-005	1689		1	1	300	450	1200
IE1D-010	1690		1	1	200	300	800
IE1D-015	1690		2	2	140	200	500

Halfpenny

Coins dated 1689 and 1690 were struck in pewter at Dublin to augment the larger gunmoney denominations. After James had left Ireland, his supporters held out in Limerick until 3rd October 1691, and during this time coined halfpence and farthings dated 1691 with a reverse depicting Hibernia. These pieces are of varying thickness and some exhibit traces of other legends. It appears that the halfpence were over large gunmoney shillings and also from metal obtained from melting gunmoney of various denominations.

James Simon (1749) and Batty describe a pewter halfpenny of 1689 'probably struck at Limerick', which depicts James on horseback, with two round specks of brass on the horse, and legend IACOBVS II DEI GRATIA. The reverse depicts two sceptres in saltire through a crown of brass with lion, with a harp under the crown, and legend HALF PENNY; MAG BR FRA ET HIB REX 1689. This piece is unknown today.

Denomination	Metal	Weight (grams)	Diameter (mm)	Rev. alignment
Halfpenny Obv 1/Rev 1	Pewter	4.7	23	↑
Halfpenny Obv 2/Rev 2	Pewter with brass or copper plug	4.1 – 4.7	23	↑
Halfpenny Obv 3/Rev 3	Gun metal	4.7 – 8.7	24 – 26	↑

Obverse 1   Head 1, left; IACOBVS II DEI GRATIA

Obverse 2   Head 2, smaller, left; floral ornament below; same legend

Obverse 3   Head 3, left; same legend

Reverse 1   Crowned harp, (date) above; MAG BR FRA ET HIB REX

Reverse 2   Similar but smaller crown dividing date as 16 90; same legend

Reverse 3   Hibernia seated, facing left, holding cross, with left arm resting on harp; HIBERNIA 1691 (N is reversed)

Edge   milled (diagonally)

Obv. 1   Obv. 2   Obv. 3

Rev. 1   Rev. 2   Rev. 3

No.	Date	Features	Obv.	Rev.	VG	F	VF	EF
IEHD-005	1689		1	1	300	500		
IEHD-010	1690		1	1	180	300		
IEHD-015	1690	reverse ↓	1	1	240	400		
IEHD-020	1690	struck in silver; reverse ↓ [1]	1	1	150	250	400	
IEHD-025	1690	struck in silver on thin flan; reverse ↓ [2]	1	1	250	400	700	
IEHD-030	1690	struck in silver over French 5 sols of Louis XIV; edge plain; reverse ↓ [3]	1	1	280	450	800	
IEHD-035	1690		2	2	70	100	300	600
IEHD-040	1691	[4]	3	3	35	50	100	180

1. Two specimens in the British Museum weigh 4.0 and 4.8 grams.
2. A specimen in the British Museum weighs 2.1 grams.
3. The date of the 5 sols is usually 1643 or 1644; one specimen weighs 2.1 grams.
4. Thickness varies. Struck over large gunmoney shillings or from metal obtained from melting gunmoney pieces.

Farthing

Supporters of James coined this issue at Limerick after his departure from Ireland. The pieces are struck over small gunmoney shillings or from metal obtained by melting down various gunmoney denominations. Because of the shape of the numeral '1' the date may appear to read 1693.

Denomination	Metal	Weight (grams)	Diameter (mm)	Rev. alignment
Farthing	Gun metal	4.3 – 6.8	22 – 23	↑

Obverse 1   Head 1, left; IACOBVS II DEI GRATIA

Reverse 1   Hibernia seated, facing left, holding cross, with left arm resting on harp; HIBERNIA 1691

Edge   milled with double row of leaves

Obv. 1   Rev. 1

No.	Date	Features	Obv.	Rev.	VG	F	VF
IEFA-005	1691		1	1	60	100	250
IEFA-010	1691	N in HIBERNIA reversed [1]	1	1	50	80	200

1. The first 'A' in GRATIA may be unbarred (obv).

Pattern

Some of the coinage in the main listings may be regarded as patterns or proofs, but are not listed separately as they are so closely related to the main coinage, and in any event may be late strikings.

The pattern crown of 1689 below, in the British Museum and elsewhere, is of an unadopted design.

1689

No.	Date	Denomination	Metal	Weight (grams)	Diameter (mm)	Rev. align.	Price
IEPT-020	1689	Crown	Pewter with brass plug(s)	22.4	37	↑	

Obv.   Rev.

Obverse   King on horseback, facing left; IACOBVS II DEI GRATIA

Reverse   Crown; MAG BR FRA ET HIB REX 1689

The coinage of the Irish Free State & the Republic

The coinage of the Irish Free State and the Republic of Ireland is treated in this catalogue separately from the earlier coinage of Ireland, and an explanation is needed as to why this is appropriate. Years of political unrest culminated in the Anglo-Irish treaty of 1921, under which the Irish Free State was created. The territory of this included most of the island of Ireland, the notable exception being six of the counties of Ulster. These six counties constitute the province of the United Kingdom now known as Northern Ireland or (somewhat inaccurately) Ulster, or the 'North of Ireland' to many people whose aim is eventual reunification of the island.

At the time of its inception, the Irish Free State did not have a coinage of its own, and rather demeaningly used that of the United Kingdom. In 1926, a committee was set up under the chairmanship of W. B. Yeats, the poet, to advise on designs for a proposed new coinage. The committee proposed designs for eight denominations from halfcrown to farthing. Each was to depict the Irish harp on the obverse, and on the reverse a different specimen of Irish wildlife. Various artists were to be invited to submit designs, in accordance with various strictures laid down by the Committee. With his usual eloquence, Yeats described the tendering process: 'As the most famous and beautiful coins are the coins of the Greek colonies, especially those in Sicily, we decided to send photographs of some of these, and one coin of Carthage, to our selected artists, and to ask them, as far as possible, to take them as a model. But the Greek coins had two advantages that ours could not have, one side need not balance the other, and either could be stamped in high relief, whereas ours must pitch and spin to please the gambler, and pack into rolls to please the banker.'

The Committee decreed itself anxious to avoid 'hackneyed symbolism' and also considered that the shamrock had 'no dignity of age behind it', being a symbol of Ireland only since the eighteenth century. The Committee was informed that the Minister for Finance recommended:

(1) that a harp should be shown on one side of the majority of the coins, if not on all;

(2) that the inscription should be in Irish only. This made it important for the Committee to consider the utility of having the denomination of the coin shown by means of a numeral, for the assistance of persons unfamiliar with Irish;

(3) that no effigies of modern persons should be included in the designs.

It was further decided that religious symbols should be avoided; amongst the reasons cited were that it was an Irish habit to spit upon the image on a coin for luck before putting it one's pocket, and also that many people would pierce the coins and use them as talismans, thereby committing a criminal offence.

It was considered that seven artists would be sufficient to compete for the work, of which three should be Irish. Each artist would receive a fee of £50. The submitted models were considered anonymously, and the work of 32 year old Percy Metcalfe, of London, was considered 'incomparably superior' to the others; Metcalfe was a Yorkshireman who had worked previously on the coinage of Egypt and Iraq, and it is a measure of his skill that his designs were chosen by the Committee separately for each denomination, without his identity being known.

The new coinage was struck in London. It was not considered feasible to set up a mint in Ireland because it would be used for only a few months of the year, and the capital expenditure of setting it up would be very high.

The new coins made their first appearance in 1928, and a proof set was issued in a green case to mark the occasion. Rather like the British proof set of 1927, the finish of this set could perhaps be best described optimistically as prooflike. The silver coinage had a fineness of 75%, higher than that of the British coinage of the period, because the 50% silver of the British coinage was considered to discolour too quickly. Sterling silver was discounted as a possible choice because in 1920 the price of silver had risen sharply, and it was thought that this might happen again, with consequent melting down of the coinage by the public. The threepence was struck in pure nickel because it retains its colour better than cupronickel and its soapy feel made it 'more pleasant to handle' than cupronickel.

There was some opposition to the new coins. A priest wrote to The Irish Independent: 'If these pagan symbols once get a hold, then is the thin edge of the wedge of freemasonry sunk into the very life of our Catholicity, for the sole object of having these pagan symbols instead of religious emblems on our coins is to wipe out all traces of religion from our minds, to forget the 'Land of Saints', and to beget a land of devil-worshippers, where evil may reign supreme.'

In 1937 a new constitution was declared in which the Irish Free State became a republic. However, all coinage dated 1937 still retained the old nomenclature. No coins dated 1938 were issued, although a unique trial piece of a penny is known, and the coins of 1939 were thus the first to carry the Irish term EIRE to denote the Republic of Ireland. The coinage from 1939 onwards also incorporates minor modifications to the harp on the obverse. In the case of the halfcrown and penny, minor differences in design were also made to the reverses. Silver coinage was discontinued for reasons of economy after 1943 and replaced in 1951 with cupronickel issues after the passing of the 1950 Coinage Act. The threepence had already converted to cupronickel in 1942.

In 1966, an unusual commemorative coin was struck in silver, both as a currency piece and as a cased proof. The denomination, of ten shillings, had not appeared hitherto, and the coin was unusually thick (3.2mm), and had an inscribed edge. The occasion commemorated was the 50th anniversary of the Easter Rising of 1916, and the coin featured the bust of Padraig Pearse and the statue of Cuchulainn which stood in the building which symbolises Irish nationalism, the Post Office in Dublin's O'Connell Street. It was hoped that the coin would to a large extent replace the ten shilling note, but, despite its political nature, it did not prove popular and most of the pieces were melted down.

In February 1962 the Government decided to introduce decimal currency at an unspecified date, and a Working Party recommended in 1965 the establishment of a system based on the ten-shilling unit. However, in April 1968 the Minister for Finance announced in the Budget that the new decimal system would mirror that of the United Kingdom, and would be introduced on the same date, 15th February 1971. The changeover date was threatened by a bank strike from May to November 1970, but in the event the transition went through smoothly.

On the new coinage, the Irish harp was retained on the obverse, and the cupronickel coins again depicted wildlife. The reverses of the bronze coins, however, carried designs by Gabriel Hayes based on illuminations from old manuscripts of Ireland. The decimal coinage bears dates from 1969, when it was first introduced, but for some reason the pre-decimal sixpence continued to be struck during that year, although not in fact being issued until July 1970.

In 1976, a new mint opened in the Irish Republic, and this took over the manufacture of the coinage which had previously been struck at the Royal Mint.

On 1st January 1999, the Irish Republic permanently fixed the exchange rate of its currency against the new Euro denomination. At the time of writing, it is intended that Euro coinage will be introduced on 1st January 2002, and that the present coinage will be withdrawn on 1st July 2002.

Grading modern Irish coins often presents a problem to collectors used to assessing the wear on an obverse portrait as the main indication of grade. There is a tendency to overgrade Irish coins by collectors who do not handle them frequently, and it is important that the amount of wear should be especially scrutinized around the frame of the harp and on the head of the wildlife portrayed on the reverse.

Ten Shillings

The Republican obverse and reverse design details of this piece were chosen by officials at the Department of Finance, with the actual design being executed by T. H. Paget of the Royal Mint in London.

Because of the concave field of this coin, the first batch of proof coins struck were of such poor quality that they had to be returned to the mint for recoining.

The ten-shilling coin eventually proved unpopular with the public, despite its republican connotations, and most of them were called in and melted down. To some extent the unpopularity was due to confusion with the florin, and to the fact that a ten-shilling note was still in circulation.

Denomination	Metal	Weight (grams)	Diameter (mm) / Thickness (mm)	Rev. alignment
Ten shillings	Silver 83.3%; Copper 16.7%	18.1	31 / 3.2	↑

Obverse 1 Head of Padraig (Patrick) Pearse, right; EIRE 1966

Reverse 1 Statue of Cuchulainn; DEIC SCILLING

Edge (incuse) EIRI AMAC NA CASCA 1916

Obv. 1

Rev. 1

No.	Date	Features	Obv.	Rev.	VF	EF	UNC
IRTS-005	1966		1	1	5	7	8
IRTS-010	1966	NASCA instead of NA CASCA (edge)	1	1	25	35	50
IRTS-015	1966	NACASCA instead of NA CASCA (edge)	1	1	20	30	40
IRTS-018	1966	edge plain	1	1			100
IRTS-020	1966	PROOF [1]	1	1		12	18

1. Issued in green leatherette case; some are double sets.

Halfcrown

The Coinage Committee recommended an Irish hunter for the reverse, and submitted to the design competition photographs of a coin of Larissa (480–430 BC) and a coin of Carthage (342–340 BC).

Denomination	Metal	Weight (grams)	Diameter (mm)	Rev. alignment
Halfcrown 1928 – 43	Silver 75%; Copper 25%	14.1	32	↑
Halfcrown 1951 – 67	Cupronickel (Copper 75%; Nickel 25%)	14.1	32	↑

Obverse 1 Harp, flanked by divided date; SAORSTAT EIREANN

Obverse 2 Harp, with very minor differences; EIRE (date)

Reverse 1 Hunting horse with 8 tail tufts, facing left; LEATH CHOROIN; 2s6d and designer initials PM in exergue; 156 border beads

Reverse 2 Similar but horse tail slightly different, with 7 tail tufts; lettering thicker; PM smaller; 151 border beads

Edge milled

Obv. 1

Obv. 2

Rev. 1

Rev. 1 detail

Rev. 2

Rev. 2 detail (note the difference in position of leg with respect to initials)

No.	Date	Features	Obv.	Rev.	F	VF	EF	UNC
IRHC-005	1928	[1]	1	1	3	6	14	28
IRHC-010	1928	PROOF [2]	1	1				30
IRHC-015	1930		1	1	3	12	100	300
IRHC-020	1930	PROOF	1	1				1000
IRHC-025	1931		1	1	6	25	130	350
IRHC-030	1931	PROOF	1	1				1200
IRHC-035	1933		1	1	4	12	100	350

No.	Date	Features	Obv.	Rev.	F	VF	EF	UNC
IRHC-040	1933	PROOF	1	1				1200
IRHC-045	1934		1	1	3	8	50	120
IRHC-050	1934	PROOF	1	1				800
IRHC-055	1937		1	1	25	85	250	1100
IRHC-060	1937	PROOF	1	1				1500
IRHC-065	1939	3	2	2	3	6	14	30
IRHC-070	1939	PROOF	2	2				400
IRHC-075	1940	3	2	2	3	6	16	35
IRHC-080	1940	PROOF	2	2				400
IRHC-085	1941		2	2	3	8	20	40
IRHC-090	1941	PROOF	2	2				400
IRHC-095	1942	3	2	2	3	8	20	40
IRHC-100	1943	4	2	2	80	200	800	1600
IRHC-105	1951		2	2			5	20
IRHC-110	1951	PROOF	2	2				250
IRHC-115	1954		2	2			6	25
IRHC-120	1954	PROOF	2	2				500
IRHC-125	1955		2	2			5	18
IRHC-130	1955	PROOF	2	2				400
IRHC-135	1959		2	2			4	12
IRHC-140	1959	PROOF	2	2				350
IRHC-145	1961		2	1	10	25	150	500
IRHC-150	1961		2	2			5	15
IRHC-155	1961	PROOF	2	2				350
IRHC-160	1962		2	2			3	8
IRHC-165	1962	PROOF	2	2				300
IRHC-170	1963		2	2			3	6
IRHC-175	1963	PROOF	2	2				300
IRHC-180	1964		2	2			3	6
IRHC-185	1964	PROOF	2	2				300
IRHC-190	1966		2	2				4
IRHC-195	1966	PROOF	2	2				250
IRHC-200	1967		2	2				4
IRHC-205	1967	Reverse struck from polished die	2	2				25
IRHC-210	1967	PROOF	2	2				250

1. Fada accent over SAORSTAT varies.
2. Some struck around 1962; issued in cased sets.
3. Date spacing varies.
4. About 7000 issued in error in 1951 when bags of silver coinage due for remelting were mixed with bags of new cupronickel coinage.

The halfcrown ceased to be legal tender after 31st December 1969.

Florin

The Coinage Committee recommended a salmon for the reverse because of its value as a natural product and because of its place in Irish legend. Also, because the halfcrown and florin are sometimes confused, the reverse design needed to be as different as possible from that on the halfcrown.

Denomination	Metal	Weight (grams)	Diameter (mm)	Rev. alignment
Florin 1928 – 43	Silver 75% Copper 25%	11.3	28.5	↑
Florin 1951 – 68	Cupronickel (Copper 75% Nickel 25%)	11.3	28.5	↑

Obverse 1 Harp, flanked by divided date; SAORSTAT EIREANN

Obverse 2 Harp, with very minor differences; EIRE (date)

Reverse 1 Salmon; FLOIRIN; 2ˢ; 152 border beads

Reverse 2 Similar but 147 border beads

Edge milled

Obv. 1   Obv.2   Rev.1

No.	Date	Features	Obv.	Rev.	F	VF	EF	UNC
IRFL-005	1928		1	1	3	5	10	22
IRFL-010	1928	PROOF 1	1	1				24
IRFL-015	1930		1	1	3	9	60	280
IRFL-020	1930	PROOF 2	1	1				1200
IRFL-025	1931		1	1	4	14	110	350
IRFL-030	1931	PROOF	1	1				1200
IRFL-035	1933		1	1				260
IRFL-040	1933	PROOF	1	1				1000
IRFL-045	1934		1	1	8	35	220	450
IRFL-050	1934	PROOF	1	1				1200
IRFL-055	1935		1	1	3	8	50	180
IRFL-060	1935	PROOF	1	1				800
IRFL-065	1937		1	1	5	15	90	300
IRFL-070	1937	PROOF	1	1				1000
IRFL-075	1939		2	1	3	5	10	20
IRFL-080	1939	PROOF	2	1				350
IRFL-085	1940		2	1	3	6	12	25
IRFL-090	1940	PROOF	2	1				350
IRFL-095	1941		2	1	3	6	12	25
IRFL-100	1941	PROOF	2	1				350
IRFL-105	1942		2	1	3	7	14	30
IRFL-110	1942	PROOF	2	1				350
IRFL-115	1943	3	2	1	2000	3000	5000	
IRFL-120	1951		2	1			4	16
IRFL-125	1951	PROOF	2	1				250
IRFL-130	1954		2	1			4	16
IRFL-135	1954	PROOF	2	1				250
IRFL-140	1955		2	1			4	15
IRFL-145	1955	PROOF	2	1				250
IRFL-150	1959		2	2			4	15
IRFL-155	1959	PROOF	2	2				250
IRFL-160	1961		2	2			5	20
IRFL-165	1961	PROOF	2	2				250
IRFL-170	1962		2	2			4	10
IRFL-175	1962	PROOF	2	2				200
IRFL-180	1963		2	2			3	8
IRFL-185	1963	PROOF	2	2				200
IRFL-190	1964		2	2				5
IRFL-195	1964	PROOF	2	2				200
IRFL-200	1965		2	2				4
IRFL-205	1965	PROOF	2	2				200
IRFL-210	1966		2	2				3
IRFL-215	1966	PROOF	2	2				200
IRFL-220	1968	4	2	2				2
IRFL-225	1968	PROOF	2	2				200

1. Some struck around 1962; issued in cased sets.
2. Possibly unique.
3. 1000 issued in error in 1951 when one bag of silver coinage due for remelting was mixed with bags of new cupronickel coinage.
4. Issued in March 1969.

Shilling

The Coinage Committee recommended a bull for the reverse, and submitted photographs of a coin of Thurium (400–350 BC). The choice symbolises the importance of Irish cattle.

Denomination	Metal	Weight (grams)	Diameter (mm)	Rev. alignment
Shilling 1928 – 42	Silver 75%; Copper 25%	5.7	24	↑
Shilling 1951 – 68	Cupronickel (Copper 75%; Nickel 25%)	5.7	24	↑

Obverse 1 Harp, flanked by divided date; SAORSTAT EIREANN

Obverse 2   Harp, with very minor differences; EIRE (date)

Reverse 1   Bull, facing right, 1ˢ above; SCILLING in exergue

Edge   milled

	Obv. 1		Obv.2		Rev.1			

No.	Date	Features	Obv.	Rev.	F	VF	EF	UNC
IRSH-005	1928		1	1	2	4	10	18
IRSH-010	1928	PROOF [1]	1	1				20
IRSH-015	1930		1	1	2	10	75	250
IRSH-020	1930	PROOF	1	1				600
IRSH-025	1931		1	1	2	8	50	140
IRSH-030	1931	PROOF	1	1				500
IRSH-035	1933		1	1	2	8	50	140
IRSH-040	1933	PROOF	1	1				500
IRSH-045	1935		1	1	2	6	20	60
IRSH-050	1935	PROOF	1	1				400
IRSH-055	1937	[2]	1	1	4	25	150	600
IRSH-060	1937	PROOF	1	1				800
IRSH-065	1939		2	1	2	4	8	20
IRSH-070	1939	PROOF	2	1				350
IRSH-075	1940		2	1	2	4	10	25
IRSH-080	1940	PROOF	2	1				350
IRSH-085	1941		2	1	2	5	12	30
IRSH-090	1941	PROOF	2	1				350
IRSH-095	1942		2	1	2	4	10	25
IRSH-100	1942	PROOF	2	1				350
IRSH-105	1951		2	1			3	12
IRSH-110	1951	PROOF	2	1				250
IRSH-115	1954		2	1			2	10
IRSH-120	1954	PROOF	2	1				250
IRSH-125	1955		2	1			3	12
IRSH-130	1955	PROOF	2	1				250
IRSH-135	1959	[3]	2	1			3	12
IRSH-140	1962		2	1			2	6
IRSH-145	1962	PROOF	2	1				200
IRSH-150	1963		2	1			2	6
IRSH-155	1963	PROOF	2	1				200
IRSH-160	1964		2	1			1	4
IRSH-165	1964	PROOF	2	1				200
IRSH-170	1966		2	1			1	2
IRSH-175	1966	PROOF	2	1				200
IRSH-180	1968		2	1			1	2
IRSH-185	1968	PROOF	2	1				200

1. Some struck around 1962; issued in cased sets.
2. Date orientation varies.
3. Very minor design alterations introduced.

Sixpence

The wolfhound was chosen as a reverse to a large extent because it was popular in a public poll of suggested features.

Denomination	Metal	Weight (grams)	Diameter (mm)	Rev. alignment
Sixpence 1928 – 40	Nickel	4.5	21	↑
Sixpence 1942 – 69	Cupronickel (Copper 75%; Nickel 25%)	4.5	21	↑

Obverse 1   Harp, flanked by divided date; SAORSTAT EIREANN

Obverse 2   Harp, with very minor differences; EIRE (date)

Reverse 1   Wolfhound, facing left, 6ᵈ above; REUL in exergue

Edge   plain

	Obv. 1		Obv.2		Rev.1			

No.	Date	Features	Obv.	Rev.	VF	EF	UNC
IR6D-005	1928		1	1	2	4	10
IR6D-010	1928	PROOF [1]	1	1			15
IR6D-015	1934		1	1	2	8	50
IR6D-020	1934	PROOF	1	1			600
IR6D-025	1935		1	1	2	12	90
IR6D-030	1935	PROOF	1	1			600
IR6D-035	1939		2	1	2	6	30
IR6D-040	1939	PROOF	2	1			500
IR6D-045	1940		2	1	2	6	30
IR6D-050	1940	PROOF	2	1			500
IR6D-055	1942		2	1	2	6	30
IR6D-060	1942	PROOF	2	1			500
IR6D-065	1945		2	1	4	20	80
IR6D-070	1945	PROOF	2	1			600
IR6D-075	1946		2	1	7	50	180
IR6D-080	1946	PROOF	2	1			700
IR6D-085	1947		2	1	4	20	70
IR6D-090	1947	PROOF	2	1			600
IR6D-095	1948		2	1	2	10	40
IR6D-100	1948	PROOF	2	1			400
IR6D-105	1949		2	1	2	10	40
IR6D-110	1949	PROOF	2	1			400
IR6D-115	1950		2	1	3	25	85
IR6D-120	1950	PROOF	2	1			500
IR6D-125	1952		2	1	2	5	20
IR6D-130	1952	PROOF	2	1			300
IR6D-135	1953		2	1	2	5	20
IR6D-140	1953	PROOF	2	1			300
IR6D-145	1955		2	1	2	5	20
IR6D-150	1955	PROOF	2	1			300
IR6D-155	1956		2	1	2	4	15
IR6D-160	1956	PROOF	2	1			300
IR6D-165	1958		2	1	2	5	25
IR6D-170	1958	PROOF	2	1			300
IR6D-175	1959		2	1		3	15
IR6D-180	1959	PROOF	2	1			250
IR6D-185	1960		2	1		2	8
IR6D-190	1960	PROOF	2	1			200
IR6D-195	1961		2	1		2	7
IR6D-200	1961	PROOF	2	1			200
IR6D-205	1962		2	1		4	25
IR6D-210	1962	PROOF	2	1			200
IR6D-215	1963		2	1		1	2
IR6D-220	1963	PROOF	2	1			200
IR6D-225	1964		2	1		1	2
IR6D-230	1964	PROOF	2	1			200
IR6D-235	1966		2	1		1	2
IR6D-240	1966	PROOF	2	1			200
IR6D-245	1967		2	1		1	2
IR6D-250	1967	PROOF	2	1			200
IR6D-255	1968		2	1		1	2
IR6D-260	1968	PROOF	2	1			200
IR6D-265	1969	[2]	2	1		1	2
IR6D-270	1969	PROOF	2	1			200

1. Some struck around 1962; issued in cased sets.
2. Issued in July 1970; possibly intended at the time to circulate after decimal day as 2½ pence.

The sixpence was retained in circulation after Decimal Day, and the May 1971 edition of 'Irish Numismatics' reported that the Decimal Currency Board and the Central Bank of Ireland said that 'there is nothing to indicate that the sixpenny piece is staying in circulation'. The coin was later withdrawn.

Threepence

The Coinage Committee recommended a hare for the reverse because of its association with sport, providing unity with the hound on the other nickel coin, the sixpence, without being easily confused with it.

C. Douglas Deane, writing from the Ulster Museum to the Irish Times, 19th March 1969, complained that the hare depicted was the English brown variety and not a native Irish hare.

Denomination	Metal	Weight (grams)	Diameter (mm)	Rev. alignment
Threepence 1928 – 40	Nickel	3.2	18	↑
Threepence 1942 – 68	Cupronickel (Copper 75% Nickel 25%)	3.2	18	↑

Obverse 1 Harp, flanked by divided date; SAORSTAT EIREANN

Obverse 2 Harp, with very minor differences; EIRE (date)

Reverse 1 Hare, facing left; LEATH REUL; 3ᵈ in exergue

Edge plain

Obv. 1   Obv.2   Rev.1

No.	Date	Features	Obv.	Rev.	VF	EF	UNC
IR3D-005	1928		1	1	2	4	8
IR3D-010	1928	PROOF [1]	1	1			10
IR3D-015	1933		1	1	8	50	180
IR3D-020	1933	PROOF	1	1			700
IR3D-025	1934		1	1	2	10	40
IR3D-030	1934	PROOF	1	1			500
IR3D-035	1935		1	1	4	20	120
IR3D-040	1935	PROOF	1	1			600
IR3D-045	1939		2	1	8	70	200
IR3D-050	1939	PROOF	2	1			800
IR3D-055	1940		2	1	2	6	24
IR3D-060	1940	PROOF	2	1			500
IR3D-065	1942		2	1	2	5	24
IR3D-070	1942	PROOF	2	1			500
IR3D-075	1943		2	1	2	8	50
IR3D-080	1943	PROOF	2	1			500
IR3D-085	1946		2	1	2	6	20
IR3D-090	1946	PROOF	2	1			500
IR3D-095	1948		2	1	3	15	60
IR3D-100	1948	PROOF	2	1			600
IR3D-105	1949		2	1	2	5	16
IR3D-110	1949	PROOF	2	1			500
IR3D-115	1950		2	1	2	4	12
IR3D-120	1950	PROOF	2	1			500
IR3D-125	1953		2	1	2	4	8
IR3D-130	1953	PROOF	2	1			400
IR3D-135	1956		2	1		3	6
IR3D-140	1956	PROOF	2	1			400
IR3D-145	1961		2	1		2	4
IR3D-150	1961	PROOF	2	1			300
IR3D-155	1962		2	1		2	6
IR3D-160	1962	PROOF	2	1			300
IR3D-165	1963		2	1		1	2
IR3D-170	1963	PROOF	2	1			200
IR3D-175	1964		2	1		1	2
IR3D-180	1964	PROOF	2	1			200
IR3D-185	1965		2	1		1	2
IR3D-190	1965	PROOF	2	1			200
IR3D-195	1966		2	1		1	2
IR3D-200	1966	PROOF	2	1			200
IR3D-205	1967		2	1		1	2
IR3D-210	1967	PROOF	2	1			200
IR3D-215	1968		2	1		1	2
IR3D-220	1968	PROOF	2	1			200

1. Some struck around 1962; issued in cased sets.

Penny

The Coinage Committee considered that the homeliness of a hen and chickens design would appeal to farmers and their families.

Denomination	Metal	Weight (grams)	Diameter (mm)	Rev. alignment
Penny 1928 – 58	Bronze (copper 95.5%; tin 3%; zinc 1.5%)	9.4	31	↑
Penny 1959 – 68	Bronze (copper 97%; zinc 2.5%; tin 0.5%)	9.4	31	↑

Obverse 1 Harp, flanked by divided date; SAORSTAT EIREANN

Obverse 2 Harp, with very minor differences; EIRE (date)

Reverse 1 Hen and chicks, facing left, 1ᵈ above; PINGIN in exergue

Reverse 2 Similar but very minor differences to hen

Edge plain

Obv. 1   Obv.2

Rev.2

No.	Date	Features	Obv.	Rev.	VF	EF	UNC
IR1D-005	1928		1	1	2	4	15
IR1D-010	1928	PROOF [1]	1	1			18
IR1D-015	1931		1	1	2	6	30
IR1D-020	1931	PROOF	1	1			400
IR1D-025	1933		1	1	3	10	70
IR1D-030	1933	PROOF	1	1			500
IR1D-035	1935		1	1	2	5	20
IR1D-040	1935	PROOF	1	1			400
IR1D-045	1937		1	1	2	7	40
IR1D-050	1937	PROOF	1	1			400
IR1D-055	1938	[2]	2	2			10000
IR1D-060	1940		2	2	5	50	400
IR1D-065	1940	PROOF	2	2			1200
IR1D-070	1941		2	2		5	20
IR1D-075	1941	PROOF	2	2			300
IR1D-080	1942		2	2		4	10
IR1D-085	1942	PROOF	2	2			300
IR1D-090	1943		2	2		5	20
IR1D-095	1943	PROOF	2	2			300
IR1D-100	1946		2	2		4	16
IR1D-105	1946	PROOF	2	2			300
IR1D-110	1948		2	2		4	14
IR1D-115	1948	PROOF	2	2			300
IR1D-120	1949		2	2		4	10
IR1D-125	1949	PROOF	2	2			250
IR1D-130	1950		2	2		3	10
IR1D-135	1950	PROOF	2	2			250
IR1D-140	1952		2	2		2	4
IR1D-145	1952	PROOF	2	2			200
IR1D-150	1962		2	2		2	8

No.	Date	Features	Obv.	Rev.	VF	EF	UNC
IR1D-155	1962	PROOF	2	2			200
IR1D-160	1963		2	2		1	3
IR1D-165	1963	PROOF	2	2			200
IR1D-170	1964		2	2		1	2
IR1D-175	1964	PROOF	2	2			200
IR1D-180	1965		2	2		1	2
IR1D-185	1965	PROOF	2	2			200
IR1D-190	1966		2	2		1	2
IR1D-195	1966	PROOF	2	2			200
IR1D-200	1967		2	2		1	2
IR1D-205	1967	PROOF	2	2			200
IR1D-210	1968	[3]	2	2		1	2

1. Some struck around 1962; issued in cased sets.
2. Unique trial piece; exists in UNC condition.
3. Some have the body of one chick very weakly struck (rev); issued from 14th October.

Halfpenny

The Coinage Committee hesitated before recommending a pig as a design, but later decided that it merited inclusion as representing a valuable product of the country.

Denomination	Metal	Weight (grams)	Diameter (mm)	Rev. alignment
Halfpenny 1928 – 53	Bronze (copper 95.5%; tin 3%; zinc 1.5%)	5.7	25	↑
Halfpenny 1964 – 67	Bronze (copper 97%; zinc 2.5%; tin 0.5%)	5.7	25	↑

Obverse 1   Harp, flanked by divided date; SAORSTAT EIREANN

Obverse 2   Harp, with very minor differences; EIRE (date)

Reverse 1   Pig and piglets, facing left, ½ᵈ above; LEATH PINGIN in exergue

Edge   plain

Obv. 1	Obv.2	Rev.1

No.	Date	Features	Obv.	Rev.	VF	EF	UNC
IRHD-005	1928		1	1	2	4	12
IRHD-010	1928	PROOF [1]	1	1			15
IRHD-015	1933		1	1	10	50	250
IRHD-020	1933	PROOF	1	1			500
IRHD-025	1935		1	1	5	25	150
IRHD-030	1935	PROOF	1	1			400
IRHD-035	1937		1	1	2	8	30
IRHD-040	1937	PROOF	1	1			300
IRHD-045	1939		2	1	8	25	80
IRHD-050	1939	PROOF	2	1			400
IRHD-055	1940		2	1	3	25	120
IRHD-060	1940	PROOF	2	1			400
IRHD-065	1941		2	1	2	4	18
IRHD-070	1941	PROOF	2	1			300
IRHD-075	1942		2	1	2	4	12
IRHD-080	1943		2	1	2	4	18
IRHD-085	1943	PROOF	2	1			300
IRHD-090	1946		2	1	3	12	40
IRHD-095	1946	PROOF	2	1			300
IRHD-100	1949		2	1		2	12
IRHD-105	1949	PROOF	2	1			250
IRHD-110	1953		2	1		1	3
IRHD-115	1953	PROOF	2	1			200
IRHD-120	1964		2	1		1	2
IRHD-125	1964	PROOF	2	1			200
IRHD-130	1965		2	1		1	2
IRHD-135	1965	PROOF	2	1			200
IRHD-140	1966		2	1		1	2
IRHD-145	1966	PROOF	2	1			200
IRHD-150	1967		2	1		1	2
IRHD-155	1967	PROOF	2	1			200

1. Some struck around 1962; issued in cased sets.

The halfpenny ceased to be legal tender after 31st July 1969.

Farthing

The woodcock was chosen as a design to appeal to sportsmen.

Denomination	Metal	Weight (grams)	Diameter (mm)	Rev. alignment
Farthing 1928 – 53	Bronze (copper 95.5%; tin 3%; zinc 1.5%)	2.8	20	↑
Farthing 1959 – 66	Bronze (copper 97%; zinc 2.5%; tin 0.5%)	2.8	20	↑

Obverse 1   Harp, flanked by divided date; SAORSTAT EIREANN

Obverse 2   Harp, with very minor differences; EIRE (date)

Reverse 1   Woodcock in flight, ¼ᵈ above; FEOIRLING

Edge   plain

Obv. 1	Obv.2	Rev.1

No.	Date	Features	Obv.	Rev.	VF	EF	UNC
IRFA-005	1928		1	1	2	4	8
IRFA-010	1928	PROOF [1]	1	1			10
IRFA-015	1930		1	1	2	5	14
IRFA-020	1930	PROOF	1	1			250
IRFA-025	1931		1	1	3	8	20
IRFA-030	1931	PROOF	1	1			250
IRFA-035	1932		1	1	4	12	24
IRFA-040	1932	PROOF	1	1			250
IRFA-045	1933		1	1	3	8	20
IRFA-050	1933	PROOF	1	1			250
IRFA-055	1935		1	1	5	15	25
IRFA-060	1935	PROOF	1	1			250
IRFA-065	1936		1	1	5	15	30
IRFA-070	1936	PROOF	1	1			250
IRFA-075	1937		1	1	2	4	10
IRFA-080	1937	PROOF	1	1			200
IRFA-085	1939		2	1	2	4	10
IRFA-090	1939	PROOF	2	1			200
IRFA-095	1940		2	1	3	6	14
IRFA-100	1940	PROOF	2	1			200
IRFA-105	1941		2	1	2	4	10
IRFA-110	1941	PROOF	2	1			200
IRFA-115	1943		2	1		2	5
IRFA-120	1943	PROOF	2	1			180
IRFA-125	1944		2	1		3	7
IRFA-130	1944	PROOF	2	1			180
IRFA-135	1946	[2]	2	1		2	6
IRFA-140	1946	PROOF	2	1			180
IRFA-145	1949		2	1		2	8
IRFA-150	1949	PROOF	2	1			180
IRFA-155	1953		2	1		1	2
IRFA-160	1953	PROOF	2	1			180
IRFA-165	1959	[3]	2	1		1	2
IRFA-170	1959	PROOF	2	1			180
IRFA-175	1966	[4]	2	1		1	2

1. Some struck around 1962; issued in cased sets.

No.	Date	Features	Obv. Rev.	VF	EF	UNC

2. Date spacing varies (obv).
3. Fada accent over EIRE varies in position (obv).
4. All issued in specimen sets.

The farthing ceased to be legal tender after 31st July 1969.

Ireland: Decimal Coinage

Pound

Denomination	Metal	Weight (grams)	Diameter (mm)	Rev. alignment
Pound	Cupronickel	10.0	31.1	↑

Obverse 1 Harp; EIRE (date)

Reverse 1 Irish red deer; £1 in exergue; PUNT

Edge Security design

Obv. 1   Rev. 1

No.	Date	Features	Obv.	Rev.	UNC
IRD1P/90–1	1990		1	1	4
IRD1P/90–3	1990	PROOF	1	1	14
IRD1P/94–1	1994		1	1	3
IRD1P/95–1	1995		1	1	3
IRD1P/96–1	1996		1	1	2
IRD1P/98–1	1998		1	1	2

50 Pence

The 50 pence coin was very unpopular when first introduced but was eventually accepted as a replacement for the ten-shilling note.

Denomination	Metal	Weight (grams)	Diameter (mm)	Rev. alignment
50 pence 1970 –	Cupronickel	13.5	30	↑

The coin is seven-sided but the diameter from any point on the edge across the centre of the face is constant

Obverse 1 Harp; EIRE (date)

Reverse 1 Woodcock in flight; 50P

Reverse 2 Arms of Dublin and Arms of Lord Mayor of Dublin, ribbon below reading AT CLIATH 1000 DUBLIN; 50p 988 1988 (for the Dublin Millennium)

Edge plain

Obv. 1

Rev. 1   Rev. 2

No.	Date	Features	Obv.	Rev.	UNC
IRD50/70–1	1970		1	1	3
IRD50/71–1	1971		1	1	3
IRD50/71–2	1971	PROOF or SPECIMEN [1]	1	1	4
IRD50/74–1	1974		1	1	4
IRD50/75–1	1975		1	1	4
IRD50/76–1	1976		1	1	4
IRD50/77–1	1977		1	1	3
IRD50/78–1	1978		1	1	3
IRD50/79–1	1979		1	1	3
IRD50/81–1	1981		1	1	3
IRD50/82–1	1982		1	1	3
IRD50/83–1	1983		1	1	3
IRD50/86–2	1986	PROOF or SPECIMEN [2]	1	1	10
IRD50/88–1	1988		1	1	3
IRD50/88–1C	1988		1	2	4
IRD50/88–3C	1988	PROOF [3]	1	2	15
IRD50/96–1	1996		1	1	1
IRD50/97–1	1997		1	1	1
IRD50/98–1	1998		1	1	1

1. Issued in sets.
2. Issued in sets; surplus issued for circulation.
3. Issued cased.

20 Pence

Denomination	Metal	Weight (grams)	Diameter (mm)	Rev. alignment
20 pence	Nickel-bronze (copper 79%; zinc 20%; nickel 1%)	8.6	27.1	↑

Obverse 1 Harp; EIRE (date)

Reverse 1 Hunting horse, facing left; 20P

Edge Alternately, three smooth and three milled segments

Obv. 1   Rev. 1

No.	Date	Features	Obv.	Rev.	UNC
IRD20/86–1	1986		1	1	3
IRD20/86–3	1986	PROOF [1]	1	1	4
IRD20/88–1	1988		1	1	3
IRD20/92–1	1992		1	1	2

No.	Date	Features	Obv.	Rev.	UNC
IRD20/94–1	1994		1	1	2
IRD20/95–1	1995		1	1	1
IRD20/96–1	1996		1	1	1
IRD20/98–1	1998		1	1	1

1. Issued in sets.

10 Pence

Denomination	Metal	Weight (grams)	Diameter (mm)	Rev. alignment
10 pence 1969 – 86	Cupronickel	11.3	28.5	↑
10 pence 1993 –	Cupronickel	6.5	21	↑

Obverse 1 Harp; EIRE (date)
Obverse 2 Similar but on smaller flan
Reverse 1 Salmon, facing right; 10P
Reverse 2 Salmon, facing left; 10P
Edge milled

Obv. 1

Obv. 2

Rev. 1

Rev. 2

No.	Date	Features	Obv.	Rev.	UNC
IRD10/69–1	1969		1	1	2
IRD10/71–1	1971		1	1	3
IRD10/71–2	1971	PROOF or SPECIMEN [1]	1	1	4
IRD10/73–1	1973		1	1	4
IRD10/74–1	1974		1	1	3
IRD10/75–1	1975		1	1	2
IRD10/76–1	1976		1	1	2
IRD10/78–1	1978		1	1	2
IRD10/80–1	1980		1	1	2
IRD10/82–1	1982		1	1	2
IRD10/85–1	1985		1	1	3
IRD10/86–3	1986	PROOF or SPECIMEN [1]	1	1	10
IRD10/93–1	1993		2	2	1
IRD10/94–1	1994		2	2	1
IRD10/95–1	1995		2	2	1
IRD10/96–1	1996		2	2	1
IRD10/97–1	1997		2	2	1
IRD10/98–1	1998		2	2	1

1. Issued in sets.

5 Pence

Denomination	Metal	Weight (grams)	Diameter (mm)	Rev. alignment
5 pence 1969 – 90	Cupronickel	5.65	24	↑
5 pence 1992 –	Cupronickel	3.3	18	↑

Obverse 1 Harp; EIRE (date)
Obverse 2 Similar but on smaller flan
Reverse 1 Bull, facing right; 5P
Reverse 2 Bull, facing left; 5P
Edge milled

Obv. 1

Obv. 2

Rev. 1

Rev. 2

No.	Date	Features	Obv.	Rev.	UNC
IRD05/69–1	1969		1	1	3
IRD05/70–1	1970		1	1	3
IRD05/71–1	1971		1	1	3
IRD05/71–2	1971	PROOF or SPECIMEN [1]	1	1	4
IRD05/74–1	1974		1	1	3
IRD05/75–1	1975		1	1	3
IRD05/76–1	1976		1	1	3
IRD05/78–1	1978		1	1	2
IRD05/80–1	1980		1	1	2
IRD05/82–1	1982		1	1	2
IRD05/85–1	1985		1	1	3
IRD05/86–1	1986		1	1	3
IRD05/86–3	1986	PROOF or SPECIMEN [1]	1	1	4
IRD05/90–1	1990		1	1	2
IRD05/92–1	1992		2	2	1
IRD05/93–1	1993		2	2	1
IRD05/94–1	1994		2	2	1
IRD05/95–1	1995		2	2	1
IRD05/96–1	1996		2	2	1
IRD05/98–1	1998		2	2	1

1. Issued in sets.

2 Pence

The reverse depicts a stylized bird design by Gabriel Hayes based on an illustration in a Bible in the Bibliotheque Nationale, Paris.

Denomination	Metal	Weight (grams)	Diameter (mm)	Rev. alignment
2 pence 1971 – 88	Bronze	7.1	26	↑
2 pence 1990	copper plated steel	7.1	26	↑
2 pence 1992 –	copper plated zinc	7.1	26	↑

Obverse 1 Harp; EIRE (date)

Reverse 1 Stylized design of Celtic bird; 2P

Edge plain

Obv. 1   Rev. 1

No.	Date	Features	Obv.	Rev.	UNC
IRD02/71–1	1971		1	1	2
IRD02/71–3	1971	PROOF or SPECIMEN [1]	1	1	3
IRD02/75–1	1975		1	1	2
IRD02/76–1	1976		1	1	2
IRD02/78–1	1978		1	1	2
IRD02/79–1	1979		1	1	2
IRD02/80–1	1980		1	1	1
IRD02/82–1	1982		1	1	1
IRD02/85–1	1985		1	1	2
IRD02/86–1	1986		1	1	1
IRD02/86–3	1986	PROOF or SPECIMEN [1]	1	1	2
IRD02/88–1	1988		1	1	1
IRD02/90–1	1990		1	1	1
IRD02/92–1	1992		1	1	1
IRD02/95–1	1995		1	1	1
IRD02/96–1	1996		1	1	1
IRD02/98–1	1998		1	1	1

1. Issued in sets.

Penny

The reverse depicts a stylized bird design by Gabriel Hayes based on an illustration in The Book of Kells, Trinity College, Dublin.

Denomination	Metal	Weight (grams)	Diameter (mm)	Rev. alignment
Penny 1971 – 88	Bronze	3.6	20.3	↑
Penny 1990	copper plated steel	3.6	20.3	↑
Penny 1992 –	copper plated zinc	3.6	20.3	↑

Obverse 1 Harp; EIRE (date)

Reverse 1 Stylized design of Celtic bird; 1p

Edge plain

Obv. 1   Rev. 1

No.	Date	Features	Obv.	Rev.	UNC
IRD01/71–1	1971	[1]	1	1	1
IRD01/71–2	1971	PROOF or SPECIMEN [2]	1	1	2
IRD01/74–1	1974		1	1	2
IRD01/75–1	1975		1	1	2
IRD01/76–1	1976		1	1	2
IRD01/78–1	1978		1	1	1
IRD01/79–1	1979		1	1	1
IRD01/80–1	1980		1	1	1
IRD01/82–1	1982		1	1	1
IRD01/85–1	1985		1	1	2
IRD01/86–1	1986		1	1	1

No.	Date	Features	Obv.	Rev.	UNC
IRD01/86–3	1986	PROOF or SPECIMEN [2]	1	1	2
IRD01/88–1	1988		1	1	1
IRD01/90–1	1990		1	1	1
IRD01/92–1	1992		1	1	1
IRD01/93–1	1993		1	1	1
IRD01/94–1	1994		1	1	1
IRD01/95–1	1995		1	1	1
IRD01/96–1	1996		1	1	1
IRD01/98–1	1998		1	1	1

1. Many issued in 1970.
2. Issued in sets.

Halfpenny

The reverse depicts a stylized bird design by Gabriel Hayes based on an illustration in a Celtic manuscript in the Cathedral of Cologne Library.

Denomination	Metal	Weight (grams)	Diameter (mm)	Rev. alignment
Halfpenny	Bronze	1.8	17.1	↑

Obverse 1 Harp; EIRE (date)

Reverse 1 Stylized design of Celtic bird; 1/2P

Edge plain

Obv. 1   Rev. 1

No.	Date	Features	Obv.	Rev.	UNC
IRDHP/71–1	1971	[1]	1	1	1
IRDHP/71–2	1971	PROOF or SPECIMEN [2]	1	1	2
IRDHP/75–1	1975		1	1	2
IRDHP/76–1	1976		1	1	2
IRDHP/78–1	1978		1	1	2
IRDHP/80–1	1980		1	1	2
IRDHP/82–1	1982		1	1	2
IRDHP/86–3	1986	PROOF or SPECIMEN [2]	1	1	8

1. Many issued in 1970.
2. Issued in sets.

The decimal halfpenny ceased to be legal tender after 31 December 1986.

Ireland: Proof Sets

1928

Of 6,001 sets struck, 4,001 were released. Two types of green case were used, a leatherette case and a simple card box.

No.	Date	Striking Standard	No. of coins	Price
IRPS-28	1928	Proof or prooflike	8	120

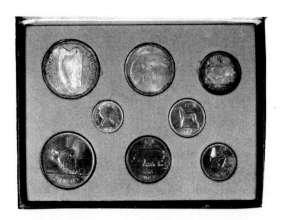

Denomination	Metal
Halfcrown	0.750 silver
Florin	0.750 silver
Shilling	0.750 silver
Sixpence	Nickel
Threepence	Nickel
Penny	Bronze
Halfpenny	Bronze
Farthing	Bronze

1928 re-issue

This restrike set was dated 1928 but, somewhat oddly, was issued in 1962/63. The standard of striking was somewhat superior to that of the original. 100 sets were released.

No.	Date	Striking Standard	No. of coins	Price
IRPS-28R	1928	Proof or prooflike	8	180

Denomination	Metal
Halfcrown	0.750 silver
Florin	0.750 silver
Shilling	0.750 silver
Sixpence	Nickel
Threepence	Nickel
Penny	Bronze
Halfpenny	Bronze
Farthing	Bronze

1966

No.	Date	Striking Standard	No. of coins	Price
IRPS-66	1966	Proof	2	60

Denomination	Metal
10 shillings	0.833 silver
10 shillings	0.833 silver

1971

No.	Date	Striking Standard	No. of coins	Price
IRDPS-71	1971	Proof	6	12

Denomination	Metal
50 pence	Cupronickel
10 pence	Cupronickel
5 pence	Cupronickel
2 pence	Bronze
Penny	Bronze
Halfpenny	Bronze

1986

No.	Date	Striking Standard	No. of coins	Price
IRDPS-86	1986	Proof	7	50

Denomination	Metal
50 pence	Cupronickel
20 pence	Nickel bronze
10 pence	Cupronickel
5 pence	Cupronickel
2 pence	Bronze
Penny	Bronze
Halfpenny	Bronze

Ireland: Specimen Sets

Issued 1966

This somewhat curious set was issued in a green 'fold-over' wallet.

No.	Date	Striking Standard	No. of coins	Price
IRMS-66	Issued 1966; dates on coins vary	Uncirculated	8	5

Denomination	Metal
Halfcrown	Cupronickel
Florin	Cupronickel
Shilling	Cupronickel
Sixpence	Cupronickel
Threepence	Cupronickel
Penny	Bronze
Halfpenny	Bronze
Farthing	Bronze

1971

No.	Date	Striking Standard	No. of coins	Price
IRDMS-71	1971	Specimen	6	8

Denomination	Metal
50 pence	Cupronickel
10 pence	Cupronickel
5 pence	Cupronickel
2 pence	Bronze
Penny	Bronze
Halfpenny	Bronze

1978

No.	Date	Striking Standard	No. of coins	Price
IRDMS-78	1978	Specimen	6	8

Denomination	Metal
50 pence	Cupronickel
10 pence	Cupronickel
5 pence	Cupronickel
2 pence	Bronze
Penny	Bronze
Halfpenny	Bronze

1982

No.	Date	Striking Standard	No. of coins	Price
IRDMS-82	1982	Specimen	6	8

Denomination	Metal
50 pence	Cupronickel
10 pence	Cupronickel
5 pence	Cupronickel
2 pence	Bronze
Penny	Bronze
Halfpenny	Bronze

1996

No.	Date	Striking Standard	No. of coins	Price
IRDMS-96	1996	Specimen	6	8

Denomination	Metal
50 pence	Cupronickel
20 pence	Nickel bronze
10 pence	Cupronickel
5 pence	Cupronickel
2 pence	Copper plated zinc
Penny	Copper plated zinc

Ecus and similar pieces

Ecus, the coins that never were...

With the economic union of the European States, there was a need for a unified currency. During the early part of the 1990s most people believed that it would be called the Ecu, but this was not to be. The EU decided to call the new currency the Euro instead.

Before the choice of name had been officially made, a number of countries and individuals struck many different medallic pieces which they labelled ecus. None of these pieces had any legal tender status but were made for collectors. Some purported to be patterns of what the currency might look like, but none had any official basis for this claim.

The pieces listed below were issued by the International Currency Bureau (ICB) and are included here for completeness. Prices reflect what is currently being charged in the numismatic market. They have become known as 'the coins that never were'.

R.L.

Obv.	Rev.

Obverse Harp with border of 12 stars; 25 ECU

Reverse Cat (on adhesive paper disc); EIRE 1995

Edge plain

Silver Ecu 1992

'Silver Ecu' is a denomination and does not refer to the metal in which the piece is struck.

No.	Date	Denomination	Metal	Weight (grams)	Diameter (mm)	Rev. align.	Current Value
IRSE-92A	1992	Silver Ecu	Cupronickel	20.0	38	↑	8
IRSE-92B	1992	Silver Ecu	Cupronickel	40.0	38	↑	25
IRSE-92C	1992	Silver Ecu	Brass		38	↑	8
IRSE-92D	1992	Silver Ecu	Silver	23.0	38	↑	25
IRSE-92E	1992	Silver Ecu	Silver	46.0	38	↑	45
IRSE-92F	1992	Silver Ecu	Gold		38	↑	295

25 Euro 1995

No.	Date	Denomination	Metal	Weight (grams)	Diameter (mm)	Rev. align.	Current Value
IR25ER-95A	1995	25 Euro	Cupronickel	20.0	38	↑	8
IR25ER-95B	1995	25 Euro	Cupronickel	40.0	38	↑	25
IR25ER-95C	1995	25 Euro	Brass		38	↑	8
IR25ER-95D	1995	25 Euro	Silver	23.0	38	↑	25
IR25ER-95E	1995	25 Euro	Silver	46.0	38	↑	45
IR25ER-95F	1995	25 Euro	Gold		38	↑	295

Obv.	Rev.

Obverse Harp with border of 12 stars; SILVER ECU

Reverse Woman playing harp; SILVER ECU 1992

Edge plain

Obv.	Rev.

Obverse Harp with border of 12 stars; 25 EURO

Reverse Cat (on adhesive paper disc); EIRE 1995

Edge plain

25 Ecu 1995

No.	Date	Denomination	Metal	Weight (grams)	Diameter (mm)	Rev. align.	Current Value
IR25E-95A	1995	25 Ecu	Cupronickel	20.0	38	↑	8
IR25E-95B	1995	25 Ecu	Cupronickel	40.0	38	↑	25
IR25E-95C	1995	25 Ecu	Brass		38	↑	8
IR25E-95D	1995	25 Ecu	Silver	23.0	38	↑	25
IR25E-95E	1995	25 Ecu	Silver	46.0	38	↑	45
IR25E-95F	1995	25 Ecu	Gold		38	↑	295

25 Ecu 1996

No.	Date	Denomination	Metal	Weight (grams)	Diameter (mm)	Rev. align.	Current Value
IR25E-96A	1996	25 Ecu	Cupronickel	20.0	38	↑	8
IR25E-96B	1996	25 Ecu	Cupronickel	40.0	38	↑	25
IR25E-96C	1996	25 Ecu	Brass		38	↑	8
IR25E-96D	1996	25 Ecu	Silver	23.0	38	↑	25
IR25E-96E	1996	25 Ecu	Silver	46.0	38	↑	45
IR25E-96F	1996	25 Ecu	Gold		38	↑	295

| Obv. | Rev. |

Obverse Harp with border of 12 stars; 25 ECU

Reverse Squirrel (on adhesive paper disc); EIRE 1996

Edge plain

25 Euro 1996

No.	Date	Denomination	Metal	Weight (grams)	Diameter (mm)	Rev. align.	Current Value
IR25ER-96A	1996	25 Euro	Cupronickel	20.0	38	↑	8
IR25ER-96B	1996	25 Euro	Cupronickel	40.0	38	↑	25
IR25ER-96C	1996	25 Euro	Brass		38	↑	8
IR25ER-96D	1996	25 Euro	Silver	23.0	38	↑	25
IR25ER-96E	1996	25 Euro	Silver	46.0	38	↑	45
IR25ER-96F	1996	25 Euro	Gold		38	↑	295

Obv.   Rev.

Obverse Harp with border of 12 stars; 25 EURO

Reverse Squirrel (on adhesive paper disc); EIRE 1996

Edge plain

Gunmoney mintage figures, according to James Simon (1749)

Denomination	Face Value £.s.d
Large halfcrown	443,498.10.0
Small halfcrown	127,200. 0.0
Large shilling	245,879.17.0
Small shilling	41,800. 0.0
Small sixpence	49,042. 6.6
Total:	**907,420.13.6**

D. Stevenson (BNJ, XXXVI, 1967) pointed out that this total is only up to 14th June 1690, and that a commonly accepted figure in the 18th century was £965,375 face value. According to other records, 10,451,099 coins totalling £779,759.14.11 were minted between 3rd August 1689 and 17th May 1690.

Letter to the Mint about gunmoney

Athlone, February the 9th 1689

This day the metall was weighed (35.0.24 lb by number at the bottom of this letter) and delivered to the carmen mentioned in the last letter, there is five hundred weight for the last gun they could not carry, and some brass that I have bought, and some brass belonging to absentees, which will be here in a few days and shall be sent by the first carrs that I can procure.

I am, sir, your honour's most humble servant.

Chr. Nicholson.

To the Honourable J. Trindar, Esq.,
Chief Commissioner of His Majesty's Mint.

Undated letter from the Mint, recipient unknown

Sir,

We have great occasion for his majesty's use to procure as much hamered or forged copper and brass as your parts can afford, and judging by the decay of trade and desolation of the country, that there may bee a great deale in your district or port, we desire you, by yourself and officers, to inform us presently what quantity you may bee able to furnish us with, and what the currant prices are of each and whatever you can gett, buy at the best rates you can, and as soon as you have four or five hundred weight, pray send it to us the commissioners of his majesty's mint, at the mint-house in Capel-street, Dublin, and what you pay shall be allowed you in your accounts at the custom house, so doing you'll oblige.

Yours &c.

Gunmoney: number of dies in use

Year and month or mark of month	Large halfcrown	Small halfcrown	Large shilling	Small shilling	Sixpence
1689 Jun					4
1689 Jul	3		5		6
1689 Aug	5		11		7
1689 Sept	9		8		4
1689 7ber					1

Year and month or mark of month	Large halfcrown	Small halfcrown	Large shilling	Small shilling	Sixpence
1689 Oct	5		9		1
1689 8ber	2		4		
1689 Nov	5		7		3
1689 9			3		
1689 9r with castle			1		
1689 Dec	5		6		4
1689 10r	1		2		
1689 Jan	4		6		7
1689 Feb	5		6		4
1689 Mar	4		2		1
1690 Mar	3		4		1
1690 Apr	9	1	4		2
1690 May	4	14		10	2
1690 Jun		4		4	1
1690 Jul		2		1	
1690 Aug		1		1	
1690 Sep		1		1	
1690 Oct		1			1

When James fled from Ireland, there was found at the Mint, according to Lord Coningsby, Vice-Treasurer of Ireland:

Number of coins	Denomination	Face value £.s.d	Devalued value per coin	Devalued total £.s.d
17,292	Crowns	4,323. 0.0	1 penny	72. 1. 0
126,503	Large halfcrowns	15,812.17.6	1 penny	527. 1.11
2,489	Small halfcrowns	311. 2.6	3 farthings	7.15. 6
9,043	Large shillings	452. 3.0	1 halfpenny	18.16. 9
4,757	Small shillings	237.17.0	1 farthing	4.19. 1
6,000	Sixpences	150. 0.0	1 farthing	6. 5. 0
4,808	Pewter crowns	1202. 0.0	1 farthing	5. 0. 0
	Total:	22,489. 0.0	Total:	641.19. 3

Wood's Coinage 1722 – 24

Table of characteristics of samples of coinage taken from parcels sent to Ireland

The different lots	Weight of halfpenny grs.	Number in 1 lb.	Current value 1722 in pence
First sort	120	58.33	29.0
Second sort	111	63.06	31.5
Third sort	103	67.96	33.5
Fourth sort	96	72.91	36.0
Average	107.5	65.11	32.5

	Quantity coined tons	Cost coined £	Current Value £ s	Loss to Public £ s
If as patent provided	360	74420	108000. 0	33580. 0
If first sort coined	360	74420	97994. 8	23574. 8
If second sort coined	360	74420	105940.16	31520.16
If third sort coined	360	74420	114172.16	39572.16
If fourth sort coined	360	74420	122488.16	48068.16
If average coined	360	74420	110149. 4	35729. 4

Irish Free State & Republic: Mintage Information & Figures

Ten shillings

Date	Mintage
1966	2,000,000 [1]
1966	20,000 [2]

1. Non-proof; over 1,200,000 melted down
2. Proof

Halfcrown

Date	Mintage
1928	2,160,000 [1]
1928	6,001 [2]
1930	352,000
1931	160,000
1933	336,000
1934	480,000
1937	40,000
1939	888,000
1940	752,000
1941	320,000
1942	285,600
1943	Not known [3]
1951	800,000
1954	400,000
1955	1,080,000
1959	1,600,000
1961	1,600,000
1962	3,200,000
1963	2,400,000
1964	3,200,000
1966	700,000
1967	2,000,000

1. Non-proof
2. Proof; probably only 4,001 released in 1928
3. Most remelted

Mintages are for non-proof specimens except where noted. For some of the dates above, the British Museum collection contains one proof specimen, and in many cases this is the only known specimen minted.

Florin

Date	Mintage
1928	2,025,000 [1]
1928	6,001 [2]
1930	330,000
1931	200,000
1933	300,000
1934	150,000
1935	390,000
1937	150,000
1939	1,080,000
1940	670,000
1941	400,000
1942	109,000
1943	Not known [3]
1951	1,000,000
1954	1,000,000
1955	1,000,000
1959	2,000,000
1961	2,000,000
1962	2,400,000
1963	3,000,000
1964	4,000,000
1965	2,000,000
1966	3,625,000
1968	1,000,000

1. Non-proof
2. Proof; probably only 4,001 released in 1928
3. Almost all remelted

Mintages are for non-proof specimens except where noted. For some of the dates above, the British Museum collection contains one proof specimen, and in many cases this is the only known specimen minted.

Shilling

Date	Mintage
1928	2,700,000 [1]
1928	6,001 [2]
1930	460,000
1931	400,000
1933	300,000
1935	400,000
1937	100,000
1939	1,140,000
1940	580,000
1941	300,000
1942	286,000
1951	2,000,000
1954	3,000,000
1955	1,000,000
1959	2,000,000
1962	4,000,000
1963	4,000,000
1964	4,000,000
1966	3,000,000
1968	4,000,000

1. Non-proof
2. Proof; probably only 4,001 released in 1928

Mintages are for non-proof specimens except where noted. For some of the dates above, the British Museum collection contains one proof specimen, and in many cases this is the only known specimen minted.

Sixpence

Date	Mintage
1928	3,201,480 [1]
1928	6,001 [2]
1934	600,000
1935	520,000
1939	876,000
1940	1,120,000
1942	1,320,000
1945	400,000

1946	720,000
1947	800,000
1948	800,000
1949	600,000
1950	800,000
1952	800,000
1953	800,000
1955	600,000
1956	600,000
1958	600,000
1959	2,000,000
1960	2,020,000
1961	3,000,000
1962	4,000,000
1963	4,000,000
1964	4,000,000
1966	2,000,000
1967	4,000,000
1968	4,000,000
1969	2,000,000

1. Non-proof
2. Proof; probably only 4,001 released in 1928

Mintages are for non-proof specimens except where noted. For some of the dates above, the British Museum collection contains one proof specimen, and in many cases this is the only known specimen minted.

Threepence

Date	Mintage
1928	1,500,000 [1]
1928	6,001 [2]
1933	320,000
1934	800,000
1935	240,000
1939	64,000
1940	720,000
1942	4,000,000
1943	1,360,000
1946	800,000
1948	1,600,000
1949	1,200,000
1950	1,600,000
1953	1,600,000
1956	1,200,000
1961	2,400,000
1962	3,200,000
1963	4,000,000
1964	6,000,000
1965	3,600,000
1966	4,000,000
1967	2,400,000
1968	4,000,000

1. Non-proof
2. Proof; probably only 4,001 released in 1928

Mintages are for non-proof specimens except where noted. For some of the dates above, the British Museum collection contains one proof specimen, and in many cases this is the only known specimen minted.

Penny

Date	Mintage
1928	9,000,000 [1]
1928	6,001 [2]
1931	2,400,000
1933	1,680,000

1935	5,472,000
1937	5,400,000
1940	312,000
1941	4,680,000
1942	17,580,000
1943	3,360,000
1946	4,800,000
1948	4,800,000
1949	4,080,000
1950	2,400,000
1952	2,400,000
1962	1,200,000
1963	9,600,000
1964	6,000,000
1965	11,160,000
1966	6,000,000
1967	2,400,000
1968	9,000,000

1. Non-proof
2. Proof; probably only 4,001 released in 1928

Mintages are for non-proof specimens except where noted. For some of the dates above, the British Museum collection contains one proof specimen, and in many cases this is the only known specimen minted.

Halfpenny

Date	Mintage
1928	2,880,000 [1]
1928	6,001 [2]
1933	720,000
1935	960,000
1937	960,000
1939	240,000
1940	1,680,000
1941	2,400,000
1942	6,931,200
1943	2,668,800
1946	720,000
1949	1,344,000
1953	2,400,000
1964	2,160,000
1965	1,440,000
1966	1,680,000
1967	1,200,000

1. Non-proof
2. Proof; probably only 4,001 released in 1928

Mintages are for non-proof specimens except where noted. For some of the dates above, the British Museum collection contains one proof specimen, and in many cases this is the only known specimen minted.

Farthing

Date	Mintage
1928	300,000 [1]
1928	6,001 [2]
1930	288,000
1931	192,000
1932	192,000
1933	480,000
1935	192,000
1936	192,000
1937	480,000
1939	768,000
1940	192,000
1941	480,000

1943	480,000
1944	480,000
1946	480,000
1949	192,000
1953	192,000
1959	192,000
1966	96,000 [3]

1. Non-proof
2. Proof; probably only 4,001 released in 1928
3. All issued in specimen sets

Mintages are for non-proof specimens except where noted. For some of the dates above, the British Museum collection contains one proof specimen, and in many cases this is the only known specimen minted.

Decimal 50 pence

Date	Mintage
1970	9,000,000
1971	600,000 [1]

1. 50,000 issued on polished blanks in wallet specimen sets.

Decimal 10 pence

Date	Mintage
1969	27,000,000
1971	4,000,000 [1]

1. 50,000 issued on polished blanks in wallet specimen sets.

Decimal 5 pence

Date	Mintage
1969	5,000,000
1970	10,000,000
1971	8,000,000 [1]

1. 50,000 issued on polished blanks in wallet specimen sets.

Decimal 2 pence

Date	Mintage
1971	75,500,000 [1]

1. 50,000 issued on polished blanks in wallet specimen sets.

Decimal penny

Date	Mintage
1971	100,500,000 [1]

1. 50,000 issued on polished blanks in wallet specimen sets.

Decimal halfpenny

Date	Mintage
1971	100,500,000

1. 50,000 issued on polished blanks in wallet specimen sets.

Channel Islands

Channel Islands: Celtic Coinage – Armorican Issues

Between 75 and 50 BC, billon coins were struck in Northwest France and the Channel Islands. All issues show a bust on the obverse and a horse on the reverse. While it is uncertain where these coins were struck, they circulated in some quantity in the Channel Islands and several large hoards have been found there. Two denominations were struck, the stater and quarter stater.

Stater

Collecting Hints

Due to the fact that several large hoards have been found, these coins are fairly common and are usually found in Fine condition. They are often found corroded and should only be cleaned by experts. These coins should never be polished or 'buffed' up as their pink copper content makes them look unsightly.

Obverse   Right-facing head.
Reverse   A horse with a boar below, Victory above, often with driver.

C1ST-005	VG £30	F £60	VF £130

Obverse   As previous.
Reverse   As previous, but no driver, horse's lash-ends made up of pellets.

C1ST-010	VG £30	F £60	VF £130

Obverse   Bust with an anchor-shaped nose.
Reverse   As C1ST-005.

C1ST-015	VG £30	F £65	VF £140

Obverse   As C1ST-005.
Reverse   Horse with reins, a lyre below the horse, lash-ends in three prongs.

C1ST-020	VG £30	F £65	VF £140

Obverse   As previous.
Reverse   As previous, but lash-ends in a long cross with four pellets.

C1ST-025	VG £30	F £60	VF £130

Obverse   As previous.
Reverse   Horse with boar below, lash-ends in the form of ladders.

C1ST-030	VG £35	F £70	VF £160

Quarter Stater

Collecting Hints

This issue is much scarcer than the stater and usually found in Fine condition.

Obverse   Right-facing bust.
Reverse   Horse.

C1QST-005	VG £40	F £100	VF £200

Jersey: Crown

Elizabeth II (1952 —)

Denomination	Metal	Weight (grams)	Diameter (mm)	Rev. alignment
Crown	Cupronickel	28.3 – 28.4	39	↑

Obverse 1 Head 1, right; QUEEN ELIZABETH THE SECOND

Reverse 1 Arms of Jersey; BAILIWICK OF JERSEY 1066 1966 FIVE SHILLINGS (for the 900th anniversary of the accession of William the Conqueror)

Edge milled

Obv. 1   Rev. 1

No.	Date	Features	Obv.	Rev.	UNC
JEL2CR-005	1966		1	1	2
JEL2CR-010	1966	PROOF [1]	1	1	4

1. Issued in cased double-crown sets.

Jersey: Three Shillings Token

George III   (1760 – 1820)

The token coinage of 1813 was authorized by the Council of the States of Jersey on 18th November 1812, with a purchase of silver bullion valued at £10,000 to provide tokens denominated at three shillings and at eighteen pence. The tokens were designed by Thomas Wyon, junior and struck at the Royal Mint; a total of £13,620 face value, to include both denominations, was struck. If these were struck in the ratio of one three shilling tokens to two eighteen pence token, the mintage figures would have been 45,400 and 90,800 respectively.

Much of the issue disappeared from circulation. A considerable number of the tokens were exported to Canada, where they circulated at a premium, but their use in Guernsey was prohibited by a Guernsey ordinance of 9th March 1813.

The tokens remained in circulation, at least in theory, until October 1834, when a decision was taken to circulate British currency. The pieces were withdrawn throughout 1834, finally leaving £1,363 face value unaccounted for.

Denomination	Metal	Weight (grams)	Diameter (mm)	Rev. alignment
Three shillings token	0.892 silver	12.8 – 12.9	35	↑

Obverse 1   Arms of Jersey; STATES OF JERSEY 1813

Reverse 1   Oak wreath encircling THREE SHILLINGS TOKEN

Edge   plain

Obv. 1   Rev. 1

No.	Date	Features	Obv.	Rev.	F	VF	EF	UNC
JG33S-005	1813		1	1	60	100	300	700
JG33S-010	1813	PROOF	1	1				
JG33S-015	1813	PROOF in copper	1	1				

Jersey: Eighteen Pence Token

George III   (1760 – 1820)

See the entry for the 1813 three shillings token. It is possible that the mintage figure for this denomination was around 90,000.

Denomination	Metal	Weight (grams)	Diameter (mm)	Rev. alignment
Eighteen pence token	0.892 silver	6.4	26.5	↑

Obverse 1   Arms of Jersey; STATES OF JERSEY 1813

Reverse 1   Oak wreath encircling EIGHTEEN PENCE TOKEN

Edge   plain

Obv. 1

Rev. 1

No.	Date	Features	Obv.	Rev.	F	VF	EF	UNC
JG318D-005	1813		1	1	40	70	180	400
JG318D-010	1813	PROOF	1	1				

Jersey: One Fourth Shilling: Threepence

Elizabeth II (1952 —)				
Denomination	Metal	Weight (grams)	Diameter (mm)	Rev. alignment
1/4 shilling 1957 – 60	Nickel-brass	4.8 – 4.9	21	↑
1/4 shilling 1964 – 66	Nickel-brass	6.7 – 6.8	21 side to side, 22 corner to corner	↑

Obverse 1   Head 1, right; QUEEN ELIZABETH THE SECOND (on round flan)

Obverse 2   Similar but on 12-sided flan

Reverse 1   Arms of Jersey flanked by divided date; BAILIWICK OF JERSEY ONE FOURTH OF A SHILLING

Reverse 2   Similar but on 12-sided flan

Reverse 3   Similar but dates 1066 1966 straddle the shield (for the 900th anniversary of the accession of William the Conqueror)

Edge   plain

Obv. 1

Obv. 2

Rev. 1

Rev. 2

Rev. 3

No.	Date	Features	Obv.	Rev.	UNC
JEL23D-005	1957		1	1	2
JEL23D-010	1957	PROOF [1]	1	1	6
JEL23D-015	1960	PROOF [1]	1	1	6
JEL23D-020	1964		2	2	1
JEL23D-025	1964	PROOF [1]	2	2	3
JEL23D-030	1966		2	3	1
JEL23D-035	1966	PROOF [1]	2	3	2

1. Issued in cased sets.

Jersey: One Thirteenth Shilling: One Twelfth Shilling: 'Penny'

The largest unit of the new Victorian coinage, this denomination was authorized by an Order in Council of 11th September 1840 and first struck at the Royal Mint in 1841, designed by William Wyon and obviously modelled on the British penny. Interestingly, the coin of 1861 was of a similar type, even though the British coin had by then been converted to the smaller bronze issue. The changeover to bronze came in 1866, and the large copper issue was withdrawn in 1869. The denomination change to the 1/12th shilling followed in 1877. The 1866 and 1877 issues were designed by L. C. Wyon, and the weight and diameter were standardized with the British penny.

In preparation for designing the 1877 issue, Wyon wrote to the Mint in 1876 to ask what the animals on the shield were supposed to be; if they are leopards, why were they not required to have spots? The Bailiff of Jersey, on being consulted, replied that they were lions according to the seal granted to Jersey by Edward I, and that spots on some previous coinage had been an error.

The early 1/13th shilling coins are difficult to find in top condition. The Elizabeth II series includes an interesting 'mule' proof of 1960, and it is always worth checking the obverse of any proof penny of this date. The 1960 penny is a somewhat unusual commemorative piece in that it celebrates the tercentenary of the Restoration of Charles II. Jersey had always championed the Royalist cause, unlike its neighbour Guernsey which supported the Commonwealth.

Obv. 1   Obv. 2

Rev. 1   Rev. 2

Victoria (1837 – 1901)

Denomination	Metal	Weight (grams)	Diameter (mm)	Rev. alignment
1/13 shilling 1841 – 65	Copper	17.4 – 17.8	34	↑
1/13 shilling 1866 – 71	Bronze (copper 95%; tin 4%; zinc 1%)	9.3 – 9.5	29	↑
1/12 shilling 1877 – 94	Bronze (copper 95%; tin 4%; zinc 1%)	9.4 – 9.6	31	↑

To maintain the weight, the one-twelfth shilling is very slightly thinner than the one-thirteenth shilling 1866–1871.

Obverse 1   Head 1, left; VICTORIA D G BRITANNIAR REGINA F D (date)

Obverse 2   Head 2, left; same legend (date)

Obverse 3   Head 2, left, star below; same legend but no date

Reverse 1   Arms on shield; STATES OF JERSEY 1/13 OF A SHILLING

Reverse 2   Similar Arms on shield; STATES OF JERSEY ONE THIRTEENTH OF A SHILLING

Reverse 3   Very different Arms on shield dividing (date); STATES OF JERSEY ONE TWELFTH OF A SHILLING

Edge   plain

No.	Date	Features	Obv.	Rev.	F	VF	EF	UNC
JV1D-005	1841		1	1	6	15	50	120
JV1D-010	1841	PROOF	1	1				250
JV1D-015	1844		1	1	8	20	70	150
JV1D-020	1844	PROOF	1	1				400
JV1D-025	1851		1	1	8	20	70	150
JV1D-030	1851	PROOF	1	1				400
JV1D-035	1858		1	1	7	18	60	140
JV1D-040	1858	PROOF	1	1				300
JV1D-045	1861		1	1	8	20	70	150
JV1D-050	1861	PROOF	1	1				400
JV1D-055	1865	PROOF [1]	1	1				900
JV1D-060	1866		2	2	4	8	24	60
JV1D-065	1866	PROOF; LCW incuse on truncation	2	2				150
JV1D-070	1866	PROOF; plain truncation [2]	2	2				400
JV1D-075	1870	[2]	2	2	4	8	24	60
JV1D-080	1870	PROOF [2]	2	2				150
JV1D-085	1871	[2]	2	2	4	8	24	60
JV1D-090	1871	PROOF [2]	2	2				150
JV1D-095	1877	'H' mintmark below head (obv) [3]	3	3	2	4	14	35
JV1D-100	1877	PROOF; 'H' mintmark below head (obv) [3]	3	3				130
JV1D-105	1877	PROOF in nickel; 'H' mintmark below head (obv) [2]	3	3				800
JV1D-110	1877	PROOF; no mintmark below head (obv)	3	3				150
JV1D-115	1877	PROOF in nickel; no mintmark below head (obv)	3	3				800
JV1D-120	1881	[4]	3	3	3	6	20	60
JV1D-125	1888		3	3	2	4	16	40
JV1D-130	1894		3	3	2	4	14	35
JV1D-135	1894	PROOF	3	3				150

1. At least one specimen weighs 19.2 grams.

Notes continued
2. The copper in the bronze used came from withdrawn copper coins.
3. Struck at Ralph Heaton and Sons, Birmingham.
4. 75,120 struck at the Royal Mint using bronze from 249,600 withdrawn 1877 forty-eighth shillings.

Edward VII   (1901 – 1910)

This issue is unusual in having the obverse legend in English rather than in Latin.

Denomination	Metal	Weight (grams)	Diameter (mm)	Rev. alignment
1/12 shilling	Bronze (copper 95%; tin 4%; zinc 1%)	9.4 – 9.6	31	↑

Obverse 1   Head 1, right; EDWARD VII KING & EMPEROR

Reverse 1   Arms on shield dividing (date); STATES OF JERSEY ONE TWELFTH OF A SHILLING

Edge   plain

Obv. 1   Rev. 1

No.	Date	Features	Obv.	Rev.	F	VF	EF	UNC
JE71D-005	1909		1	1	3	6	20	60

George V   (1910 – 1936)

Denomination	Metal	Weight (grams)	Diameter (mm)	Rev. alignment
1/12 shilling	Bronze (copper 95%; tin 4%; zinc 1%)	9.3 – 9.6	31	↑

Obverse 1   Head 1, left; GEORGIVS V D G BRITT OMN REX F D IND IMP

Reverse 1   Arms on shield dividing (date); STATES OF JERSEY ONE TWELFTH OF A SHILLING

Reverse 2   A very different Arms on shield dividing (date); STATES OF JERSEY ONE TWELFTH OF A SHILLING on two scrolls.

Reverse 3   Similar but legends not on scrolls.

Edge   plain

Obv. 1   Rev. 1

Rev. 2   Rev. 3

No.	Date	Features	Obv.	Rev.	F	VF	EF	UNC
JG51D-005	1911		1	1	1	3	8	18
JG51D-010	1913		1	1	1	3	8	18
JG51D-015	1923		1	1	1	3	8	18
JG51D-020	1923	1	1	2	1	3	9	20
JG51D-025	1926		1	2	1	3	8	18
JG51D-030	1931		1	3	1	2	5	12
JG51D-035	1931	PROOF	1	3				150
JG51D-040	1933	2	1	3	1	2	4	10
JG51D-045	1933	PROOF	1	3				130
JG51D-050	1935		1	3	1	2	4	10
JG51D-055	1935	PROOF	1	3				130

1. Struck from bronze obtained from French coinage circulating in Jersey.
2. Exists with 176 and 177 obverse border beads.

George VI   (1937 – 1952)

Denomination	Metal	Weight (grams)	Diameter (mm)	Rev. alignment
1/12 shilling	Bronze (copper 95%; tin 4%; zinc 1%)	9.4 – 9.6	31	↑

Obverse 1   Head 1, left; GEORGIVS VI D G BRITT OMN REX F D IND IMP

Obverse 2   Head 1, left; GEORGIVS VI DEI GRA BRITT OMN REX FID DEF

Reverse 1   Arms on shield dividing (date); STATES OF JERSEY ONE TWELFTH OF A SHILLING

Reverse 2   Smaller Arms on shield; ISLAND OF JERSEY LIBERATED 1945 ONE TWELFTH OF A SHILLING

Edge   plain

Obv. 1   Obv. 2

Rev. 1   Rev. 2

No.	Date	Features	Obv.	Rev.	VF	EF	UNC
JG61D-005	1937		1	1	1	3	6
JG61D-010	1937	PROOF	1	1			150
JG61D-015	1946		1	1	1	3	5
JG61D-020	1946	PROOF	1	1			130
JG61D-025	1947		1	1	1	2	4
JG61D-030	1947	PROOF	1	1			120
JG61D-035	[1]		2	2			3
JG61D-040	[1]	PROOF	2	2			130

1. Undated; issued in 1949, 1950, 1952. The date 1945 on the reverse signifies the date of liberation of Jersey from Germany.

Rev. 3   Rev. 4

No.	Date	Features	Obv.	Rev.	UNC
JEL21D-005	[1]		1	1	2
JEL21D-010	1957		2	2	1
JEL21D-015	1957	PROOF [2]	2	2	6
JEL21D-020	1960		2	3	1
JEL21D-025	1960	PROOF [2]	1	3	60
JEL21D-030	1960	PROOF [2]	2	3	5
JEL21D-035	1964		2	2	1
JEL21D-040	1964	PROOF [2]	2	2	3
JEL21D-045	1966		2	4	1
JEL21D-050	1966	PROOF [2]	2	4	2

1. Undated; issued in 1954. The date 1945 on the reverse signifies the date of liberation of Jersey from Germany.
2. Issued in cased sets.

Elizabeth II   (1952 —)

Denomination	Metal	Weight (grams)	Diameter (mm)	Rev. alignment
1/12 shilling	Bronze (copper 95%; tin 4%; zinc 1%)	9.4 – 9.6	31	↑

Obverse 1   Head 1, right; QUEEN ELIZABETH THE SECOND (legend begins at top right)

Obverse 2   Head 1, smaller, right; same legend but begins at bottom left.

Reverse 1   Arms on shield; ISLAND OF JERSEY LIBERATED 1945 ONE TWELFTH OF A SHILLING

Reverse 2   Larger Arms on shield dividing (date); BAILIWICK OF JERSEY ONE TWELFTH OF A SHILLING

Reverse 3   Smaller Arms on shield; CIIR 1660–1960 EIIR BAILIWICK OF JERSEY ONE TWELFTH OF A SHILLING (for the tercentenary of the Restoration of Charles II)

Reverse 4   Larger Arms on shield; 1066 1966 BAILIWICK OF JERSEY ONE TWELFTH OF A SHILLING (for the 900th anniversary of the Battle of Hastings)

Edge   plain

Obv. 1   Obv. 2

Rev. 1   Rev. 2

Jersey: One Twentysixth Shilling:
One Twentyfourth Shilling: 'Halfpenny'

This denomination was first issued in 1841 alongside the one-thirteenth of a shilling. Its issue closely follows that of the larger coin. The obverse die is identical to that used for the Gibraltar 2 quarts of 1841 and 1842.

Rev. 2   Rev. 3

No.	Date	Features	Obv.	Rev.	F	VF	EF	UNC
JVHD-005	1841		1	1	5	12	40	100
JVHD-010	1841	PROOF	1	1				200
JVHD-015	1844		1	1	5	12	40	100
JVHD-020	1851		1	1	5	12	35	90
JVHD-025	1858	[1]	1	1	5	12	35	90
JVHD-030	1858	PROOF	1	1				150
JVHD-035	1861		1	1	4	10	30	80
JVHD-040	1861	PROOF	1	1				140
JVHD-045	1866		2	2	2	4	12	30
JVHD-050	1866	PROOF	2	2				120
JVHD-055	1870	[2]	2	2	2	4	12	30
JVHD-060	1870	PROOF [2]	2	2				120
JVHD-065	1871	[2]	2	2	2	5	14	35
JVHD-070	1871	PROOF [2]	2	2				120
JVHD-075	1877	'H' mintmark below head (obv) [3]	3	3	1	2	5	16
JVHD-080	1877	PROOF; 'H' mintmark below head (obv) [3]	3	3				100
JVHD-085	1877	PROOF; no mintmark below head (obv)	3	3				120
JVHD-090	1888		3	3	1	2	5	16
JVHD-095	1894		3	3	1	2	5	16
JVHD-100	1894	PROOF	3	3				120

1. On some pieces a die flaw appears to make the denomination read 1/20 OF A SHILLING but the upper arc in the centre of the 6 is still visible.
2. The copper in the bronze used came from withdrawn copper coins.
3. Struck at Ralph Heaton and Sons, Birmingham.

Victoria   (1837 – 1901)

Denomination	Metal	Weight (grams)	Diameter (mm)	Rev. alignment
1/26 shilling 1841 – 61	Copper	8.7 – 8.9	28	↑
1/26 shilling 1866 – 71	Bronze (copper 95%; tin 4%; zinc 1%)	4.6 – 4.7	24	↑
1/24 shilling 1877 – 94	Bronze (copper 95%; tin 4%; zinc 1%)	5.7	25.5	↑

Obverse 1   Head 1, left; VICTORIA D G BRITANNIAR REGINA F D (date)

Obverse 2   Head 2, left; same legend (date)

Obverse 3   Head 2, left, star below; same legend but no date

Reverse 1   Arms on shield; STATES OF JERSEY 1/26 OF A SHILLING

Reverse 2   Similar Arms on shield; STATES OF JERSEY ONE TWENTY-SIXTH OF A SHILLING

Reverse 3   Very different Arms on shield dividing (date); STATES OF JERSEY ONE TWENTY-FOURTH OF A SHILLING

Edge   plain

Edward VII   (1901 – 1910)

Denomination	Metal	Weight (grams)	Diameter (mm)	Rev. alignment
1/24 shilling	Bronze (copper 95%; tin 4%; zinc 1%)	5.7	25.5	↑

Obverse 1   Head 1, right; EDWARD VII KING & EMPEROR

Reverse 1   Arms on shield dividing (date); STATES OF JERSEY ONE TWENTY-FOURTH OF A SHILLING

Edge   plain

Obv. 1   Obv. 2

Obv. 3   Rev. 1

Obv. 1   Rev. 1

No.	Date	Features	Obv.	Rev.	F	VF	EF	UNC
JE7HD-005	1909		1	1	3	7	24	70

George V (1910 – 1936)

Denomination	Metal	Weight (grams)	Diameter (mm)	Rev. alignment
1/24 shilling	Bronze (copper 95%; tin 4%; zinc 1%)	5.7	25.5	↑

Obverse 1 Head 1, left; GEORGIVS V D G BRITT OMN REX F D IND IMP

Reverse 1 Arms on shield dividing (date); STATES OF JERSEY ONE TWENTY-FOURTH OF A SHILLING

Reverse 2 A very different Arms on shield dividing (date); STATES OF JERSEY ONE TWENTYFOURTH OF A SHILLING on two scrolls

Reverse 3 Similar but legends not on scrolls

Edge plain

Obv. 1   Rev. 1

Rev. 2   Rev. 3

No.	Date	Features	Obv.	Rev.	F	VF	EF	UNC
JG5HD-005	1911		1	1	1	3	7	16
JG5HD-010	1913		1	1	1	3	7	16
JG5HD-015	1923		1	1	1	4	8	20
JG5HD-020	1923	[1]	1	2	1	3	7	16
JG5HD-025	1923	PROOF [1]	1	2				100
JG5HD-030	1926		1	2	1	2	5	10
JG5HD-035	1926	PROOF	1	2				100
JG5HD-040	1931		1	3	1	2	4	8
JG5HD-045	1931	PROOF	1	3				130
JG5HD-050	1933		1	3	1	2	4	8
JG5HD-055	1933	PROOF	1	3				120
JG5HD-060	1935		1	3	1	2	4	8
JG5HD-065	1935	PROOF	1	3				120

1. Struck from bronze obtained from French coinage circulating in Jersey; darker than previous issues.

George VI (1937 – 1952)

Denomination	Metal	Weight (grams)	Diameter (mm)	Rev. alignment
1/24 shilling	Bronze (copper 95%; tin 4%; zinc 1%)	5.7	25.5	↑

Obverse 1 Head 1, left; GEORGIVS VI D G BRITT OMN REX F D IND IMP

Reverse 1 Arms on shield dividing (date); STATES OF JERSEY ONE TWENTYFOURTH OF A SHILLING

Edge plain

Obv. 1   Rev. 1

No.	Date	Features	Obv.	Rev.	VF	EF	UNC
JG6HD-005	1937		1	1	1	2	5
JG6HD-010	1937	PROOF	1	1			120
JG6HD-015	1946		1	1	1	2	5
JG6HD-020	1946	PROOF	1	1			120
JG6HD-025	1947		1	1	1	2	5
JG6HD-030	1947	PROOF	1	1			120

Jersey: One Fifty-Second Shilling: One Forty-Eighth Shilling: 'Farthing'

The scarcest of the regular series, this denomination was struck only during the reign of Victoria, and is broadly equivalent to the British copper and bronze farthing issues. Most of the 1877 pieces were returned to the Royal Mint and recoined into twelfth shillings dated 1881.

Victoria (1837 – 1901)					
Denomination	Metal	Weight (grams)	Diameter (mm)	Rev. alignment	
1/52 shilling 1841 – 61	Copper	4.4	22	↑	
1/48 shilling 1877	Bronze (copper 95%; tin 4%; zinc 1%)	2.8	20	↑	

Obverse 1   Head 1, left; VICTORIA D G BRITANNIAR REGINA F D (date)

Obverse 2   Head 2, left, star below; same legend but no date

Reverse 1   Arms on shield; STATES OF JERSEY 1/52 OF A SHILLING

Reverse 2   Very different Arms on shield dividing 18 77; STATES OF JERSEY ONE 48TH OF A SHILLING

Edge   plain

Obv. 1

Obv. 2

Rev. 1

Rev. 2

No.	Date	Features	Obv.	Rev.	F	VF	EF	UNC
JVFA-005	1841	latter 1 over 0	1	1	18	45	80	160
JVFA-010	1841	PROOF; latter 1 over 0	1	1				500
JVFA-015	1861	PROOF	1	1				700
JVFA-020	1861	PROOF in bronze	1	1				1000
JVFA-025	1877	'H' mintmark below head (obv) [1] [2]	2	2	8	20	50	120
JVFA-030	1877	PROOF; 'H' mintmark below head (obv) [1]	2	2				100
JVFA-035	1877	PROOF; no mintmark below head (obv)	2	2				300

1. Struck at Ralph Heaton and Sons, Birmingham.
2. 249,600 withdrawn and sent to Royal Mint in May 1881 for recoining into 75,120 twelfth shillings dated 1881; 38,400 were left in circulation.

Jersey: Decimal Coinage

The introduction of decimal currency into Jersey closely followed the British pattern. In early 1969, 10 and 5 pence pieces dated 1968 were placed into circulation alongside the British florins and shillings which had been used for some time. The 50 pence (dated 1969) was introduced some months later, and the Guernsey and Jersey ten shilling notes lapsed gradually from November 1970 by allowing those in circulation to become worn out. Decimal Day was the same as in the United Kingdom, 15th February 1971.

Obv. 3

Rev. 3

No.	Date	Features	Obv.	Rev.	UNC
JD50P/72–1	1972	1	1	1	200
JD50P/72–6	1972	PROOF, individually numbered on edge 1 to 1500 [1]	1	1	240
JD50P/90–6	1990	PROOF [2]	2	2	250
JD50P/95–6	1995	PROOF [2]	3	3	250

1. Issued in cased sets. Struck at the York Mint, Birmingham.
2. Issued in cased sets.

100 Pounds

Denomination	Metal	Weight (grams)	Diameter (mm)	Rev. alignment
100 pounds	0.999 gold	31.2	33	↑

Obverse 1 Head 1, right; ELIZABETH II BAILIWICK OF JERSEY 100 POUNDS

Obverse 2 Head 1, right; QUEEN ELIZABETH THE SECOND (date)

Reverse 1 Spitfire flying over United Kingdom (for the 50th anniversary of the Battle of Britain)

Reverse 2 Dove flying over Jersey; BAILIWICK OF JERSEY LIBERATION 9 MAY 1945 1995 ONE HUNDRED POUNDS (for the 50th anniversary of liberation from Germany)

Edge milled

No.	Date	Features	Obv.	Rev.	UNC
JD100P/90 – 6	1990	PROOF [1]	1	1	500
JD100P/95 – 6	1995	PROOF [1]	2	2	500

1. Issued in cased sets.

50 Pounds

Denomination	Metal	Weight (grams)	Diameter (mm)	Rev. alignment
50 pounds 1972	0.917 gold	22.6 – 23.1	31	↑
50 pounds 1990 – 95	0.999 gold	15.6	27	↑

Obverse 1 Head 1, right; QUEEN ELIZABETH THE SECOND SILVER WEDDING 1972

Obverse 2 Head 2, right; ELIZABETH II BAILIWICK OF JERSEY 50 POUNDS

Obverse 3 Head 2, right; QUEEN ELIZABETH THE SECOND (date)

Reverse 1 Arms on shield; BAILIWICK OF JERSEY FIFTY POUNDS

Reverse 2 Royal Air Force badge (for the 50th anniversary of the Battle of Britain)

Reverse 3 Islander and British Armed Forces soldier shaking hands and holding flags; BAILIWICK OF JERSEY LIBERATION 9 MAY 1945 V 1995 FIFTY POUNDS (for the 50th anniversary of liberation from Germany)

Edge milled

25 Pounds

Denomination	Metal	Weight (grams)	Diameter (mm)	Rev. alignment
25 pounds 1972	0.917 gold	11.9 – 12.1	25	↑
25 pounds 1990 – 95	0.999 gold	7.8	22	↑

Obverse 1 Head 1, right; QUEEN ELIZABETH THE SECOND SILVER WEDDING 1972

Obverse 2 Head 2, right; ELIZABETH II BAILIWICK OF JERSEY 25 POUNDS

Obverse 3 Head 2, right; QUEEN ELIZABETH THE SECOND (date)

Reverse 1 Coat of Arms of Queen Elizabeth I at Elizabeth Castle; ROYAL ARMS 1593 ELIZABETH CASTLE; BAILIWICK OF JERSEY TWENTY FIVE POUNDS

Reverse 2 Spitfire over United Kingdom

Reverse 3 Islanders with flags; BAILIWICK OF JERSEY LIBERATION 9 MAY 1945 1995 TWENTY FIVE POUNDS (for the 50th anniversary of liberation from Germany)

Edge milled

Obv. 1

Obv. 3

Rev. 1   Rev. 3

No.	Date	Features	Obv.	Rev.	UNC
JD25P/72–1	1972	[1]	1	1	110
JD25P/72–6	1972	PROOF [1] [2]	1	1	140
JD25P/90–6	1990	PROOF [3]	2	2	150
JD25P/95–6	1995	PROOF [3]	3	3	150

1. Issued in cased sets. Struck at the York Mint, Birmingham.
2. Some examples weigh up to 12.4 grams.
3. Issued in cased sets.

20 Pounds

Denomination	Metal	Weight (grams)	Diameter (mm)	Rev. alignment
20 pounds	0.917 gold	9.3	22.5	↑

Obverse 1   Head 1, right; QUEEN ELIZABETH THE SECOND SILVER WEDDING 1972

Reverse 1   Ormer shell; BAILIWICK OF JERSEY TWENTY POUNDS

Edge   milled

Obv. 1   Rev. 1

No.	Date	Features	Obv.	Rev.	UNC
JD20P/72–1	1972	[1]	1	1	85
JD20P/72–6	1972	PROOF [1] [2]	1	1	110

1. Issued in cased sets. Struck at the York Mint, Birmingham.
2. Some examples weigh up to 9.8 grams.

10 Pounds

Denomination	Metal	Weight (grams)	Diameter (mm)	Rev. alignment
10 pounds 1972	0.917 gold	4.6 – 4.7	18	↑
10 pounds 1990	0.999 gold	3.1	16.5	↑
10 pounds 1995	0.999 gold	3.2	16.5	↑

Obverse 1   Head 1, right; QUEEN ELIZABETH THE SECOND SILVER WEDDING 1972

Obverse 2   Head 2, right; ELIZABETH II BAILIWICK OF JERSEY 10 POUNDS

Obverse 3   Head 2, right; QUEEN ELIZABETH THE SECOND (date)

Reverse 1   Gold torque of c. 1500 BC; BAILIWICK OF JERSEY TEN POUNDS

Reverse 2   Royal Air Force badge; 1940 1990 THE BATTLE OF BRITAIN 50TH ANNIVERSARY

Reverse 3   Red Cross vessel 'Vega'; BAILIWICK OF JERSEY LIBERATION 9 MAY 1945 – 1995 TEN POUNDS (for the 50th anniversary of liberation from Germany)

Edge   milled

Obv. 1   Obv. 3   Rev. 1   Rev. 3

No.	Date	Features	Obv.	Rev.	UNC
JD10P/72–1	1972	[1]	1	1	50
JD10P/72–6	1972	PROOF [1] [2]	1	1	55
JD10P/90–6	1990	PROOF [3]	2	2	70
JD10P/95–6	1995	PROOF [3]	3	3	70

1. Issued in cased sets. Struck at the York Mint, Birmingham.
2. Some examples weigh up to 5.0 grams.
3. Issued in cased sets.

5 Pounds

Denomination	Metal	Weight (grams)	Diameter (mm)	Rev. alignment
5 pounds 1972	0.917 gold	2.6 – 2.7	14.5	↑
5 pounds 1990	0.925 silver	155.6	65	↑
5 pounds 1997	Cupronickel	28.3	39	↑

Obverse 1   Head 1, right; QUEEN ELIZABETH THE SECOND SILVER WEDDING 1972

Obverse 2   Head 2, right; ELIZABETH II BAILIWICK OF JERSEY FIVE POUNDS

Obverse 3   (details not available)

Reverse 1   Lesser white-toothed shrew; BAILIWICK OF JERSEY FIVE POUNDS

Reverse 2   Spitfire over map of Britain; BATTLE OF BRITAIN 50TH ANNIVERSARY 1940 – 1990

Reverse 3   Conjoined heads of Elizabeth and Philip with Arms and view of Westminster Abbey; 1947 ELIZABETH AND PHILIP 1997 FIVE POUNDS (for the Queen's Golden Wedding Anniversary)

Edge   milled

Obv. 1   Rev. 1

Obv. 2

Obv. 1   Rev. 1

No.	Date	Features	Obv.	Rev.	UNC
JD2P50/72–1	1972	[1]	1	1	8
JD2P50/72–4	1972	PROOF [1]	1	1	10

1. Issued in cased sets. Struck at the York Mint, Birmingham.

---

2 Pounds

Denomination	Metal	Weight (grams)	Diameter (mm)	Rev. alignment
2 pounds 1972	0.925 silver	21.7 – 21.9	36	↑
2 pounds 1981	Nickel-silver [1]	28.0 – 28.3	39	↑
2 pounds 1985 – 96	Cupronickel	28.3	38 – 39	↑
2 pounds 1997 –	Cupronickel inset in nickel brass	12.0	28	↑

1. Nickel-silver is a nickel alloy which has a silvery appearance. It contains no silver, although this fact is not widely publicized.

Obverse 1   Head 1, right; QUEEN ELIZABETH THE SECOND SILVER WEDDING 1972

Obverse 2   Head 1, right; QUEEN ELIZABETH II BAILIWICK OF JERSEY TWO POUNDS

Obverse 3   Head 2, right; QUEEN ELIZABETH THE SECOND (date)

Obverse 4   Head 2, larger, right; ELIZABETH II BAILIWICK OF JERSEY TWO POUNDS

Obverse 5   Head 2, similar; QUEEN ELIZABETH THE SECOND TWO POUNDS

Obverse 6   Head 3, same legend

Obverse 7   Head 4, same legend

Reverse 1   Sailing ship 'Alexandra'; BAILIWICK OF JERSEY TWO POUNDS

Reverse 2   Heads of Charles and Diana; ROYAL WEDDING JULY 29 1981

Reverse 3   HMS Beagle; BAILIWICK OF JERSEY HMS BEAGLE LIBERATION 9 MAY 1945 – 1985 TWO POUNDS

Reverse 4   Athletes; BAILIWICK OF JERSEY TWO POUNDS 1986 (for the XIII Commonwealth Games, Edinburgh)

Reverse 5   Mauritius Pink pigeons on branches; BAILIWICK OF JERSEY TWO POUNDS WORLD WILDLIFE FUND 25TH ANNIVERSARY

Reverse 6   Jersey Mace overlaid on map of the island; BAILIWICK OF JERSEY TWO POUNDS VISIT OF HM QUEEN ELIZABETH II

Reverse 7   Spitfire over map of Britain; BATTLE OF BRITAIN 50TH ANNIVERSARY 1940 – 90

Reverse 8   Two intertwined 'E's, crown above, flanked by sprays; QUEEN ELIZABETH THE QUEEN MOTHER 1900 1990 (for the 90th Birthday of the Queen Mother)

Rev. 2

No.	Date	Features	Obv.	Rev.	UNC
JD5P/72–1	1972	[1]	1	1	30
JD5P/72–6	1972	PROOF [1] [2]	1	1	35
JD5P/90–4	1990	PROOF [3]	2	2	60
JD5P/97–1	1997		3	3	10
JD5P/97–4	1997	PROOF in silver with gold plated Arms [4]	3	3	40

1. Issued in cased sets. Struck at the York Mint, Birmingham.
2. Some examples weigh up to 3.1 grams.
3. Issued in cased sets.
4. Issued cased.

---

2 Pounds 50 Pence

Denomination	Metal	Weight (grams)	Diameter (mm)	Rev. alignment
2 pounds 50 pence	0.925 silver	27.1 – 27.3	40	↑

Obverse 1   Head 1, right; QUEEN ELIZABETH THE SECOND SILVER WEDDING 1972

Reverse 1   Lobster; BAILIWICK OF JERSEY TWO POUNDS FIFTY PENCE

Edge   milled

Reverse 9 Crown and sceptre with Arms on shield; BAILIWICK OF JERSEY CORONATION ANNIVERSARY OF QUEEN ELIZABETH II 1953 1993

Reverse 10 Dove flanked by large 'V', ribbon below inscribed 1945–1995; BAILIWICK OF JERSEY LIBERATION 9 MAY TWO POUNDS (for the 50th anniversary of liberation from Germany)

Reverse 11 Jersey Lily

Reverse 12 £2 within Parish shields; BAILIWICK OF JERSEY (date)

Edges (1986) XIII COMMONWEALTH GAMES (incuse)

(1989) 25TH MAY 1989 (twice, in very fine incuse letters)

(1997 –) INSULA CAESAREA (incuse on milling)

(others) milled

Rev. 4   Rev. 5

Rev. 6   Rev. 8

Obv. 1   Obv. 2

Obv. 3   Obv. 4

Obv. 6   Obv. 7

Rev. 1   Rev. 2

Rev. 10   Rev. 12

No.	Date	Features	Obv.	Rev.	UNC
JD2P/72–1	1972	[1]	1	1	6
JD2P/72–4	1972	PROOF [1] [2]	1	1	8
JD2P/81–1	1981		2	2	3
JD2P/81–4	1981	PROOF in 0.925 silver [3]	2	2	30
JD2P/81–6	1981	PROOF in 0.917 gold [4]	2	2	200
JD2P/85–1	1985		3	3	3
JD2P/85–4	1985	PROOF in 0.925 silver [3]	3	3	25
JD2P/85–6	1985	PROOF in 0.917 gold [3]	3	3	800
JD2P/86–1	1986		3	4	3
JD2P/86–1A	1986	no edge inscription	3	4	5
JD2P/86–1B	1986	struck in 0.500 silver	3	4	8
JD2P/86–4	1986	PROOF in 0.925 silver [3]	3	4	25
JD2P/87–1	1987		3	5	3
JD2P/87–4	1987	PROOF in 0.925 silver [3]	3	5	25
JD2P/89–1	1989	[5]	3	6	3
JD2P/89–4	1989	PROOF in 0.925 silver [3] [4]	3	6	25
JD2P/90–4A	1990	PROOF in 0.925 silver [3]	4	7	25
JD2P/90–1	1990		4	8	3
JD2P/90–4	1990	PROOF in 0.925 silver [3]	4	8	30
JD2P/90–6	1990	PROOF in 0.917 gold [4]	4	8	400
JD2P/93–1	1993		5	9	3
JD2P/93–4	1993	PROOF in 0.925 silver [3]	5	9	25
JD2P/93–6	1993	PROOF in 0.917 gold [4]	5	9	300
JD2P/95–1	1995		3	10	3
JD2P/95–4	1995	PROOF in 0.925 silver [3]	3	10	30
JD2P/95–5	1995	PIEDFORT PROOF in 0.925 silver [6]	3	10	70
JD2P/96–1	1996		N/A	11	3
JD2P/96–4	1996	PROOF in 0.925 silver [3]	N/A	11	25
JD2P/97–1	1997		6	12	3

No.	Date	Features	Obv.	Rev.	UNC
JD2P/97-4	1997	PROOF in 0.925 silver with outer ring gold plated [3]	6	12	30
JD2P/98-1	1998		7	12	3

1. Issued in cased sets. Struck at the York Mint, Birmingham.
2. Some examples weigh up to 22.6 grams.
3. Issued cased.
4. Weight 16.0 grams; diameter 28.4 mm; issued cased.
5. The mace depicted on the reverse was presented by Charles II to Jersey on 28th November 1663 for hospitality during his exile.
6. Weight 56.6 grams; issued cased.

Pound

The pound coins, struck to the specification of the United Kingdom pound, commemorate the Battle of Jersey and the twelve Parishes of Jersey, in decreasing order of population size according to the 1981 census. Some were made available in presentation wallets which included descriptions of the Parishes commemorated.

The 1981 coin depicts the Badge of the Royal Jersey Militia, which defeated the French attack force on 6th January 1781. Most of the battle centred on Royal Square, St. Helier, where the leaders of the French and Jersey forces were both killed.

The Parishes commemorated on the later coins are:

ST. HELIER: This Parish, on the south coast, was named after the hermit Saint who lived in a cave on an islet. He was murdered in A.D. 555 by Saxon marauders and the axes of the emblem are the weapons used. Today, St. Helier is the principal town of Jersey and a major offshore banking centre.

ST. SAVIOUR: The Parish, in the east of Jersey, is both a church and a civil division of the island. The church of St. Saviour dates back to the 11th century.

ST. BRELADE: This Parish lies in the south-west corner of Jersey, and has the longest coastline of any of the Parishes. The lighthouse at La Corbiere features on the decimal 20 pence coin.

ST. CLEMENT: This is geographically the smallest of the twelve Parishes and lies just east of St. Helier, in the south-east of the island. La Motte, near the shore, used to contain neolithic graves and the area is renowned as the meeting place of witches. Victor Hugo, the centenary of whose death falls in 1985, the year of issue of the St. Clement pound, lived at 3 Marine Terrace.

ST. LAWRENCE: This Parish lies in the centre of Jersey and includes Waterworks Valley.

ST. PETER: The emblem represents the keys of Heaven in the charge of St. Peter. The Parish, in western Jersey, includes two separate coastlines and also the present-day airport.

GROUVILLE: The Parish emblem comprises eight alternate bands of silver and red and dates back to Louis XI of France. Grouville lies to the south-east of the island and possesses an excellent sandy beach with many rocks visible at low tide. Queen Victoria allowed the prefix 'Royal' to be added to the Bay of Grouville on her visit in 1859.

ST. MARTIN: The emblem of St. Martin le vieux (A.D. 1042) is seven alternate silver and red bands. The Parish, in the east of Jersey, is agricultural and includes Mont Orgueil Castle.

ST. OUEN: The emblem, dating back to A.D. 1053, is a golden cross upon a blue background. St. Ouen is located at the northwest corner of Jersey. It is the only parish divided into the ancient cueillette regions, rather than the vingtaines of other parishes.

TRINITY: The emblem, La Sainte Trinite, dates to A.D. 1090 and symbolizes the Trinity, with initials of Pater, Filius, Spiritus Sanctus, and Deus. Trinity is a large Parish towards the centre of the island, but has few inhabitants. It includes Bouley Bay, a major tourist venue.

ST. JOHN: The emblem, St. Jean des Chenes, dates from A.D. 1090 and takes the form of a silver cross of the Knights of St. John of Jerusalem on a green background. St. John is at the north of the island and commands views to Guernsey, Herm, Sark and France.

ST. MARY: The emblem of this Parish dates to A.D. 1042 and is a silver Jersey Lily on a blue field. St. Mary, in the western half of the island, is not large, but is renowned for its superb views and attractive beach.

Denomination	Metal	Weight (grams)	Diameter (mm)	Rev. alignment
Pound 1972	0.925 silver	10.8 – 11.2	30	↑
Pound 1981	Cupronickel	9.0	(a)25 (b)30	↑
Pound 1983 –	Nickel brass	9.5	22.5	↑

The 1981 pound is square with rounded corners. Measurements are (a) side to side; (b) corner to corner. The weights of the 1981 and later proofs in precious metals are: 1981 silver = 10.45 grams; 1981 gold = 17.55 grams; 1983 – 1994 gold = 19.65 grams; 1983 – 1994 silver = 11.7 grams

Obverse 1   Head 1, right; QUEEN ELIZABETH THE SECOND SILVER WEDDING 1972

Obverse 2   Head 1, right; QUEEN ELIZABETH THE SECOND BAILIWICK OF JERSEY

Obverse 3   Head 1, right; QUEEN ELIZABETH THE SECOND (date)

Obverse 4   Head 2, same legend (date)

Reverse 1   Jersey lily; BAILIWICK OF JERSEY ONE POUND

Reverse 2   Crowned Arms over cross; BICENTENARY OF THE BATTLE OF JERSEY 1781 1981 ONE POUND

Reverse 3   Arms of St. Helier; BAILIWICK OF JERSEY PARISH OF ST. HELIER ONE POUND

Reverse 4   Arms of St. Saviour; BAILIWICK OF JERSEY PARISH OF ST. SAVIOUR ONE POUND

Reverse 5   Arms of St. Brelade; BAILIWICK OF JERSEY PARISH OF ST. BRELADE ONE POUND

Reverse 6   Arms of St. Clement; BAILIWICK OF JERSEY PARISH OF ST. CLEMENT ONE POUND

Reverse 7   Arms of St. Lawrence; BAILIWICK OF JERSEY PARISH OF ST. LAWRENCE ONE POUND

Reverse 8   Arms of St. Peter; BAILIWICK OF JERSEY PARISH OF ST. PETER ONE POUND

Reverse 9   Arms of Grouville; BAILIWICK OF JERSEY PARISH OF GROUVILLE ONE POUND

Reverse 10   Arms of St. Martin; BAILIWICK OF JERSEY PARISH OF ST. MARTIN ONE POUND

Reverse 11   Arms of St. Ouen; BAILIWICK OF JERSEY PARISH OF ST. OUEN ONE POUND

Reverse 12   Arms of Trinity; BAILIWICK OF JERSEY PARISH OF TRINITY ONE POUND

Reverse 13   Arms of St. John; BAILIWICK OF JERSEY PARISH OF ST. JOHN ONE POUND

Reverse 14   Arms of St. Mary; BAILIWICK OF JERSEY PARISH OF ST. MARY ONE POUND

Reverse 15   Schooner 'The Tickler'; BAILIWICK OF JERSEY ONE POUND

Reverse 16   Sailing ship 'Percy Douglas'; same legend

Reverse 17   Sailing ship 'Hebe'; same legend

Reverse 18   Coat of Arms; same legend

Reverse 19   Sailing ship 'Gemini'; same legend

Reverse 20   Sailing ship 'Century'; same legend

Reverse 21 Schooner 'Resolute'; same legend

Edges (1972) milled; (1981) plain; (1983 –) INSULA CAESAREA incuse on milling

Obv. 1   Obv. 2

Obv. 3   Obv. 4

Rev. 1   Rev. 2

Rev. 3   Rev. 4

Rev. 5   Rev. 6

Rev. 7   Rev. 8

Rev. 9   Rev. 10

Rev. 11   Rev. 12

Rev. 13   Rev. 14

Rev. 16   Rev. 21

No.	Date	Features	Obv.	Rev.	UNC
JD1P/72–1	1972	[1]	1	1	3
JD1P/72–4	1972	PROOF [1] [2]	1	1	4
JD1P/81–1	1981	[3]	2	2	2
JD1P/81–3	1981	PROOF	2	2	3
JD1P/81–4	1981	PROOF in 0.925 silver [4]	2	2	5
JD1P/81–6	1981	PROOF in 0.917 gold [4]	2	2	200
JD1P/83–1	1983		3	3	2
JD1P/83–2	1983	SPECIMEN [5]	3	3	4
JD1P/83–4	1983	PROOF in 0.925 silver [4]	3	3	7
JD1P/83–6	1983	PROOF in 0.917 gold [4]	3	3	200
JD1P/84–1	1984		3	4	2
JD1P/84–2	1984	SPECIMEN [5]	3	4	4
JD1P/84–4	1984	PROOF in 0.925 silver [4]	3	4	7
JD1P/84–6	1984	PROOF in 0.917 gold [4]	3	4	200
JD1P/84–1A	1984		3	5	2
JD1P/84–2A	1984	SPECIMEN [5]	3	5	4
JD1P/84–4A	1984	PROOF in 0.925 silver [4]	3	5	7
JD1P/84–6A	1984	PROOF in 0.917 gold [4]	3	5	200
JD1P/85–1	1985		3	6	2
JD1P/85–2	1985	SPECIMEN [5]	3	6	4
JD1P/85–4	1985	PROOF in 0.925 silver [4]	3	6	7
JD1P/85–6	1985	PROOF in 0.917 gold [4]	3	6	200
JD1P/85–1A	1985		3	7	2
JD1P/85–2A	1985	SPECIMEN [5]	3	7	4
JD1P/85–4A	1985	PROOF in 0.925 silver [4]	3	7	7
JD1P/85–6A	1985	PROOF in 0.917 gold [4]	3	7	200
JD1P/86–1	1986		3	8	2
JD1P/86–2	1986	SPECIMEN [5]	3	8	4
JD1P/86–4	1986	PROOF in 0.925 silver [4]	3	8	7
JD1P/86–6	1986	PROOF in 0.917 gold [4]	3	8	200
JD1P/86–1A	1986		3	9	2
JD1P/86–2A	1986	SPECIMEN [5]	3	9	4
JD1P/86–4A	1986	PROOF in 0.925 silver [4]	3	9	7
JD1P/86–6A	1986	PROOF in 0.917 gold [4]	3	9	200
JD1P/87–1	1987		3	10	2
JD1P/87–2	1987	SPECIMEN [5]	3	10	4
JD1P/87–4	1987	PROOF in 0.925 silver [4]	3	10	7

No.	Date	Features	Obv.	Rev.	UNC
JD1P/87–6	1987	PROOF in 0.917 gold [4]	3	10	200
JD1P/87–1A	1987		3	11	2
JD1P/87–2A	1987	SPECIMEN [5]	3	11	4
JD1P/87–4A	1987	PROOF in 0.925 silver [4]	3	11	7
JD1P/87–6A	1987	PROOF in 0.917 gold [4]	3	11	200
JD1P/88–1	1988		3	12	2
JD1P/88–2	1988	SPECIMEN [5]	3	12	4
JD1P/88–4	1988	PROOF in 0.925 silver [4]	3	12	7
JD1P/88–6	1988	PROOF in 0.917 gold [4]	3	12	200
JD1P/88–1A	1988		3	13	2
JD1P/88–2A	1988	SPECIMEN [5]	3	13	4
JD1P/88–4A	1988	PROOF in 0.925 silver [4]	3	13	7
JD1P/88–6A	1988	PROOF in 0.917 gold [4]	3	13	200
JD1P/89–1	1989		3	14	2
JD1P/89–2	1989	SPECIMEN [5]	3	14	4
JD1P/89–4	1989	PROOF in 0.925 silver [4]	3	14	7
JD1P/89–6	1989	PROOF in 0.917 gold [4]	3	14	200
JD1P/91–1	1991		3	15	2
JD1P/91–2	1991	SPECIMEN [5]	3	15	4
JD1P/91–4	1991	PROOF in 0.925 silver [4]	3	15	7
JD1P/91–6	1991	PROOF in 0.917 gold [4]	3	15	200
JD1P/91–1A	1991		3	16	2
JD1P/91–2A	1991	SPECIMEN [5]	3	16	4
JD1P/91–4A	1991	PROOF in 0.925 silver [4]	3	16	7
JD1P/91–6A	1991	PROOF in 0.917 gold [4]	3	16	200
JD1P/92–1	1992		3	17	2
JD1P/92–2	1992	SPECIMEN [5]	3	17	4
JD1P/92–4	1992	PROOF in 0.925 silver [4]	3	17	7
JD1P/92–6	1992	PROOF in 0.917 gold [4]	3	17	200
JD1P/92–1A	1992		3	18	2
JD1P/92–2A	1992	SPECIMEN [5]	3	18	4
JD1P/92–4A	1992	PROOF in 0.925 silver [4]	3	18	7
JD1P/92–6A	1992	PROOF in 0.917 gold [4]	3	18	200
JD1P/93–1	1993		3	19	2
JD1P/93–2	1993	SPECIMEN [5]	3	19	4
JD1P/93–4	1993	PROOF in 0.925 silver [4]	3	19	7
JD1P/93–6	1993	PROOF in 0.917 gold [4]	3	19	200
JD1P/93–1A	1993		3	20	2
JD1P/93–2A	1993	SPECIMEN [5]	3	20	4
JD1P/93–4A	1993	PROOF in 0.925 silver [4]	3	20	7
JD1P/93–6A	1993	PROOF in 0.917 gold [4]	3	20	200
JD1P/94–1	1994		3	21	2
JD1P/94–2	1994	SPECIMEN [5]	3	21	4
JD1P/94–4	1994	PROOF in 0.925 silver [4]	3	21	7
JD1P/94–6	1994	PROOF in 0.917 gold [4]	3	21	200
JD1P/97–1	1997		3	21	2
JD1P/97–2	1997	SPECIMEN [5]	3	21	4
JD1P/98–1	1998		4	21	2

1. Issued in cased sets. Struck at the York Mint, Birmingham.
2. Some examples weigh up to 11.6 grams.
3. Some issued in presentation wallets.
4. Issued cased.
5. Issued in card holder.

50 Pence

Denomination	Metal	Weight (grams)	Diameter (mm)	Rev. alignment
50 pence 1972	0.925 silver	5.4 – 5.5	23	↑
50 pence 1969, 1980 – 97 obv. 3	Cupronickel	13.5	30 [1]	↑
50 pence 1997 obv. 5	Cupronickel	8.0	27 [1]	↑

1. This coin is seven-sided but the diameter from any point on the edge across the centre of the face is constant.

Obverse 1 Head 1, right; QUEEN ELIZABETH THE SECOND

Obverse 2 Head 1, right; QUEEN ELIZABETH THE SECOND SILVER WEDDING 1972

Obverse 3 Head 1, right; QUEEN ELIZABETH THE SECOND (date)

Obverse 4 Head 2, right; same legend

Obverse 5 As obverse 3 but on smaller flan

Reverse 1 Arms on shield; BAILIWICK OF JERSEY FIFTY NEW PENCE (date)

Reverse 2 Jersey Mace overlaid on map of the island; BAILIWICK OF JERSEY FIFTY PENCE

Reverse 3 Arms on shield dividing date 19 81; BAILIWICK OF JERSEY FIFTY PENCE

Reverse 4 Grosnez Castle gatehouse; same legend

Reverse 5 Crossed flags above chain; BAILIWICK OF JERSEY LIBERATION FIFTY PENCE 1945 1985 (for the 40th anniversary of liberation of Jersey from Germany)

Reverse 6 As reverse 4 but on smaller flan

Edges (1972) milled; (others) plain

Obv. 1   Obv. 2

Obv. 3   Obv. 4

Obv. 5

Rev. 1   Rev. 2

Rev. 3   Rev. 4

Rev. 5   Rev. 6

No.	Date	Features	Obv.	Rev.	UNC
JD50/69–1	1969		1	1	2
JD50/72–1	1972	[1]	2	2	3
JD50/72–4	1972	PROOF [1] [2]	2	2	4
JD50/80–1	1980		1	1	3
JD50/80–2	1980	PROOF [3] [4]	1	1	3
JD50/81–1	1981		1	3	3
JD50/81–2	1981	PROOF [3] [4]	1	3	3
JD50/83–1	1983		3	4	3
JD50/83–4	1983	PROOF in 0.925 silver [3] [5]	3	4	3
JD50/84–1	1984		3	4	3
JD50/85–1	1985		4	5	2
JD50/86–1	1986		3	4	2
JD50/87–1	1987		3	4	2
JD50/88–1	1988		3	4	2
JD50/89–1	1989		3	4	2
JD50/90–1	1990		3	4	1
JD50/90–2	1990	PROOF	3	4	3
JD50/92–1	1992	[3]	3	4	2
JD50/94–1	1994		3	4	1
JD50/97–1L	1997	[3]	3	4	2
JD50/97–1S	1997		5	6	1
JD50/98–1	1998		5	6	1

1. Issued in cased sets. Struck at the York Mint, Birmingham.
2. Some examples are slightly overweight.
3. Issued in cased sets.
4. Some examples exhibit semi-circular edge markings.
5. Weight 15.7 grams.

The 30mm diameter coin ceased to be legal tender after 30th April 1998.

25 Pence

Denomination	Metal	Weight (grams)	Diameter (mm)	Rev. alignment
25 pence	Cupronickel	28.3	39	↑

Obverse 1   Head 1, right; QUEEN ELIZABETH THE SECOND 1952 – 1977 (for the Queen's Silver Jubilee)

Reverse 1   Mont Orgeuil Castle and Gorey Harbour; BAILIWICK OF JERSEY TWENTY FIVE PENCE

Edge   milled

Obv. 1   Rev. 1

No.	Date	Features	Obv.	Rev.	UNC
JD25/77–1	1977		1	1	2
JD25/77–4	1977	PROOF in 0.925 silver [1]	1	1	18

1. Issued cased. Some examples are slightly underweight.

20 Pence

La Corbiere lighthouse, depicted on this coin, lies to the south-west of Jersey and was the first concrete lighthouse built in the British Isles.

Denomination	Metal	Weight (grams)	Diameter (mm)	Rev. alignment
20 pence	Cupronickel	5.0	21[1]	↑

1. This coin is seven-sided but the diameter from any point on the edge across the centre of the face is constant.

Obverse 1   Head 1, right; QUEEN ELIZABETH THE SECOND

Obverse 2   Head 1, smaller, right; same legend (date)

Reverse 1   La Corbiere Lighthouse, 1982 incuse below; BAILIWICK OF JERSEY TWENTY PENCE

Reverse 2   Similar but no date; same legend

Edge   plain

Obv. 1   Obv. 2

Rev. 1   Rev. 2

No.	Date	Features	Obv.	Rev.	UNC
JD20/82–1	1982		1	1	1
JD20/82–4	1982	PROOF in 0.925 silver [1]	1	1	3
JD20/82–5	1982	PIEDFORT PROOF in 0.925 silver [2]	1	1	15
JD20/83–1	1983		2	2	1
JD20/83–4	1983	PROOF in 0.925 silver [1]	2	2	3
JD20/84–1	1984		2	2	1
JD20/86–1	1986		2	2	1
JD20/87–1	1987		2	2	1
JD20/89–1	1989		2	2	1
JD20/90–1	1990		2	2	1
JD20/90–2	1990	PROOF	2	2	2
JD20/92–1	1992	[3]	2	2	2
JD20/94–1	1994		2	2	1
JD20/96–1	1996		2	2	1
JD20/97–1	1997		2	2	1
JD20/98–1	1998		2	2	1

1. Issued cased. Weight 5.8 grams.
2. Issued cased. Weight 11.6 grams.
3. Issued in wallet sets.

10 Pence				
Denomination	Metal	Weight (grams)	Diameter (mm)	Rev. alignment
10 pence 1968	Cupronickel	11.0	28.5	↑
10 pence 1975 – 90	Cupronickel	11.2 – 11.5	28.5	↑
10 pence 1992	Cupronickel	6.5	24.5	↑

Obverse 1   Head 1, right; QUEEN ELIZABETH THE SECOND

Obverse 2   Head 2, right; same legend but larger lettering (date)

Obverse 3   As obverse 2 on smaller flan

Reverse 1   Arms on shield; BAILIWICK OF JERSEY TEN NEW PENCE (date)

Reverse 2   Arms on shield dividing date 19 81; BAILIWICK OF JERSEY TEN PENCE

Reverse 3   La Hougue Bie, Faldouet, St. Martin; same legend

Reverse 4   As reverse 3 on smaller flan

Edge   milled

Obv. 1   Obv. 2   Obv. 3

Rev. 2   Rev. 3   Rev. 4

No.	Date	Features	Obv.	Rev.	UNC
JD10/68–1	1968		1	1	1
JD10/75–1	1975	Early type [1]	1	1	2
JD10/75–1A	1975	Late type [1]	1	1	1
JD10/80–1	1980		1	1	1
JD10/80–2	1980	PROOF [2] [3]	1	1	2
JD10/81–1	1981		1	2	1
JD10/81–2	1981	PROOF [2] [3]	1	2	2
JD10/83–1	1983		2	3	1
JD10/83–4	1983	PROOF in 0.925 silver [2] [4]	2	3	5
JD10/84–1	1984		2	3	1
JD10/85–1	1985		2	3	1
JD10/86–1	1986		2	3	1
JD10/87–1	1987		2	3	1
JD10/88–1	1988		2	3	1
JD10/89–1	1989		2	3	1
JD10/90–1	1990		2	3	1
JD10/90–2	1990	PROOF	2	3	2
JD10/92–1	1992	[5]	3	4	1
JD10/97–1	1997		3	4	1
JD10/98–1	1998		3	4	1

1. Early type issued in 1975; late type issued in 1979 with marginally thicker flan following problems with coin-operated machinery.
2. Issued in cased sets.
3. Some examples exhibit semi-circular edge markings.
4. Weight 13.6 grams.
5. Introduced on 1st September 1992.

The 28.5 mm diameter coin ceased to be legal tender after 30th June 1993.

5 Pence				
Denomination	Metal	Weight (grams)	Diameter (mm)	Rev. alignment
5 pence 1968 – 88	Cupronickel	5.7	24	↑
5 pence 1990 –	Cupronickel	3.25	18	↑

Obverse 1   Head 1, right; QUEEN ELIZABETH THE SECOND

Obverse 2   Head 2, right; same legend but larger lettering (date)

Obverse 3   As obverse 2 on smaller flan

Reverse 1   Arms on shield; BAILIWICK OF JERSEY FIVE NEW PENCE (date)

Reverse 2   Arms on shield dividing date 19 81; BAILIWICK OF JERSEY FIVE PENCE

Reverse 3   Seymour Tower, Grouville Bay; same legend

Reverse 4   As reverse 3 on smaller flan

Edge   milled

Obv. 1   Obv. 2   Obv. 3

Rev. 1

Rev. 2   Rev. 3   Rev. 4

No.	Date	Features	Obv.	Rev.	UNC
JD05/68–1	1968		1	1	1
JD05/80–1	1980		1	1	1
JD05/80–2	1980	PROOF [1] [2]	1	1	2
JD05/81–1	1981		1	2	1
JD05/81–2	1981	PROOF [1] [2]	1	2	2
JD05/83–1	1983		2	3	1
JD05/83–4	1983	PROOF in 0.925 silver [1] [3]	2	3	4
JD05/84–1	1984		2	3	1
JD05/85–1	1985		2	3	1
JD05/86–1	1986		2	3	1
JD05/87–1	1987	[4]	2	3	2
JD05/88–1	1988		2	3	1
JD05/90–1	1990	[5]	3	4	1
JD05/91–1	1991		3	4	1
JD05/92–1	1992		3	4	1
JD05/93–1	1993		3	4	1
JD05/97–1	1997		3	4	1
JD05/98–1	1998		3	4	1

1. Issued in cased sets.
2. Some examples exhibit semi-circular edge markings.
3. Weight 6.6 grams.
4. Issued in wallet sets.

Notes continued
5. Introduced on 27th June 1990.

The 24 mm diameter coin ceased to be legal tender after 31st December 1990.

2 Pence

Denomination	Metal	Weight (grams)	Diameter (mm)	Rev. alignment
2 pence 1971 – 92	Bronze	7.0 – 7.3	26	↑
2 pence 1997 –	Copper-plated steel	7.1	26	↑

Obverse 1   Head 1, right; QUEEN ELIZABETH THE SECOND

Obverse 2   Head 2, right; same legend but larger lettering (date)

Reverse 1   Arms on shield; BAILIWICK OF JERSEY TWO NEW PENCE (date)

Reverse 2   Arms on shield dividing date 19 81; BAILIWICK OF JERSEY TWO PENCE

Reverse 3   L'Hermitage, St. Helier; same legend

Edge   plain

Obv. 1   Obv. 2

Rev. 1   Rev. 2   Rev. 3

No.	Date	Features	Obv.	Rev.	UNC
JD02/71–1	1971		1	1	1
JD02/75–1	1975	[1]	1	1	1
JD02/80–1	1980		1	1	1
JD02/80–2	1980	PROOF [2] [3]	1	1	2
JD02/81–1	1981		1	2	1
JD02/81–2	1981	PROOF [2] [3]	1	2	2
JD02/83–1	1983		2	3	1
JD02/83–4	1983	PROOF in 0.925 silver [2] [4]	2	3	4
JD02/84–1	1984		2	3	1
JD02/85–1	1985		2	3	1
JD02/86–1	1986		2	3	1
JD02/87–1	1987		2	3	1
JD02/88–1	1988		2	3	1
JD02/89–1	1989		2	3	1
JD02/90–1	1990		2	3	1
JD02/90–2	1990	PROOF	2	3	2
JD02/92–1	1992	[5]	2	3	2
JD02/92–2	1992	PROOF	2	3	1
JD02/97–1	1997		2	3	1
JD02/98–1	1998		2	3	1

1. Issued in 1976 and 1979.
2. Issued in cased sets.
3. Some examples exhibit semi-circular edge markings.
4. Weight 8.4 grams.
5. Issued in wallet sets.

Penny

Denomination	Metal	Weight (grams)	Diameter (mm)	Rev. alignment
Penny 1971	Bronze	3.5	20.3	↑
Penny 1980 – 92	Bronze	3.6	20.3	↑
Penny 1994 –	Copper plated steel	3.6	20.3	↑

Obverse 1   Head 1, right; QUEEN ELIZABETH THE SECOND

Obverse 2   Head 2, right; same legend but larger lettering (date)

Reverse 1   Arms on shield; BAILIWICK OF JERSEY ONE NEW PENNY (date)

Reverse 2   Arms on shield dividing date 19 81; BAILIWICK OF JERSEY ONE PENNY

Reverse 3   Le Hocq Tower, St. Clement; same legend

Edge   plain

Obv. 1   Obv. 2

Rev. 2   Rev. 3

No.	Date	Features	Obv.	Rev.	UNC
JD01/71–1	1971		1	1	1
JD01/80–1	1980		1	1	1
JD01/80–2	1980	PROOF [1]	1	1	2
JD01/81–1	1981		1	2	1
JD01/81–2	1981	PROOF [1] [2]	1	2	2
JD01/83–1	1983		2	3	1
JD01/83–4	1983	PROOF in 0.925 silver [1] [3]	2	3	4
JD01/84–1	1984		2	3	1
JD01/85–1	1985		2	3	1
JD01/86–1	1986		2	3	1
JD01/87–1	1987		2	3	1
JD01/88–1	1988		2	3	1
JD01/89–1	1989		2	3	1
JD01/90–1	1990		2	3	1
JD01/90–2	1990	PROOF	2	3	2
JD01/92–1	1992	[4]	2	3	2
JD01/92–2	1992	PROOF	2	3	2
JD01/94–1	1994		2	3	1
JD01/97–1	1997		2	3	1
JD01/98–1	1998		2	3	1

1. Issued in cased sets.
2. Some examples exhibit semi-circular edge markings.
3. Weight 4.2 grams.
4. Issued in wallet sets.

Halfpenny

Denomination	Metal	Weight (grams)	Diameter (mm)	Rev. alignment
Halfpenny 1971	Bronze	1.7	17	↑
Halfpenny 1980 – 81	Bronze	1.8	17	↑

Obverse 1   Head 1, right; QUEEN ELIZABETH THE SECOND

Reverse 1   Arms on shield; BAILIWICK OF JERSEY HALF NEW
PENNY (date)

Reverse 2   Arms on shield dividing date 19 81; BAILIWICK OF
JERSEY HALF PENNY

Edge   plain

Obv. 1

Rev. 1

Rev. 2

No.	Date	Features	Obv.	Rev.	UNC
JDHP/71–1	1971		1	1	1
JDHP80–1	1980		1	1	1
JDHP80–2	1980	PROOF [1]	1	1	2
JDHP81–1	1981		1	2	1
JDHP81–2	1981	PROOF [1] [2]	1	2	2

1. Issued in cased sets.
2. Some examples exhibit semi-circular edge markings.

Jersey: Proof Sets

1957

No.	Date	Striking Standard	No. of coins	Price
JPS-57	1957	Proof	4	25

Denomination	Metal
Fourth shilling	Nickel brass
Fourth shilling	Nickel brass
Twelfth shilling	Bronze
Twelfth shilling	Bronze

1960

No.	Date	Striking Standard	No. of coins	Price
JPS-60A	1960	Proof	4	140

Denomination	Metal
Fourth shilling	Nickel brass
Fourth shilling	Nickel brass
Twelfth shilling [1]	Bronze
Twelfth shilling [1]	Bronze

1. Type with obverse 1.

1960

No.	Date	Striking Standard	No. of coins	Price
JPS-60	1960	Proof	4	20

Denomination	Metal
Fourth shilling	Nickel brass
Fourth shilling	Nickel brass
Twelfth shilling [1]	Bronze
Twelfth shilling [1]	Bronze

1. Type with obverse 2.

1964

No.	Date	Striking Standard	No. of coins	Price
JPS-64	1964	Proof	4	10

Denomination	Metal
Fourth shilling	Nickel brass
Fourth shilling	Nickel brass
Twelfth shilling	Bronze
Twelfth shilling	Bronze

1966

No.	Date	Striking Standard	No. of coins	Price
JPS-66	1966	Proof	4	5

Denomination	Metal
Fourth shilling	Nickel brass
Fourth shilling	Nickel brass
Twelfth shilling	Bronze
Twelfth shilling	Bronze

1966

No.	Date	Striking Standard	No. of coins	Price
JPS-66CR	1966	Proof	2	8

Denomination	Metal
Crown	Cupronickel
Crown	Cupronickel

1972

No.	Date	Striking Standard	No. of coins	Price
JDPS-72	1972	Proof [1]	9	550

1. Although officially denoted as proofs, this set would be more accurately described as prooflike, and it is difficult to distinguish it from the specimen set which was issued in an identical case.

Denomination	Metal
50 pounds	0.917 gold
25 pounds	0.917 gold
20 pounds	0.917 gold
10 pounds	0.917 gold
5 pounds	0.917 gold
2 pounds 50 pence	0.925 silver
2 pounds	0.925 silver
Pound	0.925 silver
50 pence	0.925 silver

1980

No.	Date	Striking Standard	No. of coins	Price
JDPS-80	1980	Proof	6	12

Denomination	Metal
50 pence	Cupronickel
10 pence	Cupronickel
5 pence	Cupronickel
2 pence	Bronze
Penny	Bronze
Halfpenny	Bronze

1981

No.	Date	Striking Standard	No. of coins	Price
JDPS-81	1981	Proof	7	12

Denomination	Metal
Pound	Cupronickel
50 pence	Cupronickel
10 pence	Cupronickel
5 pence	Cupronickel
2 pence	Bronze
Penny	Bronze
Halfpenny	Bronze

1983

No.	Date	Striking Standard	No. of coins	Price
JDPS-83	1983	Proof	7	30

Denomination	Metal
Pound	0.925 silver
50 pence	0.925 silver
20 pence	0.925 silver
10 pence	0.925 silver
5 pence	0.925 silver
2 pence	0.925 silver
Penny	0.925 silver

1990

No.	Date	Striking Standard	No. of coins	Price
JDPS-90	1990	Proof	4	1000

Denomination	Metal
100 pounds	0.999 gold
50 pounds	0.999 gold
25 pounds	0.999 gold
10 pounds	0.999 gold

1995

No.	Date	Striking Standard	No. of coins	Price
JDPS-95	1995	Proof	4	1000

Denomination	Metal
100 pounds	0.999 gold
50 pounds	0.999 gold
25 pounds	0.999 gold
10 pounds	0.999 gold

Jersey: Specimen Sets

1972

No.	Date	Striking Standard	No. of coins	Price
JDMS-72	1972	Specimen [1]	9	500

1. This set is difficult to distinguish from the proof set which was issued in an identical case.

Denomination	Metal
50 pounds	0.917 gold
25 pounds	0.917 gold
20 pounds	0.917 gold
10 pounds	0.917 gold
5 pounds	0.917 gold
2 pounds 50 pence	0.925 silver
2 pounds	0.925 silver
Pound	0.925 silver
50 pence	0.925 silver

1972

No.	Date	Striking Standard	No. of coins	Price
JDMS-72A	1972	Specimen	4	15

Denomination	Metal
2 pounds 50 pence	0.925 silver
2 pounds	0.925 silver
Pound	0.925 silver
50 pence	0.925 silver

1983

No.	Date	Striking Standard	No. of coins	Price
JDMS-83	1983	Specimen	7	5

Denomination	Metal
Pound	Nickel brass
50 pence	Cupronickel
20 pence	Cupronickel
10 pence	Cupronickel
5 pence	Cupronickel
2 pence	Bronze
Penny	Bronze

1987

No.	Date	Striking Standard	No. of coins	Price
JDMS-87	1987	Specimen	7	5

Denomination	Metal
Pound	Nickel brass
50 pence	Cupronickel
20 pence	Cupronickel
10 pence	Cupronickel
5 pence	Cupronickel
2 pence	Bronze
Penny	Bronze

1992

No.	Date	Striking Standard	No. of coins	Price
JDMS-92	1992	Specimen	7	10

Denomination	Metal
Pound	Nickel brass
50 pence	Cupronickel
20 pence	Cupronickel
10 pence	Cupronickel
5 pence	Cupronickel
2 pence	Bronze
Penny	Bronze

Jersey: Mintage Information & Figures

Thirteenth of a shilling (1841 – 71)
Twelfth of a shilling (1877–1949)

Date	Mintage
1841	116,480
1844	27,040
1851	160,000
1858	173,333
1861	173,333
1866	173,333
1870	160,000
1871	160,000
1877-H	240,000 [1]
1881	75,153 [2]
1888	180,000
1894	180,000
1909	180,000
1911	204,000
1913	204,000
1923 1st type	204,000
1923 2nd type	301,200 [3]
1926	82,800
1931	204,000
1933	204,000
1935	204,000
1937	204,000
1946	204,000
1947	444,000
1949 (date on coin)	1,200,000 [4]

1. Dies engraved at Royal Mint; struck at Ralph Heaton & Sons, Birmingham.
2. Struck at Royal Mint from metal obtained from withdrawn farthings.
3. Struck from metal obtained from withdrawn French currency on Jersey.
4. Struck in 1949, 50, 52.

Twenty-sixth of a shilling (1841 – 71)
Twenty-fourth of a shilling (1877–1947)

Date	Mintage
1841	232,960
1844	232,960
1851	160,000
1858	173,333
1861	173,333
1866	173,333
1870	160,000
1871	160,000
1877-H	336,000 [1]
1888	120,000
1894	120,000
1909	120,000
1911	72,000
1913	72,000
1923 1st type	72,000
1923 2nd type	72,000 [2]
1926	120,000
1931	72,000
1933	72,000
1935	72,000
1937	72,000
1946	72,000
1947	72,000

1. Dies engraved at Royal Mint; struck at Ralph Heaton & Sons, Birmingham.
2. Struck from metal obtained from withdrawn French currency on Jersey.

Fifty-second of a shilling (1841)
Forty-eighth of a shilling (1877)

Date	Mintage
1841	116,480
1877-H	288,000 [1]

1. Dies engraved at Royal Mint; struck at Ralph Heaton & Sons, Birmingham; 249,600 pieces were withdrawn and recoined into 1/12th shillings in May 1881

Letter 26th February 1877 from Royal Mint to E. Mourant, detailing costs of £2000 worth of 1877 coinage

Messrs. Ralph Heaton: metal, manufacture and packing	662.10. 0
Freight and insurance	3. 7. 3
Mr. Leonard Wyon engraving dies	132.10. 0
Royal Mint matrices, punches and trials	15.15. 0
Inspection of finished product	3. 1. 6
Total	817. 3. 9

The milled coinage of Guernsey

Guernsey is the second largest of the Channel Islands, a British dependency lying much nearer to the coast of France than to Britain. It does not form part of the United Kingdom. Guernsey formed part of the Duchy of Normandy, and so, after the Battle of Hastings in 1066 became linked to the crown of England. Subsequently, French and English/British coinage circulated on the island. Also known were the 'freluque' and the 'enseigne de palin', neither of which appears to have survived.

In 1619, an ordinance prohibited the coinage of freluques by unauthorized persons and outlawed the circulation of those pieces which were not up to the required standard. Contravention of this ordinance was to be punished by public flogging 'until blood flows'. In 1623, the Governor was petitioned to appoint an official issuer of freluques 'in order to preserve the ancient privilege of the island'.

English coinage appears to have been introduced into Guernsey in 1672 with the importation of copper halfpennies and farthings; thereafter, other English denominations circulated, but in 1696 there were riots because of the worn state of English coinage. In the 18th century French coinage was used, and various ordinances were published dictating the exchange rates of imported currency. On 28th March 1797 it was decreed that the French 6 livres piece should pass for five shillings and three pence, and that Spanish and Spanish American dollars were to be current for four shillings and nine pence. It was on to these latter pieces that the 1809 five shilling tokens of Bishop, de Jersey and Co. were struck.

With the outbreak of war with France in 1798, it was obviously an embarrassment that the coinage of the enemy should be legal tender on the island, but the circulation of French coinage was so entrenched that no action was taken. By the end of the war in 1815, the coinage circulating was mainly ecus, 24 and 12 sous, and also British silver (circulating unofficially), especially very worn pieces which were apparently known as 'Irish shillings and sixpences'. Prior to this, in 1813, an ordinance had prohibited the circulation of the Jersey three shillings and eighteen pence tokens of that year. In 1817, the British Government sent Commissioner General White to Guernsey to exchange all worn British coinage. Between 26th March and 6th April of that year, £8,455 was handed in.

By 1829, the coinage situation had become somewhat chaotic. Jacob's 'Annals of Guernsey' records that the coins circulating 'were formed of various sizes, thicknesses and materials, some of them being old English farthings, some Dutch or Flemish, others French or Spanish, many of them only very thin pieces of copper, whilst a few of them are soldiers' buttons, beaten flat'. In 1829 the French coinage was revised, with the earlier currency being called in. The franc was fixed at 10 pence Guernsey, and the old coinage was not accepted as currency after 31st December 1833.

For much of the 19th century French currency circulated alongside Guernsey coinage. On 1st May 1848, after French coinage had become scarce, British gold and silver coins were made legal tender on the island. The British coinage was subsequently outlawed in January 1850.

The earliest generally circulating Guernsey coins were the one and four doubles of 1830, the name being taken from the double-tournois. It should be noted that in Guernsey the word 'double' takes the French, not the English, pronunciation. The double was one-eighth of a Guernsey penny; 12 pence equalled one shilling, but 21 shillings equalled a Guernsey pound, whereas in Britain the ratio was 20 shillings to be pound. The eight doubles coin was introduced in 1834, as the old French coinage was demonetized, and the two doubles began to circulate in 1858. The first 'double' series circulated until 1864, when the coins were replaced with a new series similarly denominated but much more resembling the British coinage in size and weight. The older heavier pieces ceased to be legal tender in 1868.

On the outbreak of war with Germany in 1870, silver disappeared from circulation and British coinage was again made legal tender on the island. In 1873, Bank of England notes were legalized. French bronze coins were demonetized on the island in 1902, but continued to circulate for many years.

In March 1921, there was a changeover to a system based solely on British and Guernsey currency, with the ratio fixed at 8 doubles to the British penny. French silver coins could be exchanged at 25.2 francs to the pound sterling. Prior to this there had been considerable smuggling of currency from France to Guernsey because of anomalies in the exchange rates, despite an order that no French currency above ten pounds could be imported.

Unlike the coinage of the other countries and dependencies in this catalogue, the coins of Guernsey up to George VI do not bear the effigy of the monarch. Since there is often no change of type from one monarch to the next, the denominations in most of the Guernsey section are not divided into sections for each monarch as in the rest of the catalogue.

The issue of this unusual coinage was in later years to some extent an act of defiance against Britain, who strongly suggested in 1870 that the Channel Islands issue coins compatible with those in Britain. Jersey acquiesced in 1877 to some extent, but Guernsey retained its 'double' coinage, with the 21 shillings to the pound anomaly.

It is possibly a further indication of the fierce independent stance of the island that, while its neighbour Jersey contracted with the Royal Mint to produce its coinage, Guernsey always looked to the independent mints of Birmingham until the mid 20th century.

The French spelling of GUERNESEY was retained on the coinage until 1949.

Guernsey: Ten Shillings

The ten shilling piece of 1966, struck at the Royal Mint to commemorate the 900th anniversary of the Norman Conquest, is an unusual piece, not least because it is the only pre-decimal coin of Guernsey to depict the monarch. It takes its place alongside the threepence forming a pair which are the only coins of the island denominated in shillings and pence. As if to emphasize their difference from the regular coinage, both pieces shun the usual round format. The ten shilling coin takes the form of a square with rounded corners, a coin shape not previously seen in the British Isles but occasionally encountered in colonial coinage, and subsequently used for the Jersey pound of 1981.

Elizabeth II (1952 –)

Denomination	Metal	Weight (grams)	Diameter (mm)	Rev. alignment
10 shillings	Cupronickel	11.3 – 11.4	(a)26 (b)30	↑

The coin is square with rounded corners. Measurements are: (a) side to side; (b) corner to corner.

Obverse 1 Head 1, right; BAILIWICK OF GUERNSEY 1966

Reverse 1 Head of William the conqueror facing left; WILLIAM I KING OF ENGLAND 1066 DUKE OF NORMANDY TEN SHILLINGS

Edge plain

Obv. 1   Rev. 1

No.	Date	Features	Obv.	Rev.	EF	UNC
GTS-005	1966		1	1	1	2
GTS-010	1966	PROOF [1]	1	1	2	4

1. Issued in cased proof sets.

Guernsey: Five Shillings Token

Although not an official issue, and absent from some catalogues, the five shilling token of 1809 is worthy of inclusion in the coinage listings on account of its unique status.

At the end of the eighteenth century there was an acute shortage of currency in Guernsey similar to that in Britain. Mr. Ferdinand Tupper, discussing in the Guernsey and Jersey Magazine the period 1775 to 1789 says that 'the money in circulation was English and French gold, but principally guineas and 6 livres pieces'. During 1797, silver crown-size coins of France and Spain began to circulate on the island at an unofficial rate of approximately five Guernsey shillings. The first attempt to produce a token which would help to alleviate the situation was made by Bishop, de Jersey and Company, which rather grandiosely renamed itself The Bank of Guernsey for the occasion. It should be mentioned that 'Bishop' and 'de Jersey' are two separate Guernsey surnames. Bishop, de Jersey and Company was the first bank to issue paper money (denominated at one pound) in Guernsey. The bank was located in a triangular granite house facing the High Street, which later became the home of Lloyds Bank. Abraham Bishop, the co-founder, was nicknamed the Archbishop of Methodism. His partner, Henry de Jersey, was the Seigneur of St. Jacques, and married Mollie Bishop, the daughter of Abraham Bishop.

The crown-sized tokens of five shillings were engraved by Thomas Wyon and struck over Spanish and Spanish American silver eight real pieces by Boulton, Watt and Co. at their Birmingham mint. The issue was outlawed by an Ordinance dated 2nd October 1809, and the few pieces that escaped destruction are now greatly prized by collectors. The Bank of Guernsey failed in 1811.

On 9th March 1813 an Ordinance prohibited the circulation in Guernsey of the newly issued silver tokens of Jersey, as well as copper and silver tokens from Britain.

Denomination	Metal	Weight (grams)	Diameter (mm)	Rev. alignment
5 shillings token	0.89 Silver	c. 27	40 – 42	↑

Obverse 1   Arms on shield within beaded border, ornament below; BISHOP DE JERSEY & CO.

Reverse 1   Circular oak wreath; TOKEN OF FIVE SHILLINGS (within wreath); BANK OF GUERNSEY 1809 (outside wreath)

Edge   Ornamented (from original Spanish 8 reales)

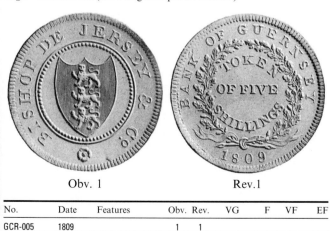

Obv. 1   Rev.1

No.	Date	Features	Obv.	Rev.	VG	F	VF	EF
GCR-005	1809		1	1				

Guernsey: Threepence

The threepence is a curious coin, not only because of its shape; it is an anomaly which does not sit easily amongst its contemporary issues denominated in doubles. The coin was struck only during the reign of Elizabeth II, but, unlike the other pre-decimal 'sterling' denominated issue, the ten shillings, the threepence does not bear the portrait of the monarch. The issue for the first year, 1956, was considered too light, and was superseded by a heavier piece in 1959. The 1966 coin was struck only for inclusion in cased proof sets.

All issues were minted at the Royal Mint.

Elizabeth II   (1952 –)

Denomination	Metal	Weight (grams)	Diameter (mm)	Rev. alignment
Threepence 1956	Cupronickel	3.4 – 3.5	21	↑
Threepence 1959, 1966	Cupronickel	6.8	21	↑

The coin has an irregular edge and the diameter given is a minimum-maximum range across the centre of the face.

Obverse 1   Shield bearing Arms, all within circle; S BALLIVIE INSVLE DE GERNEREVE

Reverse 1   Guernsey cow; GUERNSEY THREE PENCE (date)

Edge   plain

Obv. 1   Rev. 1

No.	Date	Features	Obv.	Rev.	EF	UNC
G3D-005	1956		1	1	1	2
G3D-010	1956	PROOF [1]	1	1	5	8
G3D-015	1959		1	1	1	2
G3D-020	1959	PROOF [2]	1	1		
G3D-025	1966	PROOF [1]	1	1		3

1. Issued in Royal Mint cased sets.
2. Some weigh c. 6.5 grams.

Guernsey: Eight Doubles

The largest of the copper coins, the eight doubles (i.e. penny) was first struck in 1834, four years after the four and one double pieces were issued. The size and weight were obviously based on the pre-1860 British penny, and this first type was issued for only the two years 1834 and 1858. When the next issue was made, in 1864, the British penny had been converted from copper to bronze, and considerably reduced in size; the new eight doubles reflected these alterations. After 31st December 1868, the old copper issue ceased to be legal tender, and the new basic design remained, with some modifications, until 1949. The issue for Elizabeth II, while still not carrying the portrait of the monarch, was radically redesigned.

Coins of this denomination dated 1861, 1865 and 1890 are mentioned in various reference works, but appear not to exist.

Denomination	Metal	Weight (grams)	Diameter (mm)	Rev. alignment
8 doubles 1834, 1858	Copper	20.3 – 20.8	35	↓
8 doubles 1864	Bronze	8.7 – 9.1	31	↑
8 doubles 1868 – 85	Bronze	9.0 – 10.0	32	↓
8 doubles 1889 – 93	Bronze	9.7 – 9.8	32	↑
8 doubles 1902 – 49	Bronze	9.6 – 9.9	32	↓
8 doubles 1956 – 66	Bronze	9.8 – 9.9	31	↑

Obverse 1 Arms (three lions) on shield within laurel wreath, stalk above; GUERNESEY

Obverse 2 Similar but redesigned to fit smaller flan

Obverse 3 Similar but shield different; lions now resemble leopards

Obverse 4 Very different shield bearing Arms, all within circle; S BALLIVIE INSVLE DE GERNEREVE

Reverse 1 Laurel wreath; 8 DOUBLES (date)

Reverse 2 Similar but redesigned to fit smaller flan

Reverse 3 Similar but the bows under the legend are narrower

Reverse 4 Guernsey Lily; GUERNSEY EIGHT DOUBLES (date)

Edge plain

Obv. 1   Obv. 2

Obv. 3   Obv. 4

Rev. 1   Rev. 2

Rev. 3   Rev. 4

No.	Date	Features	Obv.	Rev.	F	VF	EF	UNC
G8D-005	1834	[1] [2] [3]	1	1	8	15	50	150
G8D-010	1834	bronzed PROOF [2]	1	1				400
G8D-015	1834	bronzed PROOF; reverse ↑ [2]	1	1				800
G8D-020	1858	[4] [5]	1	1	10	20	70	200
G8D-025	1858	bronzed PROOF [5]	1	1				600
G8D-030	1858	bronzed PROOF on large flan [5]	1	1				1000
G8D-035	1864	[5] [6]	2	2	6	12	40	120
G8D-040	1864	PROOF [5]	2	2				1200
G8D-045	1868	[6] [7]	2	2	6	14	45	140
G8D-050	1874	[7]	2	2	6	12	40	120
G8D-055	1874	[7]	2	3	6	12	40	120
G8D-060	1885	mintmark H below wreath [8]	2	3	3	6	12	30
G8D-065	1885	PROOF; mintmark H below wreath [8]	2	3				300
G8D-070	1889	mintmark H below wreath [8] [9]	2	3	3	5	10	25
G8D-075	1889	PROOF on thick flan; mintmark H below wreath [8]	2	3				1000
G8D-080	1893	normal size letters and date (rev); mintmark H below wreath [8]	2	3	3	5	10	25
G8D-085	1893	larger size letters and date (rev); mintmark H below wreath [8]	2	3	3	5	10	25
G8D-090	1902	mintmark H below wreath [8] [10]	2	3	2	4	8	15
G8D-095	1902	PROOF; mintmark H below wreath [8] [10]	2	3				800
G8D-100	1903	mintmark H below wreath [8]	2	3	2	4	10	20
G8D-105	1910	mintmark H below wreath [8]	2	3	3	5	12	30
G8D-110	1910	PROOF; mintmark H below wreath [8]	2	3				800
G8D-115	1911	mintmark H below wreath [8]	2	3	3	6	15	40
G8D-120	1914	mintmark H below wreath [8]	3	3	2	4	7	15

No.	Date	Features	Obv.	Rev.	F	VF	EF	UNC
G8D-125	1918	mintmark H below wreath [8]	3	3	2	4	7	15
G8D-130	1920	mintmark H below wreath [8]	3	3	1	3	5	8
G8D-135	1934	mintmark H below wreath [8]	3	3	1	3	5	8
G8D-140	1934	burnished PROOF-LIKE; mintmark H below wreath [8] [11]	3	3				120
G8D-145	1938	mintmark H below wreath [8]	3	3			3	6
G8D-150	1945	mintmark H below wreath [8]	3	3			3	5
G8D-155	1945	mintmark H below wreath; struck in cupronickel with central hole	3	3				
G8D-160	1947	mintmark H below wreath [8]	3	3			3	5
G8D-165	1949	mintmark H below wreath [8]	3	3			3	5
G8D-170	1956	[12]	4	4			1	3
G8D-175	1956	PROOF [13]	4	4			2	5
G8D-180	1959	[12]	4	4			1	3
G8D-185	1959	PROOF	4	4				
G8D-190	1966	PROOF [13]	4	4				3

1. Leaves and berries vary in number (obv and rev).
2. Minted by Boulton, Watt and Co., Birmingham.
3. Struck in 1834, 1836, 1837, 1839.
4. Bow varies (rev).
5. Minted by Henry Toy and Co., Birmingham.
6. Several minor varieties occur.
7. Minted by Partridge and Co., Birmingham.
8. Minted by Ralph Heaton and Sons, Birmingham, later The Mint, Birmingham, Ltd.
9. Struck in 1889 and 1890.
10. Struck in 1901.
11. 500 pieces struck in 1935 for centenary of 8 doubles and for the King's Silver Jubilee.
12. Royal Mint issue.
13. Issued in Royal Mint cased sets.

Guernsey: Four Doubles

The four doubles was, together with the one double, the earliest copper coin minted for Guernsey. The denomination first appeared in 1830, during the reign of William IV but before any British coins had been struck for that reign. As with the eight doubles, the coin underwent a change of size and metal composition in 1864, and continued to be minted with a basically similar design until 1949. The Elizabeth II issue of 1956/1966 was of a very different design.

Rev. 1

Rev. 3

Rev. 4

Denomination	Metal	Weight (grams)	Diameter (mm)	Rev. alignment
4 doubles 1830	Copper	9.9 – 10.3	29	↓
4 doubles 1858	Copper	9.0 – 9.1	29	↓
4 doubles 1864	Bronze	4.8 – 5.0	26	↑
4 doubles 1868 – 85	Bronze	4.9 – 5.3	26	↓
4 doubles 1889 – 93	Bronze	4.7 – 4.9	26	↑
4 doubles 1902 – 49	Bronze	4.7 – 4.9	26	↓
4 doubles 1956 – 66	Bronze	4.8	25.5	↑

Obverse 1   Arms (three lions) on shield, stalk above; GUERNESEY

Obverse 2   Similar but redesigned to fit smaller flan. The stalk is different

Obverse 3   Similar but redesigned; the lions are larger

Obverse 4   Similar but redesigned; lions now resemble leopards

Obverse 5   Very different shield bearing Arms, all within circle; S BALLIVIE INSVLE DE GERNEREVE

Obverse SH   ST HELENA HALFPENNY 1821 within wreath (obverse of St. Helena halfpenny 1821)

Reverse 1   4 DOUBLES (date)

Reverse 2   Similar but lettering and numerals smaller and finer

Reverse 3   Similar but lettering and numerals larger

Reverse 4   Guernsey Lily; GUERNSEY FOUR DOUBLES (date)

Edge   plain

No.	Date	Features	Obv.	Rev.	F	VF	EF	UNC
G4D-005	1830	[1] [2]	1	1	4	10	40	100
G4D-010	1830	bronzed PROOF [1]	1	1				250
G4D-015	1830	[1] [3]	SH	1	400	600	1200	
G4D-020	1858	[3] [4]	1	1	6	15	60	130
G4D-025	1864	[3] [5]	2	2	5	15	70	150
G4D-030	1868	date 9mm wide [6]	2	2	5	15	70	150
G4D-035	1868	date 10mm wide [6]	2	2	5	15	70	150
G4D-040	1874	[6]	2	2	4	12	50	100
G4D-045	1885	mintmark H below date [7]	3	3	3	6	15	35
G4D-050	1885	PROOF; mintmark H below date [7]	3	3				250
G4D-055	1889	mintmark H below date [7] [8]	3	3	3	5	12	25
G4D-060	1889	PROOF on thick flan; mintmark H below date [7] [9]	3	3				1000
G4D-065	1893	mintmark H below date [7]	3	3	3	5	10	20
G4D-070	1902	mintmark H below date [7] [10]	3	3	3	5	10	20
G4D-075	1902	PROOF; mintmark H below date [7] [10]	3	3				500
G4D-080	1903	mintmark H below date [7]	3	3	3	5	10	20
G4D-085	1906	mintmark H below date [7]	3	3	3	6	12	25
G4D-090	1908	mintmark H below date [7]	3	3	4	8	15	35
G4D-095	1910	mintmark H below date [7]	3	3	3	5	10	20
G4D-100	1910	PROOF; mintmark H below wreath [7]	3	3				500
G4D-105	1911	mintmark H below date [7]	3	3	3	5	10	20
G4D-110	1914	mintmark H below date [7]	4	3	2	4	8	14
G4D-115	1918	mintmark H below date [7]	4	3	2	4	8	14
G4D-120	1920	mintmark H below date [7]	4	3	1	3	5	8
G4D-125	1945	mintmark H below date [7]	4	3			3	5
G4D-130	1949	mintmark H below date [7]	4	3			3	5

Obv. 1

Obv. 3

Obv. 4

Obv. 5

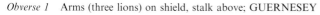

No.	Date	Features	Obv.	Rev.	F	VF	EF	UNC
G4D-135	1949	mintmark H below wreath; struck in cupronickel with central hole	4	3				
G4D-140	1956	[11]	5	4			1	3
G4D-145	1956	PROOF [12]	5	4			2	5
G4D-150	1966	PROOF [12]	5	4				2

1. Minted by Boulton, Watt and Co., Birmingham.
2. Struck in 1830, 1831, 1836, 1837, 1839.
3. Minted by Henry Toy and Co., Birmingham.
4. Legend spacing and leaves vary (obv).
5. Leaves vary (obv).
6. Minted by Partridge and Co., Birmingham.
7. Minted by Ralph Heaton and Sons, Birmingham, later The Mint, Birmingham, Ltd.
8. Alignment of 9 in date varies.
9. Weight 7.9 grams.
10. Struck in 1901.
11. Royal Mint issue.
12. Issued in Royal Mint cased sets.
13. A deliberate error coin struck c. 1850–60. The obverse is dated 1821. Weight 11.0 – 11.1 grams.

Guernsey: Two Doubles

Although the other copper denominations had first made their appearance in 1830 and 1834, the two doubles was not issued until 1858. This copper issue accordingly is a one-year type. The remainder of the issue is broadly similar to that of the 8 and 4 doubles, except that the size was not reduced on conversion to bronze, and there were no 2 doubles struck after 1929. Inflation had rendered superfluous this tiny coin, the equivalent of the British farthing.

Denomination	Metal	Weight (grams)	Diameter (mm)	Rev. alignment
2 doubles 1858	Copper	4.4 – 4.6	22	↓
2 doubles 1868 – 85	Bronze	3.6 – 3.9	22	↓
2 doubles 1889	Bronze	3.5 – 3.6	22	↑
2 doubles 1899 – 1929	Bronze	3.5 – 3.6	22.5	↓

Obverse 1 Arms (three lions) on shield, stalk above; GUERNESEY

Obverse 2 Similar but the stalk is different

Obverse 3 Similar but the lions are wider

Obverse 4 Similar but redesigned; lions now resemble leopards

Reverse 1 2 DOUBLES 1858

Reverse 2 2 DOUBLES (date); the lettering and numerals are slightly finer

Reverse 3 Similar but 2 DOUBLES is wider

Edge plain

Obv. 1

Obv. 3

Obv. 4

Rev. 1

Rev. 3

No.	Date	Features	Obv.	Rev.	F	VF	EF	UNC
G2D-005	1858	[1]	1	1	4	12	50	120
G2D-010	1868	[2] [3]	2	2	4	12	50	120
G2D-015	1874	date 7mm wide [2]	2	2	4	10	40	100
G2D-020	1874	date 9mm wide [2]	2	2	4	12	50	120
G2D-025	1885	mintmark H below date [4]	3	3	2	5	8	20
G2D-030	1885	PROOF; mintmark H below date [4]	3	3				150
G2D-035	1889	mintmark H below date [4]	3	3	2	5	8	20
G2D-040	1899	mintmark H below date [4]	3	3	2	5	8	20
G2D-045	1902	mintmark H below date [4] [5]	3	3	2	6	10	20
G2D-050	1902	PROOF; mintmark H below date [4] [6]	3	3				300
G2D-055	1903	mintmark H below date [4]	3	3	2	6	10	20
G2D-060	1906	mintmark H below date [4]	3	3	2	6	10	20
G2D-065	1908	mintmark H below date [4]	3	3	2	6	10	20
G2D-070	1911	mintmark H below date [4]	3	3	2	6	10	20
G2D-075	1914	mintmark H below date [4]	4	3	2	6	10	20
G2D-080	1917	mintmark H below date [4] [7]	4	3	5	15	25	60
G2D-085	1918	mintmark H below date [4]	4	3			4	8
G2D-090	1920	mintmark H below date [4]	4	3			4	8
G2D-095	1929	mintmark H below date [4] [6]	4	3			3	6

1. Minted by Henry Toy and Co., Birmingham.
2. Minted by Partridge and Co., Birmingham.
3. Leaves differ (obv).
4. Minted by Ralph Heaton and Sons, Birmingham, later The Mint, Birmingham, Ltd.
5. Struck in 1901.
6. Position of 7 in date varies (rev).
7. Position of mintmark varies (rev).

Guernsey: Double

The double, the unit of the currency and the equivalent of the British half farthing, was first struck in 1830. The denomination was struck until 1938, which is surprising when one considers the very low value of the coin. The British fractional farthings were not struck during the 20th century with the exception of the 1902 and 1913 third farthings struck for circulation in Malta.

Denomination	Metal	Weight (grams)	Diameter (mm)	Rev. alignment
Double 1830	Copper	2.4 – 2.5	19	↓
Double 1868 – 85	Bronze	2.2 – 2.3	19	↓
Double 1889 – 93	Bronze	2.3	19	↑
Double 1899 – 1938	Bronze	2.2 – 2.4	19	↓

Obverse 1   Arms (three lions) on shield, spray with stalk; GUERNESEY

Obverse 2   Similar but the spray has no stalk

Obverse 3   Similar but the spray is different and lettering is larger

Obverse 4   Similar but stalk is again different; lions now resemble leopards

Reverse 1   1 DOUBLE (date)

Reverse 2   Similar but the lettering and date are slightly larger

Edge   plain

Obv. 1   Obv. 3   Obv. 4

Rev. 1   Rev. 2

No.	Date	Features	Obv.	Rev.	F	VF	EF	UNC
G1D-005	1830	[1]	1	1	2	5	15	40
G1D-010	1830	stop before date (rev). [1]	1	1	5	12	40	100
G1D-015	1830	bronzed PROOF [1]	1	1				150
G1D-020	1830	bronzed PROOF; reverse ? [1]	1	1				500
G1D-025	1868	68 over 30 [2]	1	1	6	18	50	100
G1D-030	1868	[2]	2	1	8	25	70	140
G1D-035	1885	mintmark H below date (rev) [3]	3	2	1	3	8	16
G1D-040	1885	PROOF; mintmark H below date (rev) [3]	3	2				100
G1D-045	1889	mintmark H below date (rev) [3][4]	3	2		2	5	8
G1D-050	1893	mintmark H below date (rev) [3]	3	2		2	6	10
G1D-055	1899	mintmark H below date (rev) [3][5]	3	2		2	6	10
G1D-060	1902	mintmark H below date (rev) [3][6]	3	2		2	5	8
G1D-065	1902	PROOF; mintmark H below date (rev) [3][6]	3	2				200
G1D-070	1903	mintmark H below date (rev) [3][7]	3	2		2	5	8
G1D-075	1911	mintmark H below date (rev) [3]	3	2		3	7	12
G1D-080	1911	mintmark H below date (rev) [3]	4	2		3	7	12
G1D-085	1914	mintmark H below date (rev) [3]	4	2		4	9	16
G1D-090	1929	mintmark H below date (rev) [3]	4	2		2	4	7
G1D-095	1933	mintmark H below date (rev) [3]	4	2		2	4	7
G1D-100	1938	mintmark H below date (rev) [3]	4	2		2	4	7

1. Minted by Boulton, Watt and Co., Birmingham.
2. Minted by Partridge and Co., Birmingham.
3. Minted by Ralph Heaton and Co., Birmingham.
4. Struck in 1889 and 1890.
5. Spacing of 99 in date varies (rev)
6. Struck in 1901.
7. Spacing of 03 in date varies (rev)

Guernsey: Decimal Coinage

The introduction of decimal currency into Guernsey closely followed the British pattern. On 24th February 1969, 10 and 5 pence pieces dated 1968 were placed into circulation alongside the British florins and shillings which had been used for some time. The 50 pence (dated 1969) was introduced some months later, and the Guernsey and Jersey ten shilling notes lapsed gradually from November 1970 by allowing those in circulation to become worn out. Decimal Day was the same as in the United Kingdom, 15th February 1971.

100 Pounds

Denomination	Metal	Weight (grams)	Diameter (mm)	Rev. alignment
100 pounds	0.999 gold	31.2	33	↑

Obverse 1 Head 1, right; with Arms on left; ELIZABETH II BAILIWICK OF GUERNSEY

Reverse 1 Invasion scene; 50th ANNIVERSARY NORMANDY 1944–1994 100 POUNDS

Reverse 2 Liberation scene; 50th ANNIVERSARY LIBERATION 1945–1995 100 POUNDS

Edge milled

No.	Date	Features	Obv.	Rev.	UNC
GD100P/94–6	1994	PROOF [1]	1	1	500
GD100P/95–6	1995	PROOF [1]	1	2	500

1. Issued only in sets.

50 Pounds

Denomination	Metal	Weight (grams)	Diameter (mm)	Rev. alignment
50 pounds	0.999 gold	15.6	27	↑

Obverse 1 Head 1, right; with Arms on left; ELIZABETH II BAILIWICK OF GUERNSEY

Reverse 1 Invasion scene; 50th ANNIVERSARY NORMANDY 1944–1994 50 POUNDS

Reverse 2 Liberation scene; 50th ANNIVERSARY LIBERATION 1945–1995 50 POUNDS

Edge milled

Obv. 1   Rev. 1

No.	Date	Features	Obv.	Rev.	UNC
GD50P/94–6	1994	PROOF [1]	1	1	250
GD50P/95–6	1995	PROOF [1]	1	2	250

1. Issued only in sets.

25 Pounds

Denomination	Metal	Weight (grams)	Diameter (mm)	Rev. alignment
25 pounds	0.999 gold	7.8	22	↑

Obverse 1 Head 1, right; with Arms on left; ELIZABETH II BAILIWICK OF GUERNSEY

Reverse 1 Invasion scene; 50th ANNIVERSARY NORMANDY 1944–1994 25 POUNDS

Reverse 2 Liberation scene; 50th ANNIVERSARY LIBERATION 1945–1995 25 POUNDS

Reverse 3 Soccer ball with map of Europe; EUROPEAN FOOTBALL TWENTY FIVE POUNDS

Reverse 4 Elizabeth and Philip busts superimposed on Westminster Abbey; ELIZABETH AND PHILIP 1947–1997 25 POUNDS

Reverse 5 Spitfire and Lancaster Bomber, with RAF Benevolent Fund Badge, all within beaded circle; 80TH ANNIVERSARY OF THE ROYAL AIR FORCE TWENTY FIVE POUNDS

Edge milled

Obv. 1   Rev. 1

No.	Date	Features	Obv.	Rev.	UNC
GD25P/94–6	1994	PROOF [1]	1	1	150
GD25P/95–6	1995	PROOF [1]	1	2	150
GD25P/96–6	1996	PROOF	1	3	150
GD25P/97–6	1997	PROOF	1	4	200
GD25P/98–6	1998	PROOF	1	5	200

1. Issued only in sets.

10 Pounds

Denomination	Metal	Weight (grams)	Diameter (mm)	Rev. alignment
10 pounds 1994–95	0.999 gold	3.1	16	↑
10 pounds 1997	0.999 silver with 0.916 gold cameo insert	155.5	65	↑

Obverse 1 Head 1, right; with Arms on left; ELIZABETH II BAILIWICK OF GUERNSEY

Obverse 2 Head 2, right; ELIZABETH II BAILIWICK OF GUERNSEY 1997

Reverse 1   Invasion scene; 50th ANNIVERSARY NORMANDY 1944–1994 10 POUNDS

Reverse 2   Liberation scene; 50th ANNIVERSARY LIBERATION 1945–1995 10 POUNDS

Reverse 3   (details not available)

Edge   milled

Obv. 1

Rev. 1

Rev. 3

Rev. 4

No.	Date	Features	Obv.	Rev.	UNC
GD10P/94–6	1994	PROOF [1]	1	1	70
GD10P/95–6	1995	PROOF [1]	1	2	70
GD10P/97–4	1997	PROOF	2	3	60

1. Issued only in proof sets.

No.	Date	Features	Obv.	Rev.	UNC
GD5P/95–1	1995		1	1	8
GD5P/95–4	1995	PROOF in 0.925 silver	1	1	40
GD5P/95–6	1995	PROOF in 0.999 gold	1	1	150
GD5P/96–1	1996		2	2	8
GD5P/96–4	1996	PROOF in 0.925 silver	2	2	40
GD5P/96–1A	1996		2	3	8
GD5P/96–4A	1996	PROOF in 0.925 silver	2	3	40
GD5P/97–1	1997		2	4	8
GD5P/97–4A	1997	PROOF in 0.925 silver	2	4	40
GD5P/98–1	1998		2	5	8

Some recent issues (e.g. British Castles, Millennium) are not included in the table above.

5 Pounds

Denomination	Metal	Weight (grams)	Diameter (mm)	Rev. alignment
5 pounds	Cupronickel	28.3	39	↑

Obverse 1   Head 1, right; with Arms on left; ELIZABETH II BAILIWICK OF GUERNSEY (date)

Obverse 2   Head 1, smaller, right; same legend

Reverse 1   Queen Mother flanked by rose and thistle; QUEEN ELIZABETH THE QUEEN MOTHER FIVE POUNDS

Reverse 2   Soccer ball with map of Europe; EUROPEAN FOOTBALL FIVE POUNDS

Reverse 3   Queen with castle and shield; 1926 VIVAT REGINA ELIZABETHA 1996 FIVE POUNDS

Reverse 4   Elizabeth and Philip busts superimposed on Westminster Abbey; ELIZABETH AND PHILIP 1947–1997 FIVE POUNDS

Reverse 5   Spitfire and Lancaster Bomber, with RAF Benevolent Fund Badge, all within beaded circle; 80TH ANNIVERSARY OF THE ROYAL AIR FORCE FIVE POUNDS

Edge   milled

Obv. 1

2 Pounds (Commemorative)

Denomination	Metal	Weight (grams)	Diameter (mm)	Rev. alignment
2 pounds	Cupronickel	28.3	39	↑

Obverse 1   Head 1, right, with Arms on left; ELIZABETH II BAILIWICK OF GUERNSEY

Obverse 2   Similar but with date below head

Obverse 3   Head 2, right; QUEEN ELIZABETH THE SECOND TWO POUNDS

Obverse 4   Head 2, right; ELIZABETH II BAILIWICK OF GUERNSEY TWO POUNDS

Reverse 1   Doves and olive branch; GUERNSEY 1945 1985 TWO POUNDS (for the 40th anniversary of liberation of Guernsey from German occupation)

Reverse 2   Eight shields; XIII COMMONWEALTH GAMES 1986 TWO POUNDS

Reverse 3   Head of William the Conqueror; WILLIAM DUKE OF NORMANDY 1087 TWO POUNDS 1987 (for the 900th anniversary of the death of William the Conqueror)

Reverse 4   Head of William II; 1087 WILLIAM II 1100 TWO POUNDS

Reverse 5   Head of Henry I; HENRY I 1100 1135 TWO POUNDS

Reverse 6   Royal Yacht, Arms above; BAILIWICK OF GUERNSEY 1989 ROYAL VISIT

Reverse 7   Two intertwined 'E's, crown above, flanked by rose and thistle; QUEEN ELIZABETH THE QUEEN MOTHER 1900 1990 (for the Queen Mother's 90th birthday)

Reverse 8   Head of Henry II; HENRY II 1154 1189 TWO POUNDS

Reverse 9   Crowned EIIR intertwined with foliage; CORONATION ANNIVERSARY OF QUEEN ELIZABETH II 1953 1993

Reverse 10   Invasion scene; 50th ANNIVERSARY NORMANDY 1944–1994 TWO POUNDS

Reverse 11   Liberation scene; 50th ANNIVERSARY LIBERATION 1945–1995 TWO POUNDS

Reverse 12 Tiger Moth; WWF CONSERVING NATURE 1997
Reverse 13 Butterfly on plant; WWF CONSERVING NATURE 1998
Edge milled

Obv. 1   Obv. 2

Obv. 3   Obv. 4

Rev. 1   Rev. 2

Rev. 3   Rev. 4

Rev. 5   Rev. 6

Rev. 7   Rev. 8

Rev. 12   Rev. 13

No.	Date	Features	Obv.	Rev.	UNC
GD2P/85–1	1985		1	1	5
GD2P/85–3	1985	PROOF	1	1	10
GD2P/85–4	1985	PROOF in 0.925 silver	1	1	25
GD2P/85–1	1986		1	2	5
GD2P/86–1	1986	PROOF	1	2	10
GD2P/86–4	1986	PROOF in 0.500 silver	1	2	16
GD2P/86–4A	1986	PROOF in 0.925 silver	1	2	25
GD2P/87–1	1987	[1]	1	3	5
GD2P/87–3	1987	PROOF [1]	1	3	10
GD2P/87–4	1987	PROOF in 0.925 silver [1]	1	3	25
GD2P/87–6	1987	PROOF in 0.917 gold [1]	1	3	800
GD2P/88–1	1988		2	4	5
GD2P/88–3	1988	PROOF	2	4	10
GD2P/88–4	1988	PROOF in 0.925 silver	2	4	25
GD2P/89–1	1989		2	5	5
GD2P/89–3	1989	PROOF	2	5	10
GD2P/89–4	1989	PROOF in 0.925 silver	2	5	25
GD2P/89–1A	1989		3	6	5
GD2P/89–4A	1989	PROOF in 0.925 silver	3	6	25
GD2P/90–1	1990		4	7	5
GD2P/90–4	1990	PROOF in 0.925 silver	4	7	35
GD2P/90–4A	1990	PROOF in 0.925 silver	2	8	200
GD2P/91–1	1991		2	8	5
GD2P/91–4	1991	PROOF in 0.925 silver	2	8	35
GD2P/93–1	1993		4	9	5
GD2P/93–4	1993	PROOF in 0.925 silver	4	9	25
GD2P/94–1	1994		2	10	5
GD2P/94–4	1994	PROOF in 0.925 silver	2	10	25
GD2P/95–1	1995		2	11	5
GD2P/95–4	1995	PROOF in 0.925 silver	2	11	25
GD2P/95–5	1995	PIEDFORT PROOF in 0.925 silver	2	11	80

Obv. 3   Obv. 4

Rev. 1   Rev. 2

Rev. 3   Rev. 4

Rev. 5

No.	Date	Features	Obv.	Rev.	UNC
GD25/72–1	1972		1	1	3
GD25/72–4	1972	PROOF in 0.925 silver	1	1	18
GD25/77–1	1977		2	2	2
GD25/77–4	1977	PROOF in 0.925 silver	2	2	16
GD25/78–1	1978		3	3	2
GD25/78–4	1978	PROOF in 0.925 silver	3	3	16
GD25/80–1	1980		4	4	2
GD25/80–4	1980	PROOF in 0.925 silver	4	4	18
GD25/81–1	1981		4	5	2
GD25/81–4	1981	PROOF in 0.925 silver	4	5	20

20 Pence

Denomination	Metal	Weight (grams)	Diameter (mm)	Rev. alignment
20 pence	Cupronickel	5.0	21	↑

The coin is seven-sided but the diameter from any point on the edge across the centre of the face is constant.

Obverse 1   Arms on shield, all within circle; S BALLIVIE INSVLE DE GERNEREVE

Obverse 2   Head 1, right, with Arms on left; ELIZABETH II BAILIWICK OF GUERNSEY

Reverse 1   Milk can; TWENTY 20 PENCE (date)

Reverse 2   Map of Guernsey within cog-wheels, 20 below; TWENTY PENCE (date)

Edge   plain

Obv. 2   Rev. 2

No.	Date	Features	Obv.	Rev.	UNC
GD20/82–1	1982		1	1	2
GD20/83–1	1983		1	1	2
GD20/85–1	1985		2	2	2
GD20/85–3	1985	PROOF [1]	2	2	4
GD20/86–1	1986		2	2	2
GD20/86–3	1986	PROOF [1]	2	2	4
GD20/87–1	1987		2	2	2
GD20/87–3	1987	PROOF [1]	2	2	4
GD20/88–1	1988		2	2	2
GD20/88–3	1988	PROOF [1]	2	2	4
GD20/89–1	1989		2	2	2
GD20/89–3	1989	PROOF [1]	2	2	4
GD20/90–1	1990		2	2	2
GD20/90–3	1990	PROOF [1]	2	2	6
GD20/92–1	1992		2	2	2
GD20/92–3	1992	PROOF [1]	2	2	8

1. Issued in cased sets.

10 Pence

Denomination	Metal	Weight (grams)	Diameter (mm)	Rev. alignment
10 pence 1968–90	Cupronickel	11.3–11.4	28	↑
10 pence 1992–	Cupronickel	6.5	24.5	↑

Obverse 1   Arms on shield, all within circle; S BALLIVIE INSVLE DE GERNEREVE

Obverse 2   Head 1, right, with Arms on left; ELIZABETH II BAILIWICK OF GUERNSEY

Obverse 3   Similar but on smaller flan

Reverse 1   Guernsey cow; 10 NEW PENCE (date)

Reverse 2   Guernsey cow; 10 TEN PENCE (date)

Reverse 3   Guernsey tomatoes, 10 below; TEN PENCE (date)

Reverse 4   Similar but on smaller flan

Edge   milled

Obv. 1

Obv. 2

Obv. 3

Rev. 1

Rev. 2

Rev. 3

Rev. 4

5 Pence

Denomination	Metal	Weight (grams)	Diameter (mm)	Rev. alignment
5 pence 1968–90 (obvs. 1–2)	Cupronickel	5.7–5.8	24	↑
5 pence 1990–92 (obv. 3)	Cupronickel	3.25	18	↑

Obverse 1   Arms on shield, all within circle; S BALLIVIE INSVLE DE GERNEREVE

Obverse 2   Head 1, right, with Arms on left; ELIZABETH II BAILIWICK OF GUERNSEY

Obverse 3   Similar but on smaller flan

Reverse 1   Guernsey lily; 5 NEW PENCE (date)

Reverse 2   Guernsey lily; 5 FIVE PENCE (date)

Reverse 3   Sailing ship, 5 below; FIVE PENCE (date)

Reverse 4   Similar but on smaller flan

Edge   milled

Obv. 1

Obv. 2

Obv. 3

Rev. 1

Rev. 2

Rev. 3

Rev. 4

No.	Date	Features	Obv.	Rev.	UNC
GD10/68–1	1968	1	1	1	2
GD10/70–1	1970		1	1	2
GD10/71–3	1971	PROOF 2	1	1	3
GD10/77–1	1977		1	2	2
GD10/79–1	1979		1	2	2
GD10/79–3	1979	PROOF 2	1	2	3
GD10/81–3	1981	PROOF 2	1	2	4
GD10/82–1	1982		1	2	2
GD10/84–1	1984		1	2	2
GD10/85–1	1985		2	3	2
GD10/85–3	1985	PROOF 2	2	3	3
GD10/86–1	1986		2	3	2
GD10/86–3	1986	PROOF 2	2	3	4
GD10/87–1	1987		2	3	2
GD10/87–3	1987	PROOF 2	2	3	3
GD10/88–1	1988		2	3	2
GD10/88–3	1988	PROOF 2	2	3	3
GD10/89–1	1989		2	3	2
GD10/89–3	1989	PROOF 2	2	3	3
GD10/90–1	1990		2	3	2
GD10/90–3	1990	PROOF 2	2	3	4
GD10/92–1	1992		3	4	2
GD10/92–3	1992	PROOF 2	3	4	5
GD10/97–1	1997		3	4	2
GD10/97–3	1997	PROOF	3	4	4

1. Issued from 24th February 1969.
2. Issued in cased sets.

No.	Date	Features	Obv.	Rev.	UNC
GD05/68–1	1968	1	1	1	1
GD05/71–3	1971	PROOF 2	1	1	2
GD05/77–1	1977		1	2	1
GD05/77–9	1979		1	2	1
GD05/79–3	1979	PROOF 2	1	2	2
GD05/81–3	1981	PROOF 2	1	2	2
GD05/82–1	1982		1	2	1
GD05/85–1	1985		2	3	1
GD05/85–3	1985	PROOF 2	2	3	2
GD05/86–1	1986		2	3	1
GD05/86–3	1986	PROOF 2	2	3	2
GD05/87–1	1987		2	3	1
GD05/87–3	1987	PROOF 2	2	3	2
GD05/88–1	1988		2	3	1
GD05/88–3	1988	PROOF 2	2	3	2
GD05/89–1	1989		2	3	1
GD05/89–3	1989	PROOF 2	2	3	2
GD05/90–1L	1990		2	3	1
GD05/90–3L	1990	PROOF 2	2	3	3
GD05/90–1S	1990		3	4	1
GD05/90–3S	1990	PROOF 2	3	4	3
GD05/92–1	1992		3	4	1

No.	Date	Features		Obv.	Rev.	UNC
GD05/92–3	1992	PROOF [2]		3	4	5
GD05/97–1	1997			3	4	1
GD05/97–3	1997	PROOF		3	4	3

1. Issued from 24th February 1969.
2. Issued in cased sets.

---

2 Pence

The Sark mill, depicted on the first reverses, was built in 1571. The 1971 issue thus commemorates its 400th anniversary.

Denomination	Metal	Weight (grams)	Diameter (mm)	Rev. alignment
2 pence 1977–90	Bronze	7.1	26	↑
2 pence 1992–	Copper-plated steel	7.1	26	↑

Obverse 1 Arms on shield, all within circle; S BALLIVIE INSVLE DE GERNEREVE

Obverse 2 Head 1, right, with Arms on left; ELIZABETH II BAILIWICK OF GUERNSEY

Reverse 1 Sark mill; 2 NEW PENCE 1971

Reverse 2 Sark mill; 2 TWO PENCE (date)

Reverse 3 Guernsey cow, 2 below; TWO PENCE (date)

Edge plain

Obv. 1   Obv. 2

Rev. 1   Rev. 2   Rev. 3

No.	Date	Features		Obv.	Rev.	UNC
GD02/71–1	1971			1	1	1
GD02/71–3	1971	PROOF [1]		1	1	2
GD02/77–1	1977			1	2	1
GD02/79–1	1979			1	2	1
GD02/79–3	1979	PROOF [1]		1	2	2
GD02/81–1	1981	PROOF [1]		1	2	2
GD02/85–1	1985			2	3	1
GD02/85–3	1985	PROOF [1]		2	3	2
GD02/86–1	1986			2	3	1
GD02/86–3	1986	PROOF [1]		2	3	2
GD02/87–1	1987			2	3	1
GD02/87–3	1987	PROOF [1]		2	3	2
GD02/88–1	1988			2	3	1
GD02/88–3	1988	PROOF [1]		2	3	2
GD02/89–1	1989			2	3	1
GD02/89–3	1989	PROOF [1]		2	3	2
GD02/90–1	1990			2	3	1
GD02/90–3	1990	PROOF [1]		2	3	3
GD02/92–1	1992	[1]		2	3	1
GD02/92–3	1992	PROOF [1]		2	3	4
GD02/97–1	1997			2	3	1

No.	Date	Features		Obv.	Rev.	UNC
GD02/97–3	1997	PROOF		2	3	3

1. Issued in cased sets.

Penny

The first issues depict a gannet, a symbol of Alderney, which at the time did not possess any coinage of its own.

Denomination	Metal	Weight (grams)	Diameter (mm)	Rev. alignment
Penny 1971–90	Bronze	3.6	20	↑
Penny 1992–	Copper-plated steel	3.6	20	↑

Obverse 1 Arms on shield, all within circle; S BALLIVIE INSVLE DE GERNEREVE

Obverse 2 Head 1, right, with Arms on left; ELIZABETH II BAILIWICK OF GUERNSEY

Reverse 1 Gannet in flight; 1 NEW PENNY 1971

Reverse 2 Gannet in flight; 1 ONE PENNY (date)

Reverse 3 Crab, 1 below; ONE PENNY (date)

Edge plain

Obv. 1   Obv. 2

Rev. 1   Rev. 2   Rev. 3

No.	Date	Features		Obv.	Rev.	UNC
GD01/71–1	1971			1	1	1
GD01/71–3	1971	PROOF [1]		1	1	2
GD01/77–1	1977			1	2	1
GD01/79–1	1979			1	2	1
GD01/79–3	1979	PROOF [1]		1	2	2
GD01/81–3	1981	PROOF [1]		1	2	2
GD01/85–1	1985			2	3	1
GD01/85–3	1985	PROOF [1]		2	3	2
GD01/86–1	1986			2	3	1
GD01/86–3	1986	PROOF [1]		2	3	2
GD01/87–1	1987			2	3	1
GD01/87–3	1987	PROOF [1]		2	3	2
GD01/88–1	1988			2	3	1
GD01/88–3	1988	PROOF [1]		2	3	2
GD01/89–1	1989			2	3	1
GD01/89–3	1989	PROOF [1]		2	3	2
GD01/90–1	1990			2	3	1
GD01/90–3	1990	PROOF [1]		2	3	3
GD01/92–1	1992	[1]		2	3	1
GD01/92–3	1992	PROOF [1]		2	3	3
GD01/94–1	1994			2	3	1
GD01/97–1	1997			2	3	1
GD01/97–3	1997	PROOF		2	3	3

1. Issued in cased sets.

Halfpenny

Denomination	Metal	Weight (grams)	Diameter (mm)	Rev. alignment
Halfpenny	Bronze	1.8	17	↑

Obverse 1 Arms on shield, all within circle; S BALLIVIE INSVLE DE GERNEREVE

Reverse 1 1/2 NEW PENNY 1971

Reverse 2 1/2 HALF PENNY 1979

Edge plain

Obv. 1

Rev. 2

No.	Date	Features	Obv.	Rev.	UNC
GDHP/71–1	1971		1	1	1
GDHP/71–3	1971	PROOF [1]	1	1	2
GDHP/79–3	1979	PROOF [1]	1	2	2

1. Issued in cased sets.

Guernsey: Proof Sets

1902

No.	Date	Striking Standard	No. of coins	Price
GPS-02	1902	Proof	4	2000

Denomination	Metal
8 doubles	Bronze
4 doubles	Bronze
2 doubles	Bronze
double	Bronze

1910

No.	Date	Striking Standard	No. of coins	Price
GPS-10	1910	Proof	2	1500

Denomination	Metal
8 doubles	Bronze
4 doubles	Bronze

1956

No.	Date	Striking Standard	No. of coins	Price
GPS-56	1956	Proof	6	50

Denomination	Metal
Threepence	Cupronickel
Threepence	Cupronickel
8 doubles	Bronze
8 doubles	Bronze
4 doubles	Bronze
4 doubles	Bronze

1966

No.	Date	Striking Standard	No. of coins	Price
GPS-66	1966	Proof	4	18

Denomination	Metal
10 shillings	Cupronickel
Threepence	Cupronickel
8 doubles	Bronze
4 doubles	Bronze

1971

No.	Date	Striking Standard	No. of coins	Price
GDPS-71	1971	Proof	6	15

Denomination	Metal
50 pence	Cupronickel
10 pence	Cupronickel
5 pence	Cupronickel
2 pence	Bronze
Penny	Bronze
Halfpenny	Bronze

1979

No.	Date	Striking Standard	No. of coins	Price
GDPS-79	1979	Proof	6	16

Denomination	Metal
50 pence	Cupronickel
10 pence	Cupronickel
5 pence	Cupronickel
2 pence	Bronze
Penny	Bronze
Halfpenny	Bronze

1981

No.	Date	Striking Standard	No. of coins	Price
GDPS-81	1981	Proof	6	18

Denomination	Metal
Pound	Nickel brass
50 pence	Cupronickel
10 pence	Cupronickel
5 pence	Cupronickel
2 pence	Bronze
Penny	Bronze

1985

No.	Date	Striking Standard	No. of coins	Price
GDPS-85	1985	Proof	8	40

Denomination	Metal
2 pounds	Cupronickel
Pound	Nickel brass
50 pence	Cupronickel
20 pence	Cupronickel
10 pence	Cupronickel
5 pence	Cupronickel
2 pence	Bronze
Penny	Bronze

1986

No.	Date	Striking Standard	No. of coins	Price
GDPS-86	1986	Proof	8	40

Denomination	Metal
2 pounds	Cupronickel
Pound	Nickel brass
50 pence	Cupronickel
20 pence	Cupronickel
10 pence	Cupronickel
5 pence	Cupronickel
2 pence	Bronze
Penny	Bronze

1987

No.	Date	Striking Standard	No. of coins	Price
GDPS-87	1987	Proof	8	40

Denomination	Metal
2 pounds	Cupronickel
Pound	Nickel brass
50 pence	Cupronickel
20 pence	Cupronickel
10 pence	Cupronickel
5 pence	Cupronickel
2 pence	Bronze
Penny	Bronze

1988

No.	Date	Striking Standard	No. of coins	Price
GDPS-88	1988	Proof	8	40

Denomination	Metal
2 pounds	Cupronickel
Pound	Nickel brass
50 pence	Cupronickel
20 pence	Cupronickel
10 pence	Cupronickel
5 pence	Cupronickel
2 pence	Bronze
Penny	Bronze

1989

No.	Date	Striking Standard	No. of coins	Price
GDPS-89	1989	Proof	8	40

Denomination	Metal
2 pounds	Cupronickel
Pound	Nickel brass
50 pence	Cupronickel
20 pence	Cupronickel
10 pence	Cupronickel
5 pence	Cupronickel
2 pence	Bronze
Penny	Bronze

1990

No.	Date	Striking Standard	No. of coins	Price
GDPS-90	1990	Proof	8	50

Denomination	Metal
Pound	Nickel brass
50 pence	Cupronickel
20 pence	Cupronickel
10 pence	Cupronickel
5 pence (24 mm)	Cupronickel
5 pence (18 mm)	Cupronickel
2 pence	Bronze
Penny	Bronze

1992

No.	Date	Striking Standard	No. of coins	Price
GDPS-92	1992	Proof	7	55

Denomination	Metal
Pound	Nickel brass
50 pence	Cupronickel
20 pence	Cupronickel
10 pence	Cupronickel
5 pence	Cupronickel
2 pence	Copper-plated steel
Penny	Copper-plated steel

1994

No.	Date	Striking Standard	No. of coins	Price
GDPS-94	1994	Proof	4	1000

Denomination	Metal
100 pounds	0.999 gold
50 pounds	0.999 gold
25 pounds	0.999 gold
10 pounds	0.999 gold

1995

No.	Date	Striking Standard	No. of coins	Price
GDPS-95	1995	Proof	4	1000

Denomination	Metal
100 pounds	0.999 gold
50 pounds	0.999 gold
25 pounds	0.999 gold
10 pounds	0.999 gold

1996

No.	Date	Striking Standard	No. of coins	Price
GDPS-96	1996	Proof	2	200

Denomination	Metal
25 pounds	0.999 gold
5 pounds	0.925 silver

1997

No.	Date	Striking Standard	No. of coins	Price
GDPS-97	1997	Proof	3	280

Denomination	Metal
25 pounds	0.999 gold
5 pounds	0.925 silver
Pound	0.925 silver

No.	Date	Striking Standard	No. of coins	Price
GDPS-97A	1997	Proof	10	40

Denomination	Metal
5 pounds	0.925 silver
2 pounds	Bimetallic

Pound	Nickel brass
50 pence (30 mm)	Cupronickel
50 pence (27 mm)	Cupronickel
20 pence	Cupronickel
10 pence	Cupronickel
5 pence	Cupronickel
2 pence	Copper-plated steel
Penny	Copper-plated steel

Specimen Sets

1985

No.	Date	Striking Standard	No. of coins	Price
GDMS-85	1985	Specimen	8	12

Denomination	Metal
2 pounds	Cupronickel
Pound	Nickel brass
50 pence	Cupronickel
20 pence	Cupronickel
10 pence	Cupronickel
5 pence	Cupronickel
2 pence	Bronze
Penny	Bronze

1986

No.	Date	Striking Standard	No. of coins	Price
GDMS-86	1986	Specimen	7	8

Denomination	Metal
Pound	Nickel brass
50 pence	Cupronickel
20 pence	Cupronickel
10 pence	Cupronickel
5 pence	Cupronickel
2 pence	Bronze
Penny	Bronze

1987

No.	Date	Striking Standard	No. of coins	Price
GDMS-87	1987	Specimen	7	8

Denomination	Metal
Pound	Nickel brass
50 pence	Cupronickel
20 pence	Cupronickel
10 pence	Cupronickel
5 pence	Cupronickel
2 pence	Bronze
Penny	Bronze

1988

No.	Date	Striking Standard	No. of coins	Price
GDMS-88	1988	Specimen	7	8

Denomination	Metal
Pound	Nickel brass
50 pence	Cupronickel
20 pence	Cupronickel
10 pence	Cupronickel
5 pence	Cupronickel
2 pence	Bronze
Penny	Bronze

1989

No.	Date	Striking Standard	No. of coins	Price
GDMS-89	1989	Specimen	7	8

Denomination	Metal
Pound	Nickel brass
50 pence	Cupronickel
20 pence	Cupronickel
10 pence	Cupronickel
5 pence	Cupronickel
2 pence	Bronze
Penny	Bronze

1990

No.	Date	Striking Standard	No. of coins	Price
GDMS-90	1990	Specimen	8	10

Denomination	Metal
Pound	Nickel brass
50 pence	Cupronickel
20 pence	Cupronickel
10 pence	Cupronickel
5 pence (24 mm)	Cupronickel
5 pence (18 mm)	Cupronickel
2 pence	Bronze
Penny	Bronze

1992

No.	Date	Striking Standard	No. of coins	Price
GDMS-92	1992	Specimen	7	8

Denomination	Metal
Pound	Nickel brass
50 pence	Cupronickel
20 pence	Cupronickel
10 pence	Cupronickel
5 pence	Cupronickel
2 pence	Copper-plated steel
Penny	Copper-plated steel

1997

No.	Date	Striking Standard	No. of coins	Price
GDMS-97	1997	Specimen	9	20

Denomination	Metal
2 pounds	Bimetallic
Pound	Nickel brass
50 pence (30 mm)	Cupronickel
50 pence (27 mm)	Cupronickel
20 pence	Cupronickel
10 pence	Cupronickel

Specimen Sets

5 pence	Cupronickel
2 pence	Copper-plated steel
Penny	Copper-plated steel

Guernsey: Mintage Information & Figures

Billet d'Etat of 13th September 1922

The value of the coins exported, i.e. Francs	73853.17.10
Export charges	18.15.1
Commission to banks for collection of the old coinage and putting into circulation of new	1500.0.0
Balance, i.e. profit on the conversion	5679.9.9
Total = Silver received from British Government in exchange for French coins	81052.2.8

Mintage figures

For Guernsey, the entry in the date column signifies the date on the coin rather than the year of production.

10 shillings

Date	Mintage
1966	300,000 [1]
1966	10,000 [2]

1. Non-proof
2. Proof

3 pence

Date	Mintage
1956	500,000+ [1]
1956	2,100 [2]
1959	480,000
1966	10,000 [2]

1. Non-proof
2. Proof

8 doubles

Date	Mintage
1834	221,760 [1]
1858	111,469 [2]
1864	284,736 [3]
1868	54,720 [4]
1874	73,248 [4]
1885-H	69,696 [5]
1889-H	215,620 [6]
1893-H	117,600
1902-H	235,200 [7]
1903-H	117,600
1910-H	91,467
1911-H	78,400
1914-H	156,800
1918-H	156,800
1920-H	156,800
1934-H	123,600 [8]
1934-H burnished flan	500
1938-H	120,000
1945-H	192,000
1947-H	240,000
1949-H	230,400
1956	480,000 [9]

Date	Mintage
1956	2,100 [10]
1959	480,000
1966	10,000 [10]

1. Struck at Boulton, Watt & Co. Figures include coins struck in 1834, 36, 37, 39
2. Struck at Henry Toy & Co.
3. Struck at Henry Toy & Co. Includes some struck in 1865 but dated 1864.
4. Struck at Partridge & Co.
5. This and later dates struck at Ralph Heaton & Sons, later The Mint (Birmingham) Ltd.
6. Figure includes some struck in 1890 but dated 1889.
7. All struck in 1901
8. Not including burnished flan variety.
9. Non-proof
10. Proof

4 doubles

Date	Mintage
1830	655,200 [1]
1858	114,060 [2]
1864	212,976 [3]
1868	57,696 [4]
1874	69,216 [4]
1885-H	69,696 [5]
1889-H	103,744 [6]
1893-H	52,224
1902-H	104,534 [7]
1903-H	52,267
1906-H	52,266
1908-H	25,760
1910-H	52,267
1911-H	52,267
1914-H	209,067
1918-H	156,800
1920-H	156,800
1945-H	96,000
1949-H	19,200
1956	240,000 [8]
1956	2,100 [9]
1966	10,000

1. Struck at Boulton, Watt & Co. Figures include coins struck in 1830, 31, 36, 37, 39
2. Struck at Henry Toy & Co.
3. Struck at Henry Toy & Co. Includes some struck in 1865 but dated 1864.
4. Struck at Partridge & Co.
5. This and later dates struck at Ralph Heaton & Sons, later The Mint (Birmingham) Ltd.
6. Figure includes some struck in 1890 but dated 1889.
7. All struck in 1901
8. Non-proof
9. Proof

2 doubles

Date	Mintage
1858	56,128 [1]
1868	35,136 [2]
1874	45,216 [2]
1885-H	76,800 [3]
1889-H	35,616
1899-H	35,636
1902-H	17,818 [4]
1903-H	17,818
1906-H	17,820
1908-H	17,780
1911-H	28,509
1914-H	28,509
1917-H	14,524

1918-H	57,018
1920-H	57,018
1929-H	79,100

1. Struck at Henry Toy & Co.
2. Struck at Partridge & Co.
3. This and later dates struck at Ralph Heaton & Sons, later The Mint (Birmingham) Ltd.
4. All struck in 1901

Double

Date	Mintage
1830	1,648,640 [1]
1868	64,368 [2]
1885-H	76,800 [3]
1889-H	112,016 [4]
1893-H	56,016
1899-H	56,000
1902-H	84,000 [5]
1903-H	112,000
1911-H	67,200
1914-H	44,800
1929-H	79,100
1933-H	96,000
1938-H	96,000

1. Struck at Boulton, Watt & Co.
2. Struck at Partridge & Co.
3. This and later dates struck at Ralph Heaton & Sons, later The Mint (Birmingham) Ltd.
4. Figure includes some struck in 1890 but dated 1889.
5. All struck in 1901

The milled coinage of Alderney
Decimal Coinage

Alderney, the most northerly of the Channel Islands, has no history of coinage struck specifically for the island until the issues of 1989 and later, which are more in the nature of commercial souvenir issues than circulatory pieces.

100 Pounds

Denomination	Metal	Weight (grams)	Diameter (mm)	Rev. alignment
100 pounds	0.999 gold	31.2	33	↑

Obverse 1   Head 1, right; QUEEN ELIZABETH THE SECOND 1994

Reverse 1   Invasion scene; ALDERNEY D-DAY ANNIVERSARY 100 POUNDS

Edge   milled

Obv. 1   Rev. 1

No.	Date	Features	Obv.	Rev.	Unc
AD100P/94–6	1994	PROOF [1]	1	1	500

1. Issued in cased sets.

50 Pounds

Denomination	Metal	Weight (grams)	Diameter (mm)	Rev. alignment
50 pounds	0.999 gold	15.6	27	↑

Obverse 1   Head 1, right; QUEEN ELIZABETH THE SECOND 1994

Reverse 1   Invasion scene with gliders; ALDERNEY D-DAY ANNIVERSARY 50 POUNDS

Edge   milled

Obv. 1   Rev. 1

No.	Date	Features	Obv.	Rev.	Unc
AD50P/94–6	1994	PROOF [1]	1	1	200

1. Issued in cased sets.

25 Pounds

Denomination	Metal	Weight (grams)	Diameter (mm)	Rev. alignment
25 pounds 1993	0.917 gold	8.5	22	↑
25 pounds 1994	0.999 gold	7.8	21	↑

Obverse 1   Head 1, right; QUEEN ELIZABETH THE SECOND (date)

Reverse 1   Coronation coach; CORONATION ANNIVERSARY £25 ALDERNEY

Reverse 2   Invasion scene with fighter planes and tank; ALDERNEY D-DAY ANNIVERSARY 25 POUNDS

Edge   milled

Obv. 1   Rev. 1

No.	Date	Features	Obv.	Rev.	Unc
AD25P/93–6	1993	PROOF [1]	1	1	130
AD25P/94–6	1994	PROOF [2]	1	2	130

1. Issued cased.
2. Issued in cased sets.

10 Pounds

Denomination	Metal	Weight (grams)	Diameter (mm)	Rev. alignment
10 pounds	0.999 gold	3.1	16	↑

Obverse 1   Head 1, right; QUEEN ELIZABETH THE SECOND 1994

Reverse 1   Invasion scene with paratroopers; ALDERNEY D-DAY ANNIVERSARY 10 POUNDS

Edge   milled

Obv. 1   Rev. 1

No.	Date	Features	Obv.	Rev.	Unc
AD10P/94–6	1994	PROOF [1]	1	1	65

1. Issued in cased sets.

5 Pounds

Denomination	Metal	Weight (grams)	Diameter (mm)	Rev. alignment
5 pounds	Cupronickel	28.3	39	↑

Obverse 1   Head 1, right; ELIZABETH II ALDERNEY

Reverse 1   Queen Mother with two children; QUEEN ELIZABETH THE QUEEN MOTHER 1995 5 POUNDS

Reverse 2   Rose, thistle, daffodil, clover (representing four parts of United Kingdom) with crown below; TO CELEBRATE THE 70TH YEAR OF HER MAJESTY 1996 £5 (for the Queen's 70th Birthday)

Edge   milled

Obv. 1   Rev. 1

No.	Date	Features	Obv.	Rev.	Unc
AD5P/95–1	1995		1	1	8
AD5P/95–4	1995	PROOF in 0.925 silver [1]	1	1	30
AD5P/95–5	1995	PIEDFORT PROOF in 0.925 silver [2]	1	1	70
AD5P/95–6	1995	PROOF in 0.917 gold [3]	1	1	750
AD5P/96–1	1996		1	2	8
AD5P/96–4	1996	PROOF in 0.925 silver [1]	1	2	30
AD5P/96–5	1996	PIEDFORT PROOF in 0.925 silver [2]	1	2	70
AD5P/96–6	1996	PROOF in 0.917 gold [3]	1	2	750

1. Issued cased.
2. Issued cased. Weight 56.6 grams.
3. Issued cased. Weight 47.5 grams.

2 Pounds

Denomination	Metal	Weight (grams)	Diameter (mm)	Rev. alignment
2 pounds	Cupronickel	28.3	39	↑

Obverse 1   Head 1, right; QUEEN ELIZABETH THE SECOND (date)

Obverse 2   Head 2, right; ELIZABETH II ALDERNEY

Reverse 1   Alderney Crest of lion rampant, surrounded by thrift plant; ALDERNEY ROYAL VISIT TWO POUNDS

Reverse 2   Head of Queen Mother within oval cameo of pearls, flanked by Glamis roses; THE QUEEN MOTHER NINETIETH BIRTHDAY ALDERNEY TWO POUNDS

Reverse 3   Norman longship; crowned EIIR within wreath; ALDERNEY TWO POUNDS 40TH ANNIVERSARY OF REIGN

Reverse 4   Coronation coach with Union and Alderney Flags; ALDERNEY TWO POUNDS CORONATION ANNIVERSARY

Reverse 5   Invasion scene; ALDERNEY TWO POUNDS D-DAY ANNIVERSARY (for the 50th anniversary of D-Day)

Reverse 6   SS Autocarrier approaching Alderney; OUR DEAR CHANNEL ISLANDS ARE ALSO TO BE FREED; 1945–1995 THE RETURN OF THE ISLANDERS TWO POUNDS

Reverse 7   Puffin; WWF CONSERVING NATURE 1997 TWO POUNDS (for the World Wildlife Fund)

Reverse 8   Prince of Wales Investiture scene; 1947 ELIZABETH AND PHILIP 1997 TWO POUNDS (for the Queen's Golden Wedding)

Edge   milled

Obv. 1   Rev. 1

Rev. 2   Rev. 3

No.	Date	Features	Obv.	Rev.	Unc
AD2P/89–1	1989		1	1	5
AD2P/89–4	1989	PROOF in 0.925 silver [1]	1	1	25
AD2P/89–5	1989	PIEDFORT PROOF in 0.925 silver [2]	1	1	70
AD2P/89–6	1989	PROOF in 0.917 gold [3]	1	1	750
AD2P/90–1	1990		1	2	5
AD2P/90–4	1990	PROOF in 0.925 silver [1]	1	2	25
AD2P/90–5	1990	PIEDFORT PROOF in 0.925 silver [2]	1	2	70
AD2P/90–6	1990	PROOF in 0.917 gold [3]	1	2	800
AD2P/92–1	1992		1	3	5
AD2P/92–4	1992	PROOF in 0.925 silver [1]	1	3	25
AD2P/92–5	1992	PIEDFORT PROOF in 0.925 silver [2]	1	3	65
AD2P/92–6	1992	PROOF in 0.917 gold [3]	1	3	750
AD2P/93–1	1993		1	4	5
AD2P/93–4	1993	PROOF in 0.925 silver [1]	1	4	25
AD2P/93–5	1993	PIEDFORT PROOF in 0.925 silver [2]	1	4	70
AD2P/94–1	1994		1	5	5
AD2P/94–4	1994	PROOF in 0.925 silver [1]	1	5	25
AD2P/94–5	1994	PIEDFORT PROOF in 0.925 silver [2]	1	5	70
AD2P/95–1	1995		2	6	5
AD2P/95–4	1995	PROOF in 0.925 silver [1]	2	6	25
AD2P/95–5	1995	PIEDFORT PROOF in 0.925 silver [2]	2	6	70
AD2P/95–6	1995	PROOF in 0.917 gold [3]	2	6	700
AD2P/97–1	1997		2	7	5
AD2P/97–4	1997	PROOF in 0.925 silver [1]	2	7	25
AD2P/97–6	1997	PROOF in 0.917 gold [3]	2	7	700
AD2P/97–1A	1997		2	8	5
AD2P/97–4A	1997	PROOF in 0.925 silver with gold cameo insert [1]	2	8	35
AD2P/97–6A	1997	PROOF in 0.917 gold [3]	2	8	700

1. Issued cased.
2. Issued cased. Weight 56.6 grams.
3. Issued cased. Weight 47.5 grams.

Pound				
Denomination	Metal	Weight (grams)	Diameter (mm)	Rev. alignment
Pound	0.925 silver	9.5	22	↑

Obverse 1 Head 1, right; QUEEN ELIZABETH THE SECOND 1993

Obverse 2 Head 2, right; ELIZABETH II ALDERNEY

Reverse 1 Coronation coach; CORONATION ANNIVERSARY £1 ALDERNEY

Reverse 2 VE monogram; PEACE IN EUROPE ONE POUND 1945 1995 (for the 50th anniversary of VE Day)

Edge milled

Obv. 1

Rev. 1

No.	Date	Features	Obv.	Rev.	Unc
AD1P/93–4	1993	PROOF	1	1	30
AD1P/95–4	1995	PROOF	2	2	30
AD1P/95–6	1995	PROOF in 0.917 gold [1]	2	2	250

1. Weight 15.8 grams.

Alderney: Proof Sets

	1994			
No.	Date	Striking Standard	No. of coins	Price
ADPS-94	1994	Proof	5	950

Denomination	Metal
100 pounds	0.999 gold
50 pounds	0.999 gold
25 pounds	0.999 gold
10 pounds	0.999 gold
2 pounds	0.925 silver

No.	Date	Striking Standard	No. of coins	Price
ADPS-94A	1994	Proof	4	900

Denomination	Metal
100 pounds	0.999 gold
50 pounds	0.999 gold
25 pounds	0.999 gold
10 pounds	0.999 gold

No.	Date	Striking Standard	No. of coins	Price
ADPS-94B	1994	Proof	4	450

Denomination	Metal
50 pounds	0.999 gold
25 pounds	0.999 gold
10 pounds	0.999 gold
2 pounds	0.925 silver

No.	Date	Striking Standard	No. of coins	Price
ADPS-94C	1994	Proof	3	420

Denomination	Metal
50 pounds	0.999 gold
25 pounds	0.999 gold
10 pounds	0.999 gold

Isle of Man

Isle of Man: Hiberno-Manx issue

This issue was struck between 1025 and 1035 AD. The only denomination struck was the penny and the style was greatly influenced by the Hiberno-Norse issues of Ireland which in turn copied the design from the English Aethelred II long cross penny.

This issue is very crude in style and should not be confused with issues of Ireland and England; the Hiberno-Manx penny has crude blundered legends, a cruder style bust and minor marks of design which differentiate it.

Hiberno-Manx Penny   (1025 — 1035)

Collecting Hints

This issue is extremely rare, although several coins have come on to the market in the last few years.

Obverse Legend   Blundered legend.

Reverse Legend   Blundered legend.

Obverse   Crude bust of the king facing right, a quatrefoil at the beginning of the legend, sometimes a quatrefoil on the king's neck, four pellets usually behind the king's head.

Reverse   Voided long cross, a small pellet in each quarter.

MHM1D-005   ex. rare

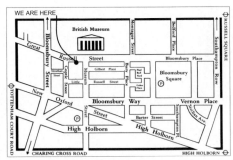

The milled coinage of the Isle of Man

The Isle of Man occupies an area of about 230 square miles, and lies in the Irish Sea about equidistantly from Scotland, Northern Ireland and England. Once an independent kingdom, it now stands as a dependency of the British Crown, yet it is not part of the United Kingdom, nor, somewhat surprisingly, is it a member of the EU; it is excluded under Protocol 3 of The Treaty of Rome. The island has its own parliament, the Tynwald, and occupies an important position as an offshore banking centre. British Acts of Parliament apply to the Isle of Man only if this fact is specifically mentioned in the relevant Act.

Roman, Saxon, Hiberno-Norse and other coinage circulated in the Isle of Man in early times, and some evidence exists that Hiberno-Norse coins were struck on the island for local use. Small quantities of Roman coins have also been found in the south of the island. While the Isle of Man was under Scottish rule in the fourteenth century, local gold and copper pieces were recorded, but appear to be unknown today. However, the gold piece reported by Nelson as a 14th century Manx coin is now considered to be a 16th century Scottish medal.

In the sixteenth century, tokens of leather are reported to have circulated. John Meyrick, a bishop of the island and the vicar of Hornchurch, Essex, wrote in 1577 in Camden's 'Britannia' that the Isle of Man has 'its own peculiar laws and money'. Henry Dodwell, in a letter of 1707 to Thomas Hearne, wrote: 'One Mr. Gilbert, a petty canon of St. Asaph ... told me that, in clearing the castle (i.e Castle Rushen) they found a room full of old leather coyn, such as he supposed to have been the current coyn of the island formerly. But they had no regard for it, and threw it away. If the Bp. can retrieve any of it, and it have any letters stamped on it, it may be of use to you'. Waldron, writing in 1730 about life on the island in the second half of the sixteenth century, noted that 'every man of substance was entitled to make leather money not exceeding a certain amount by law. On one side only was impressed with the name and the party issuing it, and the date'. Very few examples of leather tokens have been found.

In 'Liber Sacch', dated 1663 in the Rolls Office, Castle Rushen (Isle of Man), there is a reference to 'Mansk halfcrowns'. No such pieces are known today.

In the mid-seventeenth century ducatoons (known locally as 'duck(e)toons') from the Low Countries circulated at six shillings together with their halves and quarters. These were probably brought to the island as a result of barter. English coins were also in use, and many forgeries circulated alongside the genuine pieces. In 1646 an Act of Tynwald rendered it treasonable 'to falsify, forge and counterfeit, clipp and diminish any kind of current coin'. The drafting of the legislation was wider than that in force in England, where only the counterfeiting of gold and silver was actionable.

Many unofficial tokens were in use during the seventeenth century, and it fell to such a piece to become the first legally circulating coin of the island. In 1668, John Murrey issued penny tokens, probably struck in Birmingham, bearing his name and the denomination on one side, and the triune (see below) on the reverse. These circulated alongside other unofficial tokens for some years, but possibly acquired some form of respectability, since the Tynwald Act of 24th June 1679 outlawed the tokens in circulation (including St. Patrick pieces from Ireland and 'Butchers' Brass') as from 1st January 1680 (1679 old style calendar) but specifically excluded the Murrey pieces.

Anglo-Irish halfpennies of around 1680 and later were legal tender on the island as farthings, and after the routing of James II from Ireland in 1690, his issue of gunmoney halfcrowns and shillings circulated unofficially as halfpennies and farthings respectively.

The triune depicted on the Murrey coinage is a symbol of the Isle of Man, and has remained on almost all Isle of Man coinage to this day. Known also as the triquetra and the triskelis, the symbol consists of three legs, mutually joined at the hip, and symmetrically placed so that the feet appear to be running around the edge of the coin. It is an ancient symbol, and appears on, for example, pre-Christian coinage of Asia Minor and on a Panathenaic vase in the British Museum. It is possible that it was chosen to symbolize the Isle of Man because of the island's roughly equidistant location from Scotland, England and Ireland in roughly equally spaced directions. The legs of the triune frequently sport armour and spurs, a variation introduced in the 13th century. The legend QUOCUNQUE JECERIS STABIT (Whichever way you throw it, it stands) often accompanies the triune. The symbolism of the triune is elegantly represented in the words inscribed on the old House of Keys:

> 'Three legs armed,
> Armed in self-defence,
> Centrally United,
> Security from thence.'

It is perhaps not generally appreciated that, despite the variations in design of the triune on the coinage of the Isle of Man, the basic symbol itself is depicted on the coins in two distinct forms which are respectively mirror images. Hence, for cataloguing purposes, if the leg from the centre of the symbol is followed outwards and then bends at the knee to the left, this is termed 'type 1', and, if it bends to the right, this is 'type 2'.

Type 1   Type 2

In 1709, the Earl of Derby (the then current 'Lord of Man') issued cast pennies and halfpennies of poor workmanship, which were legalized on 24th June 1710. The coins, probably cast on the island but just possibly manufactured in England, were not popular, and the legends were ridiculed by the inhabitants of the island. Isaac Newton, the Master of the Royal Mint, had in 1708 refused to produce an issue of coinage for the island.

Patterns dated 1723 and 1724 of considerably superior quality are known, and it is puzzling why these were not adopted as coinage. Similar patterns dated 1732 were followed in 1733 by an issue of coinage, but the patterns differ considerably from the adopted coinage.

By 1733, the island was so overrun with counterfeits that the Tynwald Act of that year declared all previously issued coins illegal. The Earl of Derby issued penny and halfpenny coinage with a somewhat similar design to that of 1709, but the coins were struck and of high quality. Although often stated to have been struck in England, there is evidence that at least some may have been struck on the island (see main listings).

In 1736 the Isle of Man had been inherited by James Murray, the second Duke of Atholl, on the death of James, Earl of Derby, and in 1758 he issued a total of £400 worth of penny and half-penny coins bearing a coronetted monogrammed 'AD' and the date. Although this could be taken to indicate 'Anno Domini', there seems little doubt that it refers to 'Atholl Dux (or Duke)'. The coins were of inferior quality to those of 1733 and were unpopular.

In 1765, the Duke sold the island to the British Crown for £70,000, together with an annuity of £2,000; the British Government was pleased to acquire a territory which had been the seat of an extensive smuggling trade for a considerable period, to the detriment of the revenues of Britain. However, it appears to have taken little heed of the coinage needs of the island, as it waited a further 21 years before introducing regal copper currency, and this was at a time when small change was sorely needed. Crellin writes that at this time eggs were sold on the island at the rate of sixteen for a penny. The coins introduced, again with denominations of penny and halfpenny, displayed an elegant laureate bust of George III designed by Lewis Pingo, with the triune on the reverse. Interestingly, although struck at the Royal Mint, the penny was issued over ten years before the introduction of a copper penny on the British mainland. This Isle of Man coinage was issued for only one year, 1786.

In 1798 and 1813 there were issues of pennies and halfpennies which were very similar to the British 1797 cartwheel issues, and struck at the same Soho mint, Birmingham, by Matthew Boulton. Prior to the 1813 issue many tokens were in circulation on the British mainland, and the fashion for these spread to the Isle of Man. Notable amongst them were the Peel Castle tokens of 1811.

From 1813 until 1839 there were no legal coins struck specifically for the Isle of Man, and to ameliorate the situation every conceivable form of token or substitute coin was brought into circulation. Even buttons of various types were used. Special mention might be made of the 1830 token sometimes termed 'McTurk's token' or 'Cain's token', which reputedly bears the worst likeness of George III (or IV?) ever to be struck.

An Act of 10th April 1839 decreed that 'the currency of Great Britain shall be and become, and is hereby declared to be, the currency of the Isle of Man', and during that year a set of penny, halfpenny and farthing were struck at the Royal Mint specifically for the island. The obverses were identical to the British issue (except that the British penny and halfpenny of that year were struck only as proofs) and the reverse depicted the triune with its familiar accompanying legend. On 4th May 1840 a Proclamation decreed that from 21st September of that year the Manx 14-penny shilling would be abandoned in favour of a 12-penny shilling and that 'all copper coin of the currency of this island, passing after the rate of 14 pence, or 28 halfpence, for the shilling, British, shall cease to be current'. The heavy-handed approach of the British government was not appreciated, and there was rioting in the streets of Douglas and Peel, the so-called 'Copper Row', which was speedily quelled by the military. A subsequent Treasury Memorandum of 13th July 1842 noted that the old copper coin withdrawn from circulation totalled 59 pounds and 19 shillings 'and it is supposed that no more remains in circulation'.

Maud Lister, in a Paper given before the Lancashire Numismatic Society on 22nd March 1947, conjectured thus about the portrayal of the triune during the history of the island: 'If you will imagine the Legs to be a man standing on the Isle of Man, you will see that on the first Stanley coin (1709), the Man is in a kneeling posture, towards Ireland; on the 1733 coins he has

changed his position and is kneeling to England, as he also is on the Atholl issue (1758). But observe, so soon as ever the island was sold to England, the Man isn't kneeling to anybody, and he isn't even looking at England — and on the George III first issue (1786) he is running, and running at top speed, towards Ireland. He keeps on at this rate through the issues of 1798 and 1813. With the Victorian issue in 1839 his pace has decreased somewhat, but he still has his back turned on England, and is away to Ireland at as great a speed as possible'.

In 1862, the coinage of the Isle of Man and Britain were deemed to be unified, and this arrangement persisted until the reign of Elizabeth II. For much of the twentieth century, the parity of the Irish and British pounds stood at 1:1, and during this period Irish coinage also circulated on the island. In 1977, when the U.K. still had exchange controls, a report to the Tynwald parliament proposed that the Manx pound should divorce from sterling and maintain a tied parity with either the Mark, Yen or U.S. dollar, but nothing came of the proposal.

Sets of proofs and specimen gold coins for the Isle of Man were struck in 1965, together with crowns in 1970 just prior to decimalization. The decimal Royal Mint and Pobjoy issues of the Isle of Man were largely compatible with the British issues, but this period of numismatic history was complicated by the enormous output of coin-medal issues struck by the Pobjoy Mint. As an example, in 1995 this mint issued 46 different coins with the denomination of one-fifth of a crown. In this first edition, at least, many of the Pobjoy issues are covered in a summarized form.

In the tables, the 'reverse alignment' entry takes an ironical twist in the case of Isle of Man coinage, when the reverse may comprise only a symmetrical triune with a legend around the rim. On those coins where an upright stance for the reverse can be deduced from some aspect, such as a date, the reverse alignment is given; where the term becomes meaningless, this is indicated appropriately by 'QJS' (Quocunque Jeceris Stabit = Whichever way you throw it, it stands).

> However thro' the world he's tost
> However disappointed, crost,
> Reverses, losses, Fortune's frown,
> No Chance nor change can keep him down:
> Upset him any way you will,
> Upon his legs you find him still:
> For ever active, brisk and spunky,
> 'Stabit, Jeceris, Quocunque'.
>
> ANON. LOCAL POET

Isle of Man: Pre-Decimal Issues
Five Pounds

The only pre-decimal gold five pounds was struck for inclusion in the proof and specimen sets of 1965. These sets comprised three gold coins, the five pounds, sovereign (pound) and half sovereign (half pound). The sets were struck to commemorate the bicentenary of the acquisition of the Isle of Man by the Crown from the Duke of Atholl, and the two sets were issued in two slightly differently shaped green cases (see also proof and specimen set listings).

In assessing the bullion value of any proof set of 1965 being offered for sale, it must be remembered that these sets were struck in gold with the unusually high fineness standard of 0.980. Specimen issues are sometimes wrongly catalogued as proofs (e.g. in auctions), and it is helpful to remember that the proof set was issued in a square (not rectangular) case.

Denomination	Metal	Weight (grams)	Diameter (mm)	Rev. alignment
Five Pounds proof	0.980 gold	39.95	37	↑
Five Pounds non-proof	0.917 gold	39.94	37	↑

Obverse 1 Head 1, right; 1765 BICENTENARY OF THE REVESTMENT ACT 1965

Reverse 1 Triune (type 1) on shield within wreath; QUOCUNQUE JECERIS STABIT

Edge milled

Obv. 1   Rev. 1

No.	Date	Features	Obv.	Rev.	Unc
MEL25P-005	1965	[1]	1	1	400
MEL25P-010	1965	PROOF [1]	1	1	500

1. Issued cased and in cased three-coin sets.

Isle of Man: Pound (or Sovereign)

The gold pound was part of the proof and non-proof three-coin sets issued for the bicentenary of the purchase of the Isle of Man by the Crown from the Duke of Atholl. The coin was also issued cased singly, both in proof and non-proof. The weight of the proof coin is slightly above that of the British sovereign because of the marginally higher specific gravity of 0.980 gold compared with the 22 carat standard of the mainland coins.

Denomination	Metal	Weight (grams)	Diameter (mm)	Rev. alignment
Pound proof	0.980 gold	8.00	22	↑
Pound non-proof	0.917 gold	7.99	22	↑

Obverse 1 Head 1, right; 1765 BICENTENARY OF THE REVESTMENT ACT 1965

Reverse 1 Triune (type 1) on shield within wreath; QUOCUNQUE JECERIS STABIT

Edge milled

Obv. 1

Rev. 1

No.	Date	Features	Obv.	Rev.	Unc
MEL2SV-005	1965	[1]	1	1	80
MEL2SV-010	1965	PROOF [1]	1	1	100

1. Issued cased and in cased three-coin sets.

Isle of Man: Half Pound (or Half Sovereign)

The gold half pound was, like the 5 and 1 pound coins, part of the proof and non-proof three-coin sets issued for the bicentenary of the purchase of the Isle of Man by the Crown from the Duke of Atholl. The coin was also issued cased singly, both in proof and non-proof.

Denomination	Metal	Weight (grams)	Diameter (mm)	Rev. alignment
Half pound proof	0.980 gold	4.00	19	↑
Half pound non-proof	0.917 gold	3.99	19	↑

Obverse 1 Head 1, right; 1765 BICENTENARY OF THE REVESTMENT ACT 1965

Reverse 1 Triune (type 1) on shield within wreath; QUOCUNQUE JECERIS STABIT

Edge milled

Obv. 1

Rev. 1

No.	Date	Features	Obv.	Rev.	Unc
MEL2HS-005	1965	[1]	1	1	50
MEL2HS-010	1965	PROOF [1]	1	1	60

1. Issued cased and in cased three-coin sets.

Isle of Man: Crown

The only Isle of Man pre-decimal crown piece, and therefore the only Manx coin denominated at five shillings, was the 1970 'cat' crown struck at the Royal Mint. The coin was struck both as a cupronickel ordinary coin and as a sterling silver proof, the latter being issued in a white case reminiscent of that used for the Gibraltar 1967 proof crown. The coin uses the Arnold Machin bust of Elizabeth II and depicts a Christopher Ironside design of a tailless Manx cat on the reverse, and is unusual in being a pre-decimal coin not depicting the triune; this issue was the last five-shilling piece struck in the British Isles.

Denomination	Metal	Weight (grams)	Diameter (mm)	Rev. alignment
Crown (proof)	0.925 silver	28.3	39	↑
Crown (non-proof)	Cupronickel	28.3	39	↑

Obverse 1   Head 1, right; ELIZABETH THE SECOND

Reverse 1   Manx cat; ISLE OF MAN ONE CROWN 1970

Edge   milled

Obv. 1   Rev. 1

No.	Date	Features	Obv.	Rev.	Unc
MEL2CR-005	1970	[1]	1	1	4
MEL2CR-010	1970	PROOF [2]	1	1	20

1. 150,000 issued.
2. 15,000 issued in white case.

Isle of Man: Penny

John Murrey

Although having the characteristics of a token, the penny issued in 1668 by John Murrey, an opulent trader in Douglas, merits a listing in this section by virtue of being the only piece specifically excluded from the Tynwald Act of 24th June 1679, which prohibited the distribution and use of many of the tokens in circulation on the island, even including the Irish Saint Patrick pieces and Butchers' tokens. The Murrey pieces, known locally as 'Johnny Murrey's pennies', were thus immediately elevated to the status of a legal coinage. Oswald's 'Vestigia' notes: 'No insular money was ever recorded until 1679, when Governor Murrey's copper penny became a legal tender'. The coinage was redeemed in 1710 by Murrey's grandson, another John Murrey, prior to the issue of the Derby coinage, using security deposited by the original John Murrey for this purpose.

The Murrey penny, poorly struck in brass, bears a typical 17th century token obverse with the issuer's name, and a reverse depicting the triune with its customary legend. A variety bears a legend instead of the triune. The piece is sometimes said to occur in copper, but no such pieces appear to exist in this metal. The coinage is usually encountered in fair condition, and forgeries may exist.

The eminent authority on Manx coinage, Charles Clay, considered that the Murrey pieces were manufactured in Birmingham.

Denomination	Metal	Weight (grams)	Diameter (mm)	Rev. alignment
Penny obv.1; rev.1	Brass	2.0 – 2.6	20 – 22	OJS
Penny obv.2; rev.2	Brass	2.6	21	not known

Obverse 1 HIS PENNY I M within beaded circle; IOHN MVRREY 1668

Obverse 2 Similar but MVRRAY instead of MVRREY

Reverse 1 Triune (type 1) with spurs at heels within beaded circle; QVOCVNQVE GESSERIS STABIT

Reverse 2 OF DOUGLAS IN MAN within beaded circle; QVOCVNQVE GESSERIS STABIT

Edge plain

No.	Date	Features	Obv.	Rev.	VG	F
M1D-005	1668	1	1	1	2000	5000
M1D-010	1668		2	2	4000	8000

1. Thickness varies. Thin varieties are often bent.

James, tenth Earl of Derby

1709 issue

The coinage of 1709 – 10 was a sorry affair, poorly cast with part of the reverse legend misspelt and the remainder often illegible. Because the metal often did not completely fill the moulds, the date sometimes appears to read 1700, and one catalogue lists it as 1799! The issue consisted of the penny and halfpenny, and was legalized by Act of Tynwald on 12th June 1710. The coinage depicts the Stanley or Derby crest, which is an eagle and child under

which is the cap of maintenance and the date 1709 (although issued in 1710), with the legend SANS CHANGER above. The reverse is of the triune, but the JECERIS of the usual accompanying legend is spelt GESSERIS. The spurs on the triune are in such low relief that they are usually invisible. The legends were ridiculed locally, with SANS CHANGER being interpreted as 'short of change', and the triune legend said to mean 'Whenever you carry this, it will not pass'.

The use of the words 'Our Honourable Lord ... hath sent over a considerable quantity of copper pence and halfpence' in the Act of 20th October 1710 has led to speculation that the coins were cast in England, possibly at Birmingham. This may well have been the case, but some sources have suggested that the term 'hath sent over' (used again in the 1733 Act) may have had an alternative usage, or may have referred to the blanks from which the coins were struck. Freight documents of 1733 show payments for 'casks of blank pence', and there is a tradition on the island that coins were made at Ballasalla; certainly at least some of the 1733 issue appear to have struck at nearby Castletown. During excavations within the walls of Castle Rushen around 1905, remnants were found which appeared to lend weight to the theory that the 1709 coinage was cast there, but later research cast some doubt upon this.

The Derby crest of an eagle and child is said to have come about as a result of an incident in the fourteenth century when Sir Thomas de Lathom was walking with his wife in his park near a spot where an eagle was nesting. They heard the cry of a child, which was found lying in the eagle's nest. Sir Thomas and his wife, who had no child, adopted the baby, who became Sir Thomas's only heir. Later, the child's daughter, Isabel, married Sir John Stanley, who initiated the eagle and child crest.

Denomination	Metal	Weight (grams)	Diameter (mm)	Rev. alignment
Penny	Copper	7.5 – 8.9	28 – 30	OJS

Obverse 1 Eagle and child on cap of maintenance; SANS CHANGER 1709

Reverse 1 Triune (type 1) with spurs; QVOCVNQVE GESSERIS STABIT

Edge plain

No.	Date	Features	Obv.	Rev.	VG	F	VF	EF
M1D-055	1709		1	1	12	20	90	400
M1D-060	1709	In brass	1	1	20	35	150	800
M1D-065	1709	PROOF in silver 1	1	1	100	150	600	1800

1. Weight 11.0 grams.

1733 issue

By 1733, the Isle of Man was almost overrun with coin forgeries. The only solution was for the Tynwald Act of that year to declare all previously issued coinage illegal and to authorise a new issue which would be acceptable to the population. The result was an issue of pennies and halfpennies of high workmanship, but much smaller in size than the equivalent pieces would be on the British mainland. Although there was as yet no British copper penny, the Manx penny was the size of the British halfpenny, and the halfpenny corresponded in size to the farthing.

The first issue was authorised for 'three hundred pounds in copper pence and two hundred pounds in copper halfpence'. The coinage is now assumed to have been struck in Britain, possibly by adherents of William Wood, owing to the wording 'hath sent over' being used in the Act authorizing the coinage.

The population of the Isle of Man in 1733 was 15,000, and this first issue would have provided every man, woman and child on the island with eleven pieces each. However, in practice the coins disappeared from circulation as soon as they were issued and reappeared in Ireland, where they were greatly preferred to the meagre amount of then circulating Irish coinage. Twisse, in 'History of Drogheda', mentions that the 1733 Manx coinage circulated extensively in that town and all along the East coast of Ireland. A second issue of £250 in pence and £150 in halfpence in bronze was authorised, to be struck on the island by Amos Topping and Samuel Dyall (and possibly also a Mr. Garner), who arrived on Man in January 1733 with 'their chests and other instruments for coyning' and completed the work in March 1734. The exodus of coinage to Ireland continued, but the currency situation became more tolerable.

John Crellin, writing in 1879, mentions that he was told that his grandfather's grandfather had said that guns on the top of Castle Rushen were removed to provide the metal for coins. Crellin also recalls that 'forty years back' an old house in Castletown had been known as The Mint. An interesting exercise in logic provides supporting evidence that coins were struck in this town. In the 'Book of Disbursments', there is an entry for 3rd March 1733: 'Paid Ambrose Place for fetching mettle from Peele, sand from Douglas and clay for the furnas'. Five days later, an entry notes; 'Paid to William Jackson for twenty two tun of coales, delivered into the castle for the use of coyning'. The first entry indicates that the mint was not in Peel, nor in Douglas. There are, however, only two castles on the island, at Peel and Rushen (Castletown). Hence, the mint was in Castletown. Furthermore, Castletown was at that time the capital of the island and the residence of the Earl of Derby.

As well as the copper and bronze (gun metal) issues, some coins were also struck in brass, a metal similar to bronze, except that it contains a proportion of zinc rather than tin. Whether the metal for these was also obtained from cannon and similar artefacts, as with the Irish James II necessity issues, is not known. Confusion is added to the situation by the description of the gun metal by many people as 'brass'.

Maud Lister, in a Paper to the Lancashire Numismatic Society in 1947, speculated that the brass issue was manufactured on the island, but that the copper issue was brought in from England as finished coins.

Denomination	Metal	Weight (grams)	Diameter (mm)	Rev. alignment
Penny (1st issue)	Copper	7.9 – 8.0	27 – 29	↓
Penny (2nd issue)	Bronze or brass	9.4 – 11.2	29 – 30	↓

The coins are noticeably thicker in the centre than at the edge. A chemical analysis of a second issue coin gave the results: copper 97.6%, tin 2.2%, iron 0.04%, balance other including zinc.

Obverse 1 Eagle and child on cap of maintenance; SANS CHANGER 1733

Reverse 1 Triune (type 2) with spurs, with letters I D J between legs, the J being at 90 degrees alignment with I D; QUOCUNQUE IECERIS STABIT

Reverse 2 Similar but J in (0 degrees) alignment with I D; same legend

Edge plain

Obv. 1

Rev. 1

Rev. 2

1st issue

No.	Date	Features	Obv.	Rev.	VG	F	VF	EF
M1D-105	1733		1	1	10	18	60	250
M1D-110	1733	PROOF	1	1				750
M1D-115	1733	OUOCUNOUE instead of QUOCUNQUE (rev); in low relief [1]	1	2	15	30	120	

1. Possibly a forgery made in Ireland; diameter 26mm; weight 8.2 grams.

2nd issue

No.	Date	Features	Obv.	Rev.	VG	F	VF	EF
M1D-155	1733	In bronze [1]	1	2	10	18	60	250
M1D-160	1733	In bronze; annulets on triune armour	1	2	70	150	600	
M1D-165	1733	In bronze; struck on thick flan [2]	1	2	100	150	500	
M1D-170	1733	Bronze PROOF	1	2				750
M1D-175	1733	In brass	1	2	20	35	120	400
M1D-180	1733	PROOF (?) in silver [1] [3]	1	2	80	120	300	800
M1D-185	1733	PROOF (?) in silver; struck on thin flan	1	2	120	180	400	1000

1. Frosting on cap occurs on some pieces (obv).
2. Weight 13.2–13.3 grams.
3. Weight 9.2 grams.

James Murray, Duke of Atholl

By 1758, ownership of the Isle of Man had been transferred to James Murray, the second Duke of Atholl, and small change was again in short supply. The Duke authorized the issue of £400 worth of coinage, again consisting of the penny and halfpenny, bearing a coronetted AD monogram ('Atholl Dux') on the obverse, with the date below. The reverse depicts the triune, with its junction of legs resembling three arrow heads point to point, and with large caps of armour on the knees. 60,000 pence and 72,000 halfpence were issued, but they were struck in soft copper which wore down easily, and were not popular.

Denomination	Metal	Weight (grams)	Diameter (mm)	Rev. alignment
Penny	Copper	11.0 – 11.7	29 – 30	↻

Obverse 1 Coronetted AD monogram; 1758

Reverse 1 Triune (type 2); QUOCUNQUE JECERIS STABIT

Edge plain

Obv. 1   Rev. 1

Obv. 1   Obv. 2

Obv. 3

No.	Date	Features	Obv.	Rev.	VG	F	VF	EF
M1D-205	1758		1	1	15	30	50	120
M1D-210	1758	Struck on small flan	1	1	30	60	100	250
M1D-215	1758	PROOF	1	1				200
M1D-220	1758	PROOF in silver; edge milled with deep herringbone design [1]	1	1				1000

1. The inclination of the herringbone design can be either way; each type is of approximately equal rarity; weight 11.1 to 11.9 grams.

George III (1760 – 1820)

Although the ownership of the Isle of Man was transferred to the British government in 1765, a period of 21 years elapsed before any form of regal currency was introduced. The island did not, and still does not, constitute an integral part of the United Kingdom, and retained its own specifically designed coinage incorporating the triune. The 1786 coinage, again comprising the penny and halfpenny, was an attractive issue engraved by Lewis Pingo and struck at the Royal Mint. It is interesting to note that there was no corresponding issue on the mainland and, indeed, no copper pennies were issued for mainland use until 1797. The obverse was of conventional regal design, with monarch and legend, while the reverse continued the triune motif. In a departure from convention, the edge of the regular coin was diagonally milled.

The 1798 penny, designed by C. H. Küchler and struck by Matthew Boulton at the Birmingham Soho Mint, was very similar to the British 1797 penny in appearance, although considerably lighter. The 1813 issue was even lighter, very similar to the 1798 but with minor differences.

Denomination	Metal	Weight (grams)	Diameter (mm)	Rev. alignment
Penny 1786	Copper	15.1 – 16.1	34	QJS
Penny 1798	Copper	21.8 – 22.2	34	QJS
Penny 1813	Copper	20.3 – 20.6	34	QJS

Obverse 1 Head 1, right; GEORGIVS III DEI GRATIA 1786

Obverse 2 Head 2, right, with 3 pellets on truncation; GEORGIVS III D G REX 1798 incuse on broad rim

Obverse 3 Head 2, right, with pellet flanked by two annulets on truncation; GEORGIVS III D G REX 1813 incuse on slightly narrower rim

Reverse 1 Triune (type 1); QVOCVNQVE IECERIS STABIT

Reverse 2 Triune (type 1); QVOCVNQVE IECERIS STABIT incuse on broad rim

Edges (1786) milled (diagonally), (1798 and 1813) plain

Rev. 1   Rev. 2

No.	Date	Features	Obv.	Rev.	F	VF	EF	UNC
MG31D-005	1786	Without pellet below head (obv) [1]	1	1	6	20	80	150
MG31D-010	1786	Pellet below head (obv) [1]	1	1	8	35	130	250
MG31D-015	1786	Struck from dies defaced with cross [2]	1	1	300			
MG31D-020	1786	PROOF	1	1				400
MG31D-025	1786	PROOF; edge plain	1	1				800
MG31D-030	1786	PROOF in high relief on 33mm diameter thick flan; edge plain [3]	1	1				700
MG31D-035	1798		2	2	12	40	100	180
MG31D-040	1798	PROOF	2	2				300
MG31D-045	1798	Bronzed PROOF	2	2				300
MG31D-050	1798	Silver PROOF [4]	2	2				1800
MG31D-055	1798	Gilt PROOF on thin flan [5]	2	2				1500
MG31D-060	1813		3	2	8	24	70	140
MG31D-065	1813	PROOF	3	2				250
MG31D-070	1813	Gilt PROOF	3	2				1000
MG31D-075	1813	Bronzed PROOF	3	2				250

1. Date spacing varies. The pellet is irregularly shaped and may be a die flaw.
2. Not known whether with or without pellet below head.
3. Weight 18.8 grams.
4. Weight 21.4 grams. Possibly struck at a later date.
5. Weight 17.8 grams.

Restrikes exist of some of the 1798 and 1813 issues.

Victoria   (1830 – 1901)

When Victoria ascended the British throne in 1837, the currency of the Isle of Man had again degenerated largely into token issues. The situation was chaotic, and the 1839 Royal Mint issues filled the desperate need for small change having official sanction. The penny bore an obverse identical to that of the British mainland issue, but it must be remembered that the British 1839 penny was struck only for inclusion in proof sets. The reverse again depicted the triune with its accompanying legend, but the latter was in the more conventional raised lettering instead of the incuse form of the Soho Mint issues. The designer was William Wyon, and 79,680 pennies were issued.

An Act of Tynwald of 1840 demonetized Manx coinage in favour of mainland coinage, causing rioting on the island. Small quantities of pennies were struck bearing the dates 1841 and 1859, but they were not issued for circulation.

Denomination	Metal	Weight (grams)	Diameter (mm)	Rev. alignment
Penny	Copper	18.8 – 18.9	34 – 35	↑↓

Obverse 1   Head 1, left, WW incuse on truncation; VICTORIA DEI GRATIA (date)

Obverse 2   Similar but no WW on truncation

Reverse 1   Triune (type 1); QVOCVNQVE IECERIS STABIT

Edge   plain

Obv. 1   Rev. 1

No.	Date	Features	Obv.	Rev.	F	VF	EF	UNC
MV1D-005	1839		1	1	6	14	60	140
MV1D-010	2839	[1]	1	1	150			
MV1D-015	1839	Bronze PROOF	1	1				400
MV1D-020	1841		1	1	400	600	800	1000
MV1D-025	1859	[2]	2	1	400	600	800	1000

1. Date error.
2. This coin has appeared in some reference works as being struck on a thick flan. However, the weight is identical to that of the currency coin, and inspection shows that the flan is normal but the rim is unusually wide.

Isle of Man: Halfpenny

James, tenth Earl of Derby

1709 issue

As there was no halfpenny equivalent to the John Murrey penny of 1668, the first Isle of Man halfpenny having any legal status was the cast issue of 1709. The design is similar to that of the penny, and more details are to be found in that section.

Prior to this issue, the defunct Irish gunmoney halfcrowns circulated unofficially on the island as halfpennies at a time when there was a desperate shortage of small change.

Denomination	Metal	Weight (grams)	Diameter (mm)	Rev. alignment
Halfpenny	Copper	4.5 – 5.8	23 – 25	QJS

Obverse 1 Eagle and child on cap of maintenance; SANS CHANGER 1709

Reverse 1 Triune (type 1) with spurs; QVOCVNQVE GESSERIS STABIT with pellets in legend

Reverse 2 Similar but annulets instead of pellets dividing legend

Edge plain

No.	Date	Features	Obv.	Rev.	VG	F	VF	EF
MHD-005	1709		1	1	18	30	120	600
MHD-010	1709		1	2	30	50	200	1000

Cast lead pieces of high quality exist; these are modern concoctions. On some of the genuine pieces, the date appears to read 1700.

1733 issue

The first of the new issue of halfpennies for the Earl of Derby was authorized in June 1733 and struck in copper, possibly on the British mainland. They were of approximately the size of the British farthing but somewhat lighter. A further consignment in brass and bronze was struck on the island; these were of similar size but heavier. See under the penny section for further details of this issue.

Denomination	Metal	Weight (grams)	Diameter (mm)	Rev. alignment
Halfpenny 1st issue	Copper	3.7 – 3.8	24	90 degrees to right
Halfpenny 2nd issue	Bronze or brass	6.7 – 6.8	24	90 degrees to right

The coins are noticeably thicker in the centre than at the edge.

Obverse 1 Eagle and child on cap of maintenance; SANS CHANGER 1733

Reverse 1 Triune (type 2) with spurs, with symbols I D 1/2 between legs; QUOCUNQUE IECERIS STABIT

Edge plain

Obv. 1

Rev. 1

1st issue

No.	Date	Features	Obv.	Rev.	VG	F	VF	EF
MHD-055	1733		1	1	12	20	70	300
MHD-060	1733	PROOF	1	1				750

2nd issue

No.	Date	Features	Obv.	Rev.	VG	F	VF	EF
MHD-105	1733	In bronze; interior of cap frosted [1]	1	1	12	20	70	300
MHD-110	1733	In bronze; interior of cap not frosted [1]	1	1	12	20	70	300
MHD-115	1733	In bronze; struck on thin flan	1	1	80	120	400	
MHD-120	1733	Bronze PROOF; interior of cap frosted	1	1				300
MHD-125	1733	Bronze PROOF; interior of cap not frosted; eagle's wing points to E of CHANGER (obv)	1	1				400
MHD-130	1733	Bronze PROOF; interior of cap not frosted; eagle's wing points to R of CHANGER (obv)	1	1				500
MHD-135	1733	In brass	1	1	18	30	120	450
MHD-140	1733	Silver PROOF; interior of cap frosted	1	1			400	600
MHD-145	1733	Silver PROOF; interior of cap not frosted; eagle's wing points to E of CHANGER (obv)	1	1			200	400
MHD-150	1733	Silver PROOF; interior of cap not frosted; eagle's wing points to R of CHANGER (obv)	1	1			300	550

1. Alignment of lettering varies (obv).

James Murray, Duke of Atholl

An issue of 72,000 halfpennies was authorized by the new owner of the Isle of Man in 1758 to counter the shortage of small change. The coins were struck in soft copper and were not as popular as the previous issue. Some of the halfpennies were struck from a die having a long crack or flaw on the obverse to the left of the date, extending towards the coronet, and a few specimens were struck in very pale copper; forgeries exist.

Denomination	Metal	Weight (grams)	Diameter (mm)	Rev. alignment
Halfpenny	Copper	5.8	25	↑↓

Obverse 1 Coronetted 'AD' monogram; 1758

Reverse 1 Triune (type 2) ; QUOCUNQUE JECERIS STABIT

Edge plain

No.	Date	Features	Obv.	Rev.	VG	F	VF	EF
MHD-205	1758		1	1	15	30	70	200
MHD-210	1758	Struck on thin flan	1	1	40	80	200	
MHD-215	1758	Struck on thick flan	1	1	60	120	300	
MHD-220	1758	PROOF	1	1				300

George III   (1760 – 1820)

The Isle of Man was transferred to the British Government in 1765, but no coinage struck specifically for the island was issued for the occasion. Although halfpennies were struck at the Royal Mint for the mainland from 1770, it was not until 1786 that the distinctive first issue of regal halfpenny made its appearance, and no equivalent issue was struck for the mainland.

The 1798 and 1813 issues were designed by Küchler and struck by Matthew Boulton at the Soho mint, Birmingham. Although similar in appearance to the mainland cartwheel twopence and penny of 1797, they are unique of their kind, in that no equivalent British halfpenny exists.

There are two notable legend differences between the penny and halfpenny issues; on the 1786 halfpenny, the 7 of the legend is straight, whereas on the penny the stem of the 7 is markedly turned backwards at the end; on the 1798 halfpenny the King's name is spelt GEORGIUS as against GEORGIVS on the penny. Curiously, on the 1813, this reverts to GEORGIVS, and it should also be mentioned that coins of this date often appear to read 1818 owing to the style of execution of the date.

Denomination	Metal	Weight (grams)	Diameter (mm)	Rev. alignment
Halfpenny 1786	Copper	8.2 – 8.4	26 – 27	↑↓
Halfpenny 1798	Copper	10.7	27.5	↑↓
Halfpenny 1813	Copper	10.2	27.5	↑↓

Obverse 1 Head 1, right; GEORGIVS III DEI GRATIA 1786

Obverse 2 Head 2, right, with plain truncation; GEORGIUS III D G REX 1798 incuse on broad rim

Obverse 3 Head 2, right, with pellet flanked by two annulets on truncation; GEORGIVS III D G REX 1813 incuse on slightly narrower rim

Reverse 1 Triune (type 1); QVOCVNQVE IECERIS STABIT

Reverse 2 Triune (type 1); QVOCVNQVE IECERIS STABIT incuse on broad rim

Edges (1786) milled (diagonally)

(1798 and 1813) plain

Obv. 1   Obv. 2

Rev. 1   Rev. 2

No.	Date	Features	Obv.	Rev.	F	VF	EF	UNC
MG3HD-005	1786		1	1	6	24	95	180
MG3HD-010	1786	Struck on large (29mm) flan	1	1	12	50	180	400
MG3HD-015	1786	PROOF	1	1				250
MG3HD-020	1786	PROOF; edge plain [1]	1	1				500
MG3HD-025	1798		2	2	6	18	40	90
MG3HD-030	1798	PROOF	2	2				250
MG3HD-035	1798	Bronze PROOF	2	2				
MG3HD-040	1798	Gilt bronze PROOF [2]	2	2				750
MG3HD-045	1813		3	2	5	15	35	75
MG3HD-050	1813	PROOF	3	2				250
MG3HD-055	1813	Bronze PROOF	3	2				
MG3HD-060	1813	Gilt PROOF	3	2				500

1. Weight 8.5 grams; on some, the obverse border teeth are unfinished, leaving a piece of unworked metal raised above the field.
2. Some or all issued in shell.

Restrikes exist of some of the 1798 and 1813 issues. One piece, probably struck at the Soho Mint, Birmingham, bears the obverse of a pattern 1-pie of Bengal, with reverse 2 above.

Victoria   (1830 – 1901)

The striking of a Victorian regal issue of coins in 1839 came as a welcome relief to an island overrun with unofficial tokens of many sorts. The halfpenny was the most prolific of the three coins issued, both in number (214,080) and in total value (£446). However, the relief was short-lived, as the restructuring of the penny:shilling ratio from 1:14 to 1:12 caused much unrest, with rioting in the streets of Douglas and Peel. In 1840, the local coinage was replaced by British issues.

The 1839 halfpenny is sometimes encountered with a date digit 9 altered from an 8; the obverse is identical to that of the British halfpenny, which was first issued in 1838. Many specimens bear on the reverse a faint mirror image tracing of the back of the obverse portrait, the result of 'clashed dies'.

The issues of Isle of Man halfpennies dated 1841 and 1860 were not intended for circulation.

Denomination	Metal	Weight (grams)	Diameter (mm)	Rev. alignment
Halfpenny	Copper	9.4 – 9.5	28	↑↓

Obverse 1 Head 1, left, WW incuse on truncation; VICTORIA DEI GRATIA (date)

Reverse 1 Triune (type 1); QVOCVNQVE IECERIS STABIT

Edge plain

Obv. 1

Rev. 1

No.	Date	Features	Obv.	Rev.	F	VF	EF	UNC
MVHD-005	1839		1	1	4	9	25	50
MVHD-010	1839	9 over 8	1	1	8	20	60	120
MVHD-015	1839	Bronze PROOF	1	1				240
MVHD-020	1839	In silver [1]	1	1				
MVHD-025	1841		1	1	400	600	800	1000
MVHD-030	1860	[2]	1	1	600	850	1200	1500
MVHD-035	1860	PROOF (?) streaked with gold on rev.	1	1				2500

1. Reported by Philip Nelson, Num. Chron., 3rd series, Vol. XIX (1899).
2. Weight 8.6 grams. The coin has a wide rim but the actual flan is slightly thinner than the currency coin. Although the die axis alignment has little meaning with a triune reverse, it is interesting to note that the alignment is at 180 degrees to that of the currency coin.

Isle of Man: Farthing

The farthing was not an integral part of the monetary system of the Isle of Man in the earliest years of its coinage, although the Irish halfpenny issue of 1680 was granted legal tender status on the island as a farthing. The Irish gunmoney shilling issue also passed unofficially as a farthing after the Williamite victory. The only true farthings struck for the island were those of Victoria. The first of these formed part of the short-lived 1839 series. Despite the fact that the denomination had not been struck specifically for the Isle of Man before, no fewer than 213,120 were issued. A very small number of farthings dated 1841 and 1860 exist, probably fewer than twenty in total. The 1864 is a curious piece, and an equivalent coin of similar rarity exists in the British farthing series. It must be mentioned here that various writers have wrongly hitherto assumed this to be a bronze piece similar to the British currency 1864 farthing, not having seen it.

Many of the 1839 pieces bear on the reverse a faint mirror image tracing of the back of the obverse portrait, the result of 'clashed dies'.

Denomination	Metal	Weight (grams)	Diameter (mm)	Rev. alignment
Farthing	Copper	4.6 – 4.7	22	↑↓

Obverse 1   Head 1, left, WW in relief on truncation; VICTORIA DEI GRATIA (date)

Obverse 2   Similar but WW incuse; same legend

Reverse 1   Triune (type 1); QVOCVNQVE IECERIS STABIT

Edge   plain

Obv. 1   Rev. 1

No.	Date	Features	Obv.	Rev.	F	VF	EF	UNC
MVFA-005	1839	Normal rim	1	1	6	12	40	75
MVFA-010	1839	Raised rim	1	1	10	20	65	120
MVFA-015	1839	Bronzed PROOF [1]	1	1				200
MVFA-020	1839	Gilt PROOF; edge milled	1	1				1500
MVFA-025	1841		1	1	400	600	800	1000
MVFA-030	1860		2	1	600	850	1200	2500
MVFA-035	1860	PROOF (?); rev. gilt	2	1				4000
MVFA-040	1864	With figure 1 (in relief) to left of WW on truncation [2]	2	1	1500	2500	4500	9000

1. A specimen in the British Museum weighs 4.2 grams.
2. A specimen in the British Museum weighs 4.4 grams.

Isle of Man: Decimal Coinage

The Isle of Man converted to decimal currency on 15th February 1971, simultaneously with the United Kingdom. Prior to the changeover, British coinage (along with that of the Irish Republic) had been the principal coinage of the island, but the opportunity was taken with decimalization to introduce a separate coinage for the territory which was not, after all, part of the United Kingdom. Nevertheless, British and Irish coins continued to circulate after decimalization.

The Manx Decimal Coins Act, 1970 provided for a separate series of coinage which was not generally accepted as currency in the rest of the British Isles, despite the similarity in size and weight. The new coins were introduced in October, 1971, using the Arnold Machin portrait of the monarch, with reverses by Christopher Ironside, and were initially struck at the Royal Mint. In 1972, a contract was agreed with the Pobjoy Mint to take over subsequent Isle of Man issues. An exception was the 1972 crown (25 pence) piece, struck the Royal Canadian Mint at Ottawa.

The first Pobjoy Mint issues were principally currency issues similar to the 1971 Royal Mint issue, together with sets of gold coins and commemorative proof and ordinary crown issues. Bullion-type single gold pieces were also struck. Such pieces would ordinarily and rightly form the basic content of any catalogue of decimal currency of the island. However, as the years passed, the output of the Pobjoy Mint became more and more prolific and less characteristic of coinage struck for circulation on a small island. Although the items struck had legal tender status, they increasingly resembled commercial medallic products from a production line rather than the issue of a mint. By way of example, and as mentioned elsewhere, in 1995 Pobjoy issued 46 different 'one-fifth of a crown' pieces.

The quantity of material issued, running into many hundreds of different items, presents any cataloguer of Isle of Man coinage with a dilemma. To cover the output comprehensively would add about 200 pages to a catalogue which is intended to be a serious aid to collectors of coinage rather than to resemble an illustrated mail order catalogue. What, therefore, should be included, if anything? The solution has to be, as so often, a compromise. The early Pobjoy material, together with any items which are intended to circulate as coins, are obvious candidates for inclusion. Anything struck for commemorative purposes is on the suspect list, particularly if it commemorates a person of whom few people have heard, such as Pi Sheng, or celebrates the existence of the Norwegian cat. The decimal section is thus a hybrid, comprising a conventional treatment of some material, and a summary of the vast majority.

A note from the Publisher

As the publisher of Coincraft's books, I allow my authors almost total freedom in what they say and how they say it. But, being a human being, I too have opinions and so I would like to make the following remarks. I too believe that Pobjoy as well as most mints around the world issue far too many commemorative coins. These coins were never intended to circulate; they are by their very nature intended as collectors' pieces. In 1969 I tried to spend a Churchill crown on a bus and the police had to be called before the conductor would accept it in payment.

The earliest pieces struck for collectors that I can think of are the token coinage of this country of the late 1700s. They were first struck to alleviate a shortage of small change. They also allowed the merchant to make a small profit on the minting, as well as having his FREE advertising seen by everyone who used his halfpennies. Sometime later someone noticed that people were collecting the different issues and would even pay more than face value for some of the more difficult issues. That person realised that he could make pieces for collectors and charge more for them than the face value and at the same time make himself a tidy little profit. It quickly got to the point where more and more pieces were being issued for collectors and fewer for actual circulation. It might not come as a surprise, but the token halfpennies issued for collectors were much more attractive and interesting than the pieces issued for circulation. Nothing is new and everything reflects something that happened in the past.

In a more recent time, in the early 1920s, people in Germany and Austria were collecting small banknotes called Notgeld, these were again printed to make up for a shortage of small change. There were about a quarter of a million readers of a monthly magazine only about Notgeld. Again, people started to issue notes for collectors and not just for general usage. In this case there were over 125,000 different notes issued for collectors and a much smaller number for actual circulation.

Even more recently we had phone cards, where anyone could issue any card they wanted and charge as much as they wanted. What happened? The bubble burst on phone cards. Notgeld is now highly collected again and some of the prices on the rarer issues would make those original collectors turn in their graves. 18th century tokens, also known as Condor Tokens after the man who first listed them, James Condor, are alive and well and gaining new enthusiasts at a very rapid rate. The sale of James Noble's collection in Australia saw dealers and collectors from all over the world attend the sale and prices were very strong indeed. What does this all go to show? Perhaps there are too many coins being issued today, but sometime in the future, they too will be more seriously collected. How long in the future? That is anyone's guess.

Derek Pobjoy is one of my heroes. I think that he is responsible for getting more people into collecting coins than almost any other person in this country. Do I think that he has issued too many coins? Well, yes I do. On the other hand he has produced some of the most innovative designs around. I have several in my own collection, because he produced pieces that collectors want and need. He is an excellent marketer and businessman, one of the best I know. They have produced excellent quality products, with innovation and flair, and for that I salute them. But I do wish that all the world's mints would slow down the number of products they are issuing for collectors. Fewer items, more thought, more excitement and lower prices. You know if the mints issued silver proof crowns at £18 rather than £30, you would have a lot more collectors who would want them. You would make less money per piece, but overall, you would make more money because more pieces would be sold. This is sage advice which I have been telling mints for a very long time and which none of them has ever listened to. That's life...

R. L.

50 Pounds

Denomination	Metal	Weight (grams)	Diameter (mm)	Rev. alignment
50 pounds	0.999 gold	6.2	19	↑

Obverse 1   Head 1, right; ISLE OF MAN ELIZABETH II (date)

Reverse 1   Racing cars; 50 POUNDS F1 WORLD CHAMPION 1992 NIGEL MANSELL

Reverse 2   Different depiction of racing cars; PPG INDYCAR WORLD SERIES CHAMPION 1993 NIGEL MANSELL £50

Edge   milled

Obv. 1

Rev. 1

No.	Date	Features	Obv.	Rev.	UNC
MD50P/93–6	1993	PROOF	1	1	100
MD50P/94–6	1994	PROOF	1	2	100

25 Pounds

Denomination	Metal	Weight (grams)	Diameter (mm)	Rev. alignment
25 pounds	0.925 silver	28.3	39	↑

Obverse 1   Head 1, right; ELIZABETH II ISLE OF MAN 1993

Reverse 1   Racing cars; 25 POUNDS F1 WORLD CHAMPION 1992 NIGEL MANSELL

Edge   milled

Obv. 1

Rev. 1

No.	Date	Features	Obv.	Rev.	UNC
MD25P/93–4	1993	PROOF	1	1	20

10 Pounds

Denomination	Metal	Weight (grams)	Diameter (mm)	Rev. alignment
10 pounds	0.925 silver	10.0	23	↑

Obverse 1   Head 1, right; ISLE OF MAN ELIZABETH II (date)

Reverse 1   Racing cars; 10 POUNDS F1 WORLD CHAMPION 1992 NIGEL MANSELL

Reverse 2   Different depiction of racing cars; PPG INDYCAR WORLD SERIES CHAMPION 1993 NIGEL MANSELL £10

Edge   milled

Obv. 1

Rev. 1

No.	Date	Features	Obv.	Rev.	UNC
MD10P/93–4	1993	PROOF	1	1	15
MD10P/94–4	1994	PROOF	1	2	15

5 Pounds

Denomination	Metal	Weight (grams)	Diameter (mm)	Rev. alignment
5 pounds obv. 1	0.917 gold	39.8	36	↑
5 pounds obv. 2	'Virenium'	20.0	36	↑

'Virenium' is a Registered Trade Mark of Pobjoy Mint Ltd denoting a specific alloy of copper, nickel and zinc.

Obverse 1   Head 1, right; ISLE OF MAN ELIZABETH II

Obverse 2   Head 1, right; ELIZABETH THE SECOND (date)

Reverse 1   Viking warrior on horse; (date) in exergue

Reverse 2   Triune (type 1) on map of Isle of Man; ISLE OF MAN FIVE POUNDS

Reverse 3   Portraits of Charles and Diana with conjoined shields; THE WEDDING OF HRH THE PRINCE OF WALES AND THE LADY DIANA SPENCER 1981

Edge   milled

Obv. 1

Obv. 2

Rev. 1

Rev. 2

Rev. 3

Rev. 1

Rev. 2

No.	Date	Features	Obv.	Rev.	UNC
MD5P/73–1	1973		1	1	350
MD5P/73–6	1973	PROOF	1	1	400
MD5P/74–1	1974		1	1	400
MD5P/74–6	1974	PROOF	1	1	420
MD5P/75–1	1975		1	1	400
MD5P/75–6	1975	PROOF	1	1	420
MD5P/76–1	1976		1	1	380
MD5P/76–6	1976	PROOF	1	1	400
MD5P/77–1	1977		1	1	380
MD5P/77–6	1977	PROOF	1	1	400
MD5P/78–6	1978	PROOF	1	1	400
MD5P/79–1	1979		1	1	350
MD5P/79–6	1979	PROOF	1	1	400
MD5P/80–1	1980		1	1	400
MD5P/81–1	1981		2	2	8
MD5P/81–3	1981	PROOF	2	2	10
MD5P/81–4	1981	PROOF in 0.925 silver	2	2	30
MD5P/81–6	1981	PROOF in 0.917 gold	2	2	400
MD5P/81–7	1981	PROOF in 0.950 platinum	2	2	600
MD5P/81–6A	1981	PROOF	1	3	400
MD5P/82–1	1982		1	1	350
MD5P/82–6	1982	PROOF	1	1	400
MD5P/82–1A	1982		2	2	8
MD5P/82–4A	1982	PROOF in 0.925 silver	2	2	30
MD5P/82–6A	1982	PROOF in 0.917 gold	2	2	400
MD5P/82–7A	1982	PROOF in 0.950 platinum	2	2	600
MD5P/83–1	1983		2	2	8
MD5P/83–4	1983	PROOF in 0.925 silver	2	2	25
MD5P/83–6	1983	PROOF in 0.917 gold	2	2	400
MD5P/83–7	1983	PROOF in 0.950 platinum	2	2	600
MD5P/84–1	1984		2	2	8

No.	Date	Features	Obv.	Rev.	UNC
MD2P/73–1	1973		1	1	160
MD2P/73–6	1973	PROOF	1	1	180
MD2P/74–1	1974		1	1	170
MD2P/74–6	1974	PROOF	1	1	190
MD2P/75–1	1975		1	1	170
MD2P/75–6	1975	PROOF	1	1	190
MD2P/76–1	1976		1	1	170
MD2P/76–6	1976	PROOF	1	1	190
MD2P/77–1	1977		1	1	170
MD2P/77–6	1977	PROOF	1	1	190
MD2P/78–6	1978	PROOF	1	1	190
MD2P/79–1	1979		1	1	170
MD2P/79–6	1979	PROOF	1	1	190
MD2P/80–6	1980	PROOF	1	1	180
MD2P/81–6	1981	PROOF	1	2	200
MD2P/82–1	1982		1	1	170
MD2P/82–6	1982	PROOF	1	1	190

Some of the above exhibit privy marks. Later dates exist (see summary of Pobjoy issues).

Some of the above exhibit privy marks. Later dates exist (see summary of Pobjoy issues).

2 Pounds (Gold)

Denomination	Metal	Weight (grams)	Diameter (mm)	Rev. alignment
2 pounds	0.917 gold	15.9	28	↑

Obverse 1 Head 1, right; ISLE OF MAN ELIZABETH II

Reverse 1 Viking warrior on horse; (date) in exergue

Reverse 2 Portraits of Charles and Diana with conjoined shields; THE WEDDING OF HRH THE PRINCE OF WALES AND THE LADY DIANA SPENCER 1981

Edge milled

2 Pounds (Currency)

Denomination	Metal	Weight (grams)	Diameter (mm)	Rev. alignment
Two Pounds	Inner disc of cupronickel bonded to outer ring of nickel-brass	12.0	28.4	↑

Obverse 1 Head 1, right, with inner border of pellets; ISLE OF MAN ELIZABETH II (date)

Obverse 2 Head 1, smaller, right, within inner border of beads; same legend (date)

Obverse 3 Head 2, right; same legend (date)

Reverse 1 Rally cars within border of pellets; TWO POUNDS

Edge milled

Obv. 1

Obv. 1

Obv. 2

Rev. 1

No.	Date	Features	Obv	Rev	UNC
M2PC/97–1	1997		1	1	25
M2PC/97–1A	1997		2	1	4
M2PC/98–1	1998		3	1	4

Sovereign

Denomination	Metal	Weight (grams)	Diameter (mm)	Rev. alignment
Sovereign	0.917 gold	8.0	22	↑

Obverse 1   Head 1, right; ISLE OF MAN ELIZABETH II

Reverse 1   Viking warrior on horse; (date) in exergue

Edge   milled

Obv. 1   Rev. 1

No.	Date	Features	Obv.	Rev.	UNC
MDSV/73–1	1973		1	1	65
MDSV/73–6	1973	PROOF	1	1	75
MDSV/74–1	1974		1	1	65
MDSV/74–6	1974	PROOF	1	1	75
MDSV/75–1	1975		1	1	65
MDSV/75–6	1975	PROOF	1	1	75
MDSV/76–1	1976		1	1	65
MDSV/76–6	1976	PROOF	1	1	75
MDSV/77–1	1977		1	1	65
MDSV/77–6	1977	PROOF	1	1	75
MDSV/78–6	1978	PROOF	1	1	75
MDSV/79–1	1979		1	1	65
MDSV/79–6	1979	PROOF	1	1	75
MDSV/80–6	1980	PROOF	1	1	75
MDSV/82–1	1982		1	1	65
MDSV/82–6	1982	PROOF	1	1	75

Some of the above exhibit privy marks. Later dates exist, including gold versions of 'Virenium' pieces (see summary of Pobjoy issues).

Pound

Denomination	Metal	Weight (grams)	Diameter (mm)	Rev. alignment
Pound	'Virenium'	4.0	22	↑

'Virenium' is a Registered Trade Mark of Pobjoy Mint Ltd denoting a specific alloy of copper, nickel and zinc.

Obverse 1   Head 1, right; ELIZABETH THE SECOND

Reverse 1   Triune (type 1) on map of Isle of Man; ISLE OF MAN ONE POUND

Reverse 2   Portraits of Charles and Diana with conjoined shields; THE WEDDING OF HRH THE PRINCE OF WALES AND THE LADY DIANA SPENCER 1981

Edge   Alternately, three smooth and three milled segments

Obv. 1   Rev. 1   Rev. 2

No.	Date	Features	Obv.	Rev.	UNC
MD1P/78–1	1978		1	1	2
MD1P/78–2	1978	in 0.925 silver	1	1	5
MD1P/78–4	1978	PROOF in 0.925 silver	1	1	6
MD1P/78–7	1978	PROOF in 0.950 platinum	1	1	120
MD1P/79–1	1979		1	1	2
MD1P/79–3	1979	PROOF	1	1	3
MD1P/79–4	1979	PROOF in 0.925 silver	1	1	6
MD1P/79–7	1979	PROOF in 0.950 platinum	1	1	120
MD1P/80–1	1980		1	1	2
MD1P/80–3	1980	PROOF	1	1	3
MD1P/80–4	1980	PROOF in 0.500 silver	1	1	5
MD1P/80–4A	1980	PROOF in 0.925 silver	1	1	6
MD1P/80–6	1980	PROOF in 0.917 gold	1	1	70
MD1P/80–7	1980	PROOF in 0.950 platinum	1	1	120
MD1P/81–1	1981		1	1	2
MD1P/81–6	1981	PROOF in 0.917 gold	1	2	70
MD1P/82–4	1982	PROOF in 0.925 silver	1	1	6
MD1P/82–6	1982	PROOF in 0.917 gold	1	1	70
MD1P/82–7	1982	PROOF in 0.950 platinum	1	1	120

Some of the above exhibit privy marks. Later dates exist in 'Virenium' and other metals (see summary of Pobjoy issues).

Half Sovereign

Denomination	Metal	Weight (grams)	Diameter (mm)	Rev. alignment
Half sovereign	0.917 gold	4.0	19	↑

Obverse 1   Head 1, right; ISLE OF MAN ELIZABETH II

Reverse 1   Viking warrior on horse; (date) in exergue

Reverse 2   Portraits of Charles and Diana with conjoined shields; THE WEDDING OF HRH THE PRINCE OF WALES AND THE LADY DIANA SPENCER 1981

Edge   milled

Obv. 1   Rev. 1   Rev. 2

No.	Date	Features	Obv.	Rev.	UNC
MDHS/73–1	1973		1	1	40
MDHS/73–6	1973	PROOF	1	1	45
MDHS/74–1	1974		1	1	40
MDHS/74–6	1974	PROOF	1	1	45
MDHS/75–1	1975		1	1	40
MDHS/75–6	1975	PROOF	1	1	45
MDHS/76–1	1976		1	1	40
MDHS/76–6	1976	PROOF	1	1	45
MDHS/77–1	1977		1	1	40
MDHS/77–6	1977	PROOF	1	1	45
MDHS/78–6	1978	PROOF	1	1	45
MDHS/79–1	1979		1	1	40

No.	Date	Features	Obv.	Rev.	UNC
MDHS/79–6	1979	PROOF	1	1	45
MDHS/80–6	1980	PROOF	1	1	45
MDHS/81–6	1981	PROOF	1	2	45
MDHS/82–1	1982		1	1	40
MDHS/82–6	1982	PROOF	1	1	45

Some of the above exhibit privy marks. Later dates exist (see summary of Pobjoy issues).

50 Pence

The Viking ship depicted on the reverse commemorates the Norse Viking settlement on the Isle of Man in the ninth century.

Denomination	Metal	Weight (grams)	Diameter (mm)	Rev. alignment
50 pence	Cupronickel	13.5	30	↑

The coin is seven-sided but the diameter from any point on the edge across the centre of the face is constant. Proofs in silver and platinum weigh 15.5 and 30.4 grams respectively

Obverse 1 Head 1, right; ELIZABETH THE SECOND (date)

Reverse 1 Viking ship; ISLE OF MAN FIFTY NEW PENCE

Reverse 2 A different Viking ship superimposed on map of Isle of Man; ISLE OF MAN FIFTY PENCE

Edge plain

Obv. 1

Rev. 1   Rev. 2

No.	Date	Features	Obv.	Rev.	UNC
MD50/71–1	1971		1	1	2
MD50/71–3	1971	PROOF [1]	1	1	4
MD50/72–1	1972	[2]	1	1	25
MD50/73–1	1973	[2]	1	1	25
MD50/74–1	1974	[2]	1	1	25
MD50/75–1	1975		1	1	2
MD50/75–4	1975	PROOF in 0.925 silver [1]	1	1	7
MD50/75–7	1975	PROOF in 0.950 platinum [1]	1	1	400
MD50/76–1	1976		1	2	2
MD50/76–2	1976	In 0.925 silver [1]	1	2	4
MD50/76–4	1976	PROOF in 0.925 silver [1]	1	2	7
MD50/76–7	1976	PROOF in 0.950 platinum [1]	1	2	400
MD50/77–1	1977		1	2	2
MD50/77–4	1977	PROOF in 0.925 silver [1]	1	2	7
MD50/78–1	1978		1	2	2
MD50/78–3	1978	PROOF [1]	1	2	4

No.	Date	Features	Obv.	Rev.	UNC
MD50/78–4	1978	PROOF in 0.925 silver [1]	1	2	7
MD50/78–7	1978	PROOF in 0.950 platinum [1]	1	2	400
MD50/79–1	1979		1	2	2
MD50/79–4	1979	PROOF in 0.925 silver [1]	1	2	6
MD50/79–7	1979	PROOF in 0.950 platinum [1]	1	2	400

1. Issued in cased sets.
2. 1000 issued.

Later dates exist (see summary of Pobjoy issues).

25 Pence (Crown)

Denomination	Metal	Weight (grams)	Diameter (mm)	Rev. alignment
25 pence	Cupronickel	28.3	39	↑

Obverse 1 Head 1, right; ISLE OF MAN ELIZABETH II 1972

Reverse 1 Conjoined shields and 1947 1972 within wreath; SILVER WEDDING ANNIVERSARY TWENTY-FIVE PENCE

Edge milled

Obv. 1   Rev. 1

No.	Date	Features	Obv.	Rev.	UNC
MD25/72–1	1972	PROOF-LIKE [1]	1	1	3
MD25/72–4	1972	PROOF in 0.925 silver [1]	1	1	18

1. Issued in cased sets.

This issue was struck at the Royal Canadian Mint, Ottawa. Later dates exist (see summary of Pobjoy issues).

20 Pence

Denomination	Metal	Weight (grams)	Diameter (mm)	Rev. alignment
20 pence	Cupronickel	5.0	21	↑

The coin is seven-sided but the diameter from any point on the edge across the centre of the face is constant.

Obverse 1 Head 1, right; ISLE OF MAN ELIZABETH II (date)

Obverse 2 Head 2, right; same legend

Obverse 3 Head 2, smaller, right, within border; same legend around inner border

Obverse 4 Head 3, right, within border; ELIZABETH II ISLE OF MAN (date)

Reverse 1 Design symbolizing Norse history, 20 below

Reverse 2 Three Atlantic herrings, 20 below, all within ornate border

Reverse 3 Combine harvester; ELLAN VANNIN 20

Reverse 4 Similar but smaller and within border; TWENTY PENCE 20 on and around inner border

No.	Date	Features	Obv.	Rev.	UNC
MD05/78–1	1978		1	2	1
MD05/78–3	1978	PROOF [1]	1	2	2
MD05/78–2	1978	In 0.925 silver [1]	1	2	2
MD05/78–7	1978	PROOF in 0.950 platinum [1]	1	2	140
MD05/79–1	1979		1	2	1
MD05/79–4	1979	PROOF in 0.925 silver [1]	1	2	3
MD05/79–7	1979	PROOF in 0.950 platinum [1]	1	2	140
MD05/79–1A	1979		2	3	1
MD05/80–1	1980		2	3	1
MD05/80–3	1980	PROOF	2	3	2
MD05/80–4	1980	PROOF in 0.500 silver [1]	2	3	3
MD05/80–6	1980	PROOF in 0.917 gold [1]	2	3	120
MD05/80–7	1980	PROOF in 0.950 platinum	2	3	140
MD05/81–1	1981		2	3	1
MD05/82–1	1982		2	3	1
MD05/82–3	1982	PROOF	2	3	2
MD05/82–4	1982	PROOF in 0.925 silver [1]	2	3	3
MD05/82–6	1982	PROOF in 0.917 gold [1]	2	3	120
MD05/82–7	1982	PROOF in 0.950 platinum [1]	2	3	140
MD05/83–1	1983		2	3	1
MD05/83–4	1983	PROOF in 0.925 silver [1]	2	3	3
MD05/83–6	1983	PROOF in 0.917 gold [1]	2	3	120
MD05/83–7	1983	PROOF in 0.950 platinum [1]	2	3	140
MD05/84–1	1984		2	4	1
MD05/84–4	1984	PROOF in 0.925 silver [1]	2	4	3
MD05/84–6	1984	PROOF in 0.917 gold [1]	2	4	120
MD05/85–1	1985		3	4	1
MD05/85–3	1985	PROOF	3	4	2
MD05/85–4	1985	PROOF in 0.925 silver [1]	3	4	3
MD05/85–6	1985	PROOF in 0.917 gold [1]	3	4	120
MD05/85–7	1985	PROOF in 0.950 platinum [1]	3	4	140
MD05/86–1	1986		3	4	1
MD05/87–1	1987		3	4	1
MD05/88–1	1988		3	5	1
MD05/89–1	1989		3	5	1
MD05/90–1L	1990		3	5	1
MD05/90–1S	1990		4	6	1
MD05/91–1	1991		4	6	1
MD05/92–1	1992		4	6	1
MD05/94–1	1994		4	7	1
MD05/94–4	1994	PROOF in 0.925 silver	4	7	2
MD05/94–6	1994	PROOF in 0.917 gold	4	7	80
MD05/94–7	1994	PROOF in 0.950 platinum	4	7	120
MD05/95–1	1995		4	7	1
MD05/96–1	1996		4	8	1
MD05/98–1	1998		5	8	8
MD05/98–1A	1998		6	9	1

1. Issued in cased sets.
2. 1000 issued.
3. Occurs with or without mintmark PM on reverse.

Some of the above exhibit privy marks.

Some recent issues are not included in the table above.

2 Pence

Denomination	Metal	Weight (grams)	Diameter (mm)	Rev. alignment
2 pence 1971 – 95	Bronze	7.1	26	↑
2 pence 1996	Bronze-clad steel	7.1	26	↑

Proofs in silver, gold and platinum weigh 8.4, 14.2 and 16.0 grams respectively

Obverse 1   Head 1, right; ELIZABETH THE SECOND (date)

Obverse 2   Head 1, right; ISLE OF MAN ELIZABETH II (date)

Obverse 3   Head 2, right; same legend

Obverse 4   Head 3, right; same legend

Obverse 5   Head 3, slightly smaller, right; same legend, including three small triunes

Reverse 1   Falcons; ISLE OF MAN TWO NEW PENCE

Reverse 2   Manx shearwater superimposed on map of Isle of Man; ISLE OF MAN TWO PENCE

Reverse 3   Bird and ornamentation; 2

Reverse 4   Bird and 2 within ornamental border

Reverse 5   Stone cross with tools; ELLAN VANNIN 2

Reverse 6   Two cyclists; 2

Edge   plain

Obv. 1   Obv. 2   Obv. 5

Rev. 1   Rev. 2   Rev. 3

Rev. 6

No.	Date	Features	Obv.	Rev.	UNC
MD02/71–1	1971		1	1	1
MD02/71–3	1971	PROOF [1]	1	1	2
MD02/72–1	1972	[2]	1	1	18
MD02/73–1	1973	[2]	1	1	18
MD02/74–1	1974	[2]	1	1	18
MD02/75–1	1975		1	1	1
MD02/75–2	1975	In 0.925 silver [1]	1	1	2
MD02/75–7	1975	PROOF in 0.950 platinum [1]	1	1	150
MD02/76–1	1976		1	2	1
MD02/76–2	1976	In 0.925 silver [1]	1	2	2
MD02/76–7	1976	PROOF in 0.950 platinum [1]	1	2	150
MD02/77–1	1977		1	2	1
MD02/77–4	1977	PROOF in 0.925 silver [1]	1	2	3
MD02/77–7	1977	PROOF in 0.950 platinum [1]	1	2	150
MD02/78–1	1978		1	2	1
MD02/78–3	1978	PROOF [1]	1	2	2
MD02/78–2	1978	In 0.925 silver [1]	1	2	2
MD02/79–1	1979		1	2	1
MD02/79–4	1979	PROOF in 0.925 silver [1]	1	2	3
MD02/79–7	1979	PROOF in 0.950 platinum [1]	1	2	150
MD02/80–1	1980		2	3	1
MD02/80–3	1980	PROOF	2	3	2
MD02/80–4	1980	PROOF in 0.500 silver [1]	2	3	2
MD02/80–6	1980	PROOF in 0.917 gold [1]	2	3	130

No.	Date	Features	Obv.	Rev.	UNC
MD02/80–7	1980	PROOF in 0.950 platinum [1]	2	3	150
MD02/81–1	1981		2	3	1
MD02/82–1	1982		2	3	1
MD02/82–3	1982	PROOF	2	3	2
MD02/82–4	1982	PROOF in 0.925 silver [1]	2	3	3
MD02/82–6	1982	PROOF in 0.917 gold [1]	2	3	130
MD02/82–7	1982	PROOF in 0.950 platinum [1]	2	3	150
MD02/83–1	1983		2	3	1
MD02/83–4	1983	PROOF in 0.925 silver [1]	2	3	3
MD02/83–6	1983	PROOF in 0.917 gold [1]	2	3	130
MD02/83–7	1983	PROOF in 0.950 platinum [1]	2	3	150
MD02/84–1	1984		2	4	1
MD02/84–4	1984	PROOF in 0.925 silver [1]	2	4	3
MD02/84–6	1984	PROOF in 0.917 gold [1]	2	4	150
MD02/85–1	1985		3	4	1
MD02/85–3	1985	PROOF	3	4	2
MD02/85–4	1985	PROOF in 0.925 silver [1]	3	4	3
MD02/85–6	1985	PROOF in 0.917 gold [1]	3	4	130
MD02/85–7	1985	PROOF in 0.950 platinum [1]	3	4	150
MD02/86–1	1986		3	4	1
MD02/87–1	1987		3	4	1
MD02/88–1	1988		3	5	1
MD02/89–1	1989		3	5	1
MD02/90–1	1990		3	5	1
MD02/91–1	1991		3	5	1
MD02/92–1	1992		3	5	1
MD02/93–1	1993		3	5	1
MD02/96–1	1996		3	6	1
MD02/98–1	1998		4	6	8
MD02/98–1A	1998		5	6	1

1. Issued in cased sets.
2. 1000 issued.

Some of the above exhibit privy marks.

Some recent issues are not included in the table above.

Penny

The Celtic cross on the first reverse is based on decorations from 10th or 11th century Norse cross-slabs.

Denomination	Metal	Weight (grams)	Diameter (mm)	Rev. alignment
Penny 1971 – 93	Bronze	3.6	20	↑
Penny 1996 –	Bronze-clad steel	3.6	20	↑

Proofs in silver, gold and platinum weigh 4.2, 7.1 and 8.0 grams respectively.

Obverse 1 Head 1, right; ELIZABETH THE SECOND (date)

Obverse 2 Head 1, right; ISLE OF MAN ELIZABETH II (date)

Obverse 3 Head 2, right; same legend

Obverse 4 Head 3, right; same legend

Obverse 5 Head 3, slightly smaller, right; same legend, including three small triunes

Reverse 1 Celtic Cross; ISLE OF MAN ONE NEW PENNY

Reverse 2 Loagthyn Ram superimposed on map of Isle of Man; ISLE OF MAN ONE PENNY

Reverse 3 Manx Cat and ornamentation; 1

Reverse 4 Puffin and 1 within ornamental border

Reverse 5 Tools; ELLAN VANNIN 1

Reverse 6 Rugby ball and posts within wreath; 1

Edge plain

Obv. 1   Obv. 2   Obv. 3

Obv. 5   Rev. 1   Rev. 2

Rev. 3   Rev. 5   Rev. 6

No.	Date	Features	Obv.	Rev.	UNC
MD01/71–1	1971		1	1	1
MD01/71–3	1971	PROOF [1]	1	1	1
MD01/72–1	1972	[2]	1	1	18
MD01/73–1	1973	[2]	1	1	18
MD01/74–1	1974	[2]	1	1	18
MD01/75–1	1975		1	1	1
MD01/75–2	1975	In 0.925 silver [1]	1	1	2
MD01/75–7	1975	PROOF in 0.950 platinum [1]	1	1	100
MD01/76–1	1976		1	2	1
MD01/76–2	1976	In 0.925 silver [1]	1	2	2
MD01/76–7	1976	PROOF in 0.950 platinum [1]	1	2	100
MD01/77–1	1977		1	2	1
MD01/77–4	1977	PROOF in 0.925 silver [1]	1	2	2
MD01/78–1	1978		1	2	1
MD01/78–3	1978	PROOF [1]	1	2	2
MD01/78–2	1978	In 0.925 silver [1]	1	2	2
MD01/78–7	1978	PROOF in 0.950 platinum [1]	1	2	100
MD01/79–1	1979		1	2	1
MD01/79–4	1979	PROOF in 0.925 silver [1]	1	2	2
MD01/79–7	1979	PROOF in 0.950 platinum [1]	1	2	100
MD01/80–1	1980		1	2	1
MD01/80–1A	1980		2	3	1
MD01/80–3A	1980	PROOF	2	3	1
MD01/80–4A	1980	PROOF in 0.500 silver [1]	2	3	2
MD01/80–6A	1980	PROOF in 0.917 gold [1]	2	3	70
MD01/80–7A	1980	PROOF in 0.950 platinum [1]	2	3	100
MD01/81–1	1981		2	3	1
MD01/82–1	1982		2	3	1
MD01/82–3	1982	PROOF	2	3	1
MD01/82–4	1982	PROOF in 0.925 silver [1]	2	3	2
MD01/82–6	1982	PROOF in 0.917 gold [1]	2	3	70
MD01/82–7	1982	PROOF in 0.950 platinum [1]	2	3	100
MD01/83–1	1983		2	3	1
MD01/83–4	1983	PROOF in 0.925 silver [1]	2	3	2
MD01/83–6	1983	PROOF in 0.917 gold [1]	2	3	70
MD01/83–7	1983	PROOF in 0.950 platinum [1]	2	3	100
MD01/84–1	1984		2	4	1
MD01/84–4	1984	PROOF in 0.925 silver [1]	2	4	2
MD01/84–6	1984	PROOF in 0.917 gold [1]	2	4	70
MD01/85–1	1985		3	4	1
MD01/85–3	1985	PROOF	3	4	1
MD01/85–4	1985	PROOF in 0.925 silver [1]	3	4	2
MD01/85–6	1985	PROOF in 0.917 gold [1]	3	4	70

No.	Date	Features	Obv.	Rev.	UNC
MD01/85–7	1985	PROOF in 0.950 platinum [1]	3	4	100
MD01/86–1	1986		3	4	1
MD01/87–1	1987		3	4	1
MD01/88–1	1988		3	5	1
MD01/89–1	1989		3	5	1
MD01/90–1	1990		3	5	1
MD01/91–1	1991		3	5	1
MD01/92–1	1992		3	5	1
MD01/93–1	1993		3	5	1
MD01/96–1	1996		3	6	1
MD01/98–1	1998		4	6	8
MD01/98–1A	1998		5	6	1

1. Issued in cased sets.
2. 1000 issued.

Some of the above exhibit privy marks.

Some recent issues are not included in the table above.

Halfpenny

Denomination	Metal	Weight (grams)	Diameter (mm)	Rev. alignment
Halfpenny	Bronze	1.8	17	↑

Proofs in silver, gold and platinum weigh 2.1, 3.6 and 4.0 grams respectively.

Obverse 1 Head 1, right; ELIZABETH THE SECOND (date)

Obverse 2 Head 1, right; ISLE OF MAN ELIZABETH II (date)

Obverse 3 Head 2, right; same legend

Reverse 1 St. James's Weed; ISLE OF MAN HALF NEW PENNY

Reverse 2 Herring superimposed on map of Isle of Man; ISLE OF MAN HALF PENNY

Reverse 3 Similar but legend also includes F.A.O. FOOD FOR ALL

Reverse 4 Herring with ornamentation; 1/2

Reverse 5 WORLD FOOD DAY 16–10–81

Reverse 6 Fuchsia blossom and 1/2, all within border

Edge plain

No.	Date	Features	Obv.	Rev.	UNC
MDHP/71–1	1971		1	1	1
MDHP/71–3	1971	PROOF [1]	1	1	1
MDHP/72–1	1972	[2]	1	1	16
MDHP/73–1	1973	[2]	1	1	16
MDHP/74–1	1974	[2]	1	1	16
MDHP/75–1	1975		1	1	1
MDHP/75–2	1975	In 0.925 silver [1]	1	1	2
MDHP/75–7	1975	PROOF in 0.950 platinum[1]	1	1	50
MDHP/76–1	1976		1	2	1
MDHP/76–2	1976	In 0.925 silver [1]	1	2	2
MDHP/76–7	1976	PROOF in 0.950 platinum[1]	1	2	50
MDHP/77–1	1977	PM on reverse	1	3	1
MDHP/77–1A	1977	No PM on reverse	1	3	1
MDHP/77–4	1977	PROOF in 0.925 silver [1]	1	1	2
MDHP/78–1	1978		1	2	1
MDHP/78–3	1978	PROOF [1]	1	2	1
MDHP/78–2	1978	In 0.925 silver [1]	1	2	2
MDHP/78–7	1978	PROOF in 0.950 platinum[1]	1	2	50
MDHP/79–1	1979		1	2	1
MDHP/79–4	1979	PROOF in 0.925 silver [1]	1	2	2
MDHP/79–7	1979	PROOF in 0.950 platinum[1]	1	2	50
MDHP/80–1	1980		2	4	1
MDHP/80–3	1980	PROOF	2	4	1
MDHP/80–4	1980	PROOF in 0.500 silver [1]	2	4	1
MDHP/80–6	1980	PROOF in 0.917 gold [1]	2	4	40
MDHP/80–7	1980	PROOF in 0.950 platinum[1]	2	4	50
MDHP/81–1	1981		2	3	1
MDHP/81–1A	1981		2	5	1
MDHP/81–1B	1981		2	4	1
MDHP/82–1	1982		2	4	1
MDHP/82–3	1982	PROOF	2	4	1
MDHP/82–4	1982	PROOF in 0.925 silver [1]	2	4	2
MDHP/82–6	1982	PROOF in 0.917 gold [1]	2	4	40
MDHP/82–7	1982	PROOF in 0.950 platinum[1]	2	4	50
MDHP/83–1	1983		2	4	1
MDHP/83–4	1983	PROOF in 0.925 silver [1]	2	4	2
MDHP/83–6	1983	PROOF in 0.917 gold [1]	2	4	40
MDHP/83–7	1983	PROOF in 0.950 platinum[1]	2	4	50
MDHP/84–1	1984		2	6	1
MDHP/84–4	1984	PROOF in 0.925 silver [1]	2	6	2
MDHP/84–6	1984	PROOF in 0.917 gold [1]	2	6	40
MDHP/85–1	1985		3	6	1
MDHP/85–3	1985	PROOF	3	6	1
MDHP/85–4	1985	PROOF in 0.925 silver [1]	3	6	2
MDHP/85–6	1985	PROOF in 0.917 gold [1]	3	6	40
MDHP/85–7	1985	PROOF in 0.950 platinum[1]	3	6	50

1. Issued in cased sets.
2. 1000 issued.

Some of the above exhibit privy marks.

Obv. 1 Obv. 2 Obv. 3

Rev. 1 Rev. 3 Rev. 4

Rev. 6

Pobjoy Mint Commemorative Issues

After the striking of the first decimal coins for the Isle of Man at the Royal Mint and the 1972 crown piece in Ottawa, the contract for the issue of coinage for the island was signed with the Pobjoy Mint, of Sutton, Surrey. The first issues were decimal pieces intended for circulation, together with gold coins and an annual commemorative crown. As the tables below show, the output later accelerated to considerable proportions, producing a range of issues which would be impossible to cover in detail without extending this catalogue by several hundred pages. These issues were not seriously intended to circulate as currency, and, although strictly speaking they are legal tender, they might be regarded by many to be more in the nature of medallions than true coins. Because of this, they are summarized by year and subject matter only. Some of the listed types are marked by several different issues, and in some cases by a very considerable number. These are marked in the listings by (+).

1974

Churchill, centenary of birth

1975

Manx Cat

1976

American Independence, 200th anniversary
Horse Tram at Douglas

1977

Jubilee Appeal
Queen Elizabeth II, Silver Jubilee

1978

Queen Elizabeth II, 25th anniversary of coronation

1979

Manx coinage
Tynwald Millennium (+)

1980

Derby horse race
Moscow Olympics (+)
New York Exhibition
Queen Elizabeth the Queen Mother, 80th birthday
Winter Olympics

1981

Bader, Douglas
Beethoven
Braille, Louis
Charles and Diana Wedding (+)
Chichester, Francis
Christmas
Duke of Edinburgh Awards (+)
T.T. Races

1982

Christmas
Maritime Heritage (+)
T.T. Races

World Cup (+)

1983

Christmas
Manned flight (+)
T.T. Races

1984

Christmas
College of Arms, quincentenary (+)
Olympics (+)
Parliamentary Conference (+)
T.T. Races

1985

Christmas
Queen Elizabeth the Queen Mother, 85th Birthday (+)

1986

Christmas
Prince Andrew and Sarah Wedding (+)
World Cup Soccer (+)

1987

America's Cup (+)
Christmas
Hong Kong Coin Fair
U.S.A. Constitution

1988

Australian bicentennial (+)
Christmas
Computers
Manx Cat (+)
Steam Navigation (+)

1989

Christmas
Mutiny on the Bounty (+)
Persian Cat (+)
Royal Visit
Washington, George (+)
World Cup Soccer (+)

1990

Alley Cat (+)
Christmas
Churchill (+)
Penny Black, 150th anniversary (+)
Queen Elizabeth the Queen Mother, 90th birthday (+)
Soccer (+)

1991

America's Cup (+)
American Numismatic Association
Charles and Diana, 10th wedding anniversary

Christmas
Norwegian Cat (+)

1992

America's Cup (+)
Christmas
Discovery of America, 500th anniversary (+)
Siamese Cat (+)

1993

Christmas
Maine Coon Cat (+)
Mansell, Nigel
Preserve Planet Earth (+)
Year of the Rooster (+)

1994

Christmas
Japanese Bobtail Cat (+)
Legislative Building, centenary
Man in flight (+)
Mansell, Nigel
Manx Cat
Normandy Invasion (+)
Pekingese Dog (+)
Preserve Planet Earth (+)
World Cup Soccer (+)

1995

Aircraft of World War II (+)
America's Cup (+)
Christmas
Inventors (+)
Man in Flight (+)
Preserve Planet Earth (+)
Queen Elizabeth the Queen Mother, 95th birthday (+)
Turkish Cat (+)
United Nations, anniversary
World War II end, 50th anniversary
Year of the Pig (+)

1996

Burmese Cat (+)
Burns, Robert, bicentennial (+)
Christmas
Douglas centenary
Drake, Francis (+)
European Football Championship (+)
Flower fairies (+)
Inventors (+)
King Arthur (+)
La Boheme
Magellan, Ferdinand (+)
Motorcyclists

Olympics (+)
Preserve Planet Earth (+)
Queen Elizabeth II, 70th birthday
Spain

1997 (incomplete)

Eiriksson, Leiv (+)
Flower fairies (+)
History of the Cat (+)
Long-haired Smoke Cat (+)
Millennium (+)
Moore, Thomas
Motorcyclists
Nansen, Fridtjof (+)
Queen Elizabeth II and Philip, Golden Wedding
Schubert, Franz
Sweelinck, Jan
TT Races, 90th anniversary (+)

Isle of Man: Tokens and similar issues

Tokens were issued privately since before the inception of official coinage, and subsequently filled the gap created by the inadequate provision of coinage by the various authorities responsible for same. It would be impossible to detail the token issues exhaustively; consequently only the most important pieces are covered.

Since tokens do not bear any intrinsic legal denomination, the issues are listed in chronological order rather than by denomination as in the coinage section. Any denominational value intended by the issuer can generally be deduced from the legend.

17th Century Tokens

During the 17th century, various unofficial tokens were in circulation, mainly of Irish origin. Chief amongst these were the St. Patrick's halfpenny and farthing, the Mic Wilson tokens and the Limerick pieces. Some of these may be found in the section of the catalogue on Ireland. In 1679, an Act of Tynwald prohibited the use and distribution of such tokens, with the exception of the locally issued penny tokens issued by John Murrey. These were thus elevated to the status of a legal issue, and are covered in the coinage section.

The earliest known depiction of the triune on a token was on the farthing issued in 1657 by John Hutton of Norwich. The symbol also appeared on undated tokens in London at around the same time.

Peel Castle tokens

The Peel Castle series of tokens of 1811 was an ambitious issue by the short-lived self-styled Douglas Bank, otherwise Littler, Dove and Co. of Fort Street, and later Duke Street, Douglas. The tokens bore an elegant design by T. Halliday of the harbour and castle at Peel, and the tokens were struck in Birmingham by Edward Thomason, providing a much-needed medium of exchange at a time when legal currency was in short supply. At this time many tokens, mainly in silver, were struck in England, and the fashion had spread to the island.

On issuing the tokens, the bank advertised: 'The Douglas Bank Company ... feel it a duty they owe themselves and the public to declare their readiness to meet their tokens to any amount above twenty pounds by Bills upon London, at the usual Exchange of the island. Under that sum they propose to issue their own notes, but as they are not quite in readiness, they are prepared with notes and cards current in the island.'

Soon after the Peel Castle tokens were issued, disputes arose amongst the partners of the bank. The Rev. Robert Littler announced his intention to leave the island, whereupon James Dove issued a summons against him for £1,000, and Littler was imprisoned. Littler then counterclaimed against Dove, and in the Court proceedings of 3rd January, 1812, his imprisonment was set aside. The bank did not survive the scandal, and its demise followed swiftly.

No.	Date	Issued by	Metal	Weight (grams)	Diameter (mm)
MTK-010	1811	Littler, Dove and Co.	Silver	15.2	35 – 36

Obv.   Rev.

Obverse Peel Castle with two figures and fishing vessel; PEEL CASTLE ISLE OF MAN

Reverse THE DOUGLAS BANK CO AT THEIR BANK, DOUGLAS PROMISE TO PAY THE BEARER ON DEMAND 5 SHILLINGS BRITISH 1811

Edge plain
Proofs exist. Reverse axis alignment normally ↑.

F	VF	EF	PROOF
700	1000	1800	3000

No.	Date	Issued by	Metal	Weight (grams)	Diameter (mm)
MTK-020	1811	Littler, Dove and Co.	Silver	7.9	30

Obv.   Rev.

Obverse Peel Castle with two figures and fishing vessel; PEEL CASTLE ISLE OF MAN

Reverse THE DOUGLAS BANK CO AT THEIR BANK, DOUGLAS PROMISE TO PAY THE BEARER ON DEMAND 2s 6d BRITISH 1811

Edge milled (diagonally)
The orientation of the date with respect to the legend varies. Plain edge proofs exist in copper on a thick flan having a weight of 12.4 grams and diameter 28.5 mm. Reverse axis alignment normally ↑.

F	VF	EF	COPPER PROOF
700	1000	1500	1500

No.	Date	Issued by	Metal	Weight (grams)	Diameter (mm)
MTK-030	1811	Littler, Dove and Co.	Silver	2.9	22

Obv.   Rev.

Obverse Peel Castle with fishing vessel

Reverse DOUGLAS BANK TOKEN ONE SHILLING BRITISH 1811

Edge milled (diagonally)

Proofs exist. Specimens of the ordinary issue are known struck in copper with incuse 'A' countermarked on the reverse. A few trial pieces are known which have a reverse reading S.ASH in relief on a blank field, with an incuse 'A' countermarked in the field, and a plain edge (weight about 5 grams).

F	VF	EF	PROOF
150	300	600	900

No.	Date	Issued by	Metal	Weight (grams)	Diameter (mm)
MTK-040	1811	Littler, Dove and Co.	Copper	12.5	32

Obv.   Rev.

Obverse Peel Castle with fishing vessel; PEEL CASTLE ISLE OF MAN

Reverse DOUGLAS BANK TOKEN ONE PENNY 1811

Edge milled (diagonally)

Proofs exist in bronze on regular and other flans. Reverse axis alignment normally ↑.

F	VF	EF	PROOF
12	30	80	200

No.	Date	Issued by	Metal	Weight (grams)	Diameter (mm)
MTK-050	1811	Littler, Dove and Co.	Copper	12.3 – 12.5	32

Obv.   Rev.

Obverse Peel Castle with fishing vessel; PEEL CASTLE ISLE OF MAN

Reverse DOUGLAS TOKEN ONE PENNY 1811

Edge milled (diagonally)

Proofs exist, including at least one on a thin flan. Reverse axis alignment normally ↑.

F	VF	EF	PROOF
10	25	70	180

No.	Date	Issued by	Metal	Weight (grams)	Diameter (mm)
MTK-060	1811	Littler, Dove and Co.	Copper	6.2 – 6.3	25

Obverse Peel Castle with fishing vessel; PEEL CASTLE ISLE OF MAN

Reverse DOUGLAS BANK TOKEN HALFPENNY 1811

Edge milled (diagonally)

Proofs in bronze exist. The non-proof issue exists with either large and small lettering on the reverse. Reverse axis alignment normally ↑.

F	VF	EF	PROOF
10	20	60	200

Atlas Manx tokens

The Atlas tokens were issued by the Atlas Fire Insurance Company of Douglas through their bankers, Messrs. Beatson and Copeland. Reverse axis alignment normally ↓.

No.	Date	Issued by	Metal	Weight (grams)	Diameter (mm)
MTK-070	1811	Atlas Fire Insurance Company	Copper	13.6	32

Obv.   Rev.

Obverse Atlas supporting globe; PAYABLE AT THE OFFICE DOUGLAS

Reverse Triune (type 1) with spurs; MANKS TOKEN ONE PENNY 1811

Edge milled (diagonally)

Bronze proofs exist.

F	VF	EF	PROOF FDC
4	8	18	60

No.	Date	Issued by	Metal	Weight (grams)	Diameter (mm)
MTK-080	1811	Atlas Fire Insurance Company	Copper	7.5	27 – 28

Obv.   Rev.

Obverse Atlas supporting globe; PAYABLE AT THE OFFICE DOUGLAS

Reverse Triune (type 1) with spurs; MANKS TOKEN HALFPENNY 1811

Edge milled (diagonally)

This issue has 'DOUGLAS' positioned to bottom right of Atlas.

F	VF	EF
4	8	18

No.	Date	Issued by	Metal	Weight (grams)	Diameter (mm)
MTK-090	1811	Atlas Fire Insurance Company	Copper	7.1	27

Obv.   Rev.

Obverse Atlas supporting globe; PAYABLE AT THE OFFICE DOUGLAS

Reverse Triune (type 1) with spurs; MANKS TOKEN HALFPENNY 1811

Edge milled (diagonally)
This issue has 'DOUGLAS' positioned directly below Atlas; the reverse lettering is larger than that on the obverse.

VF
400

Isle of Man Bank tokens

The penny and halfpenny tokens of this issue were struck in Birmingham by the Castletown partnership of Quayle, Taubman and Kelly, formed in 1802 and reformed on 1st January 1811 as Quayle, Cotteen and Lightfoot. The designer was T. Halliday.

No.	Date	Issued by	Metal	Weight (grams)	Diameter (mm)
MTK-100	1811	Quayle and partners	Copper	14.2 – 14.3	33

Obv.   Rev.

Obverse BANK PENNY within two concentric circles; ISLE OF MAN 1811

Reverse Triune (type 2); QVOCVNQVE IECERIS STABIT

Edge milled (diagonally) in groove
Proofs exist.

F	VF	EF	PROOF FDC
10	20	60	200

No.	Date	Issued by	Metal	Weight (grams)	Diameter (mm)
MTK-110	1811	Quayle and partners	Copper	6.9	26

Obverse BANK HALF PENNY within two concentric circles; ISLE OF MAN 1811

Reverse Triune (type 2); QVOCVNQVE IECERIS STABIT

Edge milled (diagonally)
Bronze proofs exist.

F	VF	EF	PROOF FDC
5	10	20	120

Cain(e) or McTurk tokens

At the time of issue of these tokens in 1830, the situation regarding small change on the island was desperate, with every conceivable medium of exchange being used. No legal currency had been issued for the island since 1813, and the small change used was a mixture of foreign coins, tokens and even buttons. The 1830 issue was struck in a variety of metals, usually copper based alloys or copper itself, and the tokens were originally issued by John Cain(e) of Castletown, and subsequently by members of his family, John McTurk and a Mr. Carter. The issue has the distinction of bearing what is reputedly the worst likeness depicted of George III, despite the fact that the current monarch was George IV. The portrait seems to be a crude copy of Küchler's design for George III, and the triune was not represented on the tokens. Reverse axis alignment normally ↓

No.	Date	Issued by	Metal	Weight (grams)	Diameter (mm)
MTK-120	1830	John Cain(e) and family	Usually copper or copper-based alloy	14.0–14.2	34–35

Obv.   Rev.

Obverse Head of George III, right; GOD SAVE THE KING 1830

Reverse FOR PUBLICK ACCOMMODATION

Edge plain
Two main types exist: (a) pointed-top '1' and round-top '3' in date; (b) flat-top '1' and '3' in date.

F	VF	EF
4	8	20

No.	Date	Issued by	Metal	Weight (grams)	Diameter (mm)
MTK-130	1830	John Cain(e) and family	Usually copper or copper-based alloy	6.2–6.3	29–30

Obv.   Rev.

Obverse Head of George III, right; GOD SAVE THE KING 1830

Reverse FOR PUBLICK ACCOMMODATION

Edge plain

F	VF	EF
3	6	12

Callister tokens

These tokens were designated by the issuer William Callister (1808–1872), a timber importer of Ramsey at a halfpenny, and were struck by Sir Edward Thomason at Birmingham. They were designed by Thomas Halliday, and the incuse lettering design on the broad rim was probably inspired by the 1798 and 1813 coinage issues. Callister later became a Member of the House of Keys, and his grandson was the eminent collector J. D. Clucas, whose collection of Manx coins forms a prominent part of the Manx Museum.

No.	Date	Issued by	Metal	Weight (grams)	Diameter (mm)
MTK-140	1831	W. Callister	Copper	8.0 – 8.2	28 – 29

Obv.   Rev.

Obverse HALF PENNY TOKEN; PRO BONO PUBLICO 1831 incuse around broad rim

Reverse Triune (type 2); QUOCUNQUE IECERIS STABIT incuse around broad rim

Edge plain
Reverse orientation varieties exist. Proofs exist.

F	VF	EF
3	6	15

Onchan Internment Camp tokens

The Onchan tokens were struck in 1941 by J. R. Gaunt & Son Ltd., Birmingham, as part of a series (including plastic and paper denominations) for use in the internment camp for German civilians at Onchan, north of Douglas, during the second world war. Other camps existed on the island, but the brass tokens of Onchan were the only metallic tokens in use. After the closure of Onchan they were used at two other camps on the island, Granville Camp and Camp 'N'.

The larger of the two penny tokens was replaced by the smaller to deter souvenir hunters.

No.	Date	Issued by	Metal	Weight (grams)	Diameter (mm)
MTK-160	(1941)	Onchan Camp Authority	Brass	6.3 – 6.5	25 – 29

Obverse 6ᴰ ONCHAN INTERNMENT CAMP

Reverse Triune (type 2)

Edge plain

F	VF
20	40

No.	Date	Issued by	Metal	Weight (grams)	Diameter (mm)
MTK-170	(1941)	Onchan Camp Authority	Brass	6.0 – 6.3	26 – 27

Obverse 1ᴰ ONCHAN INTERNMENT CAMP

Reverse Triune (type 2)

Edge plain

F	VF

No.	Date	Issued by	Metal	Weight (grams)	Diameter (mm)
MTK-180	(1941)	Onchan Camp Authority	Brass	2.7 – 2.9	18

Obverse 1ᴰ ONCHAN INTERNMENT CAMP

Reverse Triune (type 2)

Edge plain

F	VF
12	24

No.	Date	Issued by	Metal	Weight (grams)	Diameter (mm)
MTK-190	(1941)	Onchan Camp Authority	Brass	3.8 – 4.0	21

Obverse 1/2ᴰ ONCHAN INTERNMENT CAMP

Reverse Triune (type 2)

Edge plain

F	VF
25	50

Hotel and shop tokens

A number of tokens issued by hotels are known, e.g. Gallimore's Sheffield Hotel, Brown's Theatre Royal Hotel, J. W. Birtle's Pier Inn, Trustrum York Hotel, the Quarterbridge Hotel, the Railway Hotel and the Villiers Hotel. These are generally of brass, diameter about 25mm, and denomination twopence. However, tokens of the Villiers Hotel exist from twopence up to two shillings and sixpence.

Tokens of widely varying size, mostly in brass, were issued by shops and other establishments; notable are issues from the Douglas Co-operative Society and the Grand Restaurant.

Isle of Man: Proof Sets

1965

No.	Date	Striking Standard	No. of coins	Price
MPS-65	1965	Proof	3	500

Denomination	Metal
5 pounds	0.980 gold
Sovereign	0.980 gold
Half sovereign	0.980 gold

1971

No.	Date	Striking Standard	No. of coins	Price
MDPS-71	1971	Proof	6	8

Denomination	Metal
50 pence	Cupronickel
10 pence	Cupronickel
5 pence	Cupronickel
2 pence	Bronze
Penny	Bronze
Halfpenny	Bronze

1973

No.	Date	Striking Standard	No. of coins	Price
MDPS-73	1973	Proof	4	650

Denomination	Metal
5 pounds	0.917 gold
2 pounds	0.917 gold
Sovereign	0.917 gold
Half sovereign	0.917 gold

1974

No.	Date	Striking Standard	No. of coins	Price
MDPS-74	1974	Proof	4	650

Denomination	Metal
5 pounds	0.917 gold
2 pounds	0.917 gold
Sovereign	0.917 gold
Half sovereign	0.917 gold

1975

No.	Date	Striking Standard	No. of coins	Price
MDPS-75G	1975	Proof	4	650

Denomination	Metal
5 pounds	0.917 gold
2 pounds	0.917 gold
Sovereign	0.917 gold
Half sovereign	0.917 gold

No.	Date	Striking Standard	No. of coins	Price
MDPS-75P	1975	Proof	6	1100

Denomination	Metal
50 pence	0.950 platinum
10 pence	0.950 platinum
5 pence	0.950 platinum
2 pence	0.950 platinum
Penny	0.950 platinum
Halfpenny	0.950 platinum

1976

No.	Date	Striking Standard	No. of coins	Price
MDPS-76G	1976	Proof	4	650

Denomination	Metal
5 pounds	0.917 gold
2 pounds	0.917 gold
Sovereign	0.917 gold
Half sovereign	0.917 gold

No.	Date	Striking Standard	No. of coins	Price
MDPS-76P	1976	Proof	6	1100

Denomination	Metal
50 pence	0.950 platinum
10 pence	0.950 platinum
5 pence	0.950 platinum
2 pence	0.950 platinum
Penny	0.950 platinum
Halfpenny	0.950 platinum

1977

No.	Date	Striking Standard	No. of coins	Price
MDPS-77S	1977	Proof	6	20

Denomination	Metal
50 pence	0.925 silver
10 pence	0.925 silver

5 pence	0.925 silver
2 pence	0.925 silver
Penny	0.925 silver
Halfpenny	0.925 silver

No.	Date	Striking Standard	No. of coins	Price
MDPS-77G	1977	Proof	4	650

Denomination	Metal
5 pounds	0.917 gold
2 pounds	0.917 gold
Sovereign	0.917 gold
Half sovereign	0.917 gold

1978

No.	Date	Striking Standard	No. of coins	Price
MDPS-78	1978	Proof	7	10

Denomination	Metal
Pound	'Virenium'
50 pence	Cupronickel
10 pence	Cupronickel
5 pence	Cupronickel
2 pence	Bronze
Penny	Bronze
Halfpenny	Bronze

No.	Date	Striking Standard	No. of coins	Price
MDPS-78P	1978	Proof	7	1300

Denomination	Metal
Pound	0.950 platinum
50 pence	0.950 platinum
10 pence	0.950 platinum
5 pence	0.950 platinum
2 pence	0.950 platinum
Penny	0.950 platinum
Halfpenny	0.950 platinum

1979

No.	Date	Striking Standard	No. of coins	Price
MDPS-79S	1979	Proof	7	20

Denomination	Metal
Pound	0.925 silver
50 pence	0.925 silver
10 pence	0.925 silver
5 pence	0.925 silver
2 pence	0.925 silver
Penny	0.925 silver
Halfpenny	0.925 silver

No.	Date	Striking Standard	No. of coins	Price
MDPS-79P	1979	Proof	7	1300

Denomination	Metal
Pound	0.950 platinum
50 pence	0.950 platinum
10 pence	0.950 platinum
5 pence	0.950 platinum
2 pence	0.950 platinum
Penny	0.950 platinum
Halfpenny	0.950 platinum

No.	Date	Striking Standard	No. of coins	Price
MDPS-79G	1979	Proof	4	650

Denomination	Metal
5 pounds	0.917 gold
2 pounds	0.917 gold
Sovereign	0.917 gold
Half sovereign	0.917 gold

1980

No.	Date	Striking Standard	No. of coins	Price
MDPS-80	1980	Proof	7	10

Denomination	Metal
Pound	'Virenium'
50 pence	Cupronickel
10 pence	Cupronickel
5 pence	Cupronickel
2 pence	Bronze
Penny	Bronze
Halfpenny	Bronze

No.	Date	Striking Standard	No. of coins	Price
MDPS-80S	1980	Proof	7	15

Denomination	Metal
Pound	0.500 silver
50 pence	0.500 silver
10 pence	0.500 silver
5 pence	0.500 silver
2 pence	0.500 silver
Penny	0.500 silver
Halfpenny	0.500 silver

No.	Date	Striking Standard	No. of coins	Price
MDPS-80A	1980	Proof	7	90

Denomination	Metal
Pound	0.917 gold
50 pence	0.925 silver
10 pence	0.925 silver
5 pence	0.925 silver
2 pence	0.925 silver
Penny	0.925 silver
Halfpenny	0.925 silver

No.	Date	Striking Standard	No. of coins	Price
MDPS-80G	1980	Proof	7	700

Denomination	Metal
Pound	0.917 gold
50 pence	0.917 gold
10 pence	0.917 gold
5 pence	0.917 gold
2 pence	0.917 gold
Penny	0.917 gold
Halfpenny	0.917 gold

Later sets from Pobjoy Mint proliferated, and, as with the Pobjoy single issues, are not listed. Usually, several different types of set were issued in one year, some with mintages below 100.

Isle of Man: Specimen Sets

1965				
No.	Date	Striking Standard	No. of coins	Price
MMS-65	1965	Specimen	3	450

Denomination	Metal
5 pounds	0.917 gold
Sovereign	0.917 gold
Half sovereign	0.917 gold

1971				
No.	Date	Striking Standard	No. of coins	Price
MDMS-71	1971	Uncirculated	6	5

Denomination	Metal
50 pence	Cupronickel
10 pence	Cupronickel
5 pence	Cupronickel
2 pence	Bronze
Penny	Bronze
Halfpenny	Bronze

1973				
No.	Date	Striking Standard	No. of coins	Price
MDMS-73	1973	Specimen	4	600

Denomination	Metal
5 pounds	0.917 gold
2 pounds	0.917 gold
Sovereign	0.917 gold
Half sovereign	0.917 gold

1974				
No.	Date	Striking Standard	No. of coins	Price
MDMS-74	1974	Specimen	4	600

Denomination	Metal
5 pounds	0.917 gold
2 pounds	0.917 gold
Sovereign	0.917 gold
Half sovereign	0.917 gold

1975				
No.	Date	Striking Standard	No. of coins	Price
MDMS-75	1975	Uncirculated	6	5

Denomination	Metal
50 pence	Cupronickel
10 pence	Cupronickel
5 pence	Cupronickel
2 pence	Bronze
Penny	Bronze
Halfpenny	Bronze

No.	Date	Striking Standard	No. of coins	Price
MDMS-75S	1975	Specimen	6	18

Denomination	Metal
50 pence	0.925 silver
10 pence	0.925 silver
5 pence	0.925 silver
2 pence	0.925 silver
Penny	0.925 silver
Halfpenny	0.925 silver

No.	Date	Striking Standard	No. of coins	Price
MDMS-75G	1975	Specimen	4	600

Denomination	Metal
5 pounds	0.917 gold
2 pounds	0.917 gold
Sovereign	0.917 gold
Half sovereign	0.917 gold

1976				
No.	Date	Striking Standard	No. of coins	Price
MDMS-76	1976	Specimen	6	5

Denomination	Metal
50 pence	Cupronickel
10 pence	Cupronickel
5 pence	Cupronickel
2 pence	Bronze
Penny	Bronze
Halfpenny	Bronze

No.	Date	Striking Standard	No. of coins	Price
MDMS-76S	1976	Specimen	6	18

Denomination	Metal
50 pence	0.925 silver
10 pence	0.925 silver
5 pence	0.925 silver
2 pence	0.925 silver
Penny	0.925 silver
Halfpenny	0.925 silver

No.	Date	Striking Standard	No. of coins	Price
MDMS-76G	1976	Specimen	4	600

Denomination	Metal
5 pounds	0.917 gold
2 pounds	0.917 gold
Sovereign	0.917 gold
Half sovereign	0.917 gold

1977

No.	Date	Striking Standard	No. of coins	Price
MDMS-77	1977	Specimen	6	4

Denomination	Metal
50 pence	Cupronickel
10 pence	Cupronickel
5 pence	Cupronickel
2 pence	Bronze
Penny	Bronze
Halfpenny	Bronze

No.	Date	Striking Standard	No. of coins	Price
MDMS-77G	1977	Specimen	4	600

Denomination	Metal
5 pounds	0.917 gold
2 pounds	0.917 gold
Sovereign	0.917 gold
Half sovereign	0.917 gold

1978

No.	Date	Striking Standard	No. of coins	Price
MDMS-78	1978	Specimen	6	4

Denomination	Metal
50 pence	Cupronickel
10 pence	Cupronickel
5 pence	Cupronickel
2 pence	Bronze
Penny	Bronze
Halfpenny	Bronze

No.	Date	Striking Standard	No. of coins	Price
MDMS-78	1978S	Specimen	6	18

Denomination	Metal
50 pence	0.925 silver
10 pence	0.925 silver
5 pence	0.925 silver
2 pence	0.925 silver
Penny	0.925 silver
Halfpenny	0.925 silver

1979

No.	Date	Striking Standard	No. of coins	Price
MDMS-79	1979	Specimen	6	4

Denomination	Metal
50 pence	Cupronickel
10 pence	Cupronickel
5 pence	Cupronickel
2 pence	Bronze
Penny	Bronze
Halfpenny	Bronze

No.	Date	Striking Standard	No. of coins	Price
MDMS-79G	1979	Specimen	4	600

Denomination	Metal
5 pounds	0.917 gold
2 pounds	0.917 gold
Sovereign	0.917 gold
Half sovereign	0.917 gold

1980

No.	Date	Striking Standard	No. of coins	Price
MDMS-80	1980	Specimen	6	4

Denomination	Metal
50 pence	Cupronickel
10 pence	Cupronickel
5 pence	Cupronickel
2 pence	Bronze
Penny	Bronze
Halfpenny	Bronze

1981

No.	Date	Striking Standard	No. of coins	Price
MDMS-81	1981	Specimen	6	4

Denomination	Metal
50 pence	Cupronickel
10 pence	Cupronickel
5 pence	Cupronickel
2 pence	Bronze
Penny	Bronze
Halfpenny	Bronze

1982

No.	Date	Striking Standard	No. of coins	Price
MDMS-82	1982	Specimen	6	4

Denomination	Metal
50 pence	Cupronickel
10 pence	Cupronickel
5 pence	Cupronickel
2 pence	Bronze
Penny	Bronze
Halfpenny	Bronze

Pound	'Virenium'
50 pence	Cupronickel
20 pence	Cupronickel
10 pence	Cupronickel
5 pence	Cupronickel
2 pence	Bronze
Penny	Bronze

1983

No.	Date	Striking Standard	No. of coins	Price
MDMS-83	1983	Specimen	9	14

Denomination	Metal
5 pounds	'Virenium'
Pound	'Virenium'
50 pence	Cupronickel
20 pence	Cupronickel
10 pence	Cupronickel
5 pence	Cupronickel
2 pence	Bronze
Penny	Bronze
Halfpenny	Bronze

1994

No.	Date	Striking Standard	No. of coins	Price
MDMS-94	1994	Specimen	9	18

Denomination	Metal
5 pounds	'Virenium'
2 pounds	'Virenium'
Pound	'Virenium'
50 pence	Cupronickel
20 pence	Cupronickel
10 pence	Cupronickel
5 pence	Cupronickel
2 pence	Bronze
Penny	Bronze

1989

No.	Date	Striking Standard	No. of coins	Price
MDMS-89	1989	Specimen	9	18

Denomination	Metal
5 pounds	'Virenium'
2 pounds	'Virenium'
Pound	'Virenium'
50 pence	Cupronickel
20 pence	Cupronickel
10 pence	Cupronickel
5 pence	Cupronickel
2 pence	Bronze
Penny	Bronze

1995

No.	Date	Striking Standard	No. of coins	Price
MDMS-95	1995	Specimen	9	18

Denomination	Metal
5 pounds	'Virenium'
2 pounds	'Virenium'
Pound	'Virenium'
50 pence	Cupronickel
20 pence	Cupronickel
10 pence	Cupronickel
5 pence	Cupronickel
2 pence	Bronze
Penny	Bronze

1990

No.	Date	Striking Standard	No. of coins	Price
MDMS-90	1990	Specimen	9	18

Denomination	Metal
5 pounds	'Virenium'
2 pounds	'Virenium'
Pound	'Virenium'
50 pence	Cupronickel
20 pence	Cupronickel
10 pence	Cupronickel
5 pence	Cupronickel
2 pence	Bronze
Penny	Bronze

1996

No.	Date	Striking Standard	No. of coins	Price
MDMS-96	1996	Specimen	9	18

Denomination	Metal
5 pounds	'Virenium'
2 pounds	'Virenium'
Pound	Nickel brass
50 pence	Cupronickel
20 pence	Cupronickel
10 pence	Cupronickel
5 pence	Cupronickel
2 pence	Bronze clad steel
Penny	Bronze clad steel

1992

No.	Date	Striking Standard	No. of coins	Price
MDMS-92	1992	Specimen	9	18

Denomination	Metal
5 pounds	'Virenium'
2 pounds	'Virenium'

Isle of Man: Patterns

This listing represents a selection only.

Penny 1723

The pattern pennies dated 1723–32 were considered by the eminent numismatic historians Nelson and Clay to have been the work of William Wood, better known for his work on the George I Irish coinage, on account of similarities in style and execution. Wood died in 1730, but the early patterns coincide with the production of the Irish pieces.

No.	Date	Denomination	Metal	Weight (grams)	Diameter (mm)	Rev. align.	Price
MPTN-020	1723	Penny	Copper	7.9	28	OJS	

Obv. Rev.

Obverse Eagle and child on cap of maintenance; SANS CHANGER 1723

Reverse Triune (type 2) with spurs; QVOCVNQVE GESSERIS STABIT

Edge plain

Penny 1723

No.	Date	Denomination	Metal	Weight (grams)	Diameter (mm)	Rev. align.	Price
MPTN-040	1723	Penny	Silver	8.2	28	OJS	

Obverse Eagle and child on cap of maintenance; SANS CHANGER 1723

Reverse Triune (type 2) with spurs; QVOCVNQVE GESSERIS STABIT

Edge milled (diagonally)

Halfpenny 1723

No.	Date	Denomination	Metal	Weight (grams)	Diameter (mm)	Rev. align.	Price
MPTN-060	1723	Halfpenny	Copper	4.7 – 7.9	25	OJS	700
MPTN-070	1723	Halfpenny	Silver	3.6 – 3.9	25	OJS	

Obverse Eagle and child on cap of maintenance; SANS CHANGER 1723

Reverse Triune (type 2) with spurs; QVOCVNQVE GESSERIS STABIT

Edge plain

Halfcrown (?) 1725

This piece sometimes occurs on an undersize blank, and has been catalogued as bearing the date 1705, owing to the lower half of the digits being off the flan.

No.	Date	Denomination	Metal	Weight (grams)	Diameter (mm)	Rev. align.	Price
MPTN-090	1725	Halfcrown?	Silver	14.2	33	OJS	

Obverse Eagle and child on cap of maintenance; SANS CHANGER 1725

Reverse Triune (type 2) with spurs; QUOCUNQUE GESSERIS STABIT

Edge milled (diagonally)

Halfcrown (?) 1725

This intriguing piece, in the British Museum, bears traces of an underlying coin. Just visible are GVLI...MVS DEI GRA on one side, and French Arms in a shield on the other. The edge is clearly marked DECVS ET TVTAMEN ANNO REGNI OCTAVO, the sum total of which pinpoints the underlying piece as a William III halfcrown of 1696.

No.	Date	Denomination	Metal	Weight (grams)	Diameter (mm)	Rev. align.	Price
MPTN-100	1725	Halfcrown?	Silver	14.5	33	OJS	

Obverse Eagle and child on cap of maintenance; SANS CHANGER 1725

Reverse Triune (type 2) with spurs; QUOCUNQUE GESSERIS STABIT

Edge DECVS ET TVTAMEN ANNO REGNI OCTAVO

Penny 1732

No.	Date	Denomination	Metal	Weight (grams)	Diameter (mm)	Rev. align.	Price
MPTN-140	1732	Penny	Brass	10.5	29	OJS	

Obverse Eagle and child on cap of maintenance, with olive branch of 8 leaves at head of cradle; SANS CHANGER 1732

Reverse Large triune (type 1) with spurs, with I D J between the legs; QUOCUNQUE IECERIS STABIT

Edge plain

Penny 1732

As well as this piece, a similar pattern occurs with 6 leaves in the olive branch.

No.	Date	Denomination	Metal	Weight (grams)	Diameter (mm)	Rev. align.	Price
MPTN-150	1732	Penny	Brass	9.1	26	OJS	

Obverse Eagle and child on cap of maintenance, with olive branch of 8 leaves at head of cradle; SANS CHANGER 1732

Reverse Large triune (type 1) with spurs, with I D J between the legs; QUOCUNQUE IECERIS STABIT

Edge plain

Isle of Man: Mintage Information & Figures

Extracts from 'Book of Disbursments on the Coynage of New Pence and Halfpence Anno 1733'

Page 1	Munday	Tuesday	Wednesday Thursday Friday Saturday
Mr. Topping	Ap^{il} 30, this day began to coyne	ditto	(all entries read ditto)
Mr. Dyall	Ap^{il} 30, at ditto	ditto	(all entries read ditto)
Geor. Wilks	Ap^{il} 30, at ditto	ditto	(all entries read ditto)
Jon. Slater	Ap^{il} 30, at ditto	ditto	(all entries read ditto)
Thos. Christian	Ap^{il} 30, at ditto	ditto	(all entries read ditto)
Richd. Slater	Ap^{il} 30, at ditto	ditto	(all entries read ditto)
Edwd. Caine		May 1st, this day began at the press	(all entries read ditto)

Page 29	Munday	Tuesday Wednesday Thursday Friday Saturday
Mr. Topping	Novr 12 at the press	(all entries read ditto)
Mr. Dyall	Turning	(all entries read ditto)
Geor. Wilks	At the furnas	(all entries read ditto)
Jon. Slater Thos. Christian	Filing	(all entries read ditto)
Richd. Slater	At the furnas	(all entries read ditto)
Edwd. Caine	At the press	(all entries read ditto)
Cesar Brew	At the press	(all entries read ditto)
Danl. Christian	Casting	(all entries read ditto)

April 28th, 1733   Pa^d Mr. Amos Topping from the time he came from London till they began work all together which was 11 weeks at 15s. per week but at that time he was putting things in order casting his lopps. Silver meddals. AMOS TOPPING   £8.5s.0d

April 17th, 1734   Pa^d Mr. Amos Topping for 50 weekes work when all togeat^r at the coyning at 15s. p. in full till this day AMOS TOPPING   £37.10s.0d

April 24th, 1734   Pa^d Mr. Topping one weekes wages AMOS TOPPING   £0.15s.0d

Feb^r 3d, 1733   Pa^d Jon. Gill for fetching a pair of bellows from the Smelt hows as p.   £0.0s.8d

For other liquor given the coyners on extraordinary occasions   £0.12s.10d

Lundy & Scilly

The milled coinage of Lundy

Lundy, an island of just over four square kilometres, lies in the Bristol Channel, off the coast of Devon, England at 51 degs. 10 mins. North, 4 degs. 40 mins. West, and has been inhabited since prehistoric times. Its name is said to be derived from LUND, a puffin (old Norse) and Y, an island. Medieval chieftains are thought to have issued silver and copper coins, replacing an ancient system of barter. Silver, mined on the North coast of Devon within sight of Lundy, may well have been used to make some of this primitive coinage. Other coinage may also have circulated, and in 1927, Lieut. Col. H. W. Morrieson, a member of the British Numismatic Society conjectured in a lecture that Thomas Bushell, who held Lundy for the Crown in the civil wars, had minted coins on the island.

Lundy was privately owned down the centuries, and records show that it was bought for £9,870 in 1836 by William Hudson Heaven, the island becoming known locally as 'the Kingdom of Heaven'. At the end of the 19th century it was owned by his son, the Reverend Hudson Grosett Heaven. In 1916 it passed to his nephew, Walter Heaven, who sold it the following year to Augustus Langham Christie. In 1925 Christie sold the island to Martin Coles Harman for £25,250. And thereby, as is said, hangs a tale.

Martin Coles Harman was a highly motivated individual who had ambitions for himself and for Lundy. A native of Caterham in Surrey, at the age of sixteen he worked for the banking firm Lazard Brothers in Threadneedle Street, London, and two years later visited Lundy, declaring on landing that 'one day I shall buy this island'.

On realising his ambition, he decided that it would be an excellent idea to issue coins for the island bearing his own effigy, with a reverse depicting a puffin, and proceeded with this aim. On 6th June 1929, he ordered from The Mint, Birmingham Ltd. a consignment of 50,000 bronze 'coins' approximating in size to a penny, and a similar quantity the size of a halfpenny. The cost to Harman was 50 shillings and ninepence per thousand for the larger pieces, and 26 shillings and sixpence per thousand for the smaller, plus £100 for preparing designs and sinking dies. Harman, on seeing the first designs for the reverse, remarked: 'There is one criticism I have to make. The puffin is a bird very tidy with his feathers. The bird in your sketch looks as if he slept in his clothes'.

The coins were to be issued on Lundy and to anyone else willing to buy them, his contention being that Lundy lay outside the territorial waters of the United Kingdom. Harman called the pieces the puffin and the half puffin, and around the edge was inscribed the Lundy motto 'Lundy lights and leads'. Harman arranged with banks in Bideford (Devon) to exchange British copper coins for Lundy coinage. On 29th November 1929, six cases of tokens weighing seven and a half hundredweight were despatched to the island, with others sent to Harman in London.

On 15th April 1930, Harman was charged 'that between 14th November 1929 and 5th March 1930 he unlawfully issued as a token for money a piece of metal to the value of one halfpenny, contrary to Section 5 of the Coinage Act, 1870'. At the trial, H. Russell Bazeley, for the defence, held that Lundy was outside the jurisdiction of the Court as 'there are no rates and taxes payable on Lundy. There are no dog licences, there are no Excise licences, there are no Customs, there is no game licence of any description except such as the owner himself levies. He levies taxes, dog licences and games licences himself, and the money goes into his

own pocket'. It was further pointed out that a collision between a British and an Italian ship near Lundy had previously been held not to have occurred within the jurisdiction of the Court. On being asked how he pleaded, Harman had observed: 'If you please, I offer no plea whatever; I refuse to plead'. A plea of Not Guilty had been entered.

Harman was subsequently convicted and fined £5 with 15 guineas costs (payable in U.K. currency), and he later appealed against the decision. The appeal was not without humour:

HARMAN: 'Lundy is a vest-pocket size self-governing dominion'.

JUSTICE AVORY: 'Does it ever happen that anyone assaults anyone else on Lundy?'

HARMAN: 'Yes, and it is put down with a heavy hand'.

AVORY: 'Whose heavy hand?'

HARMAN: 'The hand of my agent, who is 6 feet 4 inches and weighs 18 stone' (Laughter).

Finally, the Judge ruled that Lundy was part of the United Kingdom for the purposes of issuing coinage, and dismissed the appeal.

Harman died in 1954, having made his mark on numismatic history, and in 1965 the dies for his 'coins' were taken over by Modern World Coins who issued a double commemorative set to mark the 40th anniversary of Harman's purchase of the island. Harman's ghost might well have allowed himself a wry smile.

Puffin

Denomination	Metal	Weight (grams)	Diameter (mm)	Rev. alignment
Puffin	Bronze	10.0	30	↑

Obverse 1   Head of Harman, left; MARTIN COLES HARMAN (date)
Reverse 1   Puffin standing on rocky ground; LUNDY ONE PUFFIN
Edge   (in relief): LUNDY LIGHTS AND LEADS

Obv. 1   Rev. 1

No.	Date	Features	Obv.	Rev.	VF	EF	UNC
L1P-005	1929		1	1	6	10	18
L1P-010	1965	PROOF; edge plain [1]	1	1			8
L1P-015	1965	PROOF in nickel-brass; edge plain [1]	1	1			8
L1P-020	1965	PROOF in gold; edge plain [1]	1	1			300

1. Issued by Modern World Coins in sets to commemorate the 40th anniversary of Harman's purchase of Lundy.

Half Puffin

Denomination	Metal	Weight (grams)	Diameter (mm)	Rev. alignment
Half puffin	Bronze	5.5	24	↑

Obverse 1   Head of Harman, left; MARTIN COLES HARMAN (date)
Reverse 1   Head of puffin; LUNDY HALF PUFFIN
Edge   (in relief): LUNDY LIGHTS AND LEADS

Obv. 1   Rev. 1

No.	Date	Features	Obv.	Rev.	VF	EF	UNC
LHP-005	1929		1	1	6	10	18
LHP-010	1965	PROOF; edge plain [1]	1	1			8
LHP-015	1965	PROOF in nickel-brass; edge plain [1]	1	1			8
LHP-020	1965	PROOF in gold; edge plain [1]	1	1			200

1. Issued by Modern World Coins in sets to commemorate the 40th anniversary of Harman's purchase of Lundy.

Proof Sets

1965

These sets, struck by Modern World Coins, are usually omitted from catalogues but are struck from the original Harman dies and have as much legal authenticity as the original Harman pieces.

No.	Date	Striking Standard	No. of coins	Price
LPS-65	1965	Proof	4	30

Denomination	Metal
Puffin	Nickel brass
Puffin	Bronze
Half puffin	Nickel brass
Half puffin	Bronze

No.	Date	Striking Standard	No. of coins	Price
LPS-65A	1965	Proof	2	500

Denomination	Metal
Puffin	Gold
Half puffin	Gold

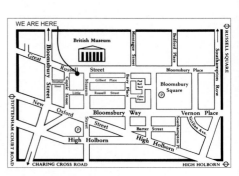

The milled coinage of the Isles of Scilly

The Isles of Scilly comprise about 140 small islands, total area 26 sq. km., off the coast of South-west England, and are part of the United Kingdom. The islands have never possessed their own currency, and there is very little documentation of the use of coinage on the islands. However, Robert Heath, writing in 'The Isles of Scilly' in 1750, mentions the use on Scilly of the Irish 'Wood's money': 'The coin is of the same kind and value here with the current coin of England, except the Irish halfpence, which are the only change in the islands for silver, not intrinsic value, but of smaller size than the English halfpence, and are not current elsewhere. These halfpence were first introduced by Irish traders hither (some of Wood's agents, employed by their honest proprietor). At which time, an inhabitant or two, more avaricious than honest, favouring the imposition, made a considerable purchase of them by weight (some say at the rate of about one-third currency) and so stocked the islands. The silver and gold coin of late brought here was principally for the payment of the King's works, by which the islanders were benefited in the circulation of some thousands of pounds among them, received of the workmen for provisions and necessaries ... the other money circulating here is chiefly from the payment of the King's Forces (who are paid every two months by the commanding officer) also from ships putting in.'

Bibliography

Bibliography

Bibliography

Anon, *Dublin, Observations on coin in general*, 1729.
Anon, *Scheme of money matters of Ireland*, 1729.
Bateson, D, *Scottish Coins*, 1987.
Bateson, J, *Coinage in Scotland*, 1997.
Bateson, J.D. & N.J. Mayhew, *Sylloge of Coins of the British Isles*, 1935.
Batty, D, *Catalogue of copper coinage*, 1868–95.
Boundy, W. S, *Bushell & Harman of Lundy*.
Budesa, C, *Coinage and Banknotes of Ireland*, 1994.
Burns, E., *The Coinage of Scotland*, 1887.
Cardonnel, *Series on the Scottish coinage*, 1786.
Clay, *Currency of the Isle of Man*, 1869.
Cleeve, B, *W B Yeats and the designing of Ireland's Coinage*, 1972.
Cochran, Patrick R.W., *Records of the Scottish Coinage*, 1876.
Coffey, G.A., *A catalogue of the Anglo-Irish coins in the collection of the Royal Irish Academy*, 1911.
Collectors' Coins, Ireland, 1981.
Conder, *Arrangement of provincial coins of Great Britain and Ireland*, 1799.
Crellin, J, *Manx Coinage of 1733*, 1880.
Davis, W. J, *The 19th century token Coinage of Great Britain*, 1904.
Dolley, M, *Some Irish dimensions to Manx history*, 1976.
Dolley, M, *Sylloge of coins of the British Isles*, 1975.
Dolley, M. & W. Seaby, *Sylloge of Coins of the British Isles. Ulster Museum, Part 1. Anglo Irish Coins, John — Edward III*, 1968.
Dolley, M., *Medieval Anglo Irish Coins*, 1972.
Dolley, R., *The Hiberno Norse coins in the British Museum*, 1966.
Dowle, A., & P. Finn, *A guide Book to the coinage of Ireland from 995 AD to the present day*, 1969.
England, *The Irish Pound, 1797–1826*, 1955.
Etherton, P. & Barlow, V, *Lundy, the tempestuous isle*, 1960.
Exley, W, *Guernsey Coinage*, 1969.
Farquhar, H, *Patterns and Medals bearing the legend Iacobus III or Iacobus VIII*.
Galster, G., M. Dolley & J. Jensen, *Sylloge of Coins of the British Isles, Royal collection of coins and medals, National Museum Copenhagen*, 1975.
Grueber, H, *Handbook of Coins of Great Britain in the British Museum*, 1899.
Grueber, H.A., *Handbook of the Coinage of Great Britain and Ireland in the British Museum*, 1901.
Heath, *The Isles of Scilly*, 1750, repr 1967.
Hocking, *Catalogue of coins, tokens in the museum of The Royal Mint*, 1906.
Holmes, N., *Scottish Coins, A History of small change in Scotland*, 1998.
Hoskins, *Charles II in the Channel Islands*, 1854.
Ireland, *Answer to remonstrances*, 1736.
Ireland, *The coinage of Saorstat Eireann 1928*, 1929.
James II, *Proclamations relating to Ireland*, 1689–90.
James, S, *Essay on Irish Coins*, 1749.
Kelly, *Spanish dollars and silver tokens*, 1976.
Krause, Mishler & Bruce, *Standard Catalog of World Coins, 26th edition*, 1999.
Langham, *Lundy*, 1970.
Leake, S. M, *Historical Account of English Money*, 1793.
Lindsay, J., *View of the Coinage of Scotland*, 1845.
Lindsay, J., *A view of the coinage of Ireland from the invasion of the Danes to the reign of George IV*, 1839.

Manx Museum, *The J. D. Clucas collection*, 1965.

Marles, R, *Collectors Coins, (Ireland)*, 1995.

Marshall, *View of silver coin & coinage of GB*, 1838.

Marshall-Fraser, *The history of banking in the Channel Islands*, 1949.

McCammon, A, *Currencies of the Anglo-Norman Isles*, 1984.

Martin, *The course of Irish history*, 1994.

Nelson, P, *The coinage of William Wood*, 1959.

Nolan, *The monetary history of Ireland*, 1926.

O'Sullivan, W., *The Earliest Irish Coinage*, 1981.

Pridmore, F, *Coins of the British Commonwealth of Nations*, 1960.

Quarmby, *Banknotes & banking in IOM*, 1971.

Rayner, *Designers & engravers of English milled coinage*, 1954.

Richardson, A.B., *Scottish Coins In the National Museum Of Antiquities, Edinburgh*, 1901, repr 1977.

Robertson, J.D., *Handbook of the Coinage of Scotland*, 1878.

Roth, B., *Hiberno Danish Coins*, 1910.

Ruding, *Annals of the coinage of Great Britain, 1840.*

Sainthill, *Numismatic Crumbs*, 1855.

Sanders, *British and Irish coin price guide*, 1970.

Scotish Coins in the Ashmolean Museum, Oxford and the Hunterian Museum, Glasgow.

Seaby, P. & F. Purvey, *Coins of Scotland, Ireland and the islands*, 1984.

Seaby, P., *Coins and Tokens of Ireland*, 1970.

Seaby, P., *Coins and Tokens of Scotland*, 1972.

Sear, D., *Greek Coins and their values, Vol. I: Europe*, 1978.

Simon, J., *Essay towards an Historical Account of Irish Coins*, 1749 repr 1810.

Snelling, *A view of the silver coins and coinage of Scotland*, 1774.

Snelling, *View of the silver coins of England*

Societe Guernesiaise, Report & Transactions, 1948.

Spink, *Coins of England and the United Kingdom*, 1999.

Stewart, I.M., *The Scottish Coinage*, 1955.

Thorburn, W, *Coins of Great Britain and Ireland*, 1884.

Trowbridge, R, *Irish gunmoney coins*, 1991.

Tynwald, *Sound Money for the Isle of Man*, 1977.

Went, A, *Irish coins and medals*, 1978.

Westropp, *Notes on Irish money*, 1916.

Young, *Coin catalogue of Ireland*, 1968.

Index

Index

435